The Herbicide Glyphosate

The Herbicide Glyphosate

Edited by

E. Grossbard, BSc, PhD, DIC
School of Natural Sciences,
Hatfield Polytechnic, Hatfield, Herts, UK

D. Atkinson, BSc, PhD, MIBiol
Pomology Department, East Malling Research Station, Maidstone, Kent, UK

BUTTERWORTHS
London Boston Durban Singapore Sydney Toronto Wellington

First published, 1985

© **Butterworth & Co. (Publishers) Ltd, 1985**

British Library Cataloguing in Publication Data

The Herbicide glyphosate.
  1. Glyphosate
  I. Grossbard, E.   II. Atkinson, D.
  632'.954   SB952.G58

  ISBN 0-408-11153-4

Library of Congress Cataloging in Publication Data
Main entry under title:

The Herbicide glyphosate.

  Includes bibliographical references and index.
  1. Glyphosate.   I. Grossbard, E.   II. Atkinson, D.
  SB952.G58H47   1984   632'.954   83–27118
  ISBN 0-408-11153-4

Typeset by Phoenix Photosetting, Chatham, Kent.
Printed by Thetford Press Ltd, Thetford, Norfolk.
Bound by Dorstel Press Ltd, Harlow, Essex.

Foreword

When, in August 1970, I made my first visit to the Monsanto Research Centre at St Louis, I remember vividly being shown some field plots that had been treated with new experimental herbicides. One of these herbicides, I was told, had some very exciting properties and was thought by the company to have an exceptionally bright commercial future. Little did I realize that I was a privileged witness to the early evaluation of what subsequently proved to be one of the most important agrochemical discoveries of this century—the herbicide glyphosate.

Since that time I have observed with much interest and admiration the processes of commercial manufacture and development, the worldwide marketing and the ever-increasing range of benefits which this compound has brought to agriculture and to the management of land and water resources. I have been fascinated by the research that has steadily gathered momentum on the properties of glyphosate, on its behaviour in the environment, on the factors which influence its unique performance and on many other aspects.

When the idea of producing a book devoted to glyphosate was first mooted, and my advice sought, I was aware that such a venture would not command universal support. Critics told me that the information was in any case already available in the literature; that any review would quickly become out of date in such a rapidly moving field; that the difficulties of finding a team of competent authors and reviewers would be insuperable. None the less I had little hesitation in giving my strong support and encouragement to my ex-colleague Dr Erna Grossbard, who had been proposed as editor, and to the would-be publishers Messrs Butterworths. Glyphosate is inherently so important and commands such massive use throughout the world that in my mind there could be no doubt about the desirability, after a decade of development, of collecting together in a single volume as much information and data as possible about it and its many uses.

Now that the book is completed, I am more than ever convinced of the need for it and the important part it will play as a source of information and guidance to all who have an interest in glyphosate and its many roles. The task has not been an easy one, but I believe that the obvious value of the volume will more than compensate for the tremendous effort that has been put into it by the joint editors, the reviewers and the publishers. Much credit must go to Erna Grossbard for her perseverance in creating this book and to her and her co-editor, Dr David Atkinson, for welding the many diverse contributions into an integrated text.

Regrettably, much of the research which has been undertaken on glyphosate remains for commercial reasons unpublished, but the willingness of the manufacturers, Monsanto Ltd, to contribute such material as can be released has greatly enhanced the contents. Their support and encouragement has been an essential feature.

It must surely be important for the well-being of this unique product, glyphosate, that the many people concerned with its distribution and use can, if they wish, easily find out what is known about it. I hope that the publication of this volume will not only be widely welcomed, but will encourage the public release of further information about glyphosate and in due course the production of new editions or supplements. In the meantime, my warm compliments to all who have been involved in this book.

J. D. Fryer
Agricultural and Food Research Council
Weed Research Organization,
Yarnton, Oxford

Preface

'There has never been a herbicide like this before' was the title of a paper presented by R. P. Thompson at the 'Simposium herbicida Roundup III', Medan, Indonesia, in 1979. The contributions included in this volume may provide the information whereby this enthusiastic statement could be judged.

Glyphosate, discovered in 1971 by J. E. Franz and sold commercially as Roundup, is a post-emergence non-selective herbicide which was commercially introduced in Europe, in 1974, by Monsanto Agricultural Products Co., St Louis, USA. It is now being marketed in 119 countries and is labelled for use in more than 50 agricultural crops and in industrial sites. Worldwide sales of Roundup in 1981 exceeded $410 million. It is projected that by 1986 it will be the first 'one-thousand million dollar herbicide molecule'. It is just over a decade since Baird and his co-workers introduced, at the 1971 North Central Weed Conference in the USA, 'A new broad spectrum post-emergence herbicide class with utility for herbaceous perennial weed control'. One may wonder whether, at that time, even the authors fully realized just what they had introduced.

There is never a perfect time to write a book on a developing subject such as a herbicide. Soon after the herbicide's introduction there is great interest in the subject but little information. When much of the research has been done there is much information but the volume is in danger of being merely a historical record. This monograph reviews studies on the herbicide glyphosate, as a reference source, on what has been done and as a springboard to future research and agricultural development.

It was the hope of the editors to bring together, in one accessible volume, most of what is known about glyphosate, reports on fundamental research and the practical use of the herbicide. This hope has not been completely fulfilled and probably could never have been achieved. Some information is unavailable for obvious commercial reasons. In addition, research is not uniform. While the chapter on the influence of the environment and plant factors on glyphosate behaviour contains over 100 references, that on effects on the soil fauna contains 13, because very little research has been carried out in this field. As a result, a volume with a small number of comprehensive reviews of a similar length would not have been appropriate. Here, we include an integrated series of chapters by specialist workers in the various subject areas which nevertheless brings together the extensive literature on the chemical which has not been summarized previously or evaluated critically. The large number of references quoted in the volume is an indication of the extent of the research undertaken, while the need for specialist authors illustrates the range of topics.

In addition to chapters detailing the mode of action of glyphosate in both weeds and crop plants and those evaluating its efficacy in a wide range of crops, its impact upon the environment and means of application are discussed. The environmental impact involves the effects of the removal of the vegetation cover as well as potential hazards to non-target organisms. Although this is difficult to quantify, it has been dealt with here in detail.

One of the unique features of glyphosate, and another indication of its importance, is that it has caused a wide range of new types of application machinery to be developed, especially for its safe use. These techniques are also described in detail.

Interest in glyphosate, and also in related molecules, is perhaps as great now as a decade ago. We hope that this volume will help all of those engaged in research and development work to appreciate what has been done in their own area and in related fields which have an impact on their own. The book may also serve as an introduction for those who intend to take up work on glyphosate.

Acknowledgements

We would like to thank Professor J. D. Fryer, of AFRC Weed Research Organization, for a great deal of advice and for constant encouragement and enthusiasm during the whole of the period while the volume was in preparation; Dr K. Holly, also of WRO, who inspired the idea for this monograph, for his guidance and continuous assistance; all the contributors, for their enthusiastic co-operation and for keeping to the deadline; and Dr K. Goulding of Hatfield Polytechnic and Dr R. Murray of East Malling Research Station who both read and commented on many of the papers. Inevitably, much of the information about any chemical is not in the public domain and so we are grateful to Monsanto Europe S.A. and Monsanto Agricultural Products Co., USA—in particular, Mr D. H. Evans, Dr H. W. Frazier, Mr J. F. Hebblethwaite, Mr M. G. O'Keeffe and Dr R. M. Sacher—for assistance in a wide variety of areas. All papers were read by, in addition to the editors, one or more external referees. We thank these referees, of whom there are too many to mention individually, for the hours of hard work which they so ungrudgingly gave. We also thank members of staff at Butterworths, East Malling Research Station, Hatfield Polytechnic and AFRC Weed Research Organisation for assistance in many ways.

E. Grossbard
D. Atkinson

List of contributors

D. Atkinson
Pomology Department, East Malling Research Station, Maidstone, Kent, UK

P.C. Bardalaye
Food Science and Human Nutrition Department, Pesticide Research Laboratory, University of Florida, Gainesville, Florida 32611, USA

P.R.F. Barrett
Agricultural and Food Research Council Weed Research Organization, Begbroke Hill, Yarnton, Oxford, UK

R.W. Bovey
United States Department of Agriculture, Agricultural Research Service, Department of Range Science, Texas A & M University, College Station, Texas 77843, USA

J.O. Brønstad
Grong videregående skole, 7870 Grong, Norway

M.E. Burt
New Jersey Agricultural Experiment Station, Cook College, Rutgers University, New Brunswick, New Jersey 08903, USA

J.C. Caseley
Agricultural and Food Research Council Weed Research Organization, Begbroke Hill, Yarnton, Oxford, UK

D.J. Cole
Department of Agricultural and Forest Sciences, University of Oxford, Parks Road, Oxford, UK (present address: Royal Holloway College, University of London, Egham Hill, Egham, Surrey, UK)

D. Coupland
Agricultural and Food Research Council Weed Research Organization, Begbroke Hill, Yarnton, Oxford, UK

C.W. Derting
Monsanto Agricultural Products Co., Memphis, Tennessee 38117, USA

S.O. Duke
Southern Weed Science Laboratory, United States Department of Agriculture,
Agricultural Research Service, P.O. Box 225, Stoneville, Mississippi 38776, USA

H. Eijsackers
Rijksinstituut voor Natuurbeheer, Kemperbergerweg 67, 6816 RM Arnhem, The
Netherlands

J.E. Franz
Monsanto Agricultural Products Co., 800 N. Lindbergh Boulevard, St. Louis,
Missouri 63166, USA

H.O. Friestad
Chemical Analytical Laboratory, Agricultural University of Norway, 1432 Ås-NLH,
Norway

J.D. Fryer
Agricultural and Food Research Council Weed Research Organization, Begbroke
Hill, Yarnton, Oxford, UK

E. Grossbard
School of Natural Sciences, The Hatfield Polytechnic, P.O. Box 109, College Lane,
Hatfield, Herts AL10 9AB, UK (present address: 29 Perrott Close, North Leigh,
Oxford, UK)

R.J. Haggar
Agricultural and Food Research Council Weed Research Organization, Begbroke
Hill, Yarnton, Oxford, UK

J.F. Hebblethwaite
Monsanto Europe S.A., Letter Box 1, Avenue de Tervuren 270–272, B1150 Brussels,
Belgium

R.E. Hoagland
Southern Weed Science Laboratory, United States Department of Agriculture,
Agricultural Research Service, P.O. Box 225, Stoneville, Mississippi 38776, USA

K. Holly
Agricultural and Food Research Council Weed Research Organization, Begbroke
Hill, Yarnton, Oxford, UK

H. Knuuttila
Department of Chemistry, University of Jyväskylä, SF-40100 Jyväskylä 10, Finland

P. Knuuttila
Department of Chemistry, University of Jyväskylä, SF-40100 Jyväskylä 10, Finland

R.H. Kupelian
New Jersey Agricultural Experiment Station, Cook College, Rutgers University,
New Brunswick, New Jersey 08903, USA

K. Lund-Høie
Department of Herbology, Norwegian Plant Protection Institute, N-1432 Ås-NLH,
Norway

R.J. Makepeace
21 Freehold Street, Lower Heyford, Oxford, UK

G.M. Markle
New Jersey Agricultural Experiment Station, Cook College, Rutgers University,
New Brunswick, New Jersey 08903, USA

C.G. McWhorter
Southern Weed Science Laboratory, United States Department of Agriculture,
Agricultural Research Service, P.O. Box 225, Stoneville, Mississippi 38776, USA

H.A. Moye
Food Science and Human Nutrition Department, Pesticide Research Laboratory,
University of Florida, Gainesville, Florida 32611, USA

G. Nilsson
Department of Plant Physiology, Swedish University of Agricultural Sciences,
S-750-07 Uppsala, Sweden

M.G. O'Keeffe
Monsanto Ltd, Agricultural Division, Thames Tower, Burleys Way, Leicester, UK

W.G. Richardson
Agricultural and Food Research Council Weed Research Organization, Begbroke
Hill, Yarnton, Oxford, UK

D.W. Robinson
Agricultural Institute, Kinsealy Research Centre, Malahide Road, Dublin 5, Eire

G.R. Schepens
Monsanto Europe S.A., Letter Box 1, Avenue de Tervuren 270–272, B1150 Brussels,
Belgium

T.P. Sullivan
Applied Mammal Research Institute, 23523 47th Avenue, R.R. #7, Langley, British
Columbia, Canada VRA 4R1

P.J. Terry
Agricultural and Food Research Council Weed Research Organization, Begbroke
Hill, Yarnton, Oxford, UK

T.E. Tooby
Ministry of Agriculture, Fisheries and Food, Directorate of Fisheries Research, Fisheries Laboratory, Remembrance Avenue, Burnham-on-Crouch, Essex, UK (present address: Pesticides Registration Department, Ministry of Agriculture, Fisheries and Food, Harpenden Laboratory, Harpenden, Herts, UK)

L. Torstensson
Department of Microbiology, Swedish University of Agricultural Sciences, S-750-07, Uppsala, Sweden

D.J. Turner
Agricultural and Food Research Council Weed Research Organization, Begbroke Hill, Yarnton, Oxford, UK

W.B. Wheeler
Food Science and Human Nutrition Department, Pesticide Research Laboratory, University of Florida, Gainesville, Florida 32611, USA

Contents

Note on terminology

References to crops, weeds, herbicides, fauna and microorganisms have been standardized throughout the text as described below, and two appendices are provided at the end of the book to aid the reader who may be unfamiliar with the terminology adopted in the text.

Crops (cultivated species)

Crops are referred to in the text by their common names, with the latin botanical name given at first mention. Appendix II gives an alphabetical list of crops by common name, together with their equivalent botanical names.

Weeds

Weeds are referred to in the text by their botanical names only. Appendix III gives an alphabetical list of weeds by their botanical names (including authorities), together with the equivalent common names used in the UK and the USA.

It should be noted that although *Elymus repens* (L.) Gould is the new name for *Agropyron repens* (L.) Beauv. (common name couch grass), in this book *Agropyron repens* has been retained because most authors have used it and the weed is still widely known by this name.

Herbicides

Herbicides are referred to in most instances in the text by their common names. Concentrations are given as quoted by the authors and have not been recalculated.

Fauna and microorganisms

Insects, fish, mammals, etc., are referred to in the text by their common names, with the latin name given at first mention. Microorganisms are given their latin names only.

Part I

Chemistry of Glyphosate

Chapter 1

Discovery, development and chemistry of glyphosate

J. E. Franz
Monsanto, St. Louis, USA

Introduction

N-(phosphonomethyl)glycine (glyphosate, formula *1*) and its salts were first described as herbicides in 1971 (Baird *et al.*, 1971). Due to the limited solubility (1.2% at 25°C) of the acid in water, it also was disclosed that the more soluble salts of *1* were preferred for formulation purposes. In over 7000 publications the term glyphosate generally is used to indicate both the acid and its salts, since it is commonly recognized that *1* and its ionic forms are biologically equivalent.

$$HO-\underset{\underset{\displaystyle O}{\|}}{C}-CH_2-\underset{\underset{\displaystyle H}{|}}{N}-CH_2-\underset{\underset{\displaystyle OH}{|}}{\overset{\overset{\displaystyle O}{\uparrow}}{P}}-OH$$

1

Glyphosate exhibits many unique biological properties. It is a broad-spectrum, non-selective, post-emergence herbicide with high unit activity on essentially all annual and perennial plants. In contrast to its high unit activity, when applied post-emergence, glyphosate shows no pre-emergence or residual soil activity. This is because the herbicide is tenaciously bound to soil particles and is readily metabolized by soil microorganisms to produce the plant nutrients phosphoric acid, ammonia and carbon dioxide (Sprankle, Meggitt and Penner, 1975; Rueppel *et al.*, 1977). In general, glyphosate is non-selective only when applied to foliage. When used as a directed spray on trees and certain crops such as grape vines it does not penetrate woody stems or bark. A few plants, however, such as conifers and *Cynodon dactylon* in the dormant state, show exceptional resistance to foliage treatment. This is presumably due to a low degree of uptake/transport of the herbicide in certain dormant plants.

The rapid translocation of glyphosate from the foliage of treated plants to the roots, rhizomes and apical meristems is one of its most important characteristics. This systemic property results in the total destruction of hard-to-kill perennial weeds such as rhizome *Sorghum halepense*, *Agropyron repens*, *Cirsium arvense*,

Cyperus spp., *C. dactylon*, *Imperata cylindrica* and even *Pueraria lobata*. By contrast, many herbicides often kill only the above-ground portion of these plants and the re-emergence of new shoots soon occurs from the underground storage organs. Thus, the survival of a single *A. repens* plant in this manner can result in the production of up to 140 m of new rhizomes and 200 new shoots in one growing season. Finally, glyphosate is practically non-toxic to mammals, birds, fish, insects and bacteria.

As a result of these unique properties, glyphosate may be used for broad-spectrum weed control in the following four areas:

(1) *Croplands*
    (a) diverted acres;
    (b) minimum tillage farming;
    (c) fence rows, storage areas, farmsteads;
    (d) drainage ditches and irrigation canals;
    (e) pasture renovation;
    (f) field crops: using rope-wick applicators, recirculating sprayers and rollers.
(2) *Plantations and orchards*
    (a) removal of ground cover from rubber, oil palm, coffee, tea, cocoa, pineapple, sugarcane plantations and orchards;
    (b) removal of deciduous trees, shrubs and vegetation from dormant conifer forests.
(3) *Industrial and recreational*
    (a) highways and roadsides;
    (b) fuel, power transmission and railway rights of way;
    (c) warehouse and storage areas;
    (d) public waterways and streams;
    (e) golf courses.
(4) *Home use*
    (a) patios, pavements, drives, rockeries, etc;
    (b) eradication of poison ivy, poison oak, vines, perennial weeds.
    (c) removal of tree suckers.

Because of glyphosate's broad utility, systemic properties, non-persistence and excellent environmental characteristics, it is now marketed in over 100 countries.

History and discovery

The discovery of glyphosate as a perennial herbicide of high unit activity was made after a conventional lead follow-up program had failed. Prior to 1970, over 100 tertiary aminomethyl phosphonic acids of types *2* and *3* were prepared (Moedritzer and Irani, 1966) at Monsanto from a variety of primary and secondary amines, as indicated in Scheme 1.

After biological evaluation of this group of products, only the two compounds *4* and *5*, prepared from iminodiacetic acid and glycine, respectively, were considered as leads. Both products were found to possess interesting plant-growth regulating and perennial herbicidal properties, but their unit activities were too low for development as commercial herbicides. Work was continued on the testing of *5* (now called glyphosine) as a cane ripener, however, and this eventually resulted in

Scheme 1

$$RR'NH + CH_2O + H_3PO_3 \xrightarrow[HCl]{\Delta} RR'NCH_2PO_3H_2 + H_2O$$

2

$$RNH_2 + 2CH_2O + 2H_3PO_3 \xrightarrow[HCl]{\Delta} RN(CH_2PO_3H_2)_2 + 2H_2O$$

3

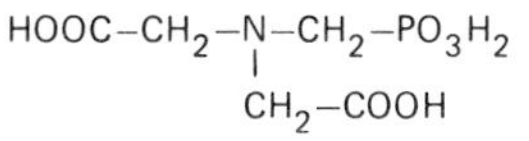

$$HOOC-CH_2-\underset{\underset{CH_2-COOH}{|}}{N}-CH_2-PO_3H_2 \qquad HOOC-CH_2-\underset{\underset{CH_2-PO_3H_2}{|}}{N}-CH_2-PO_3H_2$$

4 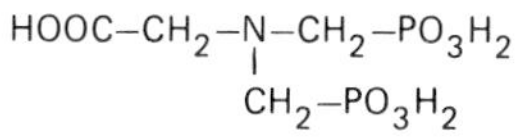   *5*

the marketing of the Polaris (Monsanto trademark) plant growth regulator. Since the discovery of a systemic perennial herbicide was a major objective of the agricultural division, many additional compounds were synthesized by the method of Scheme 1, but no improvement in unit activity was realized.

After interest in this area had waned, a synthesis programme for the preparation of some additional analogues of *4* and *5* by the phosphonomethylation of a variety of primary and secondary α-amino acids was conceived and initiated. During the course of this work, it was found that the secondary α-amino acids readily formed the expected products of type *2* (Scheme 1), but the primary α-amino acids (with the exception of glycine) formed complex coloured reaction mixtures from which pure products of type *3* were difficult to isolate. To resolve this problem the acidic phosphonomethylation reactions of two model compounds—glycine and α-alanine—were studied in more detail.

The formation of mixtures by the routes illustrated in Scheme 2 is consistent with the experimental results obtained from this study. Products of type *B* may be formed via pathway I or II. When *A* was glycine (R = H), *B* (glyphosine) was always the major product and *F* (*N*-methylglyphosate) was a minor constituent regardless of the mole ratios of reactants used. The intermediate formation of *E* was never detected, indicating that either it is formed in a rate-determining reaction or pathway II is not operative. Reduction of the azomethine *D* (presumably by formaldehyde or formic acid formed during the reaction) would produce sarcosine *C* which, although not detected, is known to readily undergo phosphonomethylation under the reaction conditions used.

Subsequently, it also was demonstrated that *E* forms *F* when heated with acidic formaldehyde. In contrast to glycine, which always produced colourless reaction solutions, the reaction of alanine *A* (R = CH₃) with formaldehyde and phosphorous acid in acid media resulted in complex coloured mixtures containing a variety of materials including *B, F, H* and polymers (presumably derived from pyruvic acid). *B* was difficult to isolate from these mixtures. Similar results were obtained with most of the remaining primary α-amino acids.

The latter results are consistent with the operation of pathway III in which the azomethine intermediate *D* undergoes isomerization to the imine *G* followed by

Scheme 2

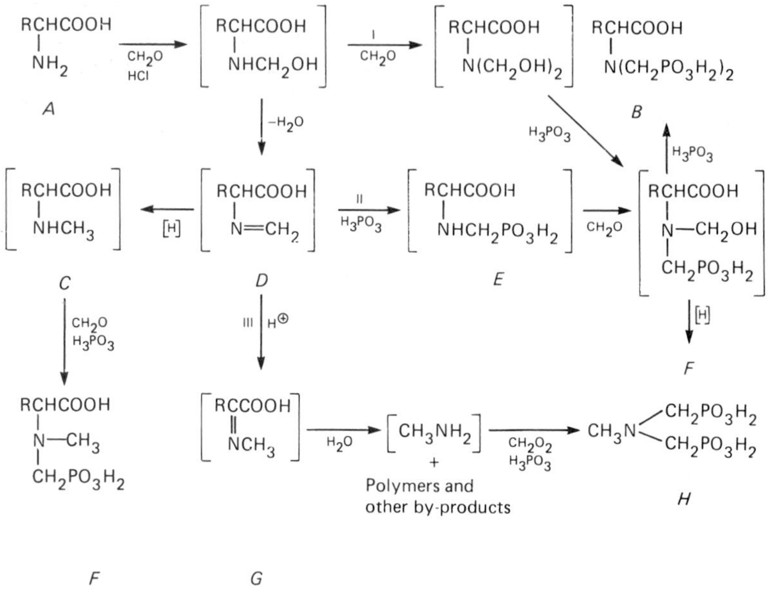

polymerization, hydrolysis and additional phosphonomethylation of the hydrolysate methyl amine to yield *H*. The operation of pathway III requires the presence in *D* of an α-hydrogen which can undergo elimination in the formation of imine *G*. It is interesting that replacement of this α-hydrogen with an alkyl group, as in 2-aminoisobutyric acid, hinders degradation reactions and makes possible the isolation of *6* in good yields (Scheme 3).

Scheme 3

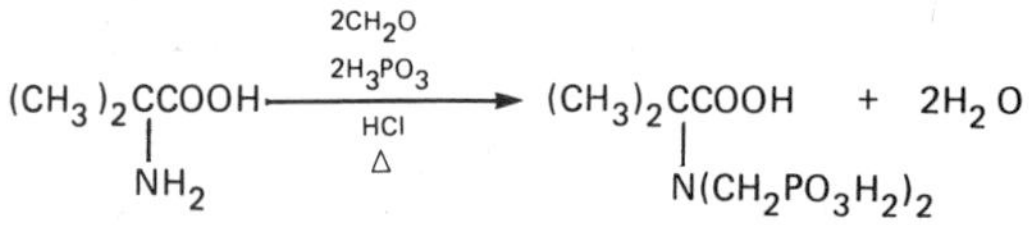

6

With these mechanistic limitations in mind, a variety of primary and secondary amino acids were converted successfully to various homologues and analogues of *4* and *5*. However, all of the tertiary aminomethylphosphonic acids thus prepared were found to exhibit very low herbicidal activity. Eventually it was concluded that the use of conventional synthetic rationale for modifying the structures of *4* and *5* to increase unit activity would not succeed and termination of the project appeared imminent. Therefore, a final effort was made to consider the problem from a different viewpoint. The notion was conceived that the similar activities of *4* and *5* might be related to their metabolic conversion in plants to some common active metabolite(s) (being aware, of course, that metabolism usually results in deactivation). One possible metabolite was *N*-methyl glyphosate, but this compound had been prepared earlier from sarcosine and exhibited very low herbicidal activity. Another possible metabolite of *4* and *5* would be *1*, as indicated in Scheme 4. According to this idea, the elimination of a carboxymethyl group from *4* and a phosphonomethyl group from *5* would have to occur to about an equal extent on metabolism. Although this type of selective metabolism did not seem probable, glyphosate was synthesized at Monsanto some time thereafter and was found to be many times more active than the lead compounds *4* and *5*.

Scheme 4

H2NCH2COOH
(C)
HN(CH2COOH)2
(C)
? (C)
(C)
CH2COOH
N-CH2COOH
CH2PO3H2
? (M)
CH2COOH
NH
CH2PO3H2
? (M)
(C)
CH2COOH
N-CH2PO3H2
CH2PO3H2

4 *1* *5*

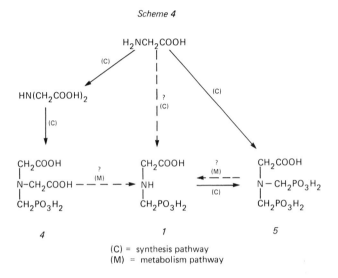

(C) = synthesis pathway
(M) = metabolism pathway

Since glyphosate could not be prepared by the phosphonomethylation of glycine in acid media, a new procedure was developed for obtaining this compound. The reaction of glycine with chloromethylphosphonic acid *7* in basic media had been reported (Westerback, Rajan and Martell, 1965) to yield *5* but not *1*. By appropriate manipulation of the reaction conditions, however, glyphosate could be obtained in moderate yields, as indicated in Scheme 5 (Franz, 1974). Yields of *1* were improved by the use of excess glycine, but the reaction products were difficult to separate. Other routes for the production of glyphosate were subsequently developed (Franz, 1979).

The idea that *4* and *5* might be converted to glyphosate *1* in plants was followed up with some additional studies. The metabolism of tertiary amines to secondary amines in biological systems can occur by either *N*-oxidation or α-oxidation pathways (Ferris, Serwe and Gapski, 1967; Beckett, 1971). The *N*-oxidation route presumably can involve *N*-oxide intermediates *9*, as indicated in Scheme 6.

To test this possibility, the *N*-oxides *9* of *4, 5* and several related compounds were

Scheme 5

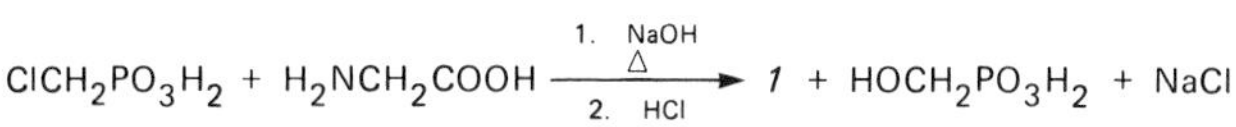

ClCH2PO3H2 + H2NCH2COOH
1. NaOH
Δ
2. HCl
1 + HOCH2PO3H2 + NaCl

7

Scheme 6

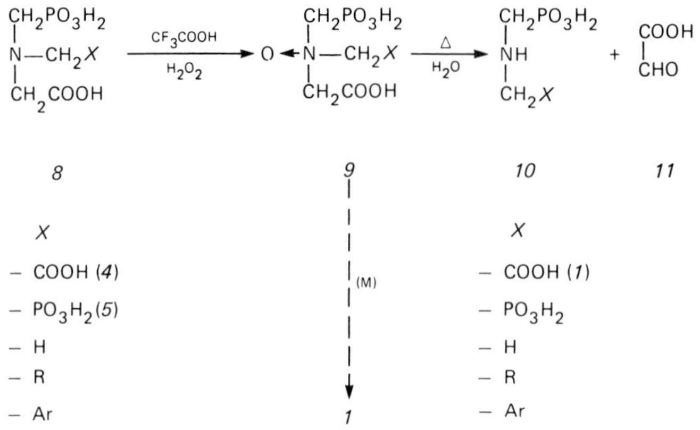

8	9	10	11
X		X	
— COOH (4)		— COOH (1)	
— PO$_3$H$_2$ (5)	(M)	— PO$_3$H$_2$	
— H		— H	
— R		— R	
— Ar	1	— Ar	

prepared by the peracid oxidation of the corresponding tertiary amines 8. It was found that these N-oxides readily decomposed in hot water to produce the secondary amines 10 in good yields, as expected. The mechanism of this decomposition possibly proceeds in the manner indicated in Scheme 7. The re-formation of some tertiary amine 8 during this decomposition apparently occurs via the reduction of N-oxide 9 by the glyoxalic acid 11 formed during the reaction.

The N-oxide of 4 (i.e. 9, X = COOH) was found to be a very active herbicide which may be related to its ease of thermal decomposition to form glyphosate 1. Contrary to expectation, however, the remaining N-oxides 9 also exhibited significant glyphosate-type activity, even though the tertiary amines 8 from which they were prepared and their secondary amine products 10 had relatively low herbicidal activity. These data appear to indicate that products of structure 9 are either uniquely active or that their metabolism in plants involve not only conversion to 10 but also, to some extent, to glyphosate 1, as indicated in Scheme 6, route (M). It is interesting that many closely related tertiary amines and their N-oxides which are not capable of glyphosate formation on metabolism (e.g. nitrilotriacetic acid N-oxide 13 and nitrilotrimethylphosphonic acid N-oxide 14) are not herbicidally active.

Scheme 7

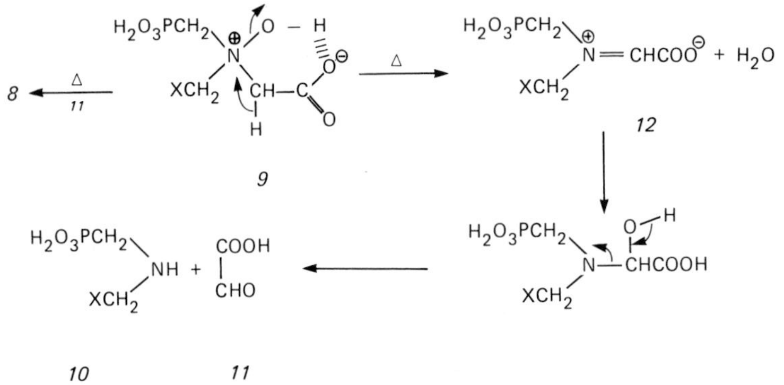

$$CH_2COOH$$
$$O \leftarrow N—CH_2COOH$$
$$CH_2COOH$$

13

$$CH_2PO_3H_2$$
$$O \leftarrow N—CH_2PO_3H_2$$
$$CH_2PO_3H_2$$

14

General properties and toxicology of glyphosate

Glyphosate or N-(phosphonomethyl)glycine has an empirical formula of $C_3H_8NO_5P$ and is a white crystalline solid which exists as a zwitterionic species *1a* in the solid state (Knuuttila and Knuuttila, 1979; see also Chapter 2).

$$HOOCCH_2\overset{H}{\underset{H}{\overset{\oplus}{N}}}CH_2PO_3H^{\ominus}$$

1a

The relatively low solubility of glyphosate *1a* in water (1.2–8% at 25–100°C) and its insolubility in organic solvents apparently is related to strong intermolecular hydrogen bonding in the crystalline lattice. The dissociation and pKa values of glyphosate in aqueous solution are indicated in Scheme 8. Values for pK_1, pK_2 and pK_3 have been reported (Madsen, Christensen and Gottlieb-Petersen, 1978) to be 2.27, 5.58 and 10.25, respectively. The pH of a 0.0067 mol 1^{-1} solution of glyphosate in 0.05 mol 1^{-1} KCl is 2.5, corresponding to about 60% of the monoanion *15* at equilibrium (Wauchope, 1976). Complete conversion of *1* to monoanion *15*, dianion *16* and trianion *17* occurs at pH values of approximately 4, 8 and 12, respectively (see *Figure 1.1*).

Plant fluids generally are buffered within rather narrow pH ranges. Thus, xylem and apoplastic solutions are acidic (pH 5–6), whereas phloem sap is basic (pH 8–8.5) (Crafts and Crisp, 1971). After penetration into leaf tissue, therefore, glyphosate exists in the apoplast primarily in its monoanionic form and is translocated via the phloem as the dianion. The similar herbicidal effectiveness of glyphosate acid and many of its soluble salts (Franz, 1974) indicates that the counter-ion may influence formulation solubility but not overall biological activity. Although the uptake of glyphosate solutions into leaf disks is invariant between pH values of 4.5 and 9.7 (Gougler and Geiger, 1981), the rate of cuticular penetration can be dependent on the particular adjuvant or surfactant utilized in the formulation (Wyrill and Burnside, 1977).

Since glyphosate is a relatively strong acid it is readily converted to essentially any salt by reaction with the appropriate base. Thus, metal salts are obtained from aqueous bicarbonate, carbonate and hydroxide solutions, whereas onium* salts are usually prepared from the corresponding hydroxides in aqueous or alcoholic media (Franz, 1974). The stability constants of the Cu^{2+}, Zn^{2+}, Ca^{2+} and Mg^{2+}

---

*'Onium' designates a generic class of cations comprising organic ammonium and its isologues, including sulfonium, phosphonium, oxonium, stilbonium, selenonium, telluronium, arsonium and iodonium (Wheland, 1949: *Hackh's Chemical Dictionary*, 1969; *Steadman's Medical Dictionary*, 1973).

Scheme 8

$$HOOCCH_2\overset{\oplus}{N}H_2CH_2PO_3H^{\ominus} \xrightarrow{pK_1} {}^{\ominus}OOCCH_2\overset{\oplus}{N}H_2CH_2PO_3H^{\ominus} + H^{\oplus}$$

1a   15

Monoanion

$${}^{\ominus}OOCCH_2\overset{\oplus}{N}H_2CH_2PO_3H^{\ominus} \xrightarrow{pK_2} {}^{\ominus}OOCCH_2\overset{\oplus}{N}H_2CH_2PO_3^{\ominus} + H^{\oplus}$$

16

Dianion

$${}^{\ominus}OOCCH_2\overset{\oplus}{N}H_2CH_2PO_3^{\ominus} \xrightarrow{pK_3} {}^{\ominus}OOCCH_2NHCH_2PO_3^{\ominus} + H^{\oplus}$$

17

Trianion

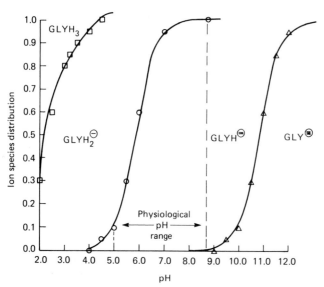

Figure 1.1. The ion species distribution is the fraction at equilibrium (after Wauchope, 1976; reprinted in part with permission, copyright 1982, ACS)

complexes of glyphosate have been reported (Madsen, Christensen and Gottlieb-Petersen, 1978). In general, the complexing properties of 1 are similar to those of iminodiacetic acid, and glyphosate has no known utility as a chelating agent. Due to its amphoteric nature, glyphosate also will dissolve in strong acids to produce salts with negative pKa values (Madsen, Christensen and Gottlieb-Petersen, 1978) and crystalline hemisalts have been isolated (Franz, 1974).

Glyphosate *1* softens and decomposes between 200°C and 230°C, with loss of water and resolidification, to form *N,N'*-diphosphonomethyl-2,5-diketopiperazine *32* (see next section).

The relevant spectral data of glyphosate are summarized in *Table 1.1* (Franz, 1979; Rueppel and Marvel, 1976; Rueppel *et al.*, 1977).

TABLE 1.1   Spectral values of glyphosate acid

ir (nujol, PS ref.): 5.80 nm (v, C=O), 6.43 nm (δNH^{2+})
^{1}H nmr (D$_2$O, TMS ref.): δ4.25 (s, $\underline{CH_2}$C=O); δ3.70 (d, $\underline{CH_2}$–P) J = 14 Hz
^{13}C nmr (D$_2$O, TMS ref.): δ174.7 (–$\underline{C}$=O), δ51.46 (–$\underline{CH_2}$C=O), δ44.66 (–$\underline{CH_2}$P)
    H decoupled
^{31}P nmr (D$_2$O, 85% H$_3$PO$_4$ ref): δ8.9 (–$\underline{PO_3H_2}$)
    H decoupled

Chemistry of glyphosate

Glyphosate acid undergoes many of the reactions typical of a secondary α-amino acid, but its low solubility in organic solvents makes some transformations difficult. The more important methods of derivatization include esterification amination, dehydration, *N*-acylation, *N*-sulfonylation, *N*-alkylation and the formation of acyl and phosphonyl halides.

Glyphosate and its esters react with halogenating agents such as phosphorus pentachloride to produce the corresponding acid chlorides *18* and *19* (R = alkyl, aryl). Although *18* and *19* readily form derivatives with a variety of nucleophiles, they exhibit poor storage stability and must be utilized as soon as possible after formation. Blockage of the secondary amine function with suitable deactivating groups, however, produces reactive stable synthons. Thus, the trifluoroacetyl derivatives *20* and *21* are sharp melting white crystalline solids (Franz, 1980) which may be stored for several months in a desiccator without deterioration. Reaction of *20* and *21* with nucleophiles produces derivatives which may be deprotected by a variety of procedures.

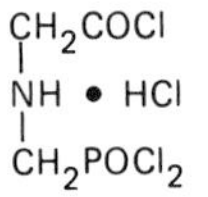

CH$_2$COCl
|
NH • HCl
|
CH$_2$POCl$_2$

18

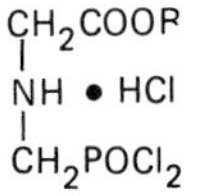

CH$_2$COOR
|
NH • HCl
|
CH$_2$POCl$_2$

19

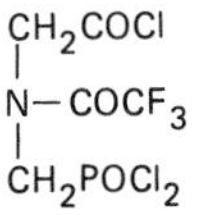

CH$_2$COCl
|
N—COCF$_3$
|
CH$_2$POCl$_2$

20

m.p. 78–81°C

CH$_2$COOC$_2$H$_5$
|
N — COCF$_3$
|
CH$_2$POCl$_2$

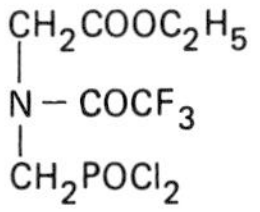

21

m.p. 77.5–79.5°C

Carboxylate ester salts *22* are readily prepared when a slurry of glyphosate is heated with an excess of an alcohol in the presence of dry HCl (Fischer esterification). The alcohol-insoluble *23* are obtained from the soluble salts *22* after treatment with an acid scavenger such as triethylamine or propylene oxide (Scheme 9). Salts of *23* undergo aminolysis to form carboxamides *24* when treated with primary and secondary amines and some of their derivatives. Triesters *25* are produced when acid chlorides *18* or *19* are allowed to react with alcohols in the presence of an acid acceptor (Scheme 10).

Scheme 9

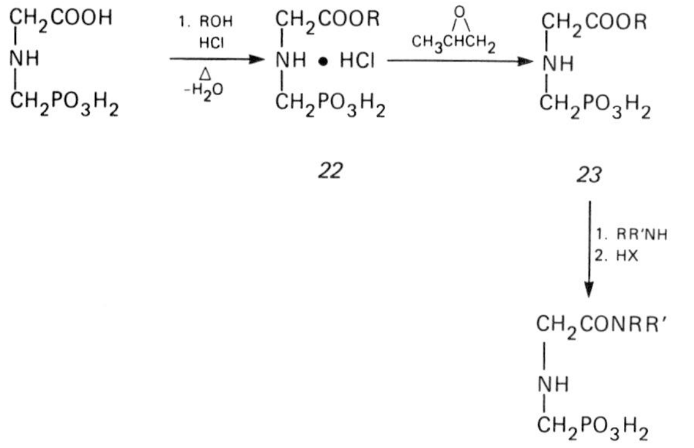

Scheme 10

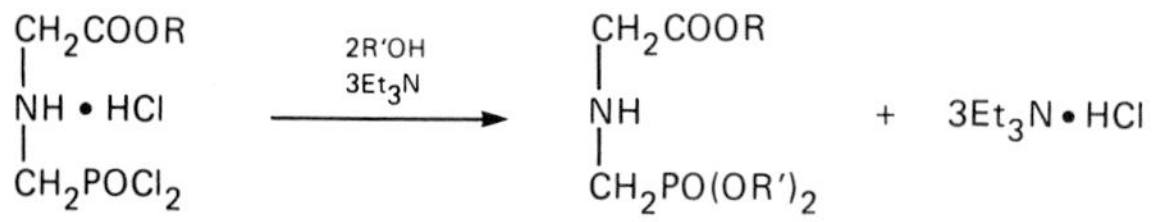

N-acyl triesters *26* may be prepared in several ways. One convenient method involves distillation of a mixture of glyphosate and an excess of an orthoester until a homogeneous solution is obtained (Scheme 11). Acylation of *25*, using Schotten–Baumann techniques, also produces products of type *26*. Finally, *N*-acyl esters (e.g. *28*) are obtained by esterification of *N*-acyl glyphosate derivatives *27* (Scheme 12). Due to the insolubility of glyphosate *1* in trifluoroacetic anhydride, formation of *27* occurs only if trifluoroacetic acid is also present (Rueppel, Suba and Marvel, 1976).

The reaction of glyphosate with aromatic acid chlorides and sulfonyl chlorides under aqueous alkaline condition produces the expected *N*-substituted products *29* and *30* in good yields (Scheme 13). Due to the higher reactivity and lower selectivity of aliphatic acid halides and sulfonyl halides relative to the aromatic analogues, however, the yields of glyphosate derivatives prepared from the aliphatic reagents are considerably lower than those obtained from the aromatic derivatives.

Scheme 11

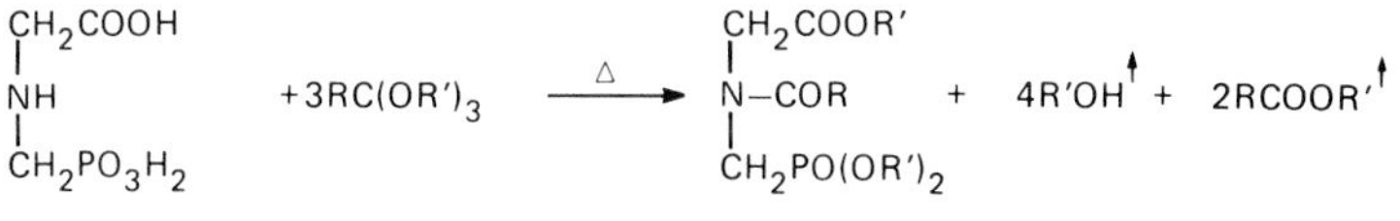

$$
\underset{\mathbf{1}}{\underset{\text{CH}_2\text{PO}_3\text{H}_2}{\overset{\text{CH}_2\text{COOH}}{\mid}}\!\!\!\!\overset{\mid}{\underset{}{\text{NH}}}}
\ +3\text{RC(OR}')_3 \ \xrightarrow{\ \Delta\ }\
\underset{\mathbf{26}}{\underset{\text{CH}_2\text{PO(OR}')_2}{\overset{\text{CH}_2\text{COOR}'}{\mid}}\!\!\!\!\overset{\mid}{\underset{}{\text{N--COR}}}}
\ +\ 4\text{R'OH}^\uparrow +\ 2\text{RCOOR}'^\uparrow
$$

Scheme 12

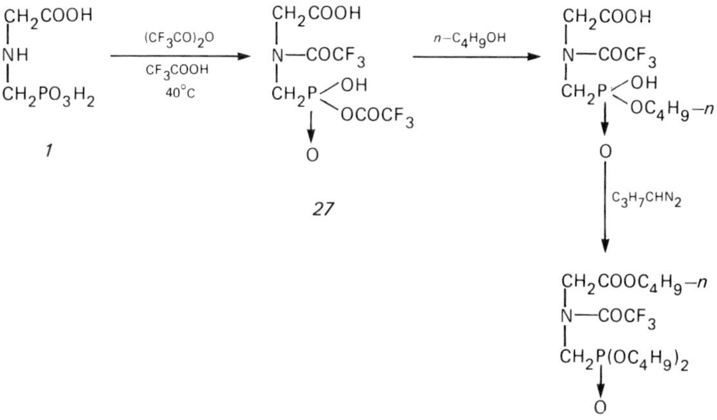

Scheme 13

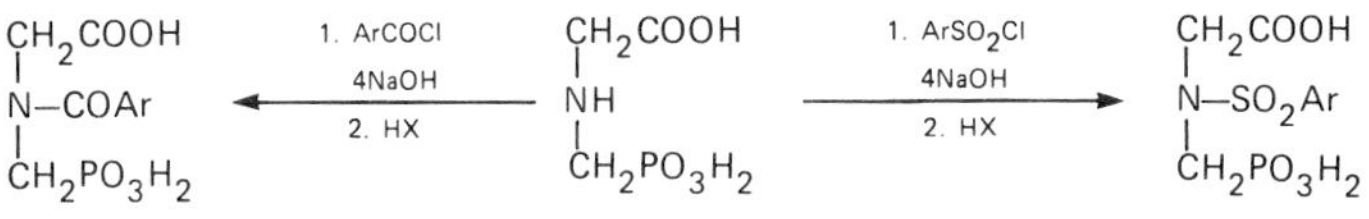

$$
\underset{29}{\overset{\text{CH}_2\text{COOH}}{\underset{\text{CH}_2\text{PO}_3\text{H}_2}{\text{N--COAr}}}}
\ \xleftarrow[\ 2.\ \text{HX}\ ]{\overset{\text{1. ArCOCl}}{4\text{NaOH}}}\
\underset{1}{\overset{\text{CH}_2\text{COOH}}{\underset{\text{CH}_2\text{PO}_3\text{H}_2}{\text{NH}}}}
\ \xrightarrow[\ 2.\ \text{HX}\ ]{\overset{\text{1. ArSO}_2\text{Cl}}{4\text{NaOH}}}\
\underset{30}{\overset{\text{CH}_2\text{COOH}}{\underset{\text{CH}_2\text{PO}_3\text{H}_2}{\text{N--SO}_2\text{Ar}}}}
$$

The *N*-alkylation of glyphosate proceeds readily in some cases. For example, glyphosine 5 is produced more rapidly from glyphosate than from glycine when phosphonomethylation is carried out in acid media (Scheme 14). Heating a mixture of glyphosate *1* and aqueous acidic formaldehyde for extended periods produces *N*-methyl glyphosate *31*. Apparently, formaldehyde functions as a reducing agent in this reaction. In alkaline media, *N*-alkylation of glyphosate proceeds smoothly, provided that activated halides (e.g. benzyl chloride) are utilized.

When glyphosate is heated at 200–230°C it softens and then resolidifies. The diketopiperazine *32* formed as a result of this dehydration (Scheme 15) is very water insoluble and is thermally stable to 316°C. Regeneration of *1* can be accomplished by refluxing *32* with strong mineral acids such as hydrobromic acid.

14

Scheme 14

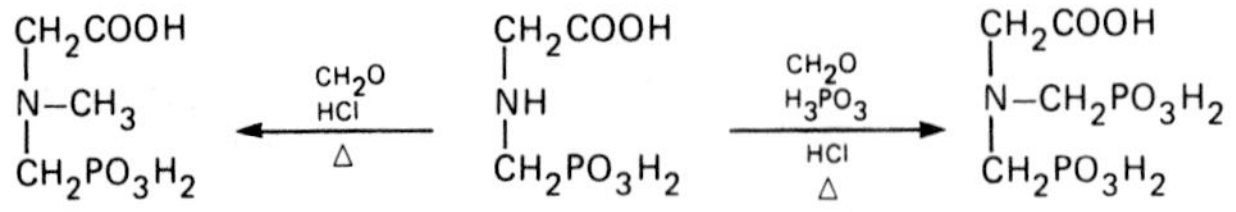

$$31 \quad \xleftarrow[\Delta]{\underset{HCl}{CH_2O}} \quad 1 \quad \xrightarrow[\Delta]{\underset{HCl}{\overset{CH_2O}{H_3PO_3}}} \quad 5$$

Compound 31:
CH₂COOH
N–CH₃
CH₂PO₃H₂

Compound 1:
CH₂COOH
NH
CH₂PO₃H₂

Compound 5:
CH₂COOH
N–CH₂PO₃H₂
CH₂PO₃H₂

Scheme 15

Compound 1:
CH₂COOH
2 NH
CH₂PO₃H₂

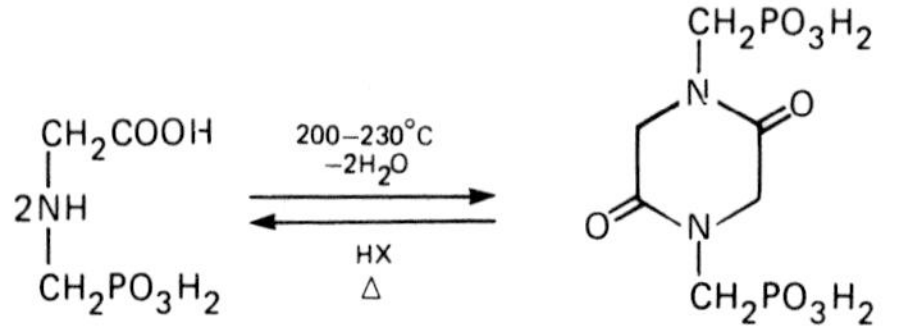

$$\underset{\Delta}{\overset{200-230°C}{\underset{HX}{-2H_2O}}}$$

Compound 32: piperazine-2,5-dione with CH₂PO₃H₂ on both nitrogens

$$\xrightarrow[\Delta]{HC(OR)_3}$$

Compound 33: piperazine-2,5-dione with CH₂PO(OR)₂ on both nitrogens

Scheme 16

Compound 23:
CH₂COOR
NH
CH₂PO₃H₂

$$\xrightarrow[25°C]{CH_3COCl}$$

Compound 34:

(ROOCCH₂⊕NH₂CH₂P)₂O with OH and O substituents   Cl⊖

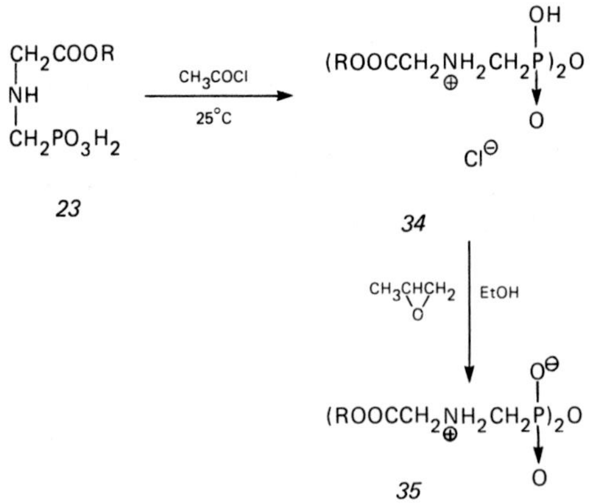

$$\xrightarrow[\text{EtOH}]{CH_3CHCH_2 \text{ (epoxide O)}}$$

Compound 35:

(ROOCCH₂⊕NH₂CH₂P)₂O with O⊖ and O substituents

Esters of type *33*, which are amenable to gas–liquid chromatography analysis, are produced when *32* is heated with orthoesters, as indicated in Scheme 15.

Treatment of glyphosate esters *23* with certain activated halides such as acetyl chloride results in dehydration of the phosphonic acid function and the formation of pyrophosphonate salts *34* (Scheme 16). The parent pyrophosphonates *35*, which are obtained by treatment of *34* with propylene oxide in ethanol, are stable in aqueous solution for several days at room temperature.

Structure/activity studies

Since the discovery of glyphosate's unique herbicidal activity, hundreds of derivatives, homologues, analogues and related compounds have been prepared and evaluated in suitable screens. The results generally indicate that glyphosate acid and its water-soluble salts are the compounds of highest unit activity, and presumably products which can easily metabolize in plants to glyphosate exhibit appreciable herbicidal properties. Thus, a series of aminomethylphosphonic acids of types *36*, *37* and *38* were prepared (Fredericks and Summers, 1981) and their post-emergence herbicidal properties were determined relative to glyphosate. The

$RNHCH_2PO_3H_2$ $R_2NCH_2PO_3H_2$

36   *37*

X (hexane ring) $NCH_2PO_3H_2$

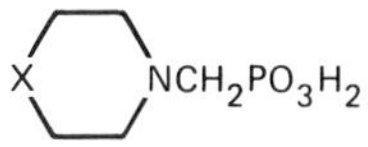

38

$HO(CH_2)_2NHCH_2PO_3H_2$ $HO(CH_2)_3NHCH_2PO_3H_2$

39   *40*

$(HOCH_2CH_2)_2NCH_2PO_3H_2$

41

only compounds which showed any activity were the alcohols *39*, *40* and *41*, but they were much less active than glyphosate. The *in vivo* oxidation of these materials to glyphosate has been suggested as a possible mode of action (Fredericks and Summers, 1981).

The synthesis and biological activity of several phosphinic acids *42* also have been reported (Takamatsu, 1977; Maier, 1980; Maier, 1981). Here again, the unit activity of these compounds is considerably less than that of glyphosate.

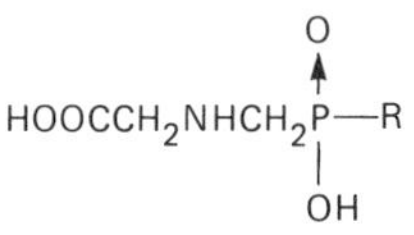

$$HOOCCH_2NHCH_2\overset{O}{\underset{OH}{\overset{\uparrow}{P}}}\!\!-\!\!R \qquad R = H, CH_3, CH_2OH, C_2H_5, C_3H_7, CHCl_2,$$
$$CCl_3, CH_2COOH, C_6H_5, CH_2Cl$$

42

Conclusions

Glyphosate effectively controls 76 of the world's 78 worst weeds, does not sterilize treated soil, is readily metabolized in soil to natural products and is essentially non-toxic to other life forms. There is no other commercial herbicide available which exhibits such diverse utility and efficacious performance in the control of almost all annual, biennial and perennial grassy and broadleaf weeds. For these reasons, the discovery of the herbicidal properties of glyphosate, its salts and other derivatives is considered to be a pioneering invention (Franz, 1983).

The unique herbicidal characteristics of glyphosate are surprising and could not have been predicted. Essentially, all analogues, homologues and isoesters of glyphosate lack a similar type of activity. Those compounds that exhibit activity, e.g. the N-oxides (9), are believed to be metabolized in plants to release the glyphosate anion which accounts for their activity.

The ionic forms of glyphosate are predominant both in the solid state and in solution. Due to the relatively high pH of plant fluids, glyphosate is converted in plants to water-soluble salts which move in the translocation stream (phloem).

Glyphosate undergoes many of the reactions typical of amino acids, such as esterification, dehydration, aminolysis, N-acylation, N-sulfonylation, N-phosphonomethylation, N-alkylation and acid chloride formation.

Acknowledgement

The author gratefully acknowledges the assistance of Mrs Alexis Massa in the preparation of this paper.

References

BAIRD, D.D., UPCHURCH, R.P., HOMESLEY, W.B. and FRANZ, J.E. (1971). Introduction of a new broadspectrum postemergence herbicide class with utility for herbaceous perennial weed control, *Proceedings of the North Central Weed Control Conference*, **26**, 64–68.

BECKETT, A.H. (1971). Metabolic oxidation of aliphatic basic nitrogen atoms and their α-carbon atoms, *Xenobiotica*, **1**, 365–383.

CRAFTS, A. and CRISP, C. (1971). *Phloem Transport in Plants*, San Francisco, Freeman.

FERRIS, J.P., SERWE, R.D. and GAPSKI, G.R. (1967). Detoxification mechanisms II. The iron-catalyzed dealkylation of trimethylamine oxide, *Journal of the American Chemical Society*, **89**, 5270–5275.

FRANZ, J.E. (1974). N-Phosphonomethylglycine phytotoxicant compositions, *U.S. Patent 3,799,758*, Monsanto Co.

FRANZ, J.E. (1979). Glyphosate and related chemistry, in *Advances in Pesticide Science*, vol. 2, Oxford and New York, Pergamon Press, pp. 139–147.

FRANZ, J.E. (1980). Derivatives of N-trifluoroacetyl-N-phosphonomethylglycine dichloride, *U.S. Patent 4,199,345*, Monsanto Co.

FRANZ, J.E. (1983). Salts of N-Phosphonomethylglycine, useful as phytotoxicants or herbicides. *U.S. Patent 4,405,531*, Monsanto Co.

FREDERICKS, P.M. and SUMMERS, L.A. (1981). Synthesis and biological activity of aminomethylphosphonic acids related to the herbicide glyphosate, *Zeitschrift für Naturforschung*, **36**, 242–245.

GOUGLER, J. and GEIGER, D. (1981). Uptake and distribution of glyphosate in sugar beet plants, *Plant Physiology*, **68**, 668.

HACKH'S CHEMICAL DICTIONARY (1969). (Ed J. Grant), New York, McGraw-Hill, p. 473.

KNUUTTILA, P. and KNUUTTILA, H. (1979). The crystal and molecular structure of N-(phosphonomethyl)glycine (glyphosate), *Acta Chemica Scandinavica*, **B33**, 623–626.

MADSEN, H.E.L., CHRISTENSEN, H.H. and GOTTLIEB-PETERSEN, C. (1978). Stability constants of copper(II), zinc, manganese(II), calcium, and magnesium complexes of N-(phosphonomethyl)glycine (glyphosate), *Acta Chemica Scandinavica*, **A32**, 79–83.

MAIER, L. (1980). Novel glycylmethylphosphinic acid derivatives, processes for their production and use thereof, *U.S. Patent 4,233,056*, Ciba–Geigy.

MAIER, L. (1981). Preparation and properties of (N-hydroxycarbonylmethyl-aminomethyl)alkyl- and -aryl-phosphinic acids, $(HO_2CCH_2NHCH_2RP(O)OH)$ and derivatives, *Phosphorus and Sulfur*, **11**, 139–147.

MOEDRITZER, K. and IRANI, R. (1966). The direct synthesis of α-aminomethylphosphonic acids. Mannich-type reactions with orthophosphorous acid, *Journal of Organic Chemistry*, **31**, 1603–1607.

RUEPPEL, M., BRIGHTWELL, B., SCHAEFER, J. and MARVEL, J. (1977). Metabolism and degradation of glyphosate in soil, *Journal of Agricultural and Food Chemistry*, **25**, 517–528.

RUEPPEL, M. and MARVEL, J. (1976). ^1H and ^{31}P nmr spectra of substituted methylphosphonic acids with indirect determination of ^{31}P shifts, *Organic Magnetic Resonance*, **8**, 19–20.

RUEPPEL, M., SUBA, L.A. and MARVEL, J. (1976). Derivatization of aminoalkylphosphonic acids for characterization by gas chromatography mass spectrometry, *Biomedical Mass Spectrometry*, **3**, 28–31.

SPRANKLE, P., MEGGITT, W. and PENNER, D. (1975). Adsorption, mobility and microbial degradation of glyphosate in soil, *Weed Science*, **23**, 229–234.

STEADMAN'S MEDICAL DICTIONARY (1973). 22nd edn, Baltimore, Williams and Wilkins, p. 275.

TAKAMATSU, H. (1977). N-[(Methylphosphino)methyl]glycine and herbicides comprising as an effective ingredient of said compound, *Japanese Patent Application 42840*, Nissan.

WAUCHOPE, D. (1976). Acid dissociation constants of arsenic acid, methylarsonic acid (MAA), dimethylarsinic acid (cacodylic acid) and N-(phosphonomethyl)glycine (glyphosate), *Journal of Agricultural and Food Chemistry*, **24**, 717–721.

WESTERBACK, S., RAJAN, K. and MARTELL, A. (1965). New multidentate ligands. III. Amino acids containing methylenephosphonate groups, *Journal of the American Chemical Society*, **87**, 2567–2572.

WHELAND, G.W. (1949). *Advanced Organic Chemistry*, 2nd edn, New York, Wiley, pp. 38–44.

WYRILL, J.B. and BURNSIDE, O.C. (1977). Glyphosate toxicity to common milkweed and hemp dogbane as influenced by surfactants, *Weed Science*, **25**, 275–287.

Chapter 2

Molecular and crystalline structure of glyphosate

P. Knuuttila and H. Knuuttila
University of Jyväskylä, Finland

Introduction

N-(phosphonomethyl)glycine (glyphosate) is a highly effective foliar herbicide. Apparently it has no effect through root absorption, perhaps because it binds to the soil in a manner similar to glycine or phosphate, or is adsorbed on soil as a zwitterion.

Franz (1971) has synthesized a large group of metal salts from glyphosate: alkaline, alkaline earth, manganese, nickel, copper and zinc salts. Glyphosate dissociates in three stages; its dissociation constants at 25°C are $pK_1 = 2.27$, $pK_2 = 5.58$ and $pK_3 = 10.25$. These values indicate that at least the alkali metals can form mono-, di- and tri-salts.

The infrared spectra of glyphosate, its potassium salt, hydrochloride and its commercial formulation Roundup have been analysed (Shoval and Yariv, 1981). The assignments of the absorption bands have been carried out for determining the relationships between the spectra and the fine structures of glyphosate and Roundup. These spectra might be useful in the identification of the herbicide in the environment.

The stability constants of Mg, Ca, Mn, Cu and Zn 1:1 complexes have been determined at 25°C by potentiometric titration (Madsen, Christensen and Gottlieb-Petersen, 1978). The replacement of one carboxylate group in iminodiacetic acid (IDA) by a phosphonic group increases the co-ordination ability a little. However, there is not always an increase for aminopolyacids (Westerback, Rajan and Martell, 1965). Although there is reason to believe that glyphosate acts as a tridentate ligand, this has not yet been confirmed through structural data*.

In the Co(II) (Głowiak *et al.*, 1980a), Cu(II) (Głowiak *et al.*, 1980b) and Zn(II) (Fenot *et al.*, 1978) complexes of aminomethylphosphonic acid, which is the metabolic product of glyphosate, the phosphono group co-ordinates through two oxygen atoms to adjacent metal atoms, forming polymeric chains across phosphono bridges. These complexes do not exhibit co-ordination through the amino group.

---

*Recent data on the behaviour of the glyphosate as a ligand have indicated that glyphosate acts as a mono- or bidentate ligand, co-ordinating only through the oxygen atoms of the phosphate group (Knuuttila and Knuuttila, unpublished). In a new calcium complex with glyphosate, the unprotonated glyphosate forms double bridges between calcium(II) ions and two protonated glyphosate ions, completing the octahedral co-ordination sphere of the calcium ion. (Preliminary information.)

Our crystallography group has a current project to synthesize and solve the structures of the metal complexes of glyphosate, including the parent glyphosate. A great difficulty has been preparation of single crystals suitable for x-ray analysis.

Crystal preparation

Glyphosate was isolated from the commercial herbicide Roundup by ion-exchange chromatography through Amberlite IRA-400. Recrystallization from hot water gave good single crystals suitable for x-ray work (Knuuttila and Knuuttila, 1979).

Structure determination

The x-ray intensities were recorded and the unit cell determined with a Syntex P2$_1$ automatic four-circle diffractometer.

The structure was solved and refined using the programs of the x-ray system (Stewart *et al.*, 1976). A final R-value of 0.03 was obtained. The R-value represents the deviation of calculated and observed structure factors and thus the quality of the structure determination. An R-value below 0.05 is usually considered good. The final atomic and thermal parameters and details of the structure determination have been published (Knuuttila and Knuuttila, 1979). All calculations and drawings were carried out on the UNIVAC 1100/60 computer of the University of Jyväskylä.

Description of the structure

Structure determination showed crystalline glyphosate to be a zwitterion $^-HO_3PCH_2NH_2^+CH_2COOH$. The molecules are connected by a network of hydrogen bonds. The backbone of each molecule is a non-planar zig-zag chain. The molecular structure is shown in *Figure 2.1* and the packing in the unit cell in *Figure 2.2*.

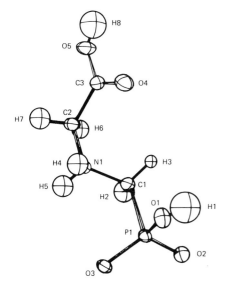

Figure 2.1 Molecular structure and atomic labelling of glyphosate. Thermal ellipsoids are drawn to enclose the 50% probability level (from Knuuttila and Knuuttila, 1979, by courtesy of *Acta Chemica Scandinavica*)

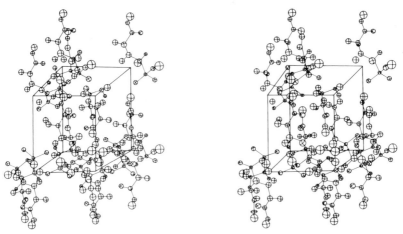

Figure 2.2. Stereoview of the molecular packing of glyphosate
(from Knuuttila and Knuuttila, 1979, by courtesy of *Acta Chemica Scandinavica*)

The atom sequences P1–C1–N1–C2 and N1–C2–C3–O5 in the zig-zag chain form almost planar groups at an angle of 75° to each other. The bond joining the phosphorus and carbon atoms is characteristically long, in this case 1.823 Å ($1 \text{ Å} = 10^{-1} \text{nm}$) which agrees well with values in the literature (Głowiak *et al.*, 1980a; 1980b; Fenot *et al.*, 1978; Emsley and Hall, 1976). Interatomic distances and their standard deviations are presented in *Table 2.1*.

Accurate structure determination showed that, in the solid state, one phosphono hydrogen has shifted to the amino group and thus a zwitterion is formed. In aqueous solution this same hydrogen atom alternates between the phosphono and amino groups at such a high frequency that its location cannot be determined. The mobility of this hydrogen atom and the formation of the zwitterion may partly explain the strong adsorption of glyphosate to soil.

The main metabolic product of glyphosate in the soil, aminomethylphosphonic acid, is formed when the N1–C2 bond is broken. The bonds N1–C1 and N1–C2 are of equal length and neither can be considered weaker than the other. The sp^3 hybridization of nitrogen should result in all bonding angles being about 109°. The atom sequence C1–N1–C2 forms an angle of 113.4°; thus the acetato and phosphono groups are in a favourable steric position with respect to each other. The angular position of the hydrogen atoms is determined by the hydrogen bonds to the neighbouring molecules.

The molecules are connected by hydrogen bonds between O–H...O and N–H···O, as shown in *Table 2.2* and *Figure 2.3*.

The hydrogen bonds, varying from 2.57 Å to 2.82 Å, are formed between phosphono, amino and carboxylic groups when C—OH, P—OH and N—H groups act as proton donors and $p{=}O$ groups as proton acceptors. The infrared study of glyphosate shows similar results in the hydrogen bond system and the zwitterion character of glyphosate (Shoval and Yariv, 1981). It has been proposed that, in Roundup, three isopropylammonium groups join through hydrogen bonds with the oxygen atoms of the phosphono group. Two oxygen atoms of the phosphono group fall in resonance with each other when the hydrogen atom moves over to the amino

TABLE 2.1 Interatomic distances and angles with their standard deviations (from Knuuttila and Knuuttila, 1979, by courtesy of *Acta Chemica Scandinavica*)

Atom pair	Distance (Å)	Atom pair	Distance (Å)	Three-atom group	Angle (°)
O1–P1	1.576(3)	O1–H1	0.711(7)	O1–P1–O2	111.7(2)
O2–P1	1.500(3)	C1–H2	1.118(6)	O1–P1–O2	106.0(2)
O3–P1	1.501(3)	C1–H3	0.975(4)	O2–P1–O3	118.7(2)
P1–C1	1.823(3)	N1–H4	0.962(5)	C1–P1–O1	104.0(2)
C1–N1	1.485(5)	N1–H5	0.914(6)	C1–P1–O2	106.3(2)
N1–C2	1.483(4)	C2–H6	1.014(5)	C1–P1–O3	109.2(2)
C2–C3	1.514(7)	C2–H7	1.017(5)	N1–C1–P1	111.5(2)
C3–O4	1.206(5)	O5–H8	0.743(8)	C2–N1–C1	113.4(3)
C3–O5	1.310(4)			C3–C2–N1	111.8(4)
				O5–C3–C2	109.6(4)
				O4–C3–C2	123.6(3)
				O4–C3–O5	126.8(4)
				H1–O1–P1	122.8(6)
				H2–C1–H3	110.8(4)
				H3–C1–P1	107.0(2)
				H3–C1–N1	110.2(2)
				P1–C1–H2	110.6(3)
				H2–C1–N1	106.8(3)
				H5–N1–H4	96.6(5)
				H5–N1–C1	112.6(4)
				H5–N1–C2	103.9(3)
				H4–N1–C1	118.8(3)
				H4–N1–C2	109.4(3)
				H6–C2–H7	112.1(4)
				H6–C2–C3	108.8(3)
				H6–C2–N1	107.7(3)
				H7–C2–C3	108.9(3)
				H7–C2–N1	107.5(3)
				H8–O5–C3	117.0(5)

TABLE 2.2 Hydrogen bonds (from Knuuttila and Knuuttila, 1979, by courtesy of *Acta Chemica Scandinavica*)

Hydrogen bond distance (Å) A–N···B	H···B	Angle (°) <AHB	Heavy atom distance (Å) A–B
O1–H1···O2	1.944(6)	157.0(66)	2.613(4)
N1–H4···O3	1.866(5)	169.3(44)	2.817(5)
N1–H5···O2	1.932(6)	144.4(47)	2.728(5)
O5–H8···O3	1.826(8)	175.8(69)	2.568(5)

group. This becomes apparent through the bonding lengths P1–O2 and P1–O3 which are 1.500 Å and 1.501 Å, respectively. The bond P1–O1 is 1.576 Å long, indicating a single bond.

Conclusions

An accurate knowledge of the structure of glyphosate is important to an understanding of its metabolism and binding to soil. Besides the structural data itself, the most important finding of this study is that crystalline glyphosate is a

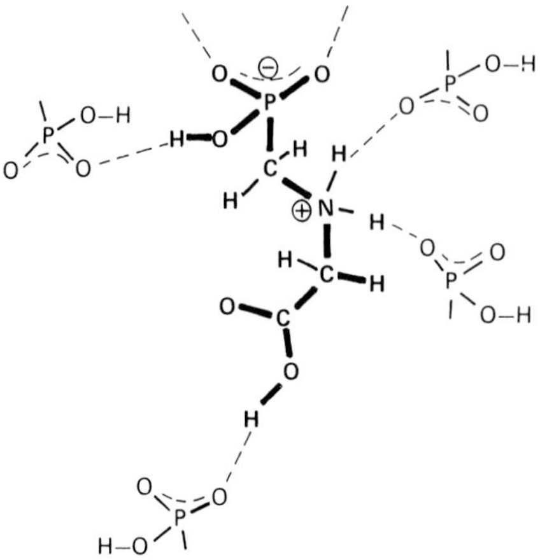

Figure 2.3. Scheme of the hydrogen bond system of glyphosate

zwitterionic species, stabilizing by strong intermolecular hydrogen bonds. The strong hydrogen bond network might explain the low solubility of glyphosate in water.

Acknowledgement

We thank Professor Jaakko Paasivirta for his continued interest in this work.

References

EMSLEY, J. and HALL, D. (1976). *The Chemistry of Phosphorus*, p. 34. London; Harper and Row.

FENOT, P., DARRIET, J., GARRIGOU-LAGRANGE, C. and CASSAIGNE, A. (1978). Crystallographic and vibrational studies of metal complexes of aminomethylphosphonic acid, *Journal of Molecular Structure*, **43**, 49–60.

FRANZ, J.E. (1971). Utilization of *N*-(phosphonomethyl)glycines and their salts as herbicides. *German Patent 2152826*, given to Monsanto Co., St. Louis, USA.

GŁOWIAK, T., SAWKA-DOBROWOLSKA, W., JEZOWSKA-TRZEBIATOWSKA, B. and ANTONÓW, A. (1980a). X-ray studies of cobaltate aminomethylphosphonic acid polymeric complex, *Inorganica Chimica Acta*, **45**, L105–L106.

GŁOWIAK, T., SAWKA-DOBROWOLSKA, W., JEZOWSKA-TRZEBIOTOWSKA, B. and ANTONÓW, A. (1980b). Crystal and molecular structure of bis(aminomethylphosphonate) copper(II). *Journal of Crystalline and Molecular Structure*, **10**, 1–10.

KNUUTTILA, P. and KNUUTTILA, H. (1979). The crystal and molecular structure of *N*-(phosphonomethyl)glycine (glyphosate), *Acta Chemica Scandinavica*, **B33**, 623–626.

MADSEN, H.E.L., CHRISTENSEN, H.H. and GOTTLIEB-PETERSEN, C. (1978). Stability constants of copper(II), zinc, manganese(II), calcium, and magnesium complexes of *N*-(phosphonomethyl)glycine(glyphosate), *Acta Chemica Scandinavica*, **A32**, 79–83.

SHOVAL, S. and YARIV, S. (1981). Infrared study of the fine structures of glyphosate and Roundup, *Agrochimica*, **25**, 377–386.

STEWART, J.M., MACHIN, P.A., DICKINSON, C.W., AMMON, H.L., HECK, H. and FLACK, H. (1976). The X-ray system of crystallographic programs, *Version of 1976 Technical Report TR-446*, Computer Science Centre, University of Maryland, USA.

WESTERBACK, S., RAJAN, K.S. and MARTELL, A.E. (1965). New multidentate ligands. III. Amino acids containing methylenephosphonate groups, *Journal of the American Chemical Society*, **87**, 2567–2572.

Part II

Behaviour of Glyphosate: In Plants

Chapter 3

Metabolism of glyphosate in plants

D. Coupland
Weed Research Organization, Oxford, UK

Terminology

Herbicide metabolism is defined as changes in the chemical structure of the herbicide within higher plants that result from the action of the plant on the herbicide. In the literature, the terms 'degradation' and (less frequently) 'decomposition' have been used interchangeably with 'metabolism'. In this chapter, 'degradation' is used to denote a reduction in the complexity of the chemical structure of the herbicide, and 'decomposition' to describe more extensive breakdown to relatively simple compounds such as water, carbon dioxide, nitrate and phosphate.

The names glyphosate and ^{14}C-glyphosate in this chapter refer to *N*-(phosphonomethyl)glycine, applied usually as the isopropylamine salt. Where the parent acid alone was used this will be stated, where this could be ascertained from the reviewed papers.

Introduction

There is very little detailed information in the literature concerning the metabolism of glyphosate in plants. This is surprising for such an important and widely used herbicide and for a compound that, physiologically, is very interesting. There are probably many reasons for this lack of information, although the difficulties inherent in the analysis of glyphosate and its potential metabolites (*Figures 3.1* and *3.2*) in extracts of plant tissues must be a major factor. Most research workers have relied on thin layer chromatography (t.l.c.) procedures and the use of ^{14}C-labelled glyphosate to determine the extent of metabolism and to characterize partially any metabolites. While these methods go some way to describe the chemical changes which glyphosate undergoes within plants, they have not been able to characterize, unequivocally, the parent acid or any of its metabolites, in the same way as can, for example, gas chromatography/mass spectroscopy methods (Rueppel *et al.*, 1975). This must be kept in mind when considering the literature on this topic. Also, the methods of extraction, purification, analysis and detection are crucial in this type of work and the reader is strongly advised to consult the original references for this information.

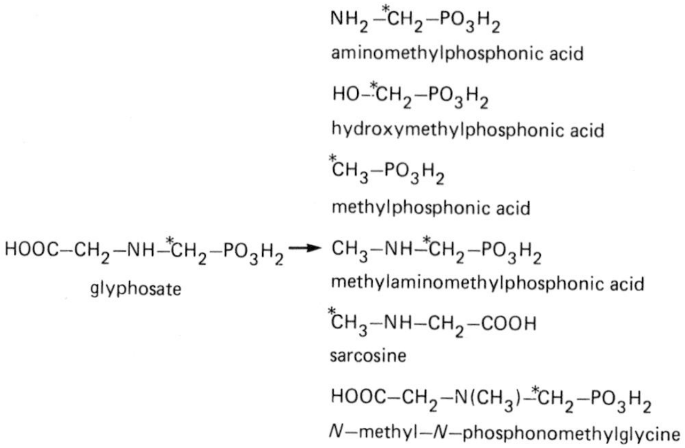

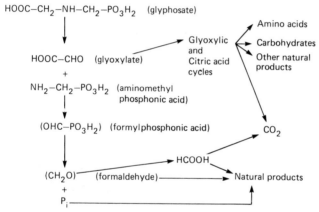

$$NH_2-\overset{*}{C}H_2-PO_3H_2$$

aminomethylphosphonic acid

$$HO-\overset{*}{C}H_2-PO_3H_2$$

hydroxymethylphosphonic acid

$$\overset{*}{C}H_3-PO_3H_2$$

methylphosphonic acid

$$HOOC-CH_2-NH-\overset{*}{C}H_2-PO_3H_2 \longrightarrow CH_3-NH-\overset{*}{C}H_2-PO_3H_2$$

glyphosate   methylaminomethylphosphonic acid

$$\overset{*}{C}H_3-NH-CH_2-COOH$$

sarcosine

$$HOOC-CH_2-N(CH_3)-\overset{*}{C}H_2-PO_3H_2$$

N—methyl—N—phosphonomethylglycine

Figure 3.1. Potential labelled metabolites arising directly from
N-phosphono-^{14}C-methylglycine (* = radiocarbon)

$HOOC-CH_2-NH-CH_2-PO_3H_2$ (glyphosate)

$HOOC-CHO$ (glyoxylate)

$+$

$NH_2-CH_2-PO_3H_2$ (aminomethyl phosphonic acid)

$(OHC-PO_3H_2)$ (formylphosphonic acid)

(CH_2O) (formaldehyde)

$+$

P_i

Glyoxylic and Citric acid cycles

Amino acids

Carbohydrates

Other natural products

CO_2

HCOOH

Natural products

Figure 3.2. Proposed metabolic pathways of glyphosate in
plants (after Rueppel *et al.*, 1975)

This chapter reviews and discusses the available literature, and indicates areas of
research which would merit further study to provide a greater understanding of the
metabolism of glyphosate in plants.

Literature review

Published results can be divided into two groups: those studies which have found no
metabolism (or in some cases no metabolites, which may or may not be the same);
and those studies which have detected metabolites. The inability to detect
metabolites in plant extracts does not necessarily mean that there is no metabolism.
Herbicide decomposition to CO_2 could be involved with the subsequent loss of
glyphosate from the plant. Conversely, loss of glyphosate (or of ^{14}C in radiotracer
work) does not necessarily mean a degradative loss. Glyphosate, like some other

phloem-mobile herbicides, is known to be exuded from the roots of treated plants as the intact molecule (Coupland and Caseley, 1979; Rodrigues, Worsham and Corbin, 1982). Unless these processes are measured, or unless a 'balance sheet' approach is made, losses such as these will be undetected and the overall picture of metabolism will be unclear. Studies in which the authors reported that no metabolism was detected will be discussed first.

Gottrup *et al.* (1976) were among the first to report on the metabolism of glyphosate in plants. The species they used were *Cirsium arvense* and *Euphorbia escula,* and the experiments lasted 1 week. All of the recovered radioactivity was present as glyphosate after t.l.c. analysis of aqueous extracts of both root and shoot tissues. However, compared to zero-time harvests, slight losses in the amounts of ^{14}C recovered were evident in some experiments. The authors thought this could have been due to decomposition to $^{14}CO_2$, but no measurements were made. However, there was the possibility that root exudation could have been the reason since the highest losses of ^{14}C were reported under high relative humidity, conditions conducive to the foliar uptake and translocation of glyphosate (see also Chapter 7).

Zandstra and Nishimoto (1977) found no evidence of glyphosate metabolism in *Cyperus rotundus* 16 days after treatment with ^{14}C-glyphosate. However, the single dimension t.l.c. method they used for the analysis of the aqueous extracts of various plant parts had a poor resolution and the glyphosate region was spread over 2 R_F units. Also, as with the above work, no attempts were made to detect losses from the plant as $^{14}CO_2$ or as root exudates.

Root exudates were specifically examined by Coupland and Caseley (1979) in *Agropyron repens*. Plants treated with ^{14}C-glyphosate and assessed after 8 days exuded, on average, 3.1% of the amount applied to the foliage. Exudates were subjected to two-dimensional t.l.c., and only one radioactive area which corresponded with glyphosate was found. Similar results were reported by Rodrigues, Worsham and Corbin (1982), using wheat (*Triticum aestivum*).

Marquis, Comes and Yang (1979) reported that no metabolism of glyphosate was detected in *Festuca rubra* and *Phalaris arundinacea*. In this study, glyphosate was applied to the roots in hydroponic solution and extracted from the roots and shoots 7 or 14 days after treatment. In contrast to the previous studies, Marquis, Comes and Yang (1979) used several techniques (three types of column chromatography and two t.l.c. solvent systems) to analyse plant extracts, but none revealed any ^{14}C-metabolites. Losses of ^{14}C, either as $^{14}CO_2$ or as exudates, were not investigated.

O'Donovan and O'Sullivan (1982) investigated metabolism in barley (*Hordeum vulgare*) treated with ^{14}C-glyphosate. Three days after treatment they used a two-dimensional t.l.c./autoradiographic technique to analyse aqueous, whole-plant extracts. No ^{14}C-metabolites were detected, but no balance sheet of counts was presented, nor were losses of ^{14}C from the plant investigated.

Finally, Devine and Bandeen (1983) have investigated the metabolic fate of glyphosate in *A. repens* over a period of several months. Plants were treated with ^{14}C-glyphosate (presumably applied as the acid) in the autumn, and the shoots and rhizomes were extracted and analysed in the following spring. Only ^{14}C-glyphosate was detected. However, there was a considerable loss of ^{14}C—over 80% of the applied amount. The authors attributed this to one or more of the following: root exudation, leaching from dead tissues and decomposition to $^{14}CO_2$ However, none f these possibilities was investigated further.

The occurrence of glyphosate metabolism has also been reported. The studies by Rueppel, Marvel and Suba (1975) were the first to be published and are the most comprehensive to date. They are considered in detail at the end of this section. Wyrill and Burnside (1976) reported 'insignificant' (less than 10%) amounts of radioactivity occurring in compounds other than glyphosate after the t.l.c. analysis of aqueous extracts of leaves and roots of *Asclepius syriaca* and *Apocynum cannabinum* 20 days after treatment with ^{14}C-glyphosate (applied as the acid). These metabolites were not investigated further and neither were potential losses of ^{14}C from the plant studied.

Putnam (1976) discovered two ^{14}C-labelled compounds in apple (*Malus domestica*) and pear (*Pyrus pyraster*) trees 90 days after treatment with ^{14}C-glyphosate. The majority of the ^{14}C-activity was associated with glyphosate (92–97%), but small amounts of aminomethylphosphonic acid (1–7%) were detected. Ion exchange chromatography and three t.l.c. systems were used to characterize these ^{14}C-compounds. No attempts were made to investigate potential loss of ^{14}C from the plants.

Lund-Høie (1976), investigating the tolerance of Norway spruce (*Picea abies*) to glyphosate (presumably applied as the acid), also studied its metabolism. Unlike the reports described above, a very complex picture of metabolites was found. Seven metabolites were detected, but some chromatographed so closely together that the author decided to combine them into three distinct groups containing 2, 3 and 2 metabolites, respectively. Glyphosate was also detected and aminomethylphosphonic acid was found in the third group of metabolites. The relative amounts of these compounds were studied over a period of 32 days and a summary of the results is shown in *Table 3.1*. This complicated pattern of metabolism was explained by suggesting that glyphosate was 'complexed' (= conjugated?) with natural compounds such as sugars, amino acids and proteins, and that these metabolites were degraded back to the parent herbicide with time, and ultimately to ^{14}CO$_2$. The theory that glyphosate is translocated in the form of one or more of these 'complexes' was also put forward, but no evidence was presented to support either of these suggestions.

TABLE 3.1   Relative amounts of radioactivity found in glyphosate and metabolites extracted from mature and immature needles of Norway spruce (*Picea abies*) treated with ^{14}C-glyphosate (after Lund-Høie, 1976)

Plant tissue	Days after application	Metabolite groups			Glyphosate
		1	2 (Recovered activity, %)	3	
Mature needles	1	90	2	2	6
	2	65	15	5	15
	4	39	37	4	20
	8	13	10	0	77
	16	11	43	32	14
	32	40	26	33	1
Immature needles	1	50	14	14	22
	2	8	50	8	34
	4	23	20	20	37
	8	20	32	20	28
	16	14	20	18	48
	32	26	29	0	45

Hasegawa, Kumamoto and Jordan (1977) reported a small amount of metabolism in avocado *(Persea americana)* fruit. Ten days after treatment with ^{14}C-glyphosate (formulation unspecified), 6% of the applied ^{14}C was found metabolized. Of this, 3.6% was lost as ^{14}CO$_2$, 0.3% was recovered as aminomethylphosphonic acid, and approximately 2.0%, occurred in miscellaneous compounds not further resolved.

Alfnes (1977) studied glyphosate metabolism in *A. repens*. She found a complex pattern of metabolites, eight in all, and like Lund-Høie (1976), separated them into three distinct groups containing 1, 4 and 3 metabolites, respectively. These groups had very similar R_F values to those described by Lund-Høie (1976). Alfnes stated that none of the eight metabolites corresponded to the aminomethylphosphonic acid standard, although it developed within the R_F range of metabolite group 3. No explanation was given for this ambiguity. Glyphosate was also resolved and its concentration in plant extracts varied over the 14-day experimental period, as shown in *Table 3.2*.

These variations in the amounts of the metabolites and glyphosate were explained in the same way as by Lund-Høie (1976). Glyphosate was stated as being 'a very reactive molecule . . . and may form various unstable complexes with natural metabolites'. However, it appears that, from the data shown in *Table 3.2*, such metabolites do not degrade to form glyphosate in the same way as in Norway spruce (*Table 3.1*). Potential losses as ^{14}CO$_2$ were not investigated and a d.p.m. balance was not presented.

Sprankle *et al.* (1978) studied glyphosate metabolism in *Convolvulus arvensis* treated with ^{14}C-glyphosate. Three days after treatment, 7% of the recovered counts was identified as aminomethylphosphonic acid, 2% as glycine and 5% as sarcosine. However, similar amounts of these metabolites were present in the glyphosate treatment solution as impurities, so these data do not unequivocally indicate metabolism by *C. arvensis*. A d.p.m. balance was not presented, and here is a good example where such a method would have helped to distinguish better between the absence of metabolism and degradative metabolism, the products of which may have had only a temporary existence before being lost from the plant due to respiration.

Lund-Høie (1979), using ash (*Fraxinus excelsior*) and birch (*Betula verrucosa*), reported similar results to his earlier work, using Norway spruce (Lund-Høie,

TABLE 3.2   Relative amounts of radioactivity found in glyphosate and metabolites extracted from *Agropyron repens* **treated at the 5-leaf stage (after Alfnes, 1977)**

Plant tissue	Days after application	Metabolite groups			Glyphosate
		1	2 (Recovered activity, %)	3	
Treated leaf	1	12	35	24	29
	7	9	53	17	21
	14	29	56	4	12
New rhizome	1	0	59	0	41
	7	21	44	24	11
	14	43	49	0	8
Roots	1	15	32	27	27
	7	0	38	55	7
	14	0	0	100	0

1976). Seven ^{14}C-metabolites were extracted from these two brush species. However, none of these corresponded to the reference compounds aminomethylphosphonate, methylphosphonate and sarcosine. Additional experiments showed that approximately 7% of the ^{14}C-glyphosate applied to leaves was lost as ^{14}CO$_2$. However, only 20% of the applied glyphosate was absorbed, so, assuming no other losses, approximately 35% of the absorbed ^{14}C became decomposed to ^{14}CO$_2$ within 2 months of application. Interestingly, much less ^{14}CO$_2$ was detected (approximately 10%) after application of ^{14}C-glyphosate to exposed phloem tissue than to leaves. With this method, a higher proportion of the applied glyphosate was absorbed and translocated to the roots (approximately 80%). This result could indicate that the aerial parts of the plant had a greater ability to degrade glyphosate than the roots. Less ^{14}CO$_2$ was produced after application of ^{14}C-glyphosate to ash than to birch. The complex pattern of metabolites, and the fact that none of them corresponded to any of the reference samples of potential glyphosate metabolites, was thought to indicate refixation of the ^{14}CO$_2$, lost as a result of glyphosate decomposition; however, none of the ^{14}C-compounds was identified.

Schultz and Burnside (1980) studied metabolism in *A. cannabinum* and measured separately losses of ^{14}C as ^{14}CO$_2$ (or volatile compounds). No more than 7% of the extracted ^{14}C was in compounds other than glyphosate and less than 0.5% (of the applied activity) was lost as ^{14}CO$_2$ or volatile compounds. No distinction was made between losses as volatile compounds or as ^{14}CO$_2$ and no attempt was made to characterize the 'insignificant' metabolites.

Sandberg, Meggitt and Penner (1980) studied metabolism in *C. arvensis*, *Ipomoea purpurea* and *Cirsium arvense*. In general, all species metabolized glyphosate to aminomethylphosphonic acid to a limited extent (approximately 11% of the recovered ^{14}C). However, appreciable losses of ^{14}C were recorded. With *C. arvensis* and *I. purpurea*, approximately 50% of the applied ^{14}C was lost 25 days after application. This loss was not characterized further, but it was thought likely to be due to loss as ^{14}CO$_2$, or perhaps volatile metabolites.

The most comprehensive report to date on the metabolism of glyphosate in plants is by Rueppel, Marvel and Suba (1975). They looked specifically at herbicide metabolism in maize (*Zea mays*), cotton (*Gossypium hirsutum*), soya bean (*Glycine max*) and wheat. The use of ^{14}C-methane-, ^{14}C-1-glycine- and ^{14}C-2-glycine-labelled glyphosate enabled them to study more precisely the mechanism of metabolism. I am indebted to Dr Rueppel for providing me with a transcript of his talk to the American Chemical Society from which the abstract was taken (see also *Figure 3.2*). Plants were treated via the roots in hydroponic solution. This was considered to be the most efficient means of loading the plant with ^{14}C-glyphosate (see also Marquis, Comes and Yang, 1979). The duration of the experiment was 4 weeks and throughout this time the hydroponic solution was monitored to determine the integrity of the labelled material. A slow decomposition of the glyphosate to ^{14}CO$_2$ and ^{14}C-aminomethylphosphonic acid was discovered. This amount was not quantified, and was likely to be due to microbial activity (see also Chapter 9). Plants were extracted, using water, and these extracts passed through ion-exchange resins to remove impurities. Eluates from the columns were further chromatographed using a two-dimensional t.l.c. method.

Results showed that after exposure to ^{14}C-1-methane-labelled glyphosate (the compound supplied by Monsanto to all other researchers), the major

[14]C-compound resolved was the parent acid in all species except maize, where aminomethylphosphonic acid was the major ^{14}C-compound found. Extraction efficiency was high, and a single extraction with water gave over 90% removal of ^{14}C-activity for two out of the four species. This was considered to 'eliminate the possibility that conjugation is a major metabolic process and that any major metabolites have gone undetected'. This is undoubtedly true for the non-graminaceous species, but perhaps not so for the others. The two cereals used were the two species from which appreciable amounts of ^{14}C remained non-extractable—maize (27%) and wheat (32%). The nature of this 'bound' residue was not investigated further.

The use of glyphosate, labelled in different positions, enabled the following degradative pathway to be suggested. First, glyphosate is degraded to aminomethylphosphonate and a 2-C natural product, probably glyoxylate. Aminomethylphosphonate is then degraded by transamination to formyl phosphonate which decomposes to formaldehyde and inorganic phosphate. Formaldehyde can then be incorporated either directly into natural metabolites or by further decomposition to carbon dioxide with subsequent photochemical refixation. Use of glycine-2-^{14}C-labelled glyphosate confirmed the expected greater incorporation of the label into natural products compared to the glycine-1-^{14}C label. The reason for this is that the C-1 position of the glyoxylate has the potential to be eliminated as carbon dioxide in the glyoxylate and citric acid cycles, whereas the C-2 position is usually incorporated into several intermediate natural products and therefore is retained in the metabolite pool. Although loss of ^{14}C from the plants was predicted in this way, no data were presented confirming or quantifying this. These pathways and degradative routes are summarized in *Figure 3.2*.

Further research

Apart from techniques, there may be differences between plant species which account for some of the variability in the reports summarized in this review. Certainly, there are differences in the response of plant species towards glyphosate. Furthermore, Westra (1980) has reported differences between biotypes of *A. repens*. Differential metabolism may well be involved and there is scope for further research in this area.

Such differences between and within species may be due to genetic influences which determine the plant's ability to metabolize glyphosate. As well as this, there is an interaction with environmental factors (see also Chapter 7). Weather has the potential to influence the induction and activity of various enzyme systems within plants which, in turn, control growth and development. Thus, the activity and metabolism of glyphosate may vary under different environmental conditions. It is well known that environmental factors do affect glyphosate performance (Coupland and Caseley, 1981; see also Chapter 7), but there is virtually no information concerning the effects on herbicide metabolism. Recent research by Coupland (in press) has shown that the poorer activity of glyphosate under warm conditions during the long-term post-application period is largely due to the greater degradation of glyphosate and ultimate loss as CO_2. Further research is needed in this area, especially with regard to the enzymes involved in these degradative processes.

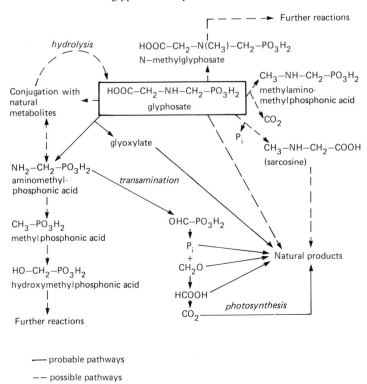

Figure 3.3. Potential metabolic pathways of glyphosate

Few research workers seem to have taken any precautions against microbial breakdown of the herbicide or its metabolites, especially during the extraction and subsequent 'clean-up' stages. Microorganisms in soil and water are known to cause the rapid degradation of both glyphosate and aminomethylphosphonate (Rueppel *et al.*, 1977; see also Chapter 9). It would be useful to know the extent of such microbial effects during sample preparation. Not only would it provide a clearer picture of glyphosate metabolism in general, but it may show whether such effects could be of agronomic significance, affecting glyphosate performance in the field.

Apart from the one report by Rueppel, Marvel and Suba (1975), there is virtually no information concerning the pathways of glyphosate metabolism in higher plants. Little is known, for example, about whether glyphosate becomes conjugated with natural metabolites. Herbicide conjugation is a process whereby phytotoxic substances may be rendered non-phytotoxic, partly due to changes in chemical structure and partly due to the compartmentalizing of the conjugates so that they do not become involved in the general metabolism of the cell. This process is well known for a variety of herbicides, and different types of natural compounds can be involved (e.g. thiols, sugars and amino acids). Although Lund-Høie (1976) and Alfnes (1977) consider glyphosate to be metabolized in this way, others (e.g. Rueppel, Marvel and Suba, 1975; Marquis, Comes and Yang, 1979) have found no evidence of this. However, those compounds identified by Lund-Høie (1976) and Alfnes (1977), which had chromatographic characteristics typical of such conjugates, have not been identified in any detail and further work is necessary to determine (a) if such compounds are real and not artefacts of the extraction procedures, and (b) their chemical nature.

Finally, glyphosate is a substituted amino acid and may or may not be incorporated into natural proteins. There is also the possibility that glyphosate may compete with natural amino acids for enzyme reactive sites, and in this way affect growth and development. To the author's knowledge no work has been published along these lines, apart from the suggestion that glyphosate may be transported across plant cell membranes by an amino acid transport system (Leonard and Shaner, 1979).

Conclusions

Glyphosate has been shown to be extensively metabolized by some plants while remaining virtually intact in others. These differences could be due to many reasons and further research is necessary, using reliable techniques of analysis and identification, to establish whether these effects are a true reflection of differential herbicide metabolism. The metabolic pathways of glyphosate described above, and other possible routes, are summarized in *Figure 3.3*.

References

ALFNES, A.T. (1977). Uptake, distribution and metabolism of glyphosate *N*-(phosphonomethyl)glycine in couch grass (*Agropyron repens* (L.) Beauv.) and the effect on couch grass and rye grass (*Lolium perenne*, L.) at different temperatures, *Dissertation for the Licentiate of Agriculture, University of Norway*, 51 pp.

COUPLAND, D. (in press). The effect of temperature on the activity and metabolism of glyphosate applied to rhizome fragments of *Elymus repens* (= *Agropyron repens*), *Pesticide Science*.

COUPLAND, D. and CASELEY, J.C. (1979). Presence of ^{14}C activity in root exudates and guttation fluid from *Agropyron repens* treated with ^{14}C labelled glyphosate, *New Phytologist*, **83**, 17–22.

COUPLAND, D. and CASELEY, J.C. (1981). Environmental influences on the effects of glyphosate on *Agropyron repens*, *Proceedings of the Association of Applied Biologists Conference 'Grass Weeds in Cereals in the United Kingdom'*, pp. 177–186.

DEVINE, M.D. and BANDEEN, J.D. (1983). Fate of glyphosate in *Agropyron repens* growing under low temperature conditions, *Weed Research*, **23**, 69–75.

GOTTRUP, O., O'SULLIVAN, P.A., SCHRAA, R.J. and VANDEN BORN, W.H. (1976). Uptake, translocation, metabolism and selectivity of glyphosate in Canada thistle and leafy spurge, *Weed Research*, **16**, 197–201.

HASEGAWA, L.S., KUMAMOTO, J. and JORDAN, L.S. (1977). Degradation of glyphosate in Avocado fruit, *Proceedings of the Western Society of Weed Science*, **30**, 55–57.

LEONARD, R.T. and SHANER, D.L. (1979). Studies on glyphosate uptake in a protoplast system, *Abstract 1979 Meeting of the Weed Science Society of America*, p. 98.

LUND-HØIE, K. (1976). The correlation between the tolerance of Norway spruce (*Picea abies*) to glyphosate (*N*-phosphonomethylglycine) and the uptake, distribution, and metabolism of the herbicide in the spruce plants, *Meldinger fra Norges landbrukshøiskole*, **55**, 1–26.

LUND-HØIE, K. (1979). The physiological fate of glyphosate-^{14}C in *Betula verrucosa* and *Fraxinus excelsior*. The effect of ammonium sulphate and the environment on the herbicide, *Meldinger fra Norges landbrukshøiskole*, **58**, 1–24.

MARQUIS, L.Y., COMES, R.D. and YANG, C.P. (1979). Selectivity of glyphosate in creeping red fescue and reed canarygrass, *Weed Research*, **19**, 335–342.

O'DONOVAN, J.T. and O'SULLIVAN, P.A. (1982). The antagonistic action of 2,4-D and bromoxynil on glyphosate phytotoxity to barley (*Hordeum vulgare*), *Weed Science*, **30**, 30–34.

PUTNAM, A.R. (1976). Fate of glyphosate in deciduous fruit trees, *Weed Science*, **24**, 425–430.

RODRIGUES, J.J.V., WORSHAM, A.D. and CORBIN, F.T. (1982). Exudation of glyphosate from wheat (*Triticum aestivum*) plants and its effects on interplanted corn (*Zea mays*) and soybeans (*Glycine max*), *Weed Science*, **30**, 316–320.

RUEPPEL, M.L., BRIGHTWELL, B.B., SCHAEFER, J. and MARVEL, J.T. (1977). Metabolism and degradation of glyphosate in soil and water, *Journal of Agricultural and Food Chemistry,* **25,** 517–528.

RUEPPEL, M.L., MARVEL, J.T. and SUBA, L.A. (1975). The metabolism of N-phosphonomethylglycine in corn, soybeans and wheat, Abstract, *Papers of the American Chemical Society,* 170th meeting, PEST 26.

RUEPPEL, M.L., MARVEL, J.T., SUBA, L.A. and SCHAEFER, J. (1975). The characterization of N-phosphonomethylglycine and its plant metabolites by NMR, derivatization, GC/MS/COM, and isotopic dilution techniques, Abstract, *Papers of the American Chemical Society,* 170th meeting, PEST 27.

SANDBERG, C.L., MEGGITT, W.F. and PENNER, D. (1980). Absorption, translocation and metabolism of ^{14}C-glyphosate in several weed species, *Weed Research,* **20,** 195–200.

SCHULTZ, M.E. and BURNSIDE, O.C. (1980). Absorption, translocation and metabolism of 2,4-D and glyphosate in hemp dogbane (*Apocynum cannabinum*), *Weed Science,* **28,** 13–20.

SPRANKLE, P., SANDBERG, C.L., MEGGITT, W.F. and PENNER, D. (1978). Separation of glyphosate and possible metabolites by thin-layer chromatography, *Weed Science,* **26,** 673–674.

WESTRA, P. (1980). Control of quackgrass (*Agropyron repens*) biotypes with glyphosate, *PhD thesis,* University of Minnesota, USA, 170 pp.

WYRILL, J.B. and BURNSIDE, O.C. (1976). Absorption, translocation and metabolism of 2,4-D and glyphosate in common milkweed and hemp dogbane, *Weed Science,* **24,** 557–566.

ZANDSTRA, B.H. and NISHIMOTO, R.K. (1977). Movement and activity of glyphosate in purple nutsedge, *Weed Science,* **25,** 268–274.

Chapter 4

Interactions between glyphosate and metals essential for plant growth

G. Nilsson
Swedish University of Agricultural Sciences, Uppsala, Sweden

Introduction

The metal-chelating properties of glyphosate, *N*-(phosphonomethyl)glycine, were mentioned in one of the first papers concerning the mode of action of this substance (Jaworski, 1972). Whether metal chelation takes place within plant cells is unknown, but there are studies on glyphosate effects on physiology where metals may be involved (Abu-Irmaileh and Jordan, 1977; Kitchen, Witt and Rieck, 1981).

The effect of metals on the effectiveness of glyphosate as a herbicide has been studied in both field and greenhouse experiments (Wills, 1973; Phillips, 1975; Sandberg, Meggitt and Penner, 1976; Stahlman and Phillips, 1979).

Glyphosate interferes with several metal ions. Its effectiveness is reduced if it is supplied together with various metal ions. Whether this phenomenon is due to the formation of a glyphosate–metal complex, unavailable to the plant, or also to interaction with metals after glyphosate has entered the plant, is not known.

Mechanisms of action other than effects on the shikimic pathway have been proposed (Brecke and Duke, 1980; Kitchen, Witt and Rieck, 1981). Its mode of action need not be restricted to one process, but could cover a complex of effects. None of the postulated mechanisms has yet been shown to be specifically connected to chelating properties. However, the possibility remains that glyphosate could bind to metals within the plant and, as other chelate complexes, affect important physiological processes.

The names glyphosate and ^{14}C-glyphosate in this chapter refer to *N*-(phosphonomethyl)glycine, which is applied usually as the isopropylamine salt of glyphosate. Where the parent acid alone was used this will be stated, where this could be ascertained from the reviewed papers.

Influence by various metal salts

The effect of metal ions on the phytotoxicity of glyphosate has been studied in several experiments. Inactivation of both monovalent and polyvalent ions have been investigated. Wills (1973) reported that potassium and sodium salts initially had little effect but extended control in long-term experiments. In short-term studies potassium, sodium and calcium increased and iron and zinc decreased the

35

toxicity of glyphosate. Phillips (1975) found that iron, aluminium and calcium reduced the phytotoxicity of glyphosate. Zinc had less effect, magnesium only a slight effect, whereas potassium and sodium did not affect the glyphosate activity at all. Hanson and Rieck (1976) studied the inhibitory effects of iron and aluminium. They found that the glyphosate–metal complex was absorbed and translocated more rapidly than the herbicide alone. Iron formed a stronger chelate with glyphosate than aluminium, and in field trials the iron–glyphosate treatments gave less control than did aluminium–glyphosate.

The effect of calcium in the spray solution was investigated by Sandberg, Meggitt and Penner (1976). They found it reduced the effectiveness of glyphosate and that inhibition was related to the diluent volume. Glyphosate activity was more sensitive to calcium at higher diluent volumes. Stahlman and Phillips (1979) obtained similar results and observed decreased inhibition at calcium concentrations higher than 10 mmol l^{-1}. There seems to be a difference between monovalent and polyvalent ions. Brecke and Duke (1980), however, observed a very rapid inhibition of the absorption of ^{86}Rb into isolated bean cells. They also postulated a mechanism of action involving inhibition of ion uptake but not due to chelation.

Glyphosate effects compared with metal deficiency

Chloroplasts and chlorophyll

When bean (*Phaseolus vulgaris*) or pea (*Pisum sativum*) plants, for example, are treated with sublethal doses of glyphosate, the youngest leaves show a very pronounced interveinal chlorosis, similar to micronutrient deficiency. During subsequent growth the chlorosis first disappears but then develops in the new leaves. Evidently there is a severe effect on chlorophyll, probably on synthesis. Kitchen, Witt and Rieck (1981) reported detrimental effects on the synthesis of δ-aminolevulinic acid (ALA), a precursor in the biosynthesis of chlorophyll, which is supposed to be iron dependent (Marsh, Evans and Matrone, 1963). Chloroplasts are damaged by glyphosate (Campbell, Evans and Reed, 1976; Pihakaski and Pihakaski, 1980) and their ultrastucture is sensitive to deficiency of manganese (Homann, 1967) and zinc (Thomson and Weier, 1962), both of which interfere with glyphosate.

Catalase

Glyphosate inhibits catalase (Abu-Irmaileh and Jordan, 1977), an iron-containing enzyme which is sensitive to iron deficiency (Agarwala, Shanna and Farooq, 1965). Kitchen, Witt and Rieck (1981) suggested that the inhibition of this enzyme could be due to decreased porphyrin synthesis through glyphosate effects on ALA formation.

Glyphosate effects in water cultures as affected by metal ions

Reversal of glyphosate activity by iron and manganese

Glyphosate is a foliar-applied herbicide and in most experiments is sprayed onto the leaves. It is also absorbed by the roots when supplied in the nutrient solution in water culture. After 5 days the fresh weight of wheat (*Triticum aestivum*) plants grown in 0.05 mmol l^{-1} glyphosate is about 60% of that of the untreated plants. A simultaneous addition of ferric citrate or $MnCl_2$ reduced the phytotoxicity of glyphosate (*Figure 4.1*). Effects on the accumulation of free amino acids (Nilsson,

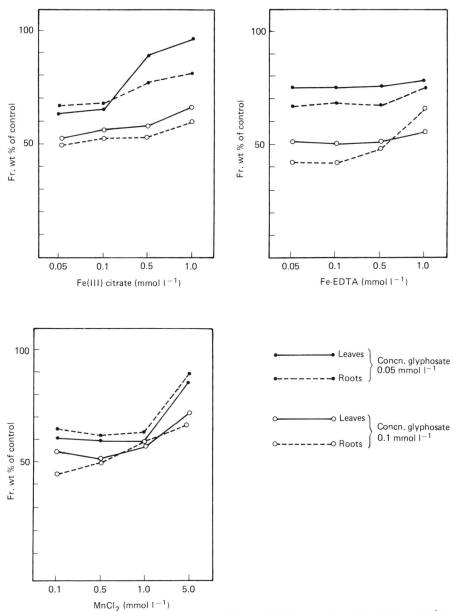

Figure 4.1. Effects of additional iron (Fe^{3+}) and manganese (Mn^{2+}) on the glyphosate efficacy in young wheat (*Triticum aestivum*) plants

1977) and on chlorophyll content are also reversed. Glyphosate effects are not inhibited when iron is added as complexes of EDDHA and EDTA. This is surprising, as ferric citrate is no better than Fe–EDTA and Fe–EDDHA as an iron source in water cultures without glyphosate. The roots of plants grown with ferric citrate are poorer than those grown in Fe–EDTA and Fe–EDDHA.

Detoxification due to the formation of an inactive iron–glyphosate complex could mean that citric iron is more available to glyphosate than iron bound to EDTA and EDDHA. However, the stability constants of iron complex with citrate and EDTA are similar (Price, 1968). In the present experiments, no precipitates were formed when metals were added in excess.

Growth effects on iron-deficient roots

Both glyphosate and EDTA have a positive effect on the root growth of iron-deficient wheat plants (*Table 4.1*). The simultaneous removal of manganese

TABLE 4.1   Growth effects of glyphosate and EDTA on iron-deficient wheat (*Triticum aestivum*) roots grown in the absence of manganese and zinc

	Control		Glyphosate, 0.05 mmol l^{-1}		EDTA, 0.05 mmol l^{-1}	
	Length (cm)	Fr. wt (mg)	Length (cm)	Fr. wt (mg)	Length (cm)	Fr. wt (mg)
Complete nutrient solution (CNS)	11.0	72	11.4	54	13.3	74
CNS–Fe	4.5	38	10.1	57	12.4	94
CNS–Fe–Mn	5.2	46	10.6	60	12.7	84
CNS–Fe–Zn	13.1	84	11.9	63	13.9	106

from the nutrient solution has no effect on either root weight or length. The positive effects of glyphosate and EDTA remain. If zinc is excluded from the medium the roots develop almost normally without further effects of glyphosate and EDTA on the root length. The stimulation of roots in an iron-free medium might be due to increased liberation of iron from the grain. Thus, glyphosate seems, by chelation or otherwise, to facilitate the release of iron allowing normal root growth. The results in *Table 4.1* suggest that glyphosate blocks the zinc ion so giving a more favourable zinc–iron balance. High concentrations of zinc are known to reduce the uptake of iron (Lingle, Tiffin and Brown, 1963; Adriano, Paulsen and Murphy, 1971). Since glyphosate and EDTA seem to stimulate root growth in a similar manner, it is likely that glyphosate forms a chelate with zinc resulting in either decreased zinc uptake or the formation of an inactive zinc complex. Analysis of glyphosate-treated plants (see *Table 4.3*) suggests decreased zinc uptake as the most probable reason.

Effects of ferric citrate and MnCl$_2$ on uptake of ^{14}C-glyphosate

Wheat plants were grown in nutrient solutions with two concentrations of either ferric citrate or MnCl$_2$ and glyphosate at 0.05 mmol l^{-1}, including labelled material. Both iron additions reversed the adverse effect of glyphosate on leaf weight, but only the higher concentration reduced the effect on the roots (*Table 4.2*). Accumulation of ^{14}C-glyphosate in the leaves was increased by ferric citrate. Compared with plants grown in the basic solution, MnCl$_2$ had a similar effect.

TABLE 4.2   Influence of Fe(III) citrate and MnCl$_2$ on the absorption and translocation of ^{14}C-glyphosate in young wheat (*Triticum aestivum*) plants

| | *Fr. wt (%) of untreated plants** | | *DPM† g^{-1} fr. wt × 1000* | |
	Leaves	Roots	Leaves	Roots
Glyphosate, 0.05 mmol l^{-1}	75	74	11.0	36
– Fe(III)–citrate, 0.5 mmol l^{-1}	101	70	16.0	39
– Fe(III)–citrate, 1 mmol l^{-1}	108	86	16.6	44
– MnCl$_2$, 1 mmol l^{-1}	81	75	20.2	48
– MnCl$_2$, mmol l^{-1}	97	91	23.9	85

* Grown with corresponding concentration of iron ɛ ɹ manganese but without glyphosate.
† Disintegrations per minute.

Stimulation of the uptake of glyphosate by iron and manganese agrees with the results of Hanson and Rieck (1976). That the herbicide is absorbed and translocated, despite the metal additions, suggests that inactivation is due to both a decreased uptake and the formation of a stable metal complex in which the glyphosate molecule remains inactive even after the entrance into the plant.

Effects on metal content and absorption of $^{65}Zn^{2+}$ and $^{59}Fe^{3+}$

Analysis of wheat leaves for copper, iron, manganese and zinc showed that glyphosate treatment increased the proportion of iron relative to copper, manganese and zinc (*Table 4.3*). The increase in iron content is probably due to glyphosate-stimulated iron absorption. Uptake experiments with $^{59}Fe^{3+}$ and $^{65}Zn^{2+}$ in wheat and pea (*Pisum sativum*) showed that the accumulation of labelled iron was higher than that of zinc in both leaves and roots. Formation of glyphosate complexes probably prevents zinc from competing with iron uptake. For the roots, iron and manganese seem to behave differently to copper and zinc. Unlike copper and zinc, the concentration of iron and manganese does not decrease continuously. This agrees with the values for glyphosate–metal complex constants (Madsen, Christensen and Gottlieb-Petersen, 1978); K_m for Cu^{2+} and Zn^{2+} are higher than that for Mn^{2+} (see also Chapter 2). Unfortunately, there are no corresponding values available for Fe^{3+}.

TABLE 4.3   Effects of glyphosate on the content of some metals in wheat (*Triticum aestivum*) plants

| *Glyphosate (mmol l^{-1})* | *μg metal g^{-1}fr. wt* | | | | | | | |
| | Leaves | | | | Roots | | | |
	Fe	Mn	Zn	Cu	Fe	Mn	Zn	Cu
0	27	13	8	12	72	41	14	40
0.01	26	13	7	15	61	36	11	34
0.05	39	18	12	9	77	38	10	20
0.1	48	19	11	10	99	41	9	14

Effects of metal ions on leaf absorption of ^{14}C-labelled glyphosate

Several metal ions reduce the activity of foliar applications of glyphosate (Wills, 1973; Phillips 1975). The effect of some divalent cations on the absorption and distribution of ^{14}C-(methyl)-labelled glyphosate was studied using auto-radiography. Calcium, iron, magnesium, manganese and zinc were supplied simul-taneously with the herbicide (*Figure 4.2*)

After 24 h, most radioactivity was retained in the metal-treated leaves. Much of the substance is probably absorbed in the leaf, but has not entered the symplast. The most pronounced effect was caused by iron, but all the metals used seemed to inhibit the uptake of glyphosate into the treated leaflet. After 72 h, the inhibition due to iron remained, while much of the radioactivity had disappeared from leaves treated with the other ions. Quantitative radioassay showed that most labelled glyphosate remained in the iron-treated leaflet. With the other treatments most of the radioactivity, lost from the treated leaflet, was in the top shoot. This indicated that translocation from the site of application to other parts of the plant is not affected by metal ions. The inhibition seems to be connected rather with entry to the cell, which is also the main barrier for glyphosate alone (Richard and Slife, 1979). The inhibition pattern in leaves is different from that of the roots, at least for iron and manganese, which stimulate rather than prevent the uptake of glyphosate through the roots.

Conclusions

Observed interactions between glyphosate and metal ions can be summarized as follows:

(1) Iron, as ferric citrate, and $MnCl_2$ reversed the inhibitory effects of glyphosate on growth. Iron, as Fe–EDTA and Fe–EDDHA, had almost no effect.
(2) Without any iron supply, glyphosate stimulated the root growth in water cultures.
(3) Ferric citrate and $MnCl_2$, at concentrations which reverse glyphosate activity, stimulated glyphosate absorption.
(4) Glyphosate increased iron in the leaves. It had some effect on manganese and zinc. In roots, copper and zinc decreased.
(5) Glyphosate stimulated the accumulation of $^{59}Fe^{3+}$ in both roots and leaves, but retarded accumulation of $^{65}Zn^{2+}$.
(6) Various metal ions delayed the absorption of glyphosate into leaf cells. Translocation from the leaf to other parts of the plant was not affected to the same extent.

Glyphosate interferes with various metal ions. The result of this is, on one hand, reduced glyphosate activity and, on the other, changed absorption and translocation of the metal ions. The formation of a metal complex, unavailable to the plant, is not sufficient to explain the inactivation by metals when glyphosate is supplied through the roots. As iron and manganese can reverse the effects of glyphosate and simultaneously stimulate absorption, it is likely that inactivation also occurs inside the plant. The plant does not show any lack of iron and manganese with glyphosate treatment, but additional supply reduces glyphosate

24 h

72 h

(a) Control

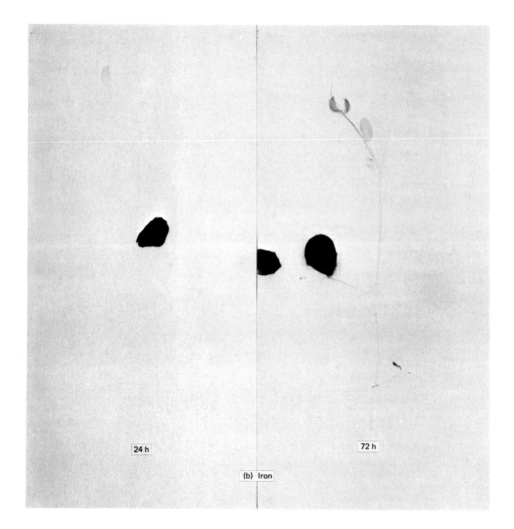

24 h

72 h

(b) Iron

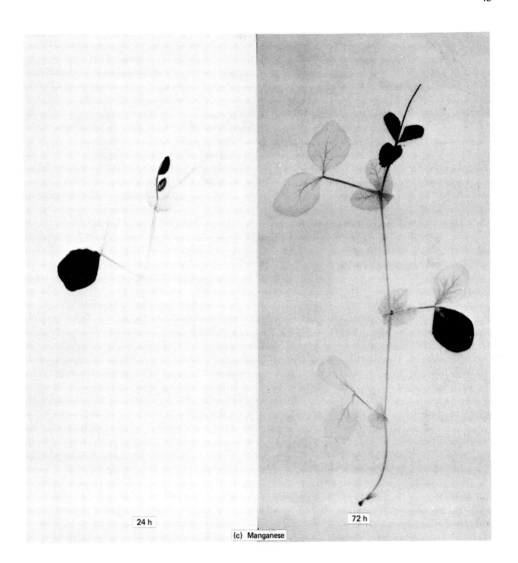

24 h   72 h

(c) Manganese

44

24 h   72 h

(d) Zinc

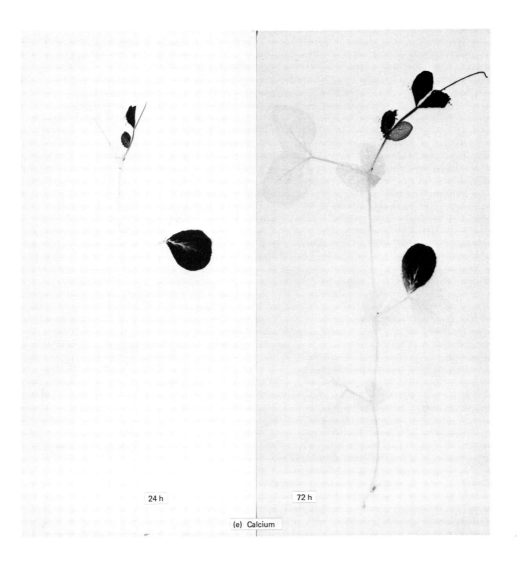

24 h

72 h

(e) Calcium

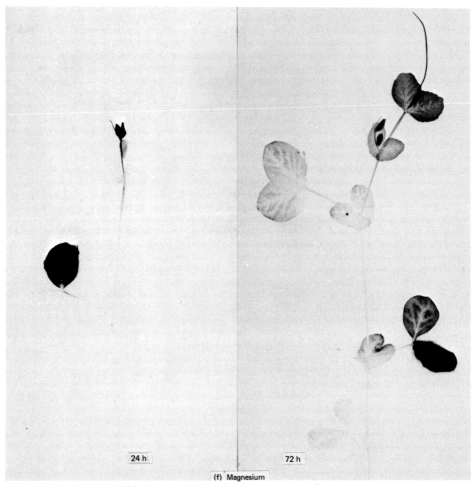

24 h

72 h

(f) Magnesium

Figure 4.2. Distribution of ^{14}C-glyphosate in pea (*Pisum sativum*) plants as affected by iron (Fe^{3+}), manganese (Mn^{2+}), zinc (Zn^{2+}), calcium (Ca^{2+}) and magnesium (Mg^{2+})

activity. Differential effects on the absorption of $^{59}Fe^{3+}$ and $^{65}Zn^{2+}$, the growth stimulation of iron-deficient roots and the decreased proportions of copper and zinc in the roots suggest that glyphosate is able to interfere with the utilization of these metals.

The fact that various metals of common occurrence in natural water delay the uptake and reduce the phytotoxicity of glyphosate is perhaps the most important consequence of the chelating properties of glyphosate. Interactions with micronutrients and iron are obvious and should not be ignored, even if they are unconnected with the central mode of action.

References

ABU-IRMAILEH, B.E. and JORDAN, L.S. (1977). Some aspects of the mechanism of action of glyphosate, *Proceedings of the Western Society of Weed Science*, **30**, 57–63.

ADRIANO, D.C., PAULSEN, G.M. and MURPHY, L.S. (1971). Phosphorus–iron and phosphorus–zinc relationship in corn (*Zea mays* L.) seedlings as affected by mineral nutrition, *Agronomy Journal*, **63**, 36–39.

AGARWALA, S.C., SHANNA, C.P. and FAROOQ, S. (1965). Effect of iron supply on growth, chlorophyll, tissue iron and activity of certain enzymes in maize and radish, *Plant Physiology*, **40**, 493–499.

BRECKE, B.J. and DUKE, W.B. (1980). Effect of glyphosate on intact bean plants (*Phaseolus vulgaris* L.) and isolated cells, *Plant Physiology*, **66**, 656–659.

CAMPBELL, W.F., EVANS, J.O. and REED, S.C. (1976). Effects of glyphosate on chloroplast ultrastructure of qwackgrass mesophyll cells, *Weed Science*, **24**, 22–25.

HANSON, C.L. and RIECK, C.E. (1976). The effect of iron and aluminium on glyphosate toxicity, *Proceedings of the Southern Weed Science Society*, **29**, 49.

HOMANN, P.E. (1967). Studies on the manganese of the chloroplast, *Plant Physiology*, **42**, 997–1007.

JAWORSKI, E.G. (1972). Mode of action of *N*-phosphonomethylglycine: inhibition of aromatic amino acid biosynthesis, *Journal of Agriculture and Food Chemistry*, **20**, 1195–1198.

KITCHEN, L.M., WITT, W.W. and RIECK, C.E. (1981). Inhibition of δ-aminolevulinic acid synthesis by glyphosate, *Weed Science*, **29**, 571–577.

LINGLE, J.C., TIFFIN, L.O. and BROWN, J.C. (1963). Iron-uptake transport of soybeans as influenced by other cations, *Plant Physiology*, **38**, 71–76.

MADSEN, H.E.L., CHRISTENSEN, H.H. and GOTTLIEB-PETERSEN, C. (1978). Stability constants of copper(II), zinc, manganese(II), calcium and magnesium complexes of *N*-(phosponomethyl)glycine (glyphosate), *Acta Chemica Scandinavica*, **A32**, 79–83.

MARSH, H.V. JR., EVANS, H.J. and MATRONE, G. (1963). Investigations on the role of iron in chlorophyll metabolism. II. Effect of iron deficiency on chlorophyll synthesis, *Plant Physiology*, **38**, 638–642.

NILSSON, G. (1977). Effects of glyphosate on the amino acid content in spring wheat plants, *Swedish Journal of Agricultural Research*, **7**, 153–157.

PHILLIPS, W.M. (1975). Glyphosate phytotoxicity as affected by carries quality and application volume, *Proceedings of the North Central Weed Control Conference*, **30**, 115.

PIHAKASKI, S. and PIHAKASKI, K. (1980). Effects of glyphosate on ultrastructure and photosynthesis of *Pellia epiphylla*, *Annals of Botany*, **46**, 133–141.

PRICE, C.A. (1968). Iron compounds and plant nutrition, *Annual Review of Plant Physiology*, **19**, 239–248.

RICHARD, E.P. JR. and SLIFE, E.P. (1979). *In vivo* and *in vitro* characterization of the foliar entry of glyphosate in hemp dogbane (*Apocynum canabinum*), *Weed Science*, **27**, 426–433.

SANDBERG, C.L., MEGGITT, W.F. and PENNER, D. (1976). Effect of spray volume and calcium on glyphosate phytotoxicity, *Proceedings of the North Central Weed Control Conference*, **31**, 31.

STAHLMAN, P.W. and PHILLIPS, W.M. (1979). Effects of water quality and spray volume on glyphosate phytotoxicity, *Weed Science*, **27**, 38–41.

THOMSON, W.W. and WEIER, T.E. (1962). The fine structure of chloroplasts from mineral-deficient leaves of *Phaseolus vulgaris*, *American Journal of Botany*, **49**, 1047–1056.

WILLS, G.D. (1973). Effects of inorganic salts on the toxicity of glyphosate to purple nutsedge, *Abstracts of Weed Science Society of America*, p.59.

Chapter 5

Mode of action of glyphosate—a literature analysis

D.J. Cole
University of Oxford, UK

Introduction

The intense interest generated by glyphosate, due to its outstanding properties and widespread use, has been paralleled by investigation into its biochemical mode of action. This has resulted in an extensive literature dealing with effects on a wide variety of cellular processes. As a consequence, the behaviour of glyphosate is now better understood than that of many longer established herbicides. Several résumés of glyphosate's action, varying in scope, have already appeared (Ashton and Crafts, 1981; Cole, 1982; Fedtke, 1982; Hoagland and Duke, 1982).

A substantial body of work has been concerned with the effects of glyphosate on the formation of aromatic amino acids. This has culminated in the establishment of glyphosate as a potent inhibitor of the shikimic acid pathway, a site of action unique among herbicides. The two major initial consequences of action at this site are the arrest of protein synthesis and the prevention of secondary compound formation. These are directly due to prevention of formation of the aromatic amino acids phenylalanine (Phe), tyrosine (Tyr) and tryptophan (Tryp), major products of the shikimic acid pathway. Glyphosate influences a plethora of other processes, several of which have potential importance. Inhibition of chlorophyll synthesis occurs in a manner which suggests that a general inhibition of porphyrin-containing compounds may occur. Reduction in the level of indolyl-3-acetic acid (IAA) appears to occur by activation of its oxidative metabolism and this may be a direct consequence of reduced secondary phenolic compound formation. The accumulation of ammonia may also be of importance.

At present, the cumulative data strongly suggest the shikimic acid pathway as a primary target. However, this does not rule out the possibility of other independent sites of action; indeed, the success of some herbicides may be due to an ability to exert several independent effects.

Several unusual properties of glyphosate have been important in both the design of experiments and interpretation of data. These are the high water solubility of its salts; extensive translocation, with accumulation only in meristematic areas; structural similarity to a number of phosphorylated metabolites; and ability to chelate divalent metal cations. However, the most significant property of glyphosate with respect to mode of action is its negligible animal toxicity; thus, inhibition of the shikimic acid pathway, which occurs only in plants and microorganisms, may explain this favourable difference in toxicity.

48

The mode of action of glyphosate has been discerned from work at a range of levels from the whole plant to cell-free reactions. For the major part, experiments involved the use of the pure free acid and, to a lesser extent, its isopropylamine salt. However, where foliar application to whole plants was used, the herbicide was normally applied as the isopropylamine salt, together with one of several surfactants. While such formulations would be expected to enhance the penetration of glyphosate, it is unlikely that the physiological activity of the pure acid would be modified significantly.

Interference with the biosynthesis of aromatic amino acids

Glyphosate is a competitive inhibitor of 5-enolpyruvylshikimic acid-3-phosphate (EPSP) synthase (Amrhein *et al.*, 1982), an enzyme of the shikimic acid pathway (*Figure 5.1*, enzyme 6). To date, this appears to be the primary site of action of the herbicide. The triple-branched pathway is of key importance in linking primary and secondary metabolism and is initiated by the condensation of phosphoenolpyruvate (PEP) with erythrose-4-phosphate. Major end-products of the pathway are the aromatic amino acids, essential for protein synthesis. In addition, Phe feeds into secondary phenolic compound pathways via the important regulatory enzyme phenylalanine ammonia-lyase (PAL) to produce a diverse array of phenolic end-products, e.g. lignin precursors, flavonoids and tannins. In graminaceous species, Tyr can also serve as a substrate for these compounds. Chorismic acid also gives rise directly to a number of phenolic compounds. The shikimic acid pathway had previously been considered as a target for rationally designed herbicides but analogues of dehydroshikimic acid, although inhibitory to shikimic acid dehydrogenase, were not herbicidal when applied to the whole plant (Baille *et al.*, 1972).

Prior to the demonstration of glyphosate as a specific enzyme inhibitor, substantial evidence had implicated inhibition of aromatic amino acid formation, but this was largely circumstantial. Initially, several workers found that growth inhibition by glyphosate in a variety of systems could be alleviated by simultaneous supplemental feeding of exogenous aromatic amino acids. Subsequently, herbicide toxicity was found to be accompanied by large increases in extractable PAL activity. Also, increases in the free aromatic amino acid content and often decreases in phenolic compound content of plants were observed. More specifically, glyphosate caused a massive accumulation of shikimic acid, indicating interference with a metabolic step subsequent to the formation of this intermediate. These phenomena are considered in detail in the following sections.

Alleviation of growth inhibition

The first indication of the interference of glyphosate in the metabolism of aromatic amino acids was the finding by Jaworski (1972) that growth inhibition of *Lemna gibba* and *Rhizobium japonicum* could be alleviated by applying mixtures of Phe, Tyr and Tryp. Although no biochemical data were presented, he expressed the likelihood that the formation of these compounds was prevented. Such reversal of toxicity was subsequently shown in a wide variety of microorganisms and cultured plant cells (*Table 5.1*). However, only in the case of *Arabidopsis thaliana* has this been demonstrated for an intact, higher terrestrial plant (Gresshoff, 1979).

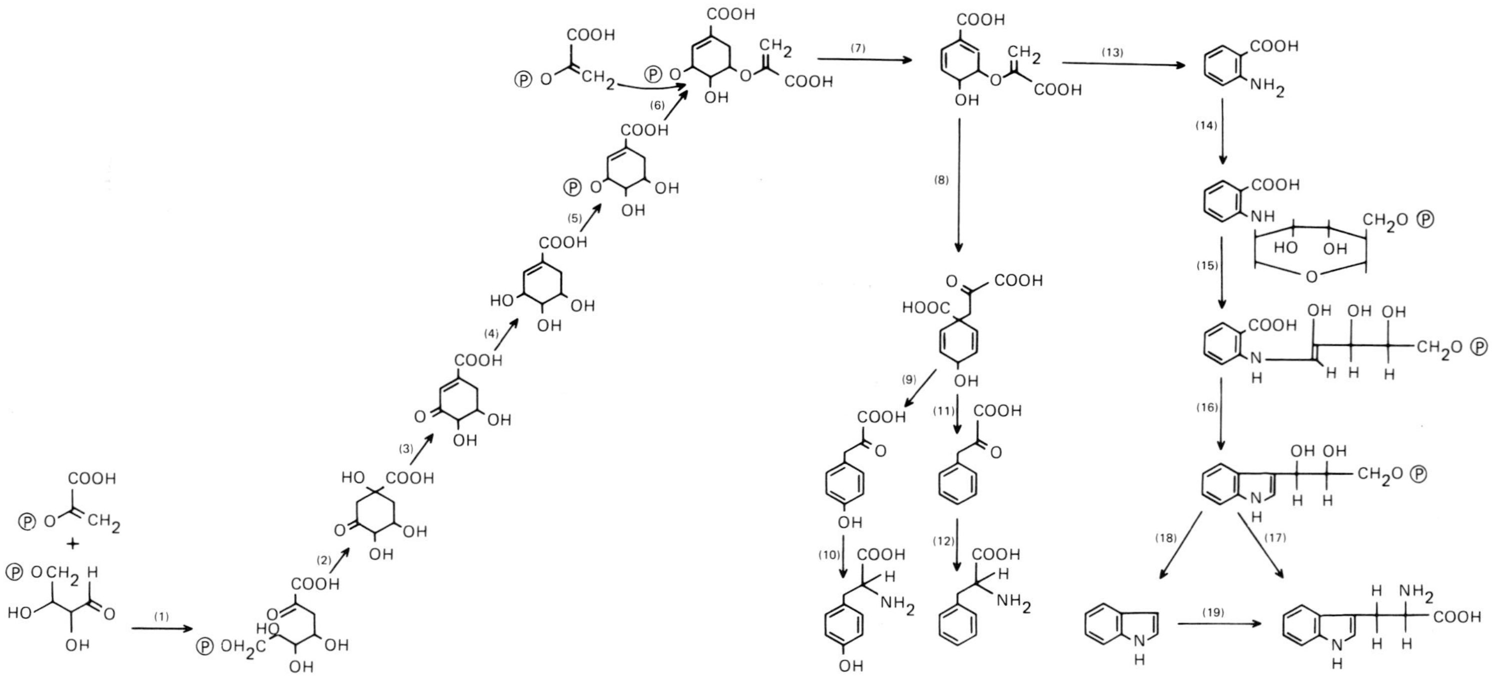

Figure 5.1. The shikimic acid pathway (see tabulated key opposite)

Key to Figure 5.1

Substrate (anion)	Enzyme
(1) Phosphoenolpyruvate and erythrose-4-phosphate	Phospho-2-keto-3-deoxy-heptonate aldolase (3-deoxy-D-*arabino*-heptulosonate-7-phosphate (DAHP) synthase) (E.C.4.1.2.15)
(2) 7-Phospho-2-keto-3-deoxy-D-*arabino*-heptonate	3-Dehydroquinate synthase (E.C.4.6.1.3)
(3) 3-Dehydroquinate	3-Dehydroquinate dehydratase (E.C.4.2.1.10)
(4) 3-Dehydroshikimate	Shikimate dehydrogenase (E.C. 1.1.1.25)
(5) Shikimate	Shikimate kinase (E.C. 2.7.1.71)
(6) Shikimate-3-phosphate	5-*enol*Pyruvylshikimate-3-phosphate (EPSP) synthase (E.C. 2.5.1.19)
(7) 5-*enol*Pyruvylshikimate-3-phosphate	Chorismate synthase (E.C. 4.6.1.4)
(8) Chorismate	Chorismate mutase (E.C. 5.4.99.4)
(9) Prephenate	Prephenate dehydrogenase (E.C. 1.3.1.13)
(10) *p*-Hydroxyphenylpyruvate	Tyrosine aminotransferase (E.C. 2.6.1.5)
(11) Prephenate	Prephenate dehydratase (E.C. 4.2.1.51)
(12) Phenylpyruvate	Phenylalanine aminotransferase (E.C. 2.6.1.58)
(13) Chorismate	Anthranilate synthase (E.C. 4.1.3.27)
(14) Anthranilate	Anthranilate phosphoribosyltransferase (E.C. 2.4.2.18)
(15) Phosphoribosyl anthranilate	Phosphoribosyl anthranilate isomerase
(16) Carboxyphenylamino-deoxyribulose-5-phosphate	Tryptophan synthase (indoleglycerol-phosate aldolase), (E.C. 4.2.1.20)
(17) Indole-3-glycerol phosphate	Tryptophan synthase
(18) Indole-3-glycerol phosphate	Tryptophan synthase
(19) Indole	Tryptophan synthase

TABLE 5.1 Growth inhibition by glyphosate: alleviatory effects of exogenous aromatic amino acids

Alleviation	Reference	Species
Successful (partial to complete)	Jaworski, 1972	*Lemna gibba, Rhizobium japonicum*
	Haderlie, Widholm and Slife (1977)	Carrot (*Daucus carota*) and tobacco (*Nicotiana tabacum*) cells
	Gresshoff (1979)	*Escherichia coli, Chlamydomonas reinhardii, Arabidopsis thaliana*, carrot and soya bean (*Glycine max*) cells
	Davis and Harvey (1979)	Lucerne (*Medicago sativa*) callus
	Amrhein *et al.* (1980)	*Galium mollugo* cells*
	Roisch and Lingens (1974; 1980)	*Escherichia coli*
Unsuccessful	Brecke (1976)	Bean (*Phaseolus vulgaris*)
	Duke and Hoagland (1978)	Maize (*Zea mays*)
	Cole, Dodge and Caseley (1980)	Wheat (*Triticum aestivum*), *Agropyron repens*
	Duke and Hoagland (1981)	Soya bean
	Lee (1980)	Tobacco callus
	Berlin and Witte (1981)	Tobacco cells†

*Alleviation with casein hydrolysate.
†Marginal alleviation only.

Generally, effectiveness of single agents was of the order Phe > Tyr > Tryp, with the mixture Phe and Tyr being particularly effective. In some cases, casein hydrolysate could be substituted. Reversal of toxicity in carrot (*Daucus carota*) cells was not due to any influence of antidotal compounds on rate of glyphosate uptake (Haderlie, Widholm and Slife, 1977). A mutant tobacco (*Nicotiana tabacum*) cell line resistant to *p*-fluorophenylalanine and having free Phe levels six times that of wild-type cells showed partial resistance to glyphosate, due apparently to lesser absorption of the herbicide (Haderlie, 1975).

In several cases, application of aromatic amino acids has no effect on toxicity of glyphosate (*Table 5.1*) despite the use, sometimes of wide ranges of potential antidotes or administration, prior to or after that of glyphosate. These were largely attempts to modify toxicity to whole higher plants or their derivitive organs. Despite the fact that growth of soya bean (*Glycine max*) could not be alleviated, roots readily absorbed ^{14}C-labelled Phe and Tyr in the presence of the herbicide and these were translocated and incorporated into secondary products. Supplemental feeding also increased the level of secondary products (Duke and Hoagland, 1981). Thus, in this case at least, the ineffectiveness of aromatic amino acids on growth could not be ascribed to a failure of these agents to enter the particular intracellular pools which are modified by glyphosate. It is known that distinct pools of these amino acids in cells can be modified independently and that some pools may be metabolically inactive (Berlin and Widholm, 1978; Nover *et al.*, 1979; Sasse, Backs-Hüsemann and Barz, 1979). Other factors may therefore be important in the toxicity of glyphosate to the whole plant.

Inhibition of the shikimic acid pathway

The direct interference of glyphosate upon the shikimic acid pathway has been shown by the effects of the compound on the metabolic fate of shikimic acid. In buckwheat (*Fagopyrum esculentum*), glyphosate inhibited ^{14}C-shikimic acid incorporation into Phe, Tyr, protein and lignin (Holländer and Amrhein, 1980). The fact that the formation of both Phe and Tyr was prevented indicated an inhibition site at or prior to chorismate mutase. Glyphosate also inhibited the incorporation of ^{14}C-shikimic acid into Phe, Tyr, protein and cinnamoyl putrescines in tobacco cells (Berlin and Witte, 1981). Evidence for inhibition of the pathway prior to its divergence at the metabolism of chorismic acid was provided by observing the incorporation of ^{14}C-shikimic acid into Tryp (Holländer and Amrhein, 1980). In buckwheat, this conversion can ordinarily be demonstrated only at low levels, but increases upon the addition of Phe which inhibits Phe/Tyr production by feedback control. In the presence of Phe, glyphosate inhibited label incorporation into Tryp (*Figure 5.2*). This was confirmed by examining anthraquinone synthesis in *Galium mollugo* cells. In this species, anthraquinones are formed from chorismic acid via *O*-succinylbenzoic acid. Glyphosate inhibited anthraquinone synthesis (*Figure 5.3*); this was negated by chorismic acid and *O*-succinylbenzoic acid, although the latter was also stimulatory in the absence of glyphosate. Neither Phe nor Tyr were active reversal agents (Amrhein *et al.*, 1980).

These observations narrowed down the possible site of action to the three enzymatic steps involved in the conversion of shikimic acid to chorismic acid. Inhibition of a particular enzyme should, in the absence of a regulatory feedback mechanism in the early part of the pathway, precipitate an accumulation of the substrate of the inhibited enzyme. An enormous accumulation of shikimic acid

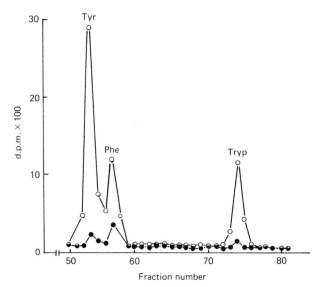

Figure 5.2. Conversion of ^{14}C-shikimic acid into aromatic amino acids in buckwheat (*Fagopyrum esculentum*) hypocotyls. Hypocotyls were incubated in light for 24 h with 0.5 µCi ^{14}C-shikimic acid and 10^{-1} mol l^{-1} Phe in the absence (○) or presence of 10^{-3} mol l^{-1} glyphosate (●). After separation on an amino acid analyser, fractions were assayed for radioactivity (From Holländer and Amrhein, 1980, by courtesy of the American Society of Plant Physiologists)

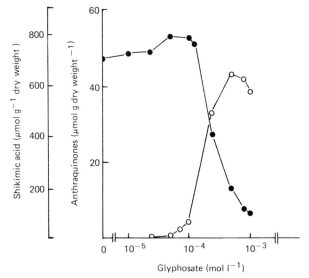

Figure 5.3. Production of shikimic acid (○) and anthraquinones (●) in *Galium mollugo* cells grown in glyphosate for 10 days (from Amrhein *et al.*, 1980, by courtesy of the American Society of Plant Physiologists)

occurred in a variety of plants, particularly cultured cells (Amrhein *et al.*, 1980; 1981; Berlin and Witte, 1981). In cells of *G. mollugo* (*Figure 5.3*) the accumulation of shikimic acid after 10 days in 5×10^{-4} mol l^{-1} glyphosate accounted for 10% total dry weight (Amrhein *et al.*, 1980). Inhibition of shikimic acid conversion was demonstrated *in vitro* using cell-free preparations from a multiply blocked mutant of the bacterium *Aerobacter aerogenes*. In this mutant, the sole product of exogenous shikimic acid is chorismic acid, but in the presence of glutamine the only product is the more easily measured anthranilic acid. Hence, this served as a measure of shikimic acid conversion to chorismic acid, a process which was strongly suppressed *in vitro*, 50% inhibition being obtained with 5×10^{-6} to 7×10^{-6} mol l^{-1} glyphosate (Amrhein *et al.*, 1980). The only product observed in this system was shikimic acid-3-phosphate and the only enzyme of the shikimic acid → chorismic acid section to be inhibited *in vitro* was EPSP synthase (Steinrücken and Amrhein, 1980; see also *Figure 5.4*). The accumulation of shikimic acid rather than shikimic acid-3-phosphate *in vivo* has been ascribed to enzymic dephosphorylation of the latter. However, some accumulation of shikimic acid-3-phosphate occurred in tomato (*Lycopersicon esculentum*) and buckwheat (Amrhein *et al.*, 1982). Shikimic acid appears to accumulate in the vacuole of the cell (Holländer-Czytko and Amrhein, 1983).

Inhibition of EPSP synthase from both *A. aerogenes* and cultured cells of *Corydalis sempervirens* is competitive with respect to PEP (Amrhein *et al.*, 1982; see also *Figure 5.5*). Inhibition by glyphosate is specific for this enzyme. It was reported that other enzymes utilizing PEP were not susceptible to glyphosate,

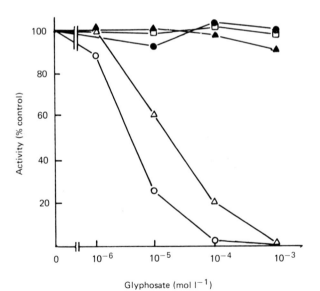

Figure 5.4. Inhibition of shikimic acid conversion to anthranilic acid *in vitro* and effect on individual enzymes in cell-free extracts of *Aerobacter aerogenes* 62-1: (○) formation of anthranilic acid, (●) shikimate kinase, (△) EPSP synthase, (▲) chorismate synthase, (□) anthranilate synthase (from Steinrücken and Amrhein, 1980, by courtesy of Academic Press Inc.)

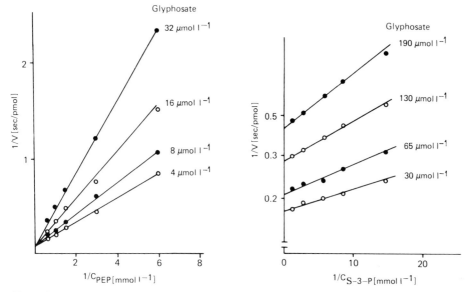

Figure 5.5. Double reciprocal plots for inhibition of EPSP synthase of *Corydalis sempervirens* by glyphosate. Inhibition is competitive with PEP, $K_I = 10\mu\text{mol l}^{-1}$. Concentration of non-varied substrate $= 5 \times 10^{-3}$ mol l^{-1} (after Amrhein *et al.*, 1982)

including 3-deoxy-D-*arabino*-heptulosonate-7-phosphate (DAHP) synthase, the initial enzyme of the shikimic acid pathway. However, a Co^{2+}-activated isozyme of DAHP synthase from mung bean (*Vigna radiata*) was inhibited by 10^{-3} mol l^{-1} glyphosate (Rubin, Gaines and Jensen, 1982). Inhibition was competitive with erythrose-4-phosphate rather than PEP and did not occur by complexing with Co^{2+}. A Mn^{2+}-stimulated isozyme was not susceptible to glyphosate and thus inhibition of only one form may not be deleterious. General inhibition of DAHP synthase activity would not be compatible with other observations on the effects of glyphosate on the pathway, particularly the accumulation of shikimic acid in a wide variety of species (Amrhein *et al.*, 1981). The *in vitro* inhibition of DAHP synthase and dehydroquinate synthase from *Escherichia coli* was abolished by the addition of the co-factor requirement, Co^{2+}. Similarly, inhibition of anthranilate synthase was removed by addition of its co-factor, Mn^{2+} (Roisch and Lingens, 1974; 1980). However, the high concentration of glyphosate required to cause inhibition (10^{-2} mol l^{-1}) suggested that these observations were of little physiological importance.

The specific activities of several shikimic acid pathway enzymes are affected by glyphosate. In *E. coli* the derepression of several enzymes provided further eloquent evidence for inhibition of end-product formation. The most sensitive enzyme was DAHP synthase, of which the Tyr-inhibited isozyme was considerably more sensitive than the Phe-inhibited isozyme (Roisch and Lingens, 1980). End-product control of enzyme levels is the major means of regulation of the pathway in microorganisms (Haslam, 1974) and DAHP synthase has more isozymes sensitive to end-products than any other of the pathway enzymes of *E. coli* (Byng, Kane and Jensen, 1982). The specific activities of chorismate mutase, prephenate dehydratase, prephenate dehydrogenase and anthranilate synthase also increased, but to lesser extents. Root tips of wheat (*Triticum aestivum*) also yielded elevated specific activities of chorismate mutase and shikimate dehydrogenase (Cole, Dodge and Caseley, 1980), but since regulation of the pathway in higher plants is exerted by direct feedback inhibition rather than modulation of enzyme levels (Gilchrist and Kosuge, 1980), these are unlikely to be true derepression responses. Shikimate dehydrogenase in soya bean was unaffected (Duke and Hoagland, 1981).

Protein content and synthesis

If the primary action of glyphosate results in a deficit of aromatic amino acids, perhaps the single most important consequence would be an inhibition of protein synthesis. Protein levels and rates of amino acid incorporation have been examined in several tissues. The soluble protein content in wheat was very sensitive to glyphosate, declining by 68% after exposure to 5×10^{-4} mol l^{-1} for 1 day. This decline was paralleled by an inhibition of tetrazolium reduction, suggesting that an inhibition of protein synthesis is associated with final toxicity (Cole, Dodge and Caseley, 1980). Comparison of the rates of incorporation of different labelled amino acids into protein can yield useful data. The incorporation of ^{14}C-leucine into TCA-insoluble material in single node rhizome buds of *Agropyron repens* was strongly inhibited by 10^{-4} mol l^{-1} glyphosate, indicating an inhibition of protein synthesis. ^{14}C-Phe, however, was considerably more readily incorporated after treatment, which suggests that glyphosate inhibited protein synthesis by depleting the Phe protein precursor pool. The fact that ^{14}C-Phe could be incorporated indicated that glyphosate had not damaged the essential machinery of protein synthesis. Neither the incorporation of Tyr nor Tryp was examined (Cole, Dodge and Caseley, 1980). These results were in contrast to those of Haderlie, Widholm and Slife (1977), who found no rapid inhibition of ^{14}C-Leu incorporation or decrease in protein content in carrot cells. Also, no significant differences in rates of incorporation of ^{14}C-Leu and ^{14}C-Phe occurred. Protein synthesis was the most sensitive biosynthetic function examined in isolated soya bean leaf cells (Tymonko and Foy, 1978a). A decrease in soluble protein content also occurred and inhibition of protein synthesis was alleviated by Phe (Tymonko and Foy, 1978b), and to a lesser extent by certain shikimic acid pathway intermediates (Tymonko, 1978). The incorporation of ^{14}C-Leu by cells isolated from glyphosate-treated bean (*Phaseolus vulgaris*) leaves was inhibited, but in this case appeared to be due to reduced uptake of the label (Brecke and Duke, 1980). Glyphosate had little effect on the soluble protein content of maize (*Zea mays*) roots (Duke and Hoagland, 1978) or soya bean axes (Hoagland, Duke and Elmore, 1979).

Free amino acids

From several studies of the effects of glyphosate on free amino acid levels (*Table 5.2*), it can be seen generally that those of Phe and Tyr decreased in response to the herbicide, although the total amount of free amino acids increased. In particular, increased formation of glutamate (Glu) and glutamine (Gln) may occur in response to increases in ammonia also observed, since the sequential formation of Glu and Gln from 2-ketoglutarate is the major means of assimilating ammonia.

   It should be stressed that the data given in *Table 5.2* are grossly simplified and

TABLE 5.2   Effect of glyphosate on free amino acid content

| Species | Major changes in free amino acid content | | Reference |
	Decrease	Increase	
Lemna gibba	Phe	Tyr	Jaworski (1972)
Carrot (*Daucus carota*) suspension culture		Glu,Gln,Arg,His	Haderlie, Widholm and Slife (1977)
Wheat (*Triticum aestivum*)	Phe,Tyr	Glu,Asp,Gln,Asn	Nilsson (1977)
Maize (*Zea mays*)	Phe,Tyr,Leu	Glu,Asp,Gln,Asn	Hoagland, Duke and Elmore (1978)
Soya bean (*Glycine max*) leaf cells	Phe,Tyr	Glu,Asp,Asn,Arg	Tymonko (1978)
Soya bean	Phe,Tyr	Gln	Hoagland, Duke and Elmore (1979)
Agropyron repens	Phe	Tyr	Ekanayake, Wickremasinghe and Liyanage (1979)
Bean (*Phaseolus vulgaris*)	Phe,Tyr		Shaner and Lyon (1980)
Buckwheat (*Fagopyrum esculentum*)	Phe	All others measured including Tyr, Tryp	Holländer and Amrhein (1980)

that not all workers separated all the amino acids of interest. There are significant differences between reports on the relationship of amino acid levels to other phenomena. Glyphosate did not reduce free Phe in carrot cells despite alleviation of toxicity by supplemental feeding (Haderlie, Widholm and Slife, 1977). The increase in total free amino acids in isolated soya bean leaf cells was concurrent with the decline in soluble protein, but preceded the decrease in free Phe and Tyr (Tymonko, 1978). Although total free amino acids increased in maize (Hoagland, Duke and Elmore, 1978) no such increase occurred in soya bean, although a similar experimental procedure was employed (Hoagland, Duke and Elmore, 1979). The data for soya bean yielded little in the way of an obvious pattern of changes. In wheat, increase in free amino acids was more notable in leaves than roots, although root growth was more sensitive to glyphosate (Nilsson, 1977).

Phenylalanine ammonia-lyase and the formation of secondary compounds

A notable biochemical characteristic of glyphosate is the ability to enhance substantially the activity of phenylalanine ammonia-lyase (PAL), a key regulatory enzyme in the link between primary and secondary metabolism. The effect has been demonstrated in a variety of species (Duke and Hoagland, 1978; Hoagland, Duke and Elmore, 1979; Cole, Dodge and Caseley, 1980) and may represent derepression of the enzyme in response to the observed declines in secondary product levels (Holländer and Amrhein, 1980; Berlin and Witte, 1981; Hoagland and Duke, 1982) brought about by inhibition of Phe and Tyr formation. A substantial amount of evidence exists to support regulation of end-product pool sizes as the major means of regulating the formation of secondary compounds (Amrhein, 1979; Engelsma, 1979), but this may not be true for all species. The lack of response of PAL to glyphosate in buckwheat (Holländer and Amrhein, 1980) supported previous evidence for lack of end-product repression of PAL in this species (Amrhein, 1979). The interference of glyphosate with secondary compound formation is fully discussed in Chapter 6.

Effects on other metabolic processes

Interaction with auxin

Recent research has indicated that an important effect of glyphosate is a rapid depression of auxin content. Tobacco calli, pretreated with 2×10^{-4} mol l^{-1} glyphosate, showed an enhanced ability to metabolize subsequently applied ^{14}C-IAA (Lee, 1982a), resulting in much lower levels of ^{14}C-IAA in treated calli (*Figures 5.6* and *5.7*). Metabolites included free acidic derivatives and conjugates. Increased metabolism was due to the promotion of IAA oxidase activity (Lee, 1982b) and since many phenolic compounds are known inhibitors of IAA oxidase (Lee, Starratt and Jevnikar, 1982), action of glyphosate on the shikimic acid pathway with subsequent inhibition of phenolic compound synthesis could cause an increase in IAA oxidase activity. An increase in oxidation of IAA would explain the alleviatory effects of exogenous auxin on callus growth (Lee, 1981; 1982a).

Auxin transport is inhibited by sub-lethal doses of glyphosate. Baur (1979a) demonstrated that exposure to glyphosate caused a simultaneous inhibition of basipetal movement of ^{14}C-IAA from donor agar blocks in excised maize shoots. In addition, an accumulation of label occurred at the basal end of the segment, which, together with a lack of diffusion of radioactivity into receiver blocks at either end, indicated binding of IAA within the tissue. Cotton (*Gossypium hirsutum*) hypocotyls were less responsive and similar phenomena could only be elicited in pretreated material. This was correlated with the higher tolerance of cotton to the herbicide. Since it is known that ethylene can inhibit auxin transport (Beyer and Morgan, 1969) it was postulated that glyphosate may induce the formation of ethylene; herbicidal concentrations produced such an effect in bean (Abu-Irmaileh,

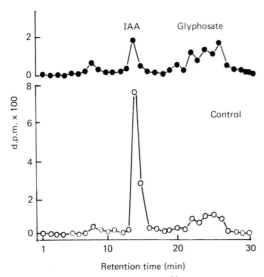

Figure 5.6. HPLC analysis of free $2-^{14}$C– IAA and acidic metabolites in tobacco (*Nicotiana tabacum*) callus. Glyphosate treatment was for 24 h, followed by incubation with ^{14}C-IAA for 4 h (from Lee, 1982a, by courtesy of the Scandinavian Society for Plant Physiology)

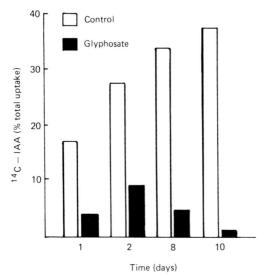

Figure 5.7. Effect of glyphosate pretreatment on free
2–14C–IAA content of tobacco (*Nicotiana tabacum*) callus
after incubation with 14C-IAA for 4 h (from Lee, 1982a, by
courtesy of the Scandinavian Society for Plant Physiology)

Jordan and Kumamoto, 1979), but not in wheat (Cole, Caseley and Dodge, 1983).
Inhibition of auxin transport may explain the extensive tillering which is
characteristic of sub-lethal doses of glyphosate (Caseley, 1972; Coupland and
Caseley, 1975; Baur, Bovey and Veech, 1977).

Chorophyll appearance

Chlorophyll is highly sensitive to glyphosate, and a notable characteristic of plants
exposed to sub-lethal doses of the herbicide is the achlorophyllous nature of
subsequent foliar growth. Experimentally, the effects of glyphosate on the
accumulation of chlorophyll have been examined by allowing etiolated material to
imbibe glyphosate with subsequent exposure to light (*Table 5.3*). The relationship
of this inhibition to that of aromatic amino acid synthesis is uncertain. In
buckwheat, inhibition of chlorophyll formation could be partially overcome by the
simultaneous admixture of Phe and Tyr, whereas Phe alone was effective in
alleviating inhibition of anthocyanin formation (Holländer and Amrhein, 1980).
However, no alleviation was evident in tobacco calli (Lee, 1981). The accumulation
of the chlorophyll precursor 5-aminolevulinic acid (ALA) was inhibited in both
maize and barley (*Hordeum vulgare*) (Kitchen, Witt and Rieck, 1981a) and further
work with barley demonstrated the specific inhibition of 14C incorporation from
glutamate, 2-ketoglutarate and glycine into ALA *in vivo*. The subsequent
transformation of ALA into chlorophyll was unaffected (Kitchen, Witt and Rieck,
1981b). In plants, ALA, which is a precursor of all porphyrins, is thought to be
synthesized from glutamate via 4,5-dioxovalerate (Beale, 1978), as shown in *Figure
5.8*. Formation from succinyl CoA and glycine, which is the route found in other
organisms, may occur in darkness (Hendry and Stobart, 1977; Meller and

TABLE 5.3   Inhibition of chlorophyll formation in six species

Species	Percentage inhibition by glyphosate (mol l^{-1})			Reference
	10^{-5}	10^{-4}	10^{-3}	
Buckwheat (*Fagopyrum esculentum*)	6	40	68	Holländer and Amrhein (1980)
Barley (*Hordeum vulgare*)	25	49	77 }	Kitchen, Witt and Rieck (1981a)
Maize (*Zea mays*)	0	24	42 }	
Soya bean* (*Glycine max*)	0	0	0 }	Lee (1981)
Tobacco* (*Nicotiana tabacum*)	0	67	100 }	
Mung bean (*Vigna radiata*)	84	98	100	Cole, Caseley and Dodge (1983)

*Callus culture.

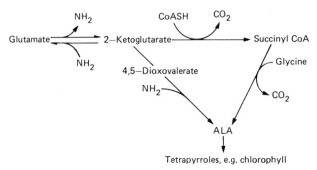

Figure 5.8. Proposed alternative pathways for the formation of 5-aminolevulinic acid (ALA) in plants

Gassman, 1982). In carrot cells, glyphosate toxicity can be alleviated by 2-ketoglutarate, in common with some other organic acids (Killmer, Widholm and Slife, 1981). Therefore a deficit of 2-ketoglutarate may be the limiting factor in chlorophyll synthesis. Since ALA plays a key role in the synthesis of porphyrins which are incorporated into such important proteins as the cytochromes, catalase and peroxidase, prevention of ALA synthesis may be of considerable importance in mode of action and may explain the decrease in catalase content of *Cyperus rotundus* leaves treated with glyphosate (Abu-Irmaileh and Jordan, 1978).

Glyphosate has also been shown to decrease chlorophyll content when applied to green tissues, although the effects are much less dramatic than the prevention of its initial appearance. Leaves of light-grown maize seedlings sprayed with glyphosate showed a decrease in chlorophyll content, but carotenoid levels were unchanged (Ali and Fletcher, 1978). Conversely, the decrease in chlorophyll in leaves of *C.rotundus* was preceded by a carotenoid decline and occurred only under illumination (Abu-Irmaileh and Jordan, 1978). A similar light-synergized effect was observed in leaf discs from tobacco and soya bean, and the similarity in response of these two species was in marked contrast to the effect on chlorophyll accumulation in callus tissues (Lee, 1981). Glyphosate also reduced chlorophyll accumulation in soya bean hypocotyls (Hoagland, 1980) and chlorophyll content of soya bean leaves in the field (Kitchen, Witt and Rieck, 1981a).

Glyphosate thus appears to exert two distinct effects upon chlorophyll. Convincing evidence for the interference of glyphosate in the inhibition of pigment synthesis has been presented (Kitchen, Witt and Rieck, 1981b), but the light-dependent decline in chlorophyll content of green tissue suggests the involvement of photodestruction in these cases. The prevention of the development of chlorophyll is a property of several herbicides of unrelated structure (Corbett, 1974; Fedtke, 1982) and, in most cases, chlorophyll undergoes photodestruction upon formation, due to an inhibition of carotenoid synthesis. Such secondary pigments provide a quenching mechanism for photo-excited chlorophylls, thus normally preventing photodestruction. In the absence of carotenoids, highly reactive oxygen species activated from oxygen by excited chlorophyll attack chloroplast components (Elstner, 1982). The bleaching of emergent maize tissue by glyphosine, N,N-bis(phosphonomethyl)glycine, was accompanied by the loss of chloroplast ribosomes and Fraction I protein (Croft *et al.*, 1974), which strongly supports the involvement of photodestruction. It appears likely that post-emergent chlorosis caused by glyphosate may involve a similar mechanism, particularly since chlorotic regrowth of *A.repens* appears to lack secondary pigments. These areas are never seen to regreen, although recovery with new chlorophyllous basal growth of the same leaf can occur (Cole, Caseley and Dodge, unpublished).

A third possible reason for the inhibition of chlorophyll appearance might be an indirect effect whereby glyphosate could be envisaged to interfere with the development of the chloroplast in some way, thus preventing insertion of the chlorophyll molecule into the thylakoid membrane. If so, other developmental processes associated with chloroplast formation might be similarly affected.

Photosynthesis

Although photosynthesis is a primary site of action for many herbicides, there is no evidence to suggest that this is an important site of action for glyphosate. The effects on rates of photosynthesis observed *in vivo* are secondary and should be considered unrelated to a primary mode of action. An effect was demonstrated by van Rensen (1974) who found that inhibition of oxygen evolution in the alga *Scenedesmus* sp. was increased by light, but could be partially abolished by washing the cells. Sprankle, Meggitt and Penner (1975) found that glyphosate had no initial effect upon carbon dioxide uptake in whole plants. Foliar application of 2.24 kg ha^{-1} to 12-day wheat plants and 24-day *A.repens* plants significantly reduced carbon dioxide uptake only after 72 h. Photosynthesis in bean was affected much more rapidly, 10^{-3} mol l^{-1} glyphosate decreasing the rate after 4 h with a maximum effect at 6 h. Inhibition concurred with that of leaf conductance (Shaner and Lyon, 1979). In a study of the effects of glyphosate on *Pellia epiphylla* over several weeks, an initial inhibition was followed by a period of recovery, after which inhibition was re-exerted (Pihakaski and Pihakaski, 1980). The assimilation of ^{14}C-bicarbonate in isolated soya bean leaf cells was less sensitive than other biosynthetic functions (Tymonko and Foy, 1978a), but the incorporation of $^{14}CO_2$ by bean leaf cells was more sensitive than protein and RNA synthesis (Brecke and Duke, 1980). Carbon dioxide uptake in detached flax (*Linum usitatissimum*) cotyledons floated on solutions was inhibited at concentrations higher than 10^{-5} mol l^{-1} after 24 h, but at sub-lethal concentrations a notable increase in photosynthetic rate was observed (Cole, Caseley and Dodge, 1983).

The influence of glyphosate on carbon dioxide uptake appears to be indirect, since the compound has no effect on partial reactions of the chloroplast (Richard, Goss and Arntzen, 1979). In isolated pea (*Pisum sativum*) chloroplasts, glyphosate had no direct effect on electron transport (Mehler reaction) and, in addition, no inhibition was observed with dark pre-incubation in glyphosate for up to 2 h. Similar pre-incubations did not inhibit cyclic or non-cyclic photophosphorylation. Fluorescence studies suggested that glyphosate had no effect on the structural organization of chloroplast membranes which might affect the light harvesting capacity of the chloroplast. This evidence contradicted findings by van Rensen (1974) that pre-incubation of isolated spinach (*Spinacea oleracea*) chloroplasts in high concentrations did inhibit electron transport. It appears likely, however, that these were artefacts due to possible lowering of reaction medium pH by glyphosate. Glyphosine had no effect on maize chloroplasts (Croft *et al.*, 1974).

Respiration

Several workers have recorded the effects of glyphosate upon respiratory activity *in vivo*. Since the arrest of respiration is an ultimate effect of any toxic compound, such studies give an estimate of the rapidity of translocation and action. However, in the absence of comparison with other effects, no conclusions can be drawn regarding the importance of respiratory inhibition in mode of action. Respiration in foliarly treated whole plants of wheat and *A.repens* was less sensitive than carbon dioxide uptake and while, after 9 days, respiration in *A.repens* was significantly reduced, that of wheat was not inhibited (Sprankle, Meggitt and Penner, 1975). Bean plants foliarly treated at 10^{-2} mol l^{-1} showed an increased rate of carbon dioxide evolution, initially evident at 24 h, although carbon dioxide cycling occurred normally for 3 days, indicating the continued operation of photosynthesis. Beyond this time a continual increase in carbon dioxide evolution was seen, due partially to inhibition of photosynthesis (Abu-Irmaileh, Jordan and Kumamoto, 1979).

Respiration in root tips of foliarly treated maize seedlings decreased rapidly at 6 h, as assayed by tetrazolium reduction, which contrasted with the much slower effects observed on foliar pigment levels. This indicated rapidity of both herbicide translocation and action at its site of accumulation (Ali and Fletcher, 1978). A decrease in the rate of tetrazolium reduction in wheat root tips correlated with increase in PAL activity and loss of soluble protein (Cole, Dodge and Caseley, 1980). Glyphosate up to 5×10^{-3} mol l^{-1} had no effect on oxygen consumption in yeast cells (Hanson and Rieck, 1975). Similarly, no effect was seen on oxygen utilization in cells isolated from treated bean leaves, although the rate of $^{14}CO_2$ liberation from ^{14}C-glucose was partially inhibited, but not to a greater degree than that of other metabolic processes examined (Brecke and Duke, 1980).

The evolution of $^{14}CO_2$ by isolated soya bean leaf cells was less sensitive than photosynthesis (Tymonko and Foy, 1978a). Carbon dioxide evolution in detached flax cotyledons was extremely insensitive to glyphosate and was not significantly affected at concentrations up to 10^{-2} mol l^{-1} after 24 h, although photosynthesis was decreased (Cole, Caseley and Dodge, 1983). It thus appears that respiration is not an initial site of action *in vivo*, although oxidative phosphorylation can be uncoupled *in vitro* (Olorunsogo, Bababunmi and Bassir, 1979).

Despite the relative insensitivity of respiration *in vivo*, Killmer, Widholm and Slife (1981) have demonstrated the amelioration of growth inhibition in carrot cells by several intermediates of glycolysis and the TCA cycle. Deficit of respiratory intermediates could be caused by inhibition at an early point in glycolysis, or by an increased utilization of respiratory substrates. It was speculated that the latter may occur by continual feeding of carbon into the shikimic acid pathway via PEP and erythrose-4-phosphate, since the accumulation of shikimic acid in glyphosate-treated tissues (Amrhein *et al.*, 1980; 1981; Berlin and Witte, 1981) indicates a lack of feedback control in the pathway prior to this point (Gilchrist and Kosuge, 1980). It was also suggested that a deficit of respiratory carbon would limit the substrate available for ammonia assimilation, thus explaining the elevated levels of ammonia and glutamine in glyphosate-treated tissues (Nilsson, 1977; Haderlie, Widholm and Slife, 1977; Hoagland, Duke and Elmore, 1978; Hoagland, Duke and Elmore, 1979). It has been suggested that accumulation of ammonia may be an important factor in the toxicity of glyphosate (Killmer, Widholm and Slife, 1981).

Macromolecule synthesis

The elaboration of nucleic acids and proteins are obvious potential targets for biocides and as such are often included in mode of action programmes. These processes are bound to be inhibited at some stage in the sequence of events leading to cell death and thus, in isolation, such studies may not be particularly informative. For example, any process dependent upon the generation of ATP will be affected by a reduction in its availability (Gruenhagen and Moreland, 1971). Nevertheless, comparative inhibition of these processes can give an idea of the proximity to the primary site of action.

Several studies have been made of the effects of glyphosate on the incorporation of labelled precursors into macromolecules *in vivo*, but there is no evidence for a direct effect upon nucleic acid or protein synthesis even though these are phenomena particularly associated with growing tissues. No rapid inhibition of RNA or protein synthesis occurred in carrot cells, but a significant reduction of ^{14}C-thymidine incorporation into DNA was due to an inhibition of uptake of the label (Haderlie, Widholm and Slife, 1977). In isolated soya bean leaf cells, synthetic functions in order of sensitivity were protein > RNA > lipid (Tymonko and Foy, 1978a). The reduction in protein and RNA synthesis observed in isolated bean leaf cells was due mainly to inhibition of precursor uptake (Brecke and Duke, 1980). Inhibition of protein synthesis would be an important consequence of the action of glyphosate on aromatic amino acids, as evidenced by a rapid decline in the protein content of wheat root tips and the differential effects on the incorporation of ^{14}C-Leu and ^{14}C-Phe into protein in *A.repens* buds (Cole, Dodge and Caseley, 1980). The inhibition of protein and nucleic acid synthesis in roots of *Xanthium pensylvanicum* may have been responsible for the rapid rise in ATP content observed (Foley *et al.*, 1983). These inhibitory effects were thus not due to an ATP deficit.

Enzymes of nitrate assimilation

In the case of a herbicide which acts specifically at meristems, it is useful to consider the effects of glyphosate on developmental processes associated with meristematic growth. Such an example of an important developmental phenomenon is the substrate-induction of nitrate reductase and nitrite reductase, consecutive and key enzymes in the nitrate assimilation pathway. In a study with excised pea tissue, glyphosate was shown to influence the behaviour of both these enzymes (Cole, Caseley and Dodge, 1983). The KNO_3-dependent induction of nitrite reductase was suppressed by glyphosate in etiolated explants, as was the appearance of chlorophyll. In explants pre-greened prior to treatment, inhibition of enzyme development correlated with inhibition of photosynthetic carbon dioxide uptake. The effect of glyphosate on NO_2^- reduction *in vivo* would be greater than the observed effect on the enzyme *in vitro* due to limited availability of reducing power in the form of reduced ferredoxin, supplied by photosynthesis. Nitrate reductase was less sensitive and in fact increased at certain times. Thus, an important metabolic consequence of glyphosate in the pea bud might be an accumulation of the highly toxic NO_2^-, implicated as a factor in the toxicity of photosynthetic inhibitor herbicides (Klepper, 1976; 1979; Fedtke, 1982). However, inhibition of NO_3^- assimilation does not seem to be an important factor in other systems where glyphosate increases total free amino acid levels (Hoagland and Duke, 1982).

Since nitrite reductase is located in the chloroplast, it is possible that glyphosate affects the development of the plastid in such a way that the insertion of components such as nitrite reductase and chlorophyll is inhibited.

Membranes

Glyphosate has negligible effects on the general permeability of the plasma membrane (Prendeville and Warren, 1977; O'Brien and Prendeville, 1979; Brecke and Duke, 1980; Fletcher, Hildebrand and Akey, 1980). However, a rapid effect on isolated bean cells was an inhibition of ^{86}Rb and ^{32}P uptake (Brecke and Duke, 1980). Since these cells were unable to absorb ^{14}C-glyphosate and essential membrane integrity was unaffected it could be envisaged that glyphosate may externally regulate inorganic ion uptake by an interaction with plasma membrane ATPases linked to ion pump mechanisms. A correlation is known to exist in plant roots between monovalent ion influx and monovalent ion-stimulated ATPase activity (Fisher, Hansen and Hodges, 1970; Leigh and Wyn-Jones, 1975; Leonard and Hotchkiss, 1976); however, 10^{-3} mol l^{-1} glyphosate had little effect *in vitro* on microsomal ATPases $\pm$ K^+ from wheat roots assayed at pH 6.0 and 9.0 (Cole, Caseley and Dodge, 1983). Although plasma membranes themselves were not isolated, the pH 6.0 component is likely to be located in this fraction (Hodges and Leonard, 1973). Further evidence that glyphosate does not affect membrane integrity was obtained by examining the effects of pre-incubation in glyphosate upon the stability of microsomal enzymes from wheat root tips. Several enzymes regarded as markers for particular intracellular membranes (Hodges and Leonard, 1973) were assayed from microsomes obtained from root tips of treated wheat seedlings, but marked decreases in specific activity were not found, indicating that glyphosate had not caused the disruption of any particular organelle membrane in such a way as to destabilize enzymes located therein. The major effect on the microsomal fraction was a loss of protein; thus, glyphosate depleted the level of microsomal enzymes per root tip (Cole, Caseley and Dodge, 1983).

Miscellaneous effects

The influence of glyphosate on a number of other physiological processes has been noted. Inhibition of transpiration and the closure of stomata occurred in foliarly treated bean leaves (Shaner, 1978; Brecke and Duke, 1980) and a further discovery was that the compound triggered cyclic opening and closing of stomata (Shaner and Lyon, 1979; see also *Figure 5.9*). Cycling could not be due to the

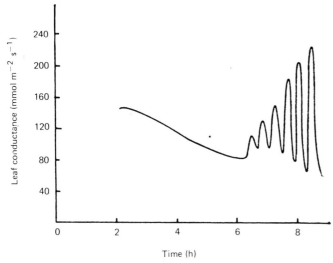

Figure 5.9. Variation in leaf conductance of bean (*Phaseolus vulgaris*) in response to 5 × 10⁻³ mol l⁻¹ glyphosate (from Shaner and Lyon, 1979, by courtesy of Elsevier/North-Holland Scientific Publishers Ltd)

inhibition of K^+ uptake, shown to be a significant effect of glyphosate (Brecke and Duke, 1980), since accumulation of K^+ is necessary for opening. Inhibition of transpiration and photosynthesis were coincident (Shaner and Lyon, 1979); thus, inhibition of transpiration could not be directly due to an initial effect on photosynthesis. Inhibition of transpiration in excised shoots was negated by Phe and Tyr, but not by Phe alone (Shaner and Lyon, 1980).

Foliar application of sub-lethal doses caused basal swelling and tillering in sorghum (*Sorghum bicolor*) (Baur, Bovey and Veech, 1977), the incidence of which was reduced by cycloheximide or Phe, whereas Tyr and IAA were ineffective (Baur, 1979b). Some genetic modification of pollen mother cells was observed in sprayed rye (*Secale cereale*) (Boyle and Evans, 1974) and the arrest of mitosis was observed in *Eichhornia crassipes* root tips (Goltenboth, 1977).

Ultrastructure

The ultrastructural effects of glyphosate are poorly understood at present. Investigations have been restricted to effects upon chlorophyllous tissues which, it is clear, are neither the initial nor major areas of glyphosate action. Campbell, Evans and Reed (1976) examined the progressive effects of foliarly applied glyphosate on leaf mesophyll cells of field-grown *A. repens* plants. Ultrastructural changes were evident at 24 h and preceded visual yellowing of leaves. Major features of cellular breakdown included disruption of the chloroplast envelope, the progressive degeneration of the chloroplast being accompanied by the accumulation of osmiophilic plastoglobuli. Swelling of the rough endoplasmic reticulum gave rise to vesicle formation, the plasma membrane became wrinkled and detached from the cell wall and mitochondria underwent swelling with degeneration of cristae. Effects on organelles were concurrent and there was no evidence to suggest that the chloroplast might be an initial site of action.

In leaf mesophyll cells of *Sinapis alba,* initial effects were observed on the chloroplast with swelling and disruption of thylakoids evident at 48 h (Uotila, Evjen and Iverson, 1980). Damage to mitochondria was observed at 2 weeks. Stem cells, examined after 2 weeks, revealed swollen chloroplasts with disrupted grana, and the appearance of plastoglobuli. Increased numbers of dictyosomes were also noted. Disruption of chloroplasts was also reported in leaves of *Prosopis juliflora* (Hull, Bleckmann and Morton, 1977) and *Cyperus rotundus* (Hoagland and Paul, 1978). In an extensive study of the epidermal cells of *P. epiphylla* (Pihakaski and Pihakaski, 1980; see also *Figure 5.10*), notable initial symptoms were the development of vesicular and tubular structures in the cytoplasm, although these were associated with chloroplasts. Also, membrane-bound granular bodies were observed; these were postulated to have formed from the chloroplast envelope. Degeneration of the large oil bodies was noted. Advanced cell damage was additionally characterized by folding and rupturing of the plasma membrane and dilation of chloroplast membranes with breakdown of grana. A notable effect on mitochondria was a lengthening of cristae. Although these workers have presented the highest resolution electron microscope studies to date, it is not clear to what extent these observations on a bryophyte can be extrapolated to higher plants. Post-emergent bleached foliar growth of maize seedlings treated with glyphosine possessed swollen chloroplasts which contained reduced levels of grana and thylakoids (Croft *et al.,* 1974).

Since glyphosate does not accumulate in mature leaves, most of these observations are probably indirect effects of glyphosate action at growing points and, therefore, probably do not represent genuine effects of glyphosate *in situ*. There is a need to examine effects on meristems and to correlate ultrastructural and biochemical phenomena in an attempt to present a united picture of events leading to cell death. So far there has been little attempt to relate the two, although it is probable that visual cell damage represents the more advanced stages of the sequence of events.

Metal ion chelation as a possible mode of action

Phosphonic acids are known chelators of metal cations (Carter, Carroll and Irani, 1967; Kabachnik *et al.,* 1974) and it has been an intriguing possibility that glyphosate may exert its action by complexing biologically important divalent and trivalent cations within the cell. If so, toxicity should be alleviated by cation addition. There is, however, little evidence to support such a hypothesis. Metal ions had no effect on the toxicity of glyphosate to *E.coli* or *C.reinhardii* (Gresshoff, 1979) or the inhibition of anthocyanin formation in buckwheat (Holländer and Amrhein, 1980). The interaction of glyphosate with metal cations is discussed in Chapter 4.

Metabolite toxicity

Most herbicides are metabolized by plants to varying degrees, which can have important implications in herbicide phytotoxicity. Plants attack what are often relatively hydrophobic compounds in such a manner as to increase water solubility. This generally results in detoxication, but in a few cases, metabolism from an inert parent compound to a toxic metabolite is a necessary prerequisite for toxicity (Cole, 1983). In contrast, glyphosate, a relatively polar herbicide, appears to be metabolized to only a very limited extent (see Chapter 3), producing a single important metabolite, aminomethylphosphonic acid (AMPA). Available evidence suggests that this is a detoxication reaction and that AMPA possesses very little biological activity. AMPA failed to inhibit the formation of anthocyanin in buckwheat or the conversion of shikimic acid to anthranilic acid in cell-free extracts of *A. aerogenes* (Amrhein *et al.*, 1980) (*Figure 5.11*). AMPA and two other possible

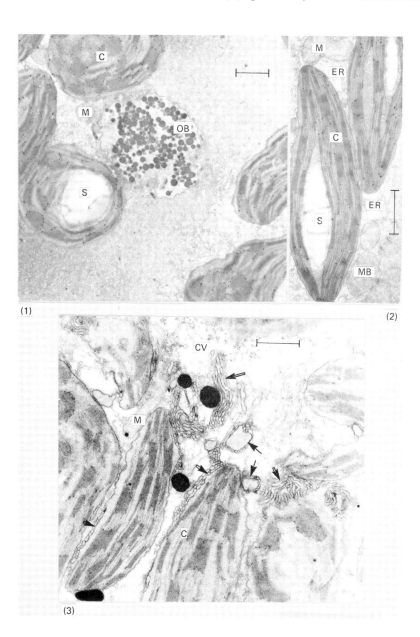

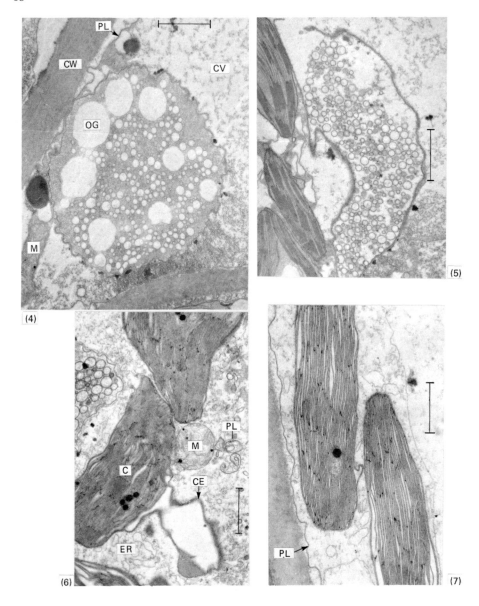

metabolites, sarcosine and glycine, had little effect on growth, anthocyanin and chlorophyll formation, phenylpropanoid levels or PAL in soya bean seedlings (Hoagland, 1980).

Conclusions

Glyphosate exerts phytotoxity by inhibiting the shikimic acid pathway and thus arresting the biosynthesis of aromatic amino acids. Specifically, the herbicide is a competitive inhibitor, with respect to PEP, of EPSP synthase. This apparent specificity has enabled the use of glyphosate as an experimental inhibitor in the resolution of questions on the nature of control mechanisms of the shikimic acid and secondary compound pathways (Amrhein and Holländer, 1981). Action at the shikimic acid pathway is unique to glyphosate and the absence of the pathway in animals is an important factor in its low animal toxicity.

The secondary effects which are responsible for bringing about cell death are the arrest of both protein synthesis and diverse phenolic compound formation. These are directly attributable to a deficit of aromatic amino acids. Other potentially significant, and possibly related, effects are the increased destruction of IAA and inhibition of porphyrin synthesis. The uncontrolled formation of shikimic acid appears to drain the cell of carbon skeletons used in the detoxication of ammonia with the accumulation of ammonia to possibly toxic levels. At the moment, the importance of these phenomena is a matter for conjecture.

The major advances on mode of action have employed cell cultures and microorganisms which are in many ways more amenable than the whole plant, but ultimately these results need to be validated in whole plants. Most workers have avoided the target weed species which encounter glyphosate in the field, an approach which is imperative in examining other facets of glyphosate's properties. There are good reasons for supposing that perennial weeds might present the biochemist with more complex problems than the aforementioned systems. The prevention of rhizome bud germination is a property unique to glyphosate. Since germination is a function of whole plant physiology, the mechanisms whereby glyphosate effects inhibition may be more complicated than its action on single cells

---

Figure 5.10. Ultrastructural effects of glyphosate in epidermal cells of *Pellia epiphylla* thalli (from Pihakaski and Pihakaski, by courtesy of *Annals of Botany*)

(1), (2)	Ultrastructure of untreated epidermal cells. Note chloroplasts containing large starch grains and oil body containing numerous oil globules. 1 × 12 000; 2 × 17 950
(3)	Cellular disruption after 1 day's treatment, characterized by tubular formations (open arrows), granular bodies (solid arrows), electron-dense bodies and vacuolated cytoplasm. × 17 250
(4), (5)	Deterioration of oil bodies after 1 day's treatment. 4, Oil body contains large electron-transparent globules. Stroma is granulated. × 19 950. 5, A further disrupted oil body, membrane has ruptured and stroma has disappeared. × 19 950
(6)	Cellular disruption after 2 weeks' treatment. Grana are indistinct, chloroplast membrane is grossly distended and particles of fragmented plasmalemma are evident. × 19 950
(7)	Chloroplast appearance after 2 weeks' treatment, characterized by separation of granal membranes. × 19 950

Glyphosate treatments were 1.3×10^{-5} mol l^{-1} to 1.3×10^{-4} mol l^{-1}. All scale bars represent 1 μm.
Key: C, chloroplast; CE, chloroplast envelope; CV, cytoplasmic vacuolation; CW, cell wall; ER, endosplasmic reticulum; M, mitochondrion; MB, microbody; OB, oil body; OG, oil globule; PL, plasmalemma; S, starch grain

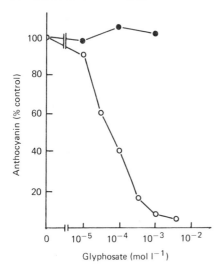

Figure 5.11. Effect of glyphosate (○) and aminomethylphosphonic acid (●) on anthocyanin formation in buckwheat (*Fagopyrum esculentum*). Etiolated hypocotyls were exposed to light and compounds for 24 h (from Amrhein *et al.*, 1980, by courtesy of the American Society of Plant Physiologists)

or lower organisms. A particularly obvious deficiency at the moment is the complete lack of ultrastructural data at sites of accumulation or the intracellular distribution of glyphosate; thus it is impossible to say which part of the cell, if any, is a primary target. Eventually it should be possible to make some correlation between biochemical and ultrastructural effects. Nevertheless the information available on the mode of action of glyphosate does currently constitute one of the most thorough studies of the interaction between a synthetic growth inhibitor and the higher plant.

References

ABU-IRMAILEH, B.E. and JORDAN, L.S. (1978). Some aspects of glyphosate action in purple nutsedge (*Cyperus rotundus*), *Weed Science*, **26**, 700–703.
ABU-IRMAILEH, B.E., JORDAN, L.S. and KUMAMOTO, J. (1979). Enhancement of CO_2 and ethylene production and cellulase activity by glyphosate in *Phaseolus vulgaris*, *Weed Science*, **27**, 103–106.
ALI, A. and FLETCHER, R.A. (1978). Phytotoxic action of glyphosate and amitrole on corn seedlings, *Canadian Journal of Botany*, **56**, 2196–2202.
AMRHEIN, N. (1979). Novel inhibitors of phenylpropanoid metabolism in higher plants, in *Regulation of Secondary Product and Plant Hormone Metabolism.*, *FEBS 12th Meeting*, vol. 55, pp. 173–182 (Eds. M. Luckner and K. Schreiber). Oxford; Pergamon.
AMRHEIN, N., DEUS, B., GEHRKE, P., HOLLANDER, H., SCHAB, J., SCHULZ, A. and STEINRÜCKEN, H.C. (1981). Interference of glyphosate with the shikimate pathway, *Proceedings of the Plant Growth Regulator Society of America*, **8**, 99–106.
AMRHEIN, N., DEUS, B., GEHRKE, P. and STEINRÜCKEN, H.C. (1980). The site of the inhibition of the shikimate pathway by glyphosate II. Interference of glyphosate with chorismate formation *in vivo* and *in vitro*, *Plant Physiology*, **66**, 830–834.
AMRHEIN, N. and HOLLÄNDER, H. (1981). Light promotes the production of shikimic acid in buckwheat, *Naturwissenschaften*, **68**, 43.
AMRHEIN, N., HOLLÄNDER-CZYTKO, H., LEIFELD, J., SCHULZ, A., STEINRÜCKEN, H.C. and TOPP, H. (1982). Inhibition of the shikimate pathway by glyphosate, in *Journées internationales d'études du Groupe Polyphenols. Bulletin de Liaison*, vol. II, pp. 21–31 (Eds. A.M. Boudet and R. Ranjeva). Toulouse.
ASHTON, F.M. and CRAFTS, A.S. (1981). *Mode of Action of Herbicides*, 2nd edn. New York; Wiley.
BAILLE, A.C., CORBETT, J.R., DOWSETT, J.R. and MCLOSKEY, P. (1972). Inhibitors of shikimate dehydrogenase as potential herbicides, *Pesticide Science*, **3**, 113–120.

BAUR, J.R. (1979a). Effects of glyphosate on auxin transport in corn and cotton tissues, *Plant Physiology*, **63**, 882–886.

BAUR, J.R. (1976b). Reduction of glyphosate induced tillering in sorghum (*Sorghum bicolor*) by several chemicals, *Weed Science*, **27**, 69–73.

BAUR, J.R., BOVEY, R.W. and VEECH, J.A. (1977). Growth responses in sorghum and wheat induced by glyphosate, *Weed Science*, **25**, 238–240.

BEALE, S.I. (1978). δ-Aminolevulinic acid in plants: its biosynthesis, regulation and role in plastid development, *Annual Reviews in Plant Physiology*, **29**, 95–120.

BERLIN, J. and WIDHOLM, J.M. (1978). Metabolism of phenylalanine and tyrosine in tobacco cell lines resistant and sensitive to *p*-fluorophenylalanine, *Phytochemistry*, **17**, 65–68.

BERLIN, J. and WITTE, L. (1981). Effects of glyphosate on shikimic acid accumulation in tobacco cell cultures with low and high yields of cinnamoyl putrescines, *Zeitschrift für Naturforschung*, **36C**, 210–214.

BEYER, E.M. and MORGAN, P.W. (1969). Ethylene modification of an auxin pulse in cotton stem sections, *Plant Physiology*, **44**, 1690–1694.

BOYLE, W.S. and EVANS, J.O. (1974). Effects of glyphosate and ethephon on meiotic chromosomes of *Secale cereale* L., *Journal of Heredity*, **65**, 250.

BRECKE, B.J. (1976). Studies into the mechanism of action of *N*-(phosphonomethyl)glycine, *Ph. D. thesis*, Cornell University.

BRECKE, B.J. and DUKE, W.B. (1980). Effects of glyphosate on intact bean plants (*Phaseolus vulgaris* L.) and isolated cells, *Plant Physiology*, **66**, 656–659.

BYNG, G.S., KANE, J.F. and JENSEN, R.A. (1982). Diversity in the routing and regulation of complex biochemical pathways as indications of biochemical relatedness, *Critical Reviews in Microbiology*, **9**, 227–252.

CAMPBELL, W.F., EVANS, J.O. and REED, F.C. (1976). Effect of glyphosate on chloroplast ultrastructure of quackgrass mesophyll cells, *Weed Science*, **24**, 22–25.

CARTER, R.P., CARROLL, R.L. and IRANI, R.R. (1967). Nitrilotri(methylenephosphonic acid), ethylimido(methylenephosphonic acid) and diethylamino methylphosphonic acid and Ca(II) and Mg(II) complexing, *Inorganic Chemistry*, **6**, 639–946.

CASELEY, J.C. (1972). The effect of environmental factors on the performance of glyphosate against *Agropyron repens*, *Proceedings of the 11th British Weed Control Conference*, pp. 641–647.

COLE, D.J. (1982). The mode of action of glyphosate, *Proceedings of the 1982 British Crop Protection Conference—Weeds*, pp. 309–315.

COLE, D.J. (1983). Oxidation of xenobiotics in plants, in *Progress in Pesticide Biochemistry*, vol. 3, pp. 199–254 (Eds. D.H. Hutson and T.R. Roberts). Chichester; Wiley (in press).

COLE, D.J., CASELEY, J.C. and DODGE, A.D. (1983). Influence of glyphosate on selected plant processes, *Weed Research*, **23**, 173–183.

COLE, D.J., DODGE, A.D. and CASELEY, J.C. (1980). Some biochemical effects of glyphosate on plant meristems, *Journal of Experimental Botany*, **31**, 1665–1674.

CORBETT, J.R. (1974). *The Biochemical Mode of Action of Pesticides*. London; Academic Press.

COUPLAND, D. and CASELEY, J.C. (1975). Reduction of silica and increase in tillering induced in *Agropyron repens* by glyphosate, *Journal of Experimental Botany*, **26**, 138–144.

CROFT, S.M., ARNTZEN, C.J., VANDERHOF, L.W. and ZETTINGER, C.S. (1974). Inhibition of chloroplast ribosome formation by *N,N*-bis(phosphonomethyl)glycine, *Biochimica et Biophysica Acta*, **335**, 211–217.

DAVIS, C. and HARVEY, R.G. (1979). Reversal of glyphosate toxicity to alfalfa calli by phenylalanine and tyrosine, *Proceedings of the Northeastern Weed Science Society*, **33**, 112–113.

DUKE, S.O. and HOAGLAND, R.E. (1978). Effects of glyphosate on metabolism of phenolic compounds I. Induction of phenylalanine ammonia-lyase activity in dark-grown maize roots, *Plant Science Letters*, **11**, 185–190.

DUKE, S.O. and HOAGLAND, R.E. (1981). Effects of glyphosate on the metabolism of phenolic compounds VII. Root-fed amino acids and glyphosate toxicity in soya bean (*Glycine max*) seedlings, *Weed Science*, **29**, 297–302.

EKANAYAKE, A., WICKREMASINGHE, R.L. and LIYANAGE, H.D.S. (1979). Studies on the mechanism of herbicidal action of *N*-(phosphonomethyl)glycine, *Weed Research*, **19**, 39–43.

ELSTNER, E.F. (1982). Oxygen activation and oxygen toxicity, *Annual Reviews in Plant Physiology*, **33**, 73–96.

ENGELSMA, G. (1979). Inhibition of phenylalanine ammonia-lyase by cinnamic acid derivatives, in *Regulation of Secondary Product and Plant Hormone Metabolism*, FEBS 12th Meeting, vol. 55, pp. 163–172 (Eds. M. Luckner and K. Schreiber). Oxford; Pergamon.

FEDTKE, C. (1982). *Biochemistry and Physiology of Herbicide Action*. Berlin; Springer-Verlag.

FISHER, J.D., HANSEN, D. and HODGES, T.K. (1970). Correlation between ion fluxes and ion-stimulated adenosine triphosphatase activity of plant roots, *Plant Physiology*, **46**, 812–814.

FLETCHER, R.A., HILDEBRAND, P. and AKEY, W. (1980). Effect of glyphosate on membrane permeability in red beet (*Beta vulgaris*) root tissue, *Weed Science*, **28**, 671–673.

FOLEY, M.E., NAFZIGER, E.D., SLIFE, F.W. and WAX, L.M. (1983). Effect of glyphosate on protein and nucleic acid synthesis and ATP levels in common cocklebur (*Xanthium pensylvanicum* Wallr.) root tissue, *Weed Science*, **31**, 76–80.

GILCHRIST, D.G. and KOSUGE, T. (1980). Aromatic amino acid biosynthesis and its regulation, in *The Biochemistry of Plants*, vol. 5, pp. 507–531 (Ed. B.J. Miflin). London; Academic Press.

GOLTENBOTH, F. (1977). The effect of glyphosate and ametryne on the root tip mitosis of waterhyacinth (*Eichhornia crassipes* (Mart.) Solms), *Proceedings of the 6th Asian–Pacific Weed Science Society Conference*, **2**, 555–556.

GRESSHOFF, P.M. (1979). Growth inhibition by glyphosate and reversal of its action by phenylalanine and tyrosine, *Australian Journal of Plant Physiology*, **6**, 177–185.

GRUENHAGEN, R.D. and MORELAND, D.E. (1971). Effects of herbicides on ATP levels in excised soya bean hypocotyls, *Weed Science*, **19**, 319–323.

HADERLIE, L.C. (1975). Biochemical action and physiological characteristics of the herbicide glyphosate, *Ph. D. thesis*, University of Illinois.

HADERLIE, L.C., WIDHOLM, J.M. and SLIFE, F.W. (1977). Effect of glyphosate on carrot and tobacco cells, *Plant Physiology*, **60**, 40–49.

HANSON, C.L. and RIECK, C.E. (1975). Effect of glyphosate on respiration, *Proceedings of the Southern Weed Science Society*, **28**, 297.

HASLAM, E. (1974). *The Shikimate Pathway*. London; Butterworths.

HENDRY, G.A.F. and STOBART, A.K. (1977). Glycine metabolism and chlorophyll synthesis in barley leaves, *Phytochemistry*, **16**, 1567–1570.

HOAGLAND, R.E. (1980). Effects of glyphosate on metabolism of phenolic compounds: VI. Effects of glyphosine and glyphosate metabolites on phenylalanine ammonia-lyase activity, growth, and protein, chlorophyll, and anthocyanin levels in soya bean (*Glycine max*) seedlings, *Weed Science*, **28**, 393–400.

HOAGLAND, R.E. and DUKE, S.O. (1982). Biochemical effects of glyphosate [*N*-(phosphonomethyl)glycine], in *Biochemical Responses Induced by Herbicides*, pp. 175–205 (Eds. D.E. Moreland, J.B. St. John and F.D. Hess), *ACS Symposium Series*, No. 181.

HOAGLAND, R.E., DUKE, S.O. and ELMORE, D. (1978). Effects of glyphosate on metabolism of phenolic compounds II. Influence on soluble hydroxyphenolic compound, free amino acid and soluble protein levels in dark-grown maize roots, *Plant Science Letters*, **13**, 291–299.

HOAGLAND, R.E., DUKE, S.O. and ELMORE, D. (1979). Effects of glyphosate on metabolism of phenolic compounds III. Phenylalanine ammonia-lyase activity, free amino acids, soluble protein and hydroxyphenolic compounds in axes of dark-grown soybeans, *Physiologia Plantarum*, **46**, 357–366.

HOAGLAND, R.E. and PAUL, R.N. (1978). Ultrastructural effects of *N*-(phosphonomethyl)glycine on mesophyll cells of *Cyperus rotundus* L. *Plant Physiology Supplement*, **61**, 42.

HODGES, T.K. and LEONARD, R.T. (1973). Purification of a plasma membrane bound adenosine triphosphatase from plant roots, *Methods in Enzymology*, **32**, 392–406.

HOLLÄNDER, H. and AMRHEIN, N. (1980). The site of the inhibition of the shikimate pathway by glyphosate I. Inhibition by glyphosate of phenylpropanoid synthesis in buckwheat (*Fagopyrum esculentum* Moench.), *Plant Physiology*, **66**, 823–829.

HOLLÄNDER-CZYTKO, H. and AMRHEIN, N. (1983). Subcellular compartmentation of shikimic acid and phenylalanine in buckwheat cell suspension cultures grown in the presence of shikimate pathway inhibitors, *Plant Science Letters*, **29**, 89–96.

HULL, H.M., BLECKMANN, C.A. and MORTON, H.L. (1977). Some effects of glyphosate on the foliar ultrastructure of velvet mesquite seedlings, *Proceedings of the Western Society of Weed Science*, **30**, 18–19.

JAWORSKI, E.G. (1972). Mode of action of *N*-phosphonomethyl-glycine: inhibition of aromatic amino acid biosynthesis, *Journal of Agricultural and Food Chemistry*, **20**, 1195–1198.

KABACHNIK, M.I., MEDVED, T.Y., DYATLOVA, N.M. and RUDOMINO, M.V. (1974). Organophosphorus complexones, *Russian Chemical Review*, **43**, 733–744.

KILLMER, J., WIDHOLM, J. and SLIFE, F. (1981). Reversal of glyphosate inhibition of carrot cell culture growth by glycolytic intermediates and organic and amino acids, *Plant Physiology*, **68**, 1299–1302.

KITCHEN, L.M., WITT, W.W. and RIECK, C.E. (1981a). Inhibition of chlorophyll accumulation by glyphosate, *Weed Science*, **29**, 513–516.

KITCHEN, L.M., WITT, W.W. and RIECK, C.E. (1981b). Inhibition of δ-aminolevulinic acid synthesis by glyphosate, *Weed Science*, **29**, 571–577.

KLEPPER, L.A. (1976). Nitrate accumulation within herbicide treated leaves, *Weed Science*, **24**, 533–535.

KLEPPER, L.A. (1979). Effects of certain herbicides and their combinations on nitrate and nitrite reduction, *Plant Physiology*, **64**, 273–275.

LEE, T.T. (1980). Characteristics of glyphosate inhibition of growth in soybean and tobacco callus cultures, *Weed Research*, **20**, 365–369.

LEE, T.T. (1981). Effect of glyphosate on synthesis and degradation of chlorophyll in soybean and tobacco cells, *Weed Research*, **21**, 161–164.

LEE, T.T. (1982a). Mode of action of glyphosate in relation to metabolism of indole-3-acetic acid, *Physiologia Plantarum*, **54**, 289–294.

LEE, T.T. (1982b). Promotion of indole-3-acetic acid oxidation by glyphosate in tobacco callus tissue, *Journal of Plant Growth Regulation*, **1**, 37–48.

LEE, T.T., STARRATT, A.N. and JEVNIKAR, J.J. (1982). Regulation of enzymic oxidation of indole-3-acetic acid by phenols: structure–activity relationships, *Phytochemistry*, **21**, 517–523.

LEIGH, R.A. and WYN-JONES, R.G. (1975). Correlation between ion-stimulated adenosine triphosphatase activities and ion influxes in maize roots, *Journal of Experimental Botany*, **26**, 508–520.

LEONARD, R.T. and HOTCHKISS, C.W. (1976). Cation-stimulated adenosine triphosphatase activity and cation transport in corn roots, *Plant Physiology*, **58**, 331–335.

MELLER, E. and GASSMAN, M.L. (1982). Biosynthesis of 5-aminolevulinic acid: two pathways in higher plants, *Plant Science Letters*, **26**, 23–29.

NILSSON, G. (1977). Effects of glyphosate on the amino acid content in spring wheat plants, *Swedish Journal of Agricultural Research*, **7**, 153–157.

NOVER, L., LERBS, W., MÜLLER, W. and LUCKNER, M. (1979). Channelling of exogenous phenylalanine to the sites of storage and the sites of alkaloid and protein biosynthesis in *Penicillium cyclopium*, *Biochimica et Biophysica Acta*, **584**, 270–283.

O'BRIEN, M.C. and PRENDEVILLE, G.N. (1979). Effects of herbicides on cell membrane permeability in *Lemna minor*, *Weed Research*, **19**, 331–334.

OLORUNSOGO, O.O., BABABUNMI, E.A. and BASSIR, O. (1979). Uncoupling of corn shoot mitochondria by *N*-(phosphonomethyl)glycine, *FEBS Letters*, **97**, 279–282.

PIHAKASKI, S. and PIHAKASKI, K. (1980). Effects of glyphosate on ultrastructure and photosynthesis of *Pellia epiphylla*, *Annals of Botany*, **46**, 133–141.

PRENDEVILLE, G.N. and WARREN, G.F. (1977). Effect of four herbicides and two oils on leaf cell membrane permeability, *Weed Research*, **30**, 251–258.

VAN RENSEN, J.J.S. (1974). Effects of *N*-(phosphonomethyl)glycine on photosynthetic reactions in *Scenedesmus* and in isolated spinach chloroplasts, *Proceedings of the 3rd International Congress on Photosynthesis*, Amsterdam.

RICHARD, E.P., GOSS, J.R. and ARNTZEN, C.J. (1979) Glyphosate does not inhibit photosynthetic electron transport and phosphorylation in pea (*Pisum sativum*) chloroplasts, *Weed Science*, **27**, 684–688.

ROISCH, U. and LINGENS, F. (1974). Effect of the herbicide *N*-(phosphonomethyl)glycine on the biosynthesis of aromatic amino acids, *Angewandte Chemie International Edition*, **13**, 400.

ROISCH, U. and LINGENS, F. (1980). The mechanism of action of the herbicide *N*-(phosphonomethyl)glycine: its effect on the growth and the enzymes of aromatic amino acid biosynthesis in *Escherichia coli*, *Hoppe-Seyler's Zeitschrift für Physiologische Chemie*, **361**, 1049–1058.

RUBIN, J.L., GAINES, C.G. and JENSEN, R.A. (1982). Enzymological basis for the herbicidal action of glyphosate, *Plant Physiology*, **70**, 833–839.

SASSE, F., BACKS-HUSEMANN, D. and BARZ, W. (1979). Isolation and characterisation of vacuoles from cell suspension cultures of *Daucus carota*, *Zeitschrift für Naturforschung*, **34C**, 848–853.

SHANER, D.L. (1978). Effects of glyphosate on transpiration, *Weed Science*, **26**, 513–518.

SHANER, D.L. and LYON, J.L. (1979). Stomatal cycling in *Phaseolus vulgaris* L. in response to glyphosate, *Plant Science Letters*, **15**, 83–87.

SHANER, D.L. and LYON, J.L. (1980). Interaction of glyphosate with aromatic amino acids on transpiration in *Phaseolus vulgaris*, *Weed Science*, **28**, 31–35.

SPRANKLE, P., MEGGITT, W.F. and PENNER, D. (1975). Absorption, action and translocation of glyphosate, *Weed Science*, **23**, 235–240.

STEINRÜCKEN, H.C. and AMRHEIN, N. (1980). The herbicide glyphosate is a potent inhibitor of 5-enolpyruvylshikimic acid-3-phosphate synthase, *Biochemical and Biophysical Research Communications*, **94**, 1207–1212.

TYMONKO, J.M. (1978). Studies on the metabolic sites of action of glyphosate, *Ph.D.thesis,* Virginia Polytechnic Institute and State University.

TYMONKO, J.M. and FOY, C.L. (1978a). Influence of glyphosate on the metabolism of separated soybean leaf cells, *Abstracts of the Weed Science Society of America,* pp. 70–71.

TYMONKO, J.M. and FOY, C.L. (1978b). Inhibition of protein synthesis by glyphosate, *Plant Physiology Supplement,* **61,** 41.

UOTILA, M., EVJEN, K. and IVERSON, T.-H. (1980). The effects of glyphosate on the development and cell ultrastructure of white mustard (*Sinapis alba* L.) seedlings, *Weed Research,* **20,** 153–158.

Chapter 6

Effects of glyphosate on metabolism of phenolic compounds

S.O. Duke and R.E. Hoagland
USDA, Stoneville, USA

Introduction

The earliest hypothesis of the mechanism of action of glyphosate was that it inhibits biosynthesis of aromatic amino acids (Jaworski, 1972; Roisch and Lingens, 1974). Such a primary effect could slow down or halt protein synthesis, resulting in the secondary and tertiary effects caused by this herbicide. However, no primary effects of glyphosate on enzymes of aromatic amino acid synthesis were demonstrated in these early studies.

Two findings led to a new hypothesis in 1978, involving phenylalanine ammonia-lyase (PAL; EC 4.3.1.5), the enzyme thought to regulate synthesis of secondary phenolic compounds (Duke and Hoagland, 1978). Elevation of PAL activity by light had been shown to increase the turnover rate of phenylalanine and tyrosine greatly, despite lowering pool sizes of these aromatic amino acids (Duke and Naylor, 1976a). Increased levels of PAL activity were suggested to reduce aromatic amino acid pools sufficiently to reduce growth in callus cultures of Jerusalem artichoke (*Helianthus tuberosus*) (Davidson and Yeoman, 1974; James and Davidson, 1976). This information led to the hypothesis that glyphosate could exert its effects on aromatic amino acid pools and on growth by enhancing the *in vivo* activity of PAL greatly (Duke and Hoagland, 1978). In addition to depletion of aromatic amino acid pools, toxic levels of the products of PAL, ammonium ion and cinnamate (and its derivatives) could exacerbate the metabolic problems of a plant cell with elevated PAL activity. Jangaard (1974) had suggested previously that inhibition of PAL activity would be an effective herbicidal mechanism, but found no evidence that any existing herbicide had such a mechanism of action. Although earlier data (Duke and Hoagland, 1978) strongly supported our hypothesis, subsequent studies indicated that PAL probably is only marginally involved in the mechanism of glyphosate action (Hoagland, Duke and Elmore, 1978;1979; Duke, Hoagland and Elmore, 1979; 1980; Duke and Hoagland, 1981; Hoagland and Duke, 1982b). During these studies, however, considerable information on the regulation of secondary aromatic compound synthesis was obtained. This chapter deals with new information of aromatic compound metabolism in higher plants resulting from studies with glyphosate.

The name glyphosate in this chapter refers to the free acid form of *N*-(phosphonomethyl)glycine.

Effects of glyphosate on aromatic amino acid synthesis

Glyphosate has been shown to strongly reduce free pool sizes of aromatic amino acids in maize (*Zea mays*) (Hoagland and Duke, 1978), soya bean (*Glycine max*) (Hoagland, Duke and Elmore, 1979; Duke, Hoagland and Elmore, 1979; 1980), cotton (*Gossypium hirsutum*) (Duke, Hoagland and Elmore, unpublished) and buckwheat (*Fagopyrum esculentum*) (Holländer and Amrhein, 1980) (*Table 6.1*).

TABLE 6.1   Effects of glyphosate on free pools of aromatic amino acids in four species

Species	Tissue	Glyphosate treatment		Lighting	Phenylalanine		Tyrosine		Reference
		Concentration (mmol l⁻¹)	Duration (h)		Control (nmol g⁻¹ fr.wt)	Treated	Control (nmol g⁻¹ fr.wt)	Treated	
Soya bean (*Glycine max*)	Root	0.5	72	Continuous	369	168	117	69	Duke, Hoagland and Elmore (1980)
Maize (*Zea mays*)	Root	1.0	72	Darkness	128	77	171	88	Duke and Hoagland (1978)
Cotton (*Gossypium hirsutum*)	Axis	0.2	72	Continuous	307	173	125	149	Duke, Hoagland and Elmore (unpubl.)
Buckwheat (*Fagopyrum esculentum*)	Hypo-cotyl	1.0	24	Continuous	44	20	59	76	Holländer and Amrhein (1980)

Agropyron repens (Ekanayake, Wickremasinghe and Liyanage, 1979), wheat (*Triticum aestivum*) (Nilsson, 1977) and bean (*Phaseolus vulgaris*) (Shaner and Lyon, 1980) also have reduced levels of aromatic amino acids as a result of glyphosate treatment. Haderlie, Widholm and Slife (1977), however, found no significant effect of growth-reducing levels of glyphosate on free pools of aromatic amino acids in carrot (*Daucus carota*) cell cultures. Unfortunately, the turnover or flow rate of aromatic amino acid pools was not determined in any of these studies. A reduced pool size does not necessarily indicate a reduction in synthesis rate (Duke and Naylor, 1976a).

Evidence from Amrhein's laboratory, however, has indicated that synthesis of aromatic amino acids is reduced considerably due to inhibition of 5-*enol*pyruvylshikimate-3-phosphate synthase (EPSP synthase: EC 2.5.1.19) by glyphosate (Amrhein, Schab and Steinrücken, 1980; Steinrücken and Amrhein, 1980; Amrhein *et al.*, 1981). In addition to the lowered aromatic amino acid levels, inhibition of EPSP synthase leads to accumulation of high levels of shikimate in the vacuole (Steinrücken and Amrhein, 1980; Amrhein *et al.*, 1981; Holländer-Czytko and Amrhein, 1983). Inhibition of EPSP synthase is the only known primary site of glyphosate activity (for more details, see Chapter 5). This primary effect results in several interesting secondary effects on the metabolism of secondary aromatic compounds.

Elevation of extractable PAL activity by glyphosate

PAL, the first enzyme in the conversion of aromatic amino acids to secondary products, is the most influential enzyme in regulating the production of secondary aromatic compounds such as flavonoids, lignins, tannins and various phenolic acids (Camm and Towers, 1977) (*Figure 6.1*). Glyphosate treatment causes large

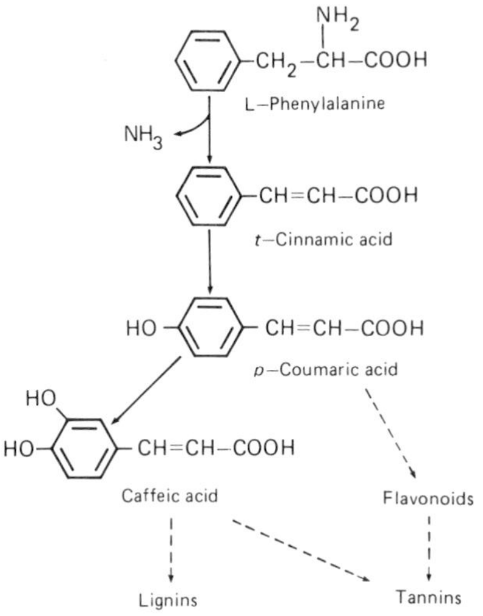

Figure 6.1. Pathway of secondary phenolic compounds controlled by PAL

increases in extractable PAL activities from all higher plant species thus far examined (Duke and Hoagland, 1978; Duke, Hoagland and Elmore, 1979; Cole, Dodge and Caseley, 1980; Hoagland and Duke, 1982a), except buckwheat (Holländer and Amrhein, 1980). In buckwheat there is apparently no effect of end-products of PAL on its extractable activity, as found in other species (Amrhein, 1979). Glyphosate has no direct *in vitro* effect on the activity of PAL (Duke and Hoagland, 1978; Hoagland, Duke and Elmore, 1979). Glyphosine [*N*,*N*-bis(phosphonomethyl)glycine], a growth regulator and other structural analogues of glyphosate have little or no effect on extractable or *in vitro* PAL activity (Hoagland, 1980).

Of all the environmental factors known to increase extractable PAL activity, the effect of light has been most studied (Zucker, 1972; Smith, Billett and Giles, 1977). The effect that glyphosate has on extractable PAL activity is apparently different from that of light. In maize roots, continuous white light causes an increase in extractable PAL activity which disappears after 72 h (Duke and Naylor, 1974; 1976b) (*Figure 6.2a*). A pronounced increase in PAL activity followed by a decrease to lower levels is the typical pattern of light-induced PAL activity (Camm and Towers, 1977). Glyphosate treatment in darkness, however, causes a continual increase in PAL activity, with the greatest effect at the longest exposure time in maize (Duke and Hoagland, 1978) (*Figure 6.2a*). The long-lived increases in PAL activity may be related to the lack of metabolism or detoxification of this herbicide in higher plant tissues (see also Chapter 3). In soya bean, both light and glyphosate cause continual increases in PAL activity for 96 h (Duke, Hoagland and Elmore, 1979) (*Figure 6.2b*). Light and glyphosate enhancements of PAL activity are more

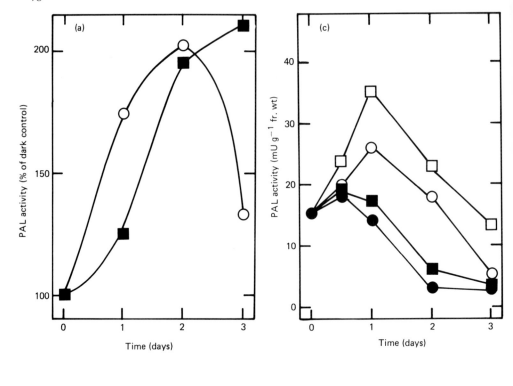

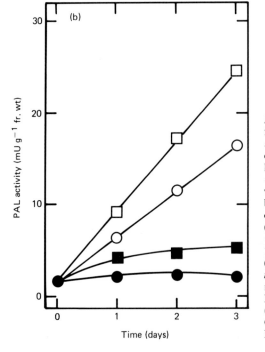

Figure 6.2. Effects of light and root-fed glyphosate on extractable PAL activity from three species. ● 2 = control, darkness; ○ = control, light; ■ = glyphosate, darkness; □ = glyphosate, light. All species were grown in darkness for 3 days before exposure to glyphosate and/or light. (a) Root tissue of maize (*Zea mays*) seedlings. Glyphosate = 1 mmol l^{-1} (Duke and Naylor, 1976b; Duke and Hoagland, 1978). (b) Axis of soya bean (*Glycine max*) seedlings. Glyphosate = 0.5 mmol l^{-1} (Duke, Hoagland and Elmore, 1979). (c) Axis of cotton (*Gossypium hirsutum*) seedlings. Glyphosate = 0.2 mmol l^{-1} (Duke and Hoagland, unpublished)

than additive in soya bean, suggesting that the mechanism of increased extractable activity is different for these stimuli. In cotton, the effects of light and glyphosate generally are more than additive, but the patterns of extractable PAL activity are similar (*Figure 6.2c*) (Duke and Hoagland, unpublished). Results of Holländer and Amrhein (1980) support the view that the mechanisms of effects on extractable PAL activity differ for light and glyphosate. They found light to have a strong enhancing effect on extractable PAL from buckwheat, whereas glyphosate had no effect. Differences between the mechanisms and kinetics of light- and glyphosate-caused increases in PAL activity may be related to differences in end-product accumulation.

Effects of glyphosate on accumulation of aromatic secondary compounds

In our studies, glyphosate caused significant decreases in the amount of soluble hydroxyphenolic compounds in plants on a per plant (or per organ) basis, while increasing their concentration within the tissues (Hoagland, Duke and Elmore, 1978; Duke, Hoagland and Elmore, 1979) (*Figure 6.3*). Using an assay similar to ours, however, Lee (1982b) found that glyphosate caused marked decreases in the amount of phenolic compounds per unit of dry weight in tobacco (*Nicotiana tabacum*) callus. The non-specific technique (Singleton and Rossi, 1965) that we used for quantification of soluble hydroxyphenolics could have been misleading for several reasons: (1) individual hydroxyphenolic compounds give grossly different results with this technique, so that qualitative changes in the hydroxyphenolic composition during glyphosate treatment could confound the results; (2) catabolic degradation of phenolic compounds may be altered by glyphosate; and (3) glyphosate may affect movement of soluble hydroxyphenolic compounds into insoluble compounds such as lignin.

Some of our data suggest that the first of these equivocations is unlikely to be a major source of error. We found glyphosate to have no significant effect on the proportion of ethanol-soluble hydroxyphenolics that were flavonoids (Duke and Hoagland, 1981). We obtained similar results with an ultraviolet spectrophotometric assay of phenolic compounds (Duke and Hoagland, unpublished). However, glyphosate greatly decreased anthocyanin (a specific phenolic compound) formation in soya bean hypocotyls (Hoagland, 1980 and buckwheat cotyledons (Holländer and Amrhein, 1980). Levels of glyceollin, a phenolic phytoalexin, were reduced greatly in soya bean hypocotyls and leaves by glyphosate (Holliday and Keen, 1982; Keen, Holliday and Yoshikawa, 1982; see also Chapter 11).

Whether the second problem, that of turnover or degradation of hydroxyphenolics, has confounded our results also is not certain. This probably is not a major source of error, however, because turnover of soluble secondary phenolic constituents of higher plants normally is very slow or absent in developing seedlings (Amrhein and Diederich, 1980).

The third criticism of the method probably is also not a significant source of error either, because glyphosate was shown to have no effect in soya bean seedlings on the proportion of ^{14}C-labelled aromatic amino acids incorporated into non-hydrolysable, ethanol-insoluble compounds which probably were lignins and tannins (Duke and Hoagland, 1981). Thus, despite possible criticisms of the method of Singleton and Rossi (1965), the finding that glyphosate often causes increases in the concentration of soluble hydroxyphenolic compounds probably is correct.

This conclusion seems incompatible with glyphosate inhibition of aromatic amino acid synthesis. In developing seedlings, however, the concentration effect may be a secondary result of the inhibition of cellular enlargement. The loss in concentration in the control over time in dark-grown tissues, despite an increase in the hydroxyphenolic content per plant organ (*Figure 6.3*), supports this theory. Also,

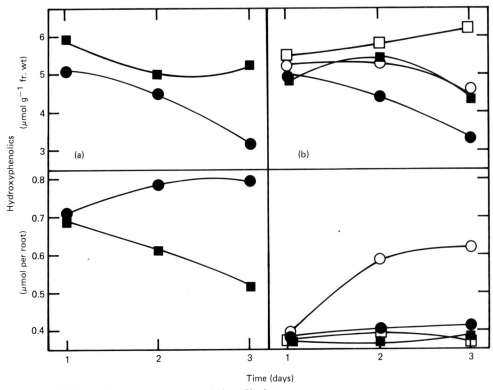

Time (days)

Figure 6.3. Effects of glyphosate on accumulation of hydroxyphenolic compounds in (a) maize (*Zea mays*) and (b) soya bean
(*Glycine max*) seedling roots. (From (a) Hoagland, Duke and
Elmore, 1978; (b) Duke, Hoagland and Elmore, 1979).
○ = control, grown in continuous white light; ● = control, grown
in darkness; □ = glyphosate-treated, grown in continuous
white light; ■ = glyphosate-treated, grown in darkness.

glyphosate could cause increases in synthesis of phenolic compounds not derived from aromatic amino acids (see Heinstein *et al.*, 1979; Gross, 1981), especially benzoic acids derived from shikimate precursors. Indeed, Amrhein *et al.* (1983) reported that glyphosate can cause a fourfold increase in gallic acid content, presumably via dehydroshikimic acid.

The mechanism of glyphosate effects on extractable PAL activity

Extractable PAL activity levels are known to be under the feedback control of end-products (Lamb and Rubery, 1976; Amrhein, 1979; Engelsma, 1979). Until the discovery of the effect of glyphosate on aromatic amino acid synthesis, the only proofs of this were: (1) the inhibition of extractable PAL activity by feeding *t*-cinnamic acid, an immediate product of PAL (Lamb and Rubery, 1976; Engelsma, 1979); (2) the increase in extractable activity in PAL caused by feeding PAL inhibitors such as D-phenylalanine (Szkutnicks and Lewaki, 1975; Huault and Klein-Eude, 1978) or L-α-aminooxy-β-phenylpropionic acid (AOPP) (Amrhein and Gerhardt, 1979); and (3) the increase in PAL activity caused by converting hydroxycinnamic acids to other compounds *in vivo* (Engelsma, 1979). A secondary effect of reduced aromatic amino acid synthesis by glyphosate treatment apparently is an increase in extractable PAL activity. In the only exception, buckwheat, neither AOPP (Amrhein, 1979) nor glyphosate (Holländer and Amrhein, 1980) affected PAL activity, suggesting that feedback control or end-product gene repression does not exist in this tissue. In most tissues there is a close correlation between increases in PAL activity and decreases in phenylalanine and hydroxyphenolic compound levels caused by glyphosate on a per plant or plant-organ basis (Hoagland and Duke, 1982a) (*Figure 6.4*). These results are compatible with the theory of end-product regulation of PAL activity.

AOPP, a specific inhibitor of PAL with little phytotoxicity (Amrhein and Gödeke, 1977), has been useful in understanding further the effects of glyphosate on PAL activity. The effects of AOPP on extractable PAL activity and soluble hydroxyphenolic compound levels in soya bean are almost identical to those of glyphosate (Duke, Hoagland and Elmore, 1980). Obviously, AOPP is removed from PAL during partial purification. The effects of AOPP and glyphosate on phenylalanine and tyrosine levels are opposite, with AOPP increasing greatly the free pools of these aromatic amino acids (*Figure 6.5*).

Noé and Seitz (1982) showed that AOPP increased levels of PAL activity due to *de novo* synthesis of the enzyme. Their findings suggest that increases in extractable PAL activity, resulting from reduced levels of end-products, are due to *de novo* synthesis of PAL. Therefore, glyphosate probably causes enhanced PAL activity levels by this mechanism.

A serious objection to this view is that there is no reduction in the actual tissue concentration of soluble hydroxyphenolic compounds, as there is with AOPP (*Table 6.2*). Also, glyphosate causes elevated PAL activity, even when high concentrations of aromatic amino acids are fed to soya bean seedlings (Duke and Hoagland, 1981). In order to resolve this paradox, additional information on (1) intra- and intercellular compartmentalization of PAL and its products, (2) qualitative effects of glyphosate on secondary phenolic compounds and (3) quantitative differences between the effects of different phenolic compounds on *de novo* synthesis of PAL will be necessary. In soya bean, PAL levels correlate poorly with total hydroxyphenolic levels, but correlate very well with anthocyanin levels (Hoagland and Duke, 1983), indicating that the hydroxyphenolic assay does not reflect the relative concentration of those phenolic compounds that regulate PAL synthesis.

Aminooxyacetic acid (AOA) very effectively inhibits both transaminase enzymes requiring pyridoxyl phosphate and PAL (Amrhein, Gödeke and Kefeli, 1976; John, Charteris and Fowler, 1978) and is extremely phytotoxic (Hoagland and Duke, 1982b). In the light, AOA reduces PAL levels below those of the control; however, the effect of glyphosate with AOA is practically the same as that of glyphosate alone (*Figure 6.6*). Data of Havir (1981) and Hoagland and Duke (1982b) indicated that AOA inhibits synthesis of PAL. The mechanism of this

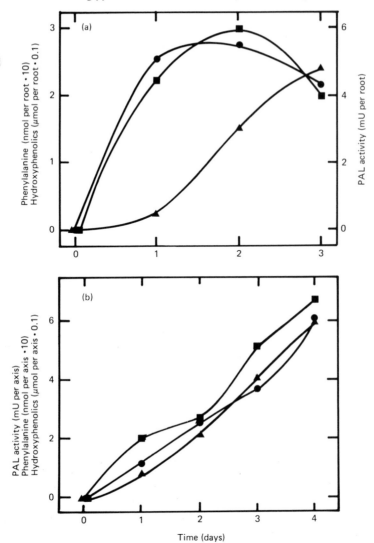

Figure 6.4. Correlation of extractable PAL activity increases
(●) with decreases in PAL substrate (phenylalanine) (■) and
end-products (hydroxyphenolics) (▲) during glyphosate treatment in dark-grown roots of (a) maize (*Zea mays*) and light-
grown (b) soya bean (*Glycine max*) axes (from Hoagland and
Duke, 1982a).

effect probably is through alteration of amino acid metabolism by binding of AOA
to certain transaminase enzymes at the pyridoxal phosphate binding site.
Glyphosate, a possible pyridoxal phosphate analogue, could protect this site from
AOA without inhibiting the transaminase reaction strongly. This possibility is
supported by free amino acid pool data in which the effect of glyphosate generally
predominates over that of AOA in those cases where the effects of AOA and
glyphosate differ (Hoagland and Duke, 1982b).

The prolonged increase in extractable PAL activity during glyphosate exposure (*Figure 6.2*) is difficult to reconcile with the theory that glyphosate strongly retards protein synthesis. The half-life of PAL has been reported to range from 3 to 4 h in mustard (*Sinapis alba*) cotyledons (Acton and Gupta, 1979) and to 5 to 10 h in parsley (*Petroselinum hortense*) cell suspension cultures (Betz, Schafer and Hahlbrock, 1978). Therefore, the prolonged increases in extractable PAL activity over several days in glyphosate-treated plants are probably due, at least in part, to *de novo* synthesis of the enzyme. In some systems, decreases in extractable PAL activity after environmentally-stimulated increases have been attributed to increased synthesis of a proteinaceous PAL inhibitor after PAL induction (Hanson and Havir, 1981). If substantial inhibition of protein synthesis occurs only after prolonged glyphosate treatment, prevention of synthesis of this inhibitor could prolong the half-life of PAL in glyphosate-treated tissues.

Specificity of the effect of glyphosate on aromatic compound metabolism

Although Jangaard (1974) and Duke and Hoagland (1978) have speculated that PAL might be the site of action of some herbicides, no clear evidence of a key role of PAL in the mechanism of action of any herbicide has yet been produced. In a study of 17 herbicides, representing 15 herbicide classes, we found a strong positive correlation (>99% probability) between PAL activity and anthocyanin accumulation (Hoagland and Duke, 1981; 1983) (*Figure 6.7*). Only glyphosate caused PAL activity to increase while decreasing product levels. None of the herbicides had *in vitro* effects on PAL activity. Apparently, the effect of glyphosate on PAL activity is related closely to its mechanism of action and is not the tertiary result of herbicidal stress.

Does PAL regulate synthesis of secondary phenolic compounds?

Margna (1977) and Laanest (1981) have argued that PAL activity is not limiting to phenylpropanoid synthesis in most cases, but that substrate supply is the major limitation. The alternative view, that PAL regulates the production of cinnamate and its derivatives, is held widely (Camm and Towers, 1977). Work with glyphosate has not favoured either hypothesis, but has suggested that either factor can control flow of aromatic amino acids into secondary compounds, depending on the system.

In two cell lines of tobacco which accumulate grossly different amounts of cinnamoyl putrescines and have correspondingly large differences in PAL activity, Berlin and Witte (1981) found little difference in shikimate accumulation caused by glyphosate. This finding is strong evidence that PAL activity regulates secondary phenolic compound levels in this system. In buckwheat, however, Amrhein and Holländer (1981) found light to increase greatly glyphosate-caused shikimate accumulation over that in darkness. This effect was unrelated to glyphosate uptake. In this system, light-caused increases in phenylpropanoid content are apparently largely due to increased aromatic amino acid synthesis. As mentioned earlier, light but not glyphosate increases PAL activity in buckwheat (Holländer and Amrhein, 1980).

Results from our work suggest that, in most systems, both substrate supply and

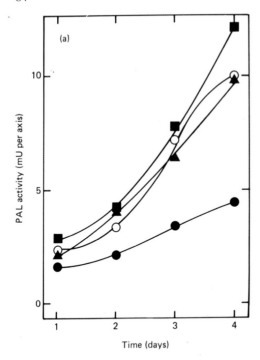

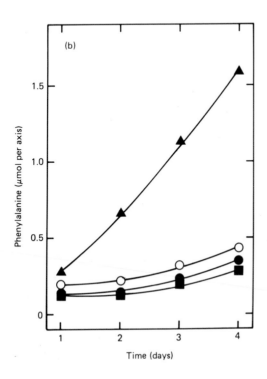

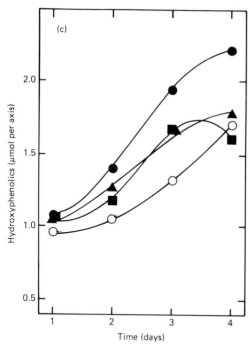

Figure 6.5. Effects of glyphosate and AOPP on extractable PAL (a), phenylalanine (b) and hydroxyphenolic levels (c), in axes of soya bean (*Glycine max*) seedlings. Glyphosate was root-fed at 0.5 mmol l^{-1} and AOPP at 0.1 mmol l^{-1}. ● = control, ■ = glyphosate, ▲ = AOPP, ○ = glyphosate plus AOPP (from Duke, Hoagland and Elmore, 1980)

TABLE 6.2   Effect of glyphosate (0.5 mmol l^{-1}) and AOPP (0.1 mmol l^{-1}) on concentration of extractable PAL activity and soluble hydroxyphenolic compounds from soya bean (*Glycine max*) seedling roots after 3 days of chemical treatment (from Duke, Hoagland and Elmore, 1980). Numbers in parentheses are percentages of control

Treatment	PAL activity (mU g^{-1} fr. wt)	Hydroxyphenolics (μmol g^{-1} fr. wt)
Control	9.6	5.9
Glyphosate	30.5 (318)	6.3 (107)
AOPP	21.3 (222)	4.5 (77)
AOPP and glyphosate	25.7 (268)	6.3 (107)

PAL activity play a role in regulating flow of aromatic amino acids into secondary plant products. The strong positive correlation between extractable PAL activity and anthocyanin content under a wide variety of chemical influences indicates that PAL normally controls production of anthocyanin (Hoagland and Duke, 1983) (*Figure 6.7*). In the same system, however, glyphosate-caused reduction of PAL substrate levels cannot be compensated for by glyphosate-caused increases in PAL activity. In fact, our studies with AOPP (Duke, Hoagland and Elmore, 1980) suggest that only a small proportion of the phenylalanine/tyrosine pool is accessible to PAL. In studies in which aromatic amino acids were root-fed to soya bean seedlings (Duke and Hogland, 1981), the concentration of hydroxyphenolic compounds in the root tissue was not increased (*Table 6.3*), suggesting that there is no substrate limitation in this system. This conclusion is supported further by the finding that exogenously fed phenylalanine was converted to secondary phenolic compounds. In glyphosate-treated plants, however, exogenous aromatic amino

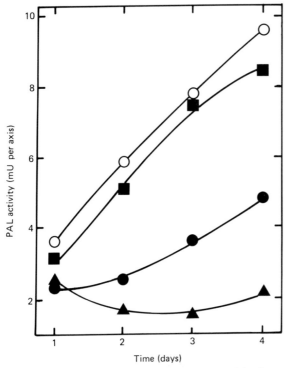

Figure 6.6. Effects of AOA on extractable PAL activity from axes of soya bean (*Glycine max*) seedlings. ● = control, ■ = glyphosate (0.5 mmol l⁻¹), ▲ = AOA (50 µmol l⁻¹), ○ = glyphosate plus AOA (from Hoagland and Duke, 1982b)

acids did elevate the concentration of hydroxyphenolics. Higher than normal PAL activity was still found in glyphosate-treated tissues supplied with aromatic amino acids. Moreover, in seedlings fed aromatic amino acids, a higher proportion of the absorbed amino acids are incorporated into secondary phenolic compounds in glyphosate-treated than in control plants (Duke and Hoagland, 1981). Thus, in tissues with elevated PAL levels and lowered endogenous aromatic amino acid pool sizes, *in vivo* PAL activity apparently is substrate-limited.

A further complication regarding the question of whether PAL activity limits synthesis of secondary phenolic compounds is the possibility of alternative pathways, not involving PAL, for some phenolic compounds (Amrhein *et al.,* 1983).

Effects of glyphosate on polyphenol oxidase

The only other enzyme of secondary phenolic metabolism on which the effect of glyphosate has been examined is polyphenol oxidase (PPO). Enhancement of PPO activity has been observed under a variety of stress stimuli (Mayer and Harel, 1979), including glyphosate treatment (Cole, Dodge and Caseley, 1980; Hoagland and Duke, 1982a). Such effects are generally thought to indicate activation of latent

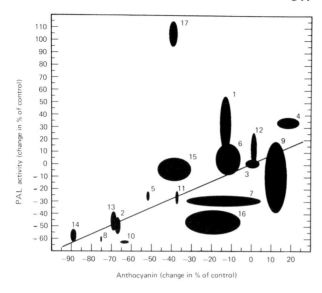

Key: 1, amitrole (0.5 mmol l^{-1}); 2, atrazine (0.1 mmol l^{-1}); 3, dichlofop-methyl (0.07 mmol l^{-1}); 4, DSMA (0.5 mmol l^{-1}); 5, fenuron (0.2 mmol l^{-1}); 6, fluridone (0.05 mmol l^{-1}); 7, MH (0.5 mmol l^{-1}); 8, metribuzin (0.5 mmol l^{-1}); 9, nitralin, (0.0018 mmol l^{-1}); 10, norflurazon (0.05 mmol l^{-1}); 11, paraquat (0.05 mmol l^{-1}); 12, perfluidone (0.15 mmol l^{-1}); 13, propanil (0.2 mmol l^{-1}); 14, propham (0.1 mmol l^{-1}); 15, TCA (0.5 mmol l^{-1}); 16, 2,4-D (0.05 mmol l^{-1}); 17, glyphosate (0.5 mmol l^{-1})

Figure 6.7. Correlation of effects of 17 herbicides on extractable PAL activity and anthocyanin content of axes of soya bean (*Glycine max*) seedlings (from Hoagland and Duke, 1983)

TABLE 6.3   Effects of exogenously fed aromatic amino acids on ethanol-soluble hydroxyphenolic and PAL concentration in axis tissues of control and 0.5 mmol l^{-1} glyphosate-treated soya bean (*Glycine max*) seedlings. Three-day-old, dark-grown seedlings were exposed to light and amino acids for 1 day and then exposed to glyphosate for 2 or 3 days (calculated from data in Duke and Hoagland, 1981)

Treatment	PAL activity (mU g^{-1} fr. wt)	Hydroxyphenolics (μmol g^{-1} fr. wt)
	2 days	
Control	17.2	5.9
Glyphosate	86.7	5.6
Amino acids	12.1	5.6
Glyphosate and amino acids	43.1	7.5
	3 days	
Control	18.6	4.7
Glyphosate	84.4	5.9
Amino acids	9.9	4.8
Glyphosate and amino acids	66.2	6.7

enzyme rather than *de novo* synthesis. If the increased PPO had access to the more concentrated hydroxyphenolics in glyphosate-treated tissues, toxic *ortho*-quinones could be produced. Recent results, however, strongly suggest that in undamaged tissue the plastid enzyme, PPO, never comes in contact with vacuolar hydroxyphenolic compounds (Duke and Vaughn, 1982). Moreover, these results indicate that peroxidase (POD) is probably the enzyme normally involved in phenolic oxidation and hydroxylation *in vivo* in healthy tissues. The assay used by Cole, Dodge and Caseley (1980) and Hoagland and Duke (1982a) did not distinguish between PPO and POD, so the effect they detected could well have been a POD effect. If so, the results of Lee (1982a; 1982b) could be partially explained by these findings. Lee found glyphosate to enhance oxidative degradation of indole-3-acetic acid (IAA). IAA-oxidase is known to be a form of POD that is strongly affected by secondary phenolic compounds (Moore, 1979). Thus, the effects of glyphosate on IAA metabolism and physiology observed by Lee (1982a; 1982b) and Baur (1979) could be an indirect effect of glyphosate-caused reductions in secondary phenolic compounds and, thereby, of altered IAA-oxidase activity.

Conclusions

Glyphosate is unique in that it is the only compound known to specifically inhibit the synthesis of aromatic amino acids. This property results in profound effects on metabolism of secondary aromatic compounds including: (1) increased extractable PAL activity; (2) decreased levels of secondary aromatic compounds; and (3) reversal of AOA-reduced PAL levels. These findings have provided further evidence for strong end-product repression of extractable PAL activity in most higher plant species, as well as suggesting possible pyridoxyl phosphate analogue properties of glyphosate. Several questions must be resolved, however, in order to understand the effect of glyphosate on secondary phenolic compound metabolism more fully. The most important of these include: (1) does glyphosate cause *de novo* synthesis of PAL; (2) does glyphosate strongly affect any enzymes of secondary phenolic metabolism other than PAL; (3) are glyphosate-caused increases in extractable PAL activity caused by decreased end-product concentration? Unequivocal answers to these questions will produce a clearer understanding of the mechanism of glyphosate action and of secondary phenolic compound metabolism.

References

ACTON, G.J. and GUPTA, G. (1979). A relationship between protein-degradation rates *in vivo*, isoelectric points, and molecular weights obtained by using density labelling, *Biochemical Journal*, **184**, 367–377.

AMRHEIN, N. (1979). Novel inhibitors of phenylpropanoid metabolism in higher plants, in *Regulation of Secondary Product and Plant Hormone Metabolism*, pp. 173–182 (Eds. M. Luckner and K. Schreiber). Oxford; Pergamon Press.

AMRHEIN, N., DEUS, B., GEHRKE, P., HOLLÄNDER, H., SCHAB, J., SCHULZ, A. and STEINRÜCKEN, H.C. (1981). Interference of glyphosate with the shikimate pathway, *Proceedings of the Plant Growth Regulator Working Group*, **8**, 99–106.

AMRHEIN, N. and DIEDERICH, E. (1980). Turnover of isoflavones in *Cicer arietinum*, *Naturwissenschaften*, **67**, 40.

AMRHEIN, N. and GERHARDT, J. (1979). Superinduction of phenylalanine ammonia-lyase in gherkin hypocotyls caused by the inhibitor, L-α-aminooxy-β-phenylpropionic acid, *Biochemica et Biophysica Acta*, **583**, 434–442.

AMRHEIN, N. and GÖDEKE, K.H. (1977). α-Aminooxy-β-phenylpropionic acid—a potent inhibitor of L-phenylalanine ammonia-lyase *in vitro* and *in vivo*, *Plant Science Letters*, **8**, 313–317.

AMRHEIN, N., GÖDEKE, K.-H. and KEFELI, V.I. (1976). The estimation of relative intracellular phenylalanine ammonia-lyase (PAL)-activities and the modulation *in vivo* and *in vitro* by competitive inhibitors, *Berichte der Deutschen Botanischen Gesellschaft*, **89**, 247–259.

AMRHEIN, N. and HOLLÄNDER, H. (1981). Light promotes the production of shikimic acid in buckwheat, *Naturwissenschaften*, **68**, 43.

AMRHEIN, N., HOLLÄNDER-CZYTKO, H., LEIFELD, J., SCHULZ, A., STEINRÜCKEN, H.-C. and TOPP, H. (1983). Inhibition of the shikimate pathway by glyphosate, in *Journées internationales d'études du Groupe Polyphenols. Bulletin de Liaison*, vol. II, pp. 21–31 (Eds. A.M. Boudet and R. Ranjeva). Toulouse.

AMRHEIN, N., SCHAB, J. and STEINRÜCKEN, H.L. (1980). The mode of action of the herbicide glyphosate, *Naturwissenschaften*, **67**, 356–357.

BAUR, J.R. (1979). Effect of glyphosate on auxin transport in corn and cotton tissues, *Plant Physiology*, **63**, 882–886.

BERLIN, J. and WITTE, L. (1981). Effects of glyphosate on shikimic acid accumulation in tobacco cell cultures with low and high yields of cinnamoyl putrescines, *Zeitschift für Naturforschung*, **36C**, 210–214.

BETZ, B., SCHAFER, E. and HAHLBROCK, K. (1978). Light-induced phenylalanine ammonia-lyase in cell-suspension cultures of *Petroselinum hortense*, *Archives of Biochemistry and Biophysics*, **190**, 126–135.

CAMM, E.L. and TOWERS, G.H.N. (1977). Phenylalanine ammonia-lyase, in *Progress in Phytochemistry*, vol. 4, pp. 169–188 (Eds. L. Reinhold, J.B. Harborne and T. Swain). New York; Pergamon Press.

COLE, D.J., DODGE, A.D. and CASELEY, J.C. (1980). Some biochemical effects of glyphosate on plant meristems, *Journal of Experimental Botany*, **31**, 1665–1674.

DAVIDSON, A.W. and YEOMANN, M.M. (1974). A phytochrome-mediated sequence of reactions regulating cell division in developing callus cultures, *Annals of Botany*, **38**, 545–554.

DUKE, S.O. and HOAGLAND, R.E. (1978). Effects of glyphosate on metabolism of phenolic compounds. I. Induction of phenylalanine ammonia-lyase activity in dark-grown maize roots, *Plant Science Letters*, **11**, 185–190.

DUKE, S.O. and HOAGLAND, R.E. (1981). Effects of glyphosate on metabolism of phenolic compounds. VII. Root-fed amino acids and glyphosate toxicity in soybean (*Glycine max*) seedlings, *Weed Science*, **29**, 297–302.

DUKE, S.O., HOAGLAND, R.E. and ELMORE, C.D. (1979). Effects of glyphosate on metabolism of phenolic compounds. IV. Phenylalanine ammonia-lyase activity, free amino acids, and soluble hydroxyphenolic compounds in axes of light-grown soybeans, *Physiologia Plantarum*, **46**, 307–317.

DUKE, S.O., HOAGLAND, R.E. and ELMORE, C.D. (1980). Effects of glyphosate on metabolism of phenolic compounds. V. L-α-aminooxy-β-phenylpropionic acid and glyphosate effects on phenylalanine ammonia-lyase in soybean seedlings, *Plant Physiology*, **65**, 17–21.

DUKE, S.O. and NAYLOR, A.W. (1974). Effects of light on phenylalanine ammonia-lyase activity in dark-grown *Zea mays* (L.) seedlings, *Plant Science Letters*, **2**, 289–293.

DUKE, S.O. and NAYLOR, A.W. (1976a). Light effects on phenylalanine ammonia-lyase substrate levels and turnover rates in maize seedlings, *Plant Science Letters*, **6**, 361–367.

DUKE, S.O. and NAYLOR, A.W. (1976b). Light control of anthocyanin biosynthesis in *Zea* seedlings, *Physiologia Plantarum*, **37**, 62–68.

DUKE, S.O. and VAUGHN, K.C. (1982). Lack of involvement of polyphenol oxidase in ortho-hydroxylation of phenolic compounds in mung bean seedlings, *Physiologia Plantarum*, **54**, 381–385.

EKANAYAKE, A., WICHREMASINGHE, R.L. and LIYANAGE, H.D.S. (1979). Studies on the mechanism of herbicidal action of *N*-(phosphonomethyl)glycine, *Weed Research*, **19**, 39–43.

ENGELSMA, G. (1979). Inhibition of phenylalanine ammonia-lyase by cinnamic acid derivatives, in *Regulation of Secondary Product and Plant Hormone Metabolism*, pp. 163–172 (Eds. M. Luckner and K. Schreiber). Oxford; Pergamon Press.

GROSS, G.G. (1981). Phenolic acids, in *The Biochemistry of Plants*, vol. 7, *Secondary Plant Products*, pp. 301–316 (Eds. P.K. Stumpf and E.E. Conn). New York; Academic Press.

HADERLIE, L.C., WIDHOLM, J.M. and SLIFE, F.W. (1977). Effect of glyphosate on carrot and tobacco cells, *Plant Physiology*, **60**, 40–43.

HANSON, K.R. and HAVIR, E.A. (1981). Phenylalanine ammonia-lyase, in *The Biochemistry of Plants*, vol. 7, *Secondary Plant Products*, pp. 577–625 (Eds. P.K. Stumpf and E.E. Conn). New York; Academic Press.

HAVIR, E.A. (1981). Modification of L-phenylalanine ammonia-lyase in soybean cell suspension cultures by 2-aminooxyacetate and L-2-aminooxy-3-phenylpropionate, *Planta*, **152**, 124–130.

HEINSTEIN, P., WIDMAIER, R., WEGNER, P. and HOWE, J. (1979). Biosynthesis of gossypol, *Recent Advances in Phytochemistry*, **12**, 313–337.

HOAGLAND, R.E. (1980). Effects of glyphosate on metabolism of phenolic compounds. VI. Effects of glyphosine and glyphosate metabolites on phenylalanine ammonia-lyase activity, growth, and protein, chlorophyll, and anthocyanin levels in soybean (*Glycine max*) seedlings, *Weed Science*, **28**, 393–400.

HOAGLAND, R.E. and DUKE, S.O. (1981). Effects of herbicides on growth and extractable phenylalanine ammonia-lyase activity in light- and dark-grown soybean (*Glycine max*) seedlings, *Weed Science*, **29**, 433–439.

HOAGLAND, R.E. and DUKE, S.O. (1982a). Biochemical effects of glyphosate [*N*-(phosphonomethyl)glycine], in *Biochemical Responses Induced by Herbicides*, pp. 175–205 (Eds. D.E. Moreland, J.B. St. John and F.D. Hess), ACS Symp. Series No. 181. American Chemical Soc.

HOAGLAND, R.E. and DUKE, S.O. (1982b). Effects of glyphosate on metabolism of phenolic compounds. VIII. Comparison of the effects of aminooxyacetate and glyphosate, *Plant and Cell Physiology*, **23**, 1081–1088.

HOAGLAND, R.E. and DUKE, S.O. (1983). Relationships between phenylalanine ammonia-lyase activity and physiological responses of soybean (*Glycine max*) seedlings to herbicides, *Weed Science*, **31**, 845–852.

HOAGLAND, R.E., DUKE, S.O. and ELMORE, C.D. (1978). Effects of glyphosate on metabolism of phenolic compounds. II. Influence on soluble hydroxyphenolic compound, free amino acid and soluble protein levels in dark-grown maize roots, *Plant Science Letters*, **13**, 291–299.

HOAGLAND, R.E., DUKE, S.O. and ELMORE, C.D. (1979). Effects of glyphosate on metabolism of phenolic compounds. III. Phenylalanine ammonia-lyase activity, free amino acids, soluble protein and hydroxyphenolic compounds in axes of dark-grown soybeans. *Physiologia Plantarum*, **46**, 357–366.

HOLLÄNDER, H. and AMRHEIN, N. (1980). The site of the inhibition of the shikimate pathway by glyphosate. I. Inhibition by glyphosate of phenylpropanoid synthesis in buckwheat (*Fagopyrum esculentum Moench*), *Plant Physiology*, **66**, 823–829.

HOLLÄNDER-CZYTKO, H. and AMRHEIN, N. (1983). Subcellular compartmentalization of shikimic acid and phenylalanine in buckwheat cell suspension cultures grown in the presence of shikimate pathway inhibitors, *Plant Science Letters*, **29**, 89–96.

HOLLIDAY, M.J. and KEEN, N.T. (1982). The role of phytoalexins in the resistance of soybean leaves to bacteria: effect of glyphosate on glyceollin accumulation, *Phytopathology*, **72**, 1470–1474.

HUAULT, C. and KLEIN-EUDE, D. (1978). L'acide *trans*-cinnamique et l'evolution de l'activite de la phenylalanine ammoniac-lyase dans les cotyledons de radis exposes a la lumiere rouge lointain, *Plant Science Letters*, **13**, 185–192.

JAMES, D.J. and DAVIDSON, A.W. (1976). Phenylalanine ammonia-lyase and the regulation of cell division in Jerusalem artichoke (*Helianthus tuberosus* L.) callus cultures, *Annals of Botany*, **40**, 957–968.

JANGAARD, N.O. (1974). The effect of herbicides, plant growth regulators and other compounds on phenylalanine ammonia-lyase activity, *Phytochemistry*, **13**, 1769–1775.

JAWORSKI, E.G. (1972). Mode of action of *N*-phosphonomethly glycine: inhibition of aromatic amino acid biosynthesis, *Journal of Agriculture and Food Chemistry*, **20**, 1195–1198.

JOHN, R.A., CHARTERIS, A. and FOWLER, L.J. (1978). The reaction of amino-oxyacetate with pyridoxal phosphate-dependent enzymes, *Biochemical Journal*, **171**, 771–779.

KEEN, N.T., HOLLIDAY, M.J. and YOSHIKAWA, M. (1982). Effects of glyphosate on glyceollin production and the expression of resistance to *Phytophthora megasperma* f. sp. *glycinea* in soybean, *Phytopathology*, **72**, 1467–1470.

LAANEST, L.E. (1981). Utilization of exogenous phenylalanine and tyrosine in biosynthesis of C-glycosyl-flavones in barley, *Fiziologiya Rastenii*, **28**, 103–110.

LAMB, C.J. and RUBERY, P.H. (1976). Phenylalanine ammonia-lyase and cinnamic acid 4-hydroxylase: product repression of the level of enzyme activity in potato tuber discs, *Planta*, **130**, 283–290.

LEE, T.T. (1982a). Mode of action of glyphosate in relation to metabolism in indole-3-acetic acid, *Physiologia Plantarum*, **54**, 289–294.

LEE, T.T. (1982b). Promotion of indole-3-acetic acid oxidation by glyphosate in tobacco callus tissues, *Journal of Plant Growth Regulation*, **1**, 37–48.

MARGNA, U. (1977). Control at the level of substrate supply—an alternative in the regulation of phenylpropanoid accumulation in plant cells, *Phytochemistry*, **16**, 419–426.

MAYER, A.M. and HAREL, E. (1979). Polyphenol oxidases in plants, *Phytochemistry*, **18**, 193–215.

MOORE, T.C. (1979). *Biochemistry and Physiology of Plant Hormones*. New York; Springer-Verlag.

NILSSON, G. (1977). Effects of glyphosate on the amino acid content in spring wheat plants, *Swedish Journal of Agricultural Research*, **7**, 153–157.

NOÉ, N. and SEITZ, H.U. (1982). Induction of *de novo* synthesis of phenylalanine ammonia-lyase by

L-α-aminooxy-β-phenylpropionic acid in suspension cultures of *Daucus carota* L, *Planta,* **154,** 454–458.

ROISCH, U. and LINGENS, F. (1974). Effect of the herbicide *N*-phosphonomethyl-glycine on the biosynthesis of aromatic amino acids, *Angewandte Chemie,* International Edition in English, **13,** 400.

SHANER, D.L. and LYON, J.L. (1980). Interaction of glyphosate with aromatic amino acids on transpiration in *Phaseolus vulgaris, Weed Science,* **28,** 31–35.

SINGLETON, Y.L. and ROSSI, J.A. (1965). Colorimetry of total phenolics with phosphomolybdic-phosphotungstic acid reagents, *American Journal of Enology and Viticulture,* **16,** 144–158.

SMITH, H., BILLETT, E.E. and GILES, A.B. (1977). The photocontrol of gene expression in higher plants, in *Regulation of Enzyme Synthesis and Activity in Higher Plants,* pp. 93–127. (Ed. H. Smith). London; Academic Press.

STEINRÜCKEN, H.C. and AMRHEIN, N. (1980). The herbicide glyphosate as a potent inhibitor of 5-enolpyruvylshikimic acid-3-phosphate synthase, *Biochemical and Biophysical Research Communications,* **94,** 1207–1212.

SZKUTNICKS, K. and LEWAKI, S. (1975). Stimulation of L-phenylalanine ammonia-lyase (PAL) activity by D-phenylalanine in germinating seeds, *Plant Science Letters,* **5,** 147–156.

ZUCKER, M. (1972). Light and enzymes, *Annual Review of Plant Physiology,* **23,** 133–156.

Chapter 7

Environmental and plant factors affecting glyphosate uptake, movement and activity

J.C. Caseley and D. Coupland
Weed Research Organization, Oxford, UK

Introduction

Glyphosate is a post-emergence herbicide which normally enters plants through the aerial, usually chlorophyll-containing, parts. Since the shoot is, in practice, the only portal of entry for glyphosate, its development, as judged by the number of leaves, their area, angle, surface characteristics and physiological condition, is of key importance in relation to interception, retention and penetration. As the primary site of action of glyphosate is associated with inhibition of meristematic activity, translocation from the intercepting leaves to both above and below ground meristems is an essential stage in successful glyphosate treatments. Thus the aerial environment is of prime concern in relation to shoot development, while the soil environment is of importance with regard to its effect on the physiological status of the plant and the development of the shoots and underground perennating organs. The steps involved in glyphosate activity and the main factors that influence them are outlined in *Figure 7.1.*

In this chapter we are primarily concerned with the influence of environmental factors on glyphosate entry, movement and activity. These interactions are in turn affected by other factors, for example application and formulation, which are considered in detail elsewhere in this book and will only be discussed here where they impinge on the topics of this review.

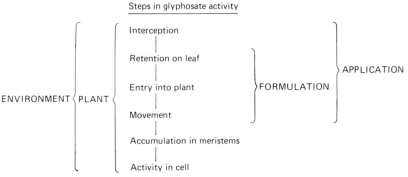

Figure 7.1. Factors affecting the steps involved in glyphosate activity

92

The duration of a particular environmental regime and the time of its imposition in relation to herbicide application are of signal importance in understanding the relationship between environmental factors and glyphosate performance. In this review we have divided the time course of experiments around the moment of application into long- and short-term, pre- and post-spraying periods (*Figure 7.2*).

Unless stated otherwise, citation of the common name glyphosate refers to its use as the isopropylamine salt applied with surfactant. Doses of active ingredient and concentration of surfactant are adjusted by researchers to highlight the level of glyphosate performance on plants at different growth stages and in contrasting environments. Consequently, details of dose are provided only where there is a significant unexpected interaction with the factor under consideration.

We retrieved nearly 420 references in our literature search, but have limited citation to those papers which provided the most detailed and pertinent information.

Some general points relating to plant development and glyphosate entry, movement and performance will be made before considering these in relation to individual environmental factors.

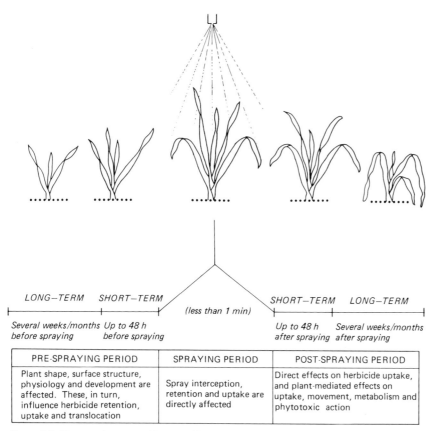

LONG—TERM   SHORT—TERM

(less than 1 min)

SHORT—TERM   LONG—TERM

Several weeks/months   Up to 48 h
before spraying   before spraying

Up to 48 h   Several weeks/months
after spraying   after spraying

PRE-SPRAYING PERIOD	SPRAYING PERIOD	POST-SPRAYING PERIOD
Plant shape, surface structure, physiology and development are affected. These, in turn, influence herbicide retention, uptake and translocation	Spray interception, retention and uptake are directly affected	Direct effects on herbicide uptake, and plant-mediated effects on uptake, movement, metabolism and phytotoxic action

Figure 7.2. How environmental factors affect glyphosate activity

Glyphosate absorption

Under most circumstances, glyphosate enters the plant through the foliage. The aerial parts of the shoot are covered by the cuticle, a lipoidal, non-cellular, non-living membrane which functions to retain water and solutes within the plant and impedes the invasion of pathogens.

Diffusion is regarded as the most likely process for transport of solutes across the cuticle. Factors that influence this process include temperature, formulation, the structure, chemical composition and thickness of cuticle and the presence and type of epicuticular wax. These topics have recently been reviewed by Price (1982). The concentration gradient between the spray deposit and the inside of the plant will also influence the rate of uptake, as demonstrated by Erickson and Duke (1981) who found that increasing the concentration of glyphosate (but not surfactant) enhanced herbicide penetration through isolated cuticles of *Agropyron repens*.

A polar, water-soluble compound such as glyphosate probably penetrates the cuticle via the hydrophilic pathway. It is believed that cutin and carbohydrate fibres provide a polar route among the non-polar waxy portions of the cuticle. When water is freely available, the polar portions hydrate and swell allowing glyphosate penetration to proceed readily, as indicated in the sections of this chapter concerned with humidity and soil moisture (see pp. 109 and 112).

Under favourable conditions, glyphosate rapidly penetrates leaves. Sprankle, Meggitt and Penner (1975) applied ^{14}C-glyphosate, at a concentration of 4.4 g l^{-1} and containing 0.8% surfactant, as a 5 µl drop held with lanolin barriers in the centre of an *A. repens* leaf. Within 4 h, 34% of the applied ^{14}C-glyphosate had penetrated, but over the next 44 h uptake proceeded much more slowly. Working with the leaves of *Apocynum cannabinum*, Schultz and Burnside (1980a) found that after one-half, 3 and 12 days, uptake was 19, 36 and 53% of the applied amount.

Initial fast entry, followed by a longer phase of slower penetration, has been widely reported and the duration of these phases is dependent on a number of factors including species, age, environmental conditions and concentration of the glyphosate and surfactant. For example, as water evaporates from spray drops, the concentration of the active ingredient and adjuvants will increase, facilitating their diffusion across the cuticle. Working with bean (*Phaseolus vulgaris*) leaves, Brecke and Duke (1980) found rapid cuticular penetration over 4 h, but very slow uptake of ^{14}C-glyphosate by mesophyll cells. Gougler and Geiger (1981) studied glyphosate entry into the mesophyll of isolated sugar beet (*Beta vulgaris*) leaf discs and concluded that the concentration dependence of uptake and slow exodiffusion from the tissue was indicative of a passive mechanism. Richard and Slife (1979) demonstrated that ^{14}C-glyphosate uptake by mesophyll cells of *A. cannabinum* was concentration dependent and that ^{14}C-glyphosate was not tightly bound to cellular components. They suggested that the negative charges of the cell wall and plasmalemma repel the strongly anionic glyphosate. This lack of strong binding would contribute to the movement of glyphosate in the apoplast.

Thus, slow penetration of the symplast could be a major barrier to the continued foliar absorption of glyphosate, but on the other hand its lack of rapid phytotoxic effect on many physiological processes may well play a major part in its success as a systemic herbicide. Some of the processes which may affect glyphosate in the leaf are outlined in *Table 7.1* (see also Chapter 5).

So far we have presented a scheme for glyphosate penetration of the cuticle and

TABLE 7.1   Some effects of glyphosate within the leaf which may, in turn, affect its uptake

Process*	Entry†	Reason
1. Stomatal aperture reduced (2–5 h)	−	Transpiration reduced, less removal of glyphosate in apoplast and concentration gradient across cuticle reduced
2. Transpiration reduced	−	
3. Water potential increased (96 h)	+	Hydrated cuticle favours uptake
4. Carbon dioxide fixation reduced (7 h)	−	Less removal of glyphosate in phloem, concentration gradient reduced across the cuticle
5. Respiration unaffected (up to 24 h)	+	Energy-consuming processes, such as phloem loading,
6. Membrane integrity unaffected (96 h)	+	still functioning

*Based on reports by Brecke and Duke (1980), Shaner and Lyon (1980), Crowley and Prendeville (1980), Fletcher, Hilderbrand and Akey (1980) and Richard and Slife (1979).
†Entry decreased (−), increased (+).

entry into the symplast. Now we shall consider techniques to investigate these processes and some of the factors that affect them.

Useful inferences about penetration may be obtained in whole plant studies where phytotoxicity is recorded. Washing glyphosate-treated plants at time intervals after treatment or following exposure to contrasting environments provides information on the time taken for a phytotoxic amount of herbicide to enter the plant (see section on Precipitation, p. 114). Merritt (1982) applied the same dose per plant at three concentrations to *Raphanus sativa* and *Avena fatua*, and the most concentrated glyphosate formulation was always the most toxic. Applying the same dose in drops of 200 or 400 μm diameter (0.004 and 0.03 μl, respectively) had no effect on phytotoxicity. In these experiments, higher phytotoxicity probably resulted from greater entry followed by enhanced transport. However, to quantify herbicide absorption, the amount of glyphosate should be determined on the surface, within the treated tissue and elsewhere in the plant. Since the chemical analysis of glyphosate is difficult, most quantitative studies are made with ^{14}C-glyphosate. For economic and safety reasons this is not usually sprayed onto the plant and, in fact, carefully positioned deposition can reveal information on sites of entry, apoplastic and symplastic movement, binding, metabolism and site of action. Typically, at time intervals after treatment, the treated area is washed to remove glyphosate from the surface, the plant divided into appropriate parts and these and the surface washings prepared for scintillation counting.

Schultz and Burnside (1980a) found no significant difference in ^{14}C-glyphosate entry and movement in *A. cannabinum* with or without a previous overall spray of formulated glyphosate, whereas McAllister and Haderlie (1980) found that pre-spraying soya bean (*Glycine max*) led to decreased ^{14}C-glyphosate entry. To reduce errors due to differences in the surface tension and therefore volume of dispensed drops of formulated and unformulated solutions, some workers apply surfactant to the leaf before dispensing unformulated ^{14}C-glyphosate (Wills, 1978). Others add adjuvants direct to the ^{14}C-glyphosate solution (Wyrill III and Burnside, 1976). Drop sizes employed typically range from 0.5 to 50 μl volumes, far in excess of those produced by conventional spray equipment. As these larger drops tend to roll off the leaf, lanolin or lanolin and starch barriers are often employed to locate the deposit. Schultz and Burnside (1980b) found that such barriers may absorb substantial quantities of herbicide and alter both the amount of ^{14}C-glyphosate absorbed by the leaf and the pattern of its transport.

There are several references in this chapter to enhanced ^{14}C-glyphosate absorption when surfactant was added. In *A. cannabinum,* initial absorption was enhanced, but the period of absorption was not prolonged (Richard and Slife, 1979). In several cases, inclusion of surfactant has, to some extent, overcome the effects of adverse environmental conditions (see p. 117). The properties of surfactants in relation to glyphosate activity are discussed at length elsewhere (see Chapter 15). However, in addition to their well-documented effects on retention, spreading and solubilization of cuticular and epicuticular waxes (with concomitantly improved diffusion across the cuticle), certain surfactants facilitate permeability of the plasmalemma to glyphosate. Wyrill III and Burnside (1977) showed that surfactants which altered the phytotoxicity of glyphosate to *A. cannabinum* and *Asclepias syriaca* had little effect on diffusion of glyphosate across isolated cuticles of these species and concluded that enhancement of plasmalemma permeability may be an important role of adjuvants. However, loss of membrane integrity due to excessive or highly toxic surfactants would reduce glyphosate performance, as symplast loading would stop. Photosynthetic inhibitor herbicides stop photosynthate export and these are antagonistic to glyphosate action, but may increase cuticular penetration and accumulation in the treated area (Ahmadi, Haderlie and Wicks, 1980).

Site of application on the foliage may have a large influence on penetration. Coupland, Taylor and Caseley (1978) found that application to the adaxial surface of the lamina tip of *A. repens* resulted in less damage than application to the lamina base, but most phytotoxicity resulted from deposition of glyphosate on the adaxial surface of the leaf sheath (Coupland, 1983). This is a smooth area free of epicuticular wax, compared with the lamina which is covered in dense wax platelets.

Glyphosate is able to enter the plant by other routes. Turner and Loader (1974) demonstrated that solubilized oil formulations enable glyphosate to penetrate the bark of woody species (see Chapter 15). Roots of plants in nutrient solution containing glyphosate absorb the herbicide which moves throughout the plant (Haderlie, Slife and Butler, 1978; Penn and Lynch, 1982). Salazar and Appleby (1982) found that seedlings of *Agrostis tenuis* were damaged following the placement of seed on organic soil previously sprayed with 3.4 kg ha^{-1} of glyphosate, but Baird, Upchurch and Selleck (1972) showed that between 8 and 32 kg ha^{-1} were required to cause damage to a range of species via the soil.

In the foregoing paragraphs a limited selection of factors that influence glyphosate entry have been cited. There is a need for increased precision in the description of experimental methods. Since the interactions between spray deposit, cuticle and symplast are subject to variation by such a large range of factors, the greatest care should be exercised in making quantitative comparisons between the results of different workers, even when studying the same species. However, trends associated with different levels of environmental factors are remarkably consistent. Many investigators have looked to epicuticular wax and the cuticle as the main barrier to entry, but results presented here suggest that behaviour of glyphosate in the mesophyll and factors relating to its entry into the symplast deserve more attention.

Glyphosate translocation

The translocation of glyphosate in plants involves cell-to-cell movement as well as longer distance transport in the vascular tissues. Transfer across cell membranes is necessary for glyphosate to enter the symplast and move within the phloem system. Apoplastic movement occurs in between cells (within the cell walls) and in the xylem tissues.

Translocation of glyphosate has been studied directly, mainly using ^{14}C-labelled herbicide, and also indirectly by measuring certain physiological responses caused by the presence of the herbicide. Examples of the former include qualitative autoradiographic techniques and quantitative measurements of the amounts of radioactivity in various plants parts. Examples of the latter include measuring the chlorosis induced in green tissues and determing viability (e.g. stem and rhizome buds).

Previous studies have looked at the distribution of glyphosate in plants after its application to leaves, stems or roots. In whole plants, absorption precedes translocation so any factors which affect herbicide absorption, for example environmental conditions, will also influence subsequent translocation. This interdependence has made it difficult to study translocation *per se*, and in almost all of the published reports no attempts have been made to study glyphosate translocation in isolation from uptake. Previously, but with other herbicides, researchers have tried to do this by damaging the plant in order to bypass the absorption stage. Leaf flap, leaf abrasion and stem injection are common examples of these techniques. However, damaged tissues may not behave in the same way as in the intact plant. Recently, Coupland (1983) has described a method which, while not avoiding the uptake process through the plant cuticle, takes advantage of the greatly facilitated absorption through the adaxial surface of the leaf sheaths in *A. repens*. This 'compromise' method has been useful in describing the influence of several environmental factors on the translocation of glyphosate in this species.

Other problems inherent in ^{14}C-tracer studies concern plant treatment. This has been discussed in the previous section dealing with glyphosate entry, and suffice it to say here that any factor affecting uptake will, directly or indirectly, also affect translocation. Because glyphosate is phloem mobile, application to plant parts that are naturally exporting photo-assimilates leads to greater translocation of glyphosate in the rest of the plant. This has been shown in several species, for example cotton (*Gossypium hirsutum*) (Wills, 1978), *Apocynum cannabinum* (Schultz and Burnside, 1980a) and *A. repens* (Coupland, Taylor and Caseley, 1978). These and other studies have demonstrated the phloem mobility of glyphosate (e.g. Sprankle, Meggitt and Penner, 1975; Wyrill III and Burnside, 1976; Coupland and Caseley, 1979; Gougler and Geiger, 1981; Smid and Hiller, 1981).

Accordingly, it might be expected that glyphosate should closely follow the same distribution pattern within plants as the photo-assimilates. This has been demonstrated in several species (Gougler and Geiger, 1981; Dewey, 1982; Lund-Høie, 1983). Gougler and Geiger (1981) treated sugar beet (*Beta vulgaris*) plants simultaneously with ^{14}C-glyphosate and ^{3}H-sucrose (as a tracer for photo-assimilates). The distribution of activity from these two compounds within the plant was remarkably consistent (*Figure 7.3*). The proportionally lower concentration of ^{3}H in the two youngest leaves was attributed to a higher rate of sucrose metabolism in these developing tissues. The slightly higher levels found in

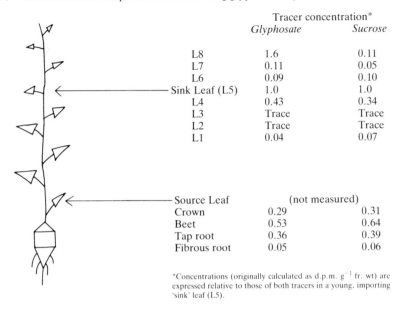

	Tracer concentration*	
	Glyphosate	*Sucrose*
L8	1.6	0.11
L7	0.11	0.05
L6	0.09	0.10
Sink Leaf (L5)	1.0	1.0
L4	0.43	0.34
L3	Trace	Trace
L2	Trace	Trace
L1	0.04	0.07
Source Leaf	(not measured)	
Crown	0.29	0.31
Beet	0.53	0.64
Tap root	0.36	0.39
Fibrous root	0.05	0.06

*Concentrations (originally calculated as d.p.m. g^{-1} fr. wt) are expressed relative to those of both tracers in a young, importing 'sink' leaf (L5).

Figure 7.3. Distribution of ^{14}C-glyphosate and ^{3}H-sucrose after simultaneous application to a mature leaf of sugar beet (*Beta vulgaris*) (after Gougler and Geiger, 1981)

one older leaf (immediately basipetal to the designated 'sink') were thought to be due to recirculation of both labels in the xylem. Thus the distribution of ^{14}C in plants treated with ^{14}C-glyphosate generally shows a typical 'source to sink' direction and it has been suggested that the greatest translocation (and perhaps herbicide efficacy) should result when the number of physiological sinks is greatest (Wyrill III and Burnside, 1976). In practice, however, this theory is too simplistic and other factors need to be taken into account. For example, the more sinks there are, the more the herbicide will be 'diluted' within the plant and therefore more herbicide is needed for a toxic amount to reach each sink. Claus and Behrens (1976) demonstrated this well in *A. repens;* plants with 20–90 rhizome nodes had a higher survival rate than those with 10 nodes. Lolas and Coble (1980) showed a direct relationship between sink activity and ^{14}C-translocation. Plants with longer rhizomes accumulated more radioactivity than those with shorter rhizomes. Also, 'more physiological sinks' generally implies a more mature growth stage. The influence of growth stage on herbicide performance, uptake and translocation will be considered later in this chapter.

Glyphosate is also translocated in the apoplast and its distribution in plants is determined by those factors which influence plant transpiration (Gottrup *et al.,* 1976; Marquis, Comes and Yang, 1979; Bingham, Segura and Foy, 1980; Lolas and Coble, 1980; Lund-Høie, 1983). Compounds, such as glyphosate, that exhibit both symplastic and apoplastic movement are termed ambimobile (Peterson, De Wildt and Edgington, 1978). Little is known, however, about those factors which determine the relative amounts of glyphosate translocated in the symplast or apoplast. Similarly, when and where this interchange between xylem and phloem occurs is little understood.

The other main factors that influence the translocation of glyphosate in plants are plant species, growth stage and the environment. A few reports describe comparative studies of glyphosate translocation in different species under the same conditions. The following data are taken from Sandberg, Meggitt and Penner (1980) and are values of the amounts of ^{14}C translocated out of a treated leaf 14 days after ^{14}C-glyphosate application: *Convolvulus arvensis* (3.5%), *C. sepium* (21.6%), *Cirsium arvense* (7.8%), *Ipomoea purpurea* (6.5%) and *Polygonum convolvulus* (5.0%) (values are expressed as percentage of applied ^{14}C). These differences between species were thought largely to be due to effects on herbicide absorption and translocation.

Environmental factors have pronounced effects on glyphosate translocation in plants, both directly and indirectly, and these effects are described in detail later in this chapter.

Plant development

It is well established for perennial grasses that a minimum amount of foliage is required for satisfactory control with glyphosate. Thus, application of glyphosate to one-and-a-half to three leaf-stage shoots arising from rhizomes of *A. repens* resulted in poor control compared with treatment of larger plants (Rioux, Bandeen and Anderson, 1974). Claus and Behrens (1976) applied glyphosate to *A. repens* with 10, 20, 30, 60 or 90 nodes when the foliage length was 13, 25 or 45 cm. The plants with the fewest nodes were affected most. Application of herbicide to the 13 cm foliage resulted in the least control, whereas treatment of both the 25 and 45 cm plants was equally and highly effective.

The results from these papers may be interpreted in relation to the steps involved in glyphosate activity outlined in *Figure 7.1*. In order to achieve good glyphosate performance, sufficient herbicide in relation to the number of propagules to be controlled must be intercepted, retained and absorbed by the foliage. For example, grasses at an early stage of development tend to have erect laminae which present a small plan area for spray interception. On commencement of tillering, a more prostrate habit develops and the inner surfaces of leaf sheaths are often exposed where entry and subsequent movement of glyphosate proceed more effectively (Coupland, Taylor and Caseley, 1978). Thus, retention and entry may be enhanced at these later growth stages. During the early development of shoots attached to a rhizome system, the flow of photosynthates tends to be towards the expanding laminae of the shoot and little glyphosate will be transported to the rhizome, but once the shoot commences export of photosynthates the rhizome becomes vulnerable (see previous section, p. 97). As shoot growth proceeds, some of the older leaves will become senescent and the rhizome system will have increased in size. This may partially explain the results of Wallgren (1979), who found increasing control of *A. repens* at the following growth stages: 1–3 < 5–7 < 3–5 leaves. Another factor which alters source–sink relationships and glyphosate efficacy is the development of flowering shoots. Lee (1973) achieved 90% control of established *C. arvense* at full flower, but earlier glyphosate treatments, when the shoots were 25–30 cm high, had little effect and application at the mature seed stage had no effect. With *Solanum carolinense*, both flowering and fruiting stages were well controlled, but glyphosate efficacy was halved at the pre-bloom stages (Banks and Santelmann, 1976).

The successful control of other temperate perennials (Davis, Fawcett and Harvey, 1979) and tropical perennials (Suwanketnikom and Penner, 1976; Baird and Upchurch, 1972; Whitwell and Santelmann, 1978; Bolt and Sweet, 1974) with shoots arising from storage organs generally appears to be dependent on adequate foliage and a source–sink relationship that favoured accumulation of glyphosate in the propagule.

In the case of a range of broad leaf and grass species growing from seed, the dose of glyphosate to achieve control increased as the plants grew larger (Brattain and Fay, 1980). Ahmadi, Haderlie and Wicks (1980) applied glyphosate to 5, 10, 15 and 20 cm *Echinochloa crus-galli* plants. The 10 cm plants were affected the most, the 5 and 15 cm were intermediate in response and the 20 cm plants were only slightly damaged. A probable explanation for these results is that the smallest plants intercepted less herbicide, whereas in the larger plants the herbicide was less mobile (see *Table 7.8*).

Plants without developed perennating organs may be controlled better than those with, when their shoots are at an earlier stage of development, since photosynthate flow will be towards the developing portions of the shoot and roots and there are no other meristems.

Tables 7.2 and *7.3* illustrate the varied response in ^{14}C-glyphosate uptake and translocation reported in the literature. Clearly, there is no simple relationship between growth stage and herbicide entry and movement, and factors such as herbicide retention, source–sink relationship and environmental conditions all interact to affect these processes.

TABLE   7.2   Effects of growth stage on ^{14}C-glyphosate absorption

Species	Growth stage	Absorption	Reference
(a) Lucerne (*Medicago sativa*)	(a) Plant height: 20 and 70 cm	(a) Plant size had no significant effect on uptake	Davis, Fawcett and Harvey (1979)
(b) *Agropyron repens*	(b) Maturity: boot and post-bloom stages	(b) The more mature *A. repens* absorbed nearly twice as much as those plants in the boot stage	
Echinochloa crus-galli	Plant height: 5, 10 and 15 cm	Absorption of ^{14}C-glyphosate decreased as plant height increased; no difference between 5 cm and 10 cm plants, but reduced absorption for 15 cm plants 3 days after treatment	Ahmadi, Haderlie and Wicks (1980)
Sorghum halepense	Maturity/plant height: 15–30 cm tall, 45–60 cm tall, seedhead stage; also rhizome length 10, 20 and 30 cm	Absorption was unaffected by plant height, maturity or rhizome length and ranged between 63 and 75% (of applied), 6 days after treatment	Lolas and Coble (1980)
Soya bean (*Glycine max*)	Leaf maturity: unifoliate and trifoliate leaves of different ages	More ^{14}C was absorbed by mature than immature leaves (69, 59, 37 and 28% for the unifoliate and 1st, 2nd and 3rd trifoliate leaves, respectively)	McWhorter, Jordan and Wills (1980)
Apocynum cannabinum	Leaf age: upper vs. lower leaves	No effect of leaf age on absorption	Schultz and Burnside (1980a)

N.B. For each study, the same amount of ^{14}C-glyphosate was applied to the various growth stages and, where specified, absorption is expressed as a percentage of applied [14]C.

TABLE 7.3   Effects of growth stage on ^{14}C-glyphosate translocation

Species	Growth stage	Translocation	Reference
Apocynum can-nabinum and *Asclepias syriaca*	Plant age; young plants 30–40 cm tall—not flowering. Mature plants 70–80 cm tall—post-bloom.	12 days after treatment there were no significant differences in the amount of ^{14}C translocated in young or mature plants of either species	Wyrill III and Burnside (1976)
(a) *Medicago sativa* (b) *Agropyron repens*	(a) Plant height: 20 and 70 cm (b) Plant maturity: boot and post-bloom stages	(a) and (b). No differences were observed in the amounts of ^{14}C translocated out of the treated leaf	Davis, Fawcett and Harvey (1979)
Echinochloa crus-galli	Plant height: 5, 10 and 15 cm	Maximum translocation observed from 10 cm plants, i.e. 3 days after treatment 24% (of absorbed ^{14}C) was translocated throughout the plant compared to 16 and 18% for 5 and 15 cm tall plants, respectively	Ahmadi, Hader-lie and Wicks (1980)
Sorghum halepense	Rhizome length: 10, 20 or 30 cm. Plant matur-ity: 15–30 cm tall and 45–60 cm tall seedhead stage	More ^{14}C was translocated to the rhizomes as rhizome length increased or with increasing plant maturity	Lolas and Coble (1980)
Soya bean (*Gly-cine max*)	Leaf age: unifoliate leaf and 1st, 2nd and 3rd tri-foliate leaves	More ^{14}C was translocated out of the 2nd trifoliate leaf than the other leaves	McWhorter, Jor-dan and Wills (1980)
Apocynum can-nabinum	Leaf age, i.e. upper vs. lower leaves	Greater, although insignificant, amounts of ^{14}C were translocated from upper than lower leaves (14 and 8%, respectively, averaged over 12 days)	Schultz and Burnside (1980a)

N.B. Comparisons between studies of the amounts of ^{14}C translocated cannot be made directly because percentage values refer to the percentage of ^{14}C absorbed or recovered (see original text for details).

Environmental factors

Light

Effects of light on herbicide performance can be due to one or more of the following: intensity, spectral quality and photoperiod. Light intensity, together with daylength and spectral characteristics, determines the total energy received by the plant. Commonly, the photoperiod, together with temperature, determines the development of the plant; for example, the vegetative to flowering transition. Finally, light quality can influence the physiology of the plant; for example, via photosynthesis and the phytochrome-mediated reactions (Smith, 1975). In addition, light, in particular the u.v. component, may also have a direct effect on the chemical on the plant surface. However, available data for glyphosate indicate that photodegradation is not an important factor. The influence of light intensity over stated photoperiods has been studied the most, and there are a few reports of day/night effects. In the literature, different types of units have been used, i.e. lux, foot-candles and W m^{-2}. The preferred unit for photosynthetically active radiation (400–700 nm) is the mole, usually expressed as µmol m^{-2} s^{-1} (numerically equivalent to µE m^{-2} s^{-1}, McFarlane, 1979). However, plants can respond to wavelengths beyond the 400–700 nm region; therefore, total irradiance should be quoted, and the preferred units for this are watts per square metre (W m^{-2}). Interconversion of units is often difficult because lamps differ in their spectral output and measuring instruments vary in their response to different wavelengths. However, for convenience in the following review, all units have been converted to W m^{-2} using the conversion factors described by Bickford and Dunn (1972).

LONG-TERM PRE-SPRAYING PERIOD

Light has a considerable influence on the growth and development of the plant during the long-term pre-spraying period. These effects are achieved at the biochemical level and are manifested in plant size, shape and physiological condition. Light can thus influence herbicide performance by affecting spray interception, retention, absorption and, to a lesser extent, herbicide translocation and metabolism. *Table 7.4* presents some data taken from two reports (Caseley, 1974; Moosavi-Nia and Dore, 1979b) showing the influence of light intensity on the growth of a temperate and a tropical grass weed.

The low light levels indicated in *Table 7.4*, often encountered within a cereal canopy, are conducive to the control with glyphosate of perennial weeds such as *A. repens*, because the plants develop with high shoot : rhizome ratios. This may be one of the reasons why the pre-harvest application of glyphosate is effective (O'Keeffe, 1981). Moosavi-nia and Dore (1979b) showed conclusively that better control of *Imperata cylindrica* and *Cyperus rotundus* was achieved with plants grown under shady conditions. The effects of light on shoot : rhizome ratios and on the reduction of total rhizome and tuber tissues were probably the main reasons for these effects, although changes in leaf morphology, cuticle and wax thickness and leaf wettability were also suggested. Similar results were obtained by Arif (1979) for *I. cylindrica*. He found that in shaded areas this tropical weed can be controlled with lower rates of glyphosate than would normally be used.

TABLE 7.4   **Effects of light intensity on the growth of** *Agropyron repens* **and** *Imperata cylindrica* **(after Caseley, 1974 and Moosavi-Nia and Dore, 1979b)**

Plant species	Light treatment*		
	High	Medium	Low
Agropyron repens			
Number of shoots	22	15	11
Rhizome fr. wt (g)	22	8	2
Number of rhizome nodes	82	37	8
Shoots/nodes ratio (approx.)	1:4	1:3	1:1
Imperata cylindrica			
Number of shoots	4	3.4	2.6
Rhizome dry wt (g)	1.6	1.0	0.2
Shoot dry wt. (g)	3.1	2.7	1.7
Shoot wt/rhizome wt. ratio (approx.)	2:1	3:1	7:1

*Light treatments were: *A. repens*, 203, 50, 13 W m^{-2} (growth cabinet experiment); *I. cylindrica*, unshaded, 50% shade, 75% shade (glasshouse experiment).

Majek (1980) studied the interaction of photoperiod and temperature on the growth of *A. repens*. As a result of these growth chamber studies, Majek predicted the best times to apply glyphosate under local field conditions (New York State, USA). These times coincided with maximum primary rhizome growth, i.e. the greatest rhizome 'sink' activity. Field trials carried out subsequently showed that the best results did occur during late May and October, the times predicted for optimum glyphosate translocation and efficacy.

SHORT-TERM PRE-SPRAYING PERIOD AND SPRAYING PERIOD

No reports have been published concerning the influence of light on glyphosate performance specifically during the short-term pre-spraying and spraying periods. High light intensities, immediately prior to spraying, may result in increased levels of photosynthate which, in turn, may cause an increase in translocation from the leaf (Ho, 1976). There is much scope for research in this area, with practical implications on when best to apply the herbicide. During the spraying period, phototropic and nyctinastic leaf movements could, in theory, affect spray interception and retention and in this way alter herbicide performance.

SHORT-TERM POST-SPRAYING PERIOD

Experiments reporting day/night effects will be discussed in this section, as well as those effects associated with the short-term post-spraying period.

Increased light intensity has been found to increase herbicide uptake and translocation and to increase the speed of development of herbicide damage. Whitwell *et al.* (1980) showed that glyphosate absorption by excised leaf tips and stem sections of *S. carolinense* was greater in the light than in the dark. They concluded that light was implicated in the active uptake of glyphosate and proposed that this could involve the production of ATP or other energy sources, but no specific mechanisms were described.

Coupland (1983) has shown that the translocation of ^{14}C-glyphosate in *A. repens* is influenced by light intensity. Plants treated by application of ^{14}C-glyphosate to the adaxial surface of the leaf sheaths translocated approximately twice as much radioactivity to the rhizomes at 117 W m^{-2} as those treated at 26 W m^{-2}. This difference was observed up to 24 h after treatment, but at 48 h after treatment there was no difference in the amounts of radioactivity found in the rhizomes. Plants sprayed with glyphosate and kept at 117 or 26 W m^{-2} showed a similar response to the ^{14}C-translocation study. Significant reductions in shoot regrowth and rhizome node viability were observed for plants kept at the higher light intensity up to 24 h after spraying. At the 48 h assessment there were no significant differences between the two light levels.

Increased light intensity enhanced the speed of development of herbicide damage (Caseley, 1972). Abu-Irmaileh and Jordan (1977) also showed that darkness delays the appearance of chlorosis on treated leaves, and Lee (1980) showed that glyphosate-induced chlorophyll degradation was accelerated by light.

Davis (1976) looked at diurnal effects on glyphosate activity by treating *A. repens* at 6 h intervals throughout a light/dark cycle in a controlled environment chamber. Treatments made 1 h after the beginning of the light cycle, in the middle of the light cycle and 1 h after the beginning of the dark cycle were all equally effective. Treatments made in the middle of the dark period were least effective. These effects were considered to be correlated with photosynthesis and associated herbicide translocation (Fawcett and Davis, 1976).

Under natural conditions, day/night differences cannot be related simply to the presence or absence of light. At night, temperatures fall and air humidity increases. Because both of these factors influence glyphosate uptake, translocation and activity, all factors should be considered. Caseley, Coupland and Hough (1983) recently have treated *A. repens* in controlled environment rooms set at contrasting conditions (day: 16°C, 48% r.h., 90 W m^{-2}; night: 10°C, 85% r.h., no light). Groups of plants were treated at the beginning, middle and end of the day or night periods (12 h daylength). Results showed insignificant differences between those plants treated during the night or day periods, although there was a slight increase in rhizome bud kill with the daytime treatments when rhizomes were fragmented 6 or 12 h after glyphosate treatment. It would seem from these results that, during the day, light can enhance glyphosate translocation, whereas at night, more humid conditions lead to increased herbicide absorption and enhance activity in this way (see Humidity section, p. 109)

LONG-TERM POST-SPRAYING PERIOD

The majority of research on the influence of light on glyphosate performance concerns the long-term post-spraying period. Most research workers agree that increased light intensity increases herbicide performance.

Upchurch and Baird (1972) found that *Sorghum halepense* was more effectively controlled at 2000 than 500 ft-candles (approx. 70 and 18 W m^{-2}), irrespective of whether the post-treatment temperature was 32° or 16°C. Suwanketnikom and Penner (1976) showed better *Cyperus esculentus* control at 48 438 lux than at 16 146 lux (approx. 157 and 52 W m^{-2}), and Caseley (1972) found better control of *A. repens* at 203 than 13 W m^{-2}, although he stressed that light intensity had the least influence on glyphosate activity compared to temperature and humidity. Several workers have found that given 'sufficient' light during the long-term post-spraying period, plants exposed to reduced light intensities for a short period after spraying will be affected to the same extent as those exposed to relatively high intensities throughout the entire post-spraying period (Upchurch and Baird, 1972; Evans, 1972; Hanson, Rieck and Harger, 1975; Coupland and Caseley, 1981).

More detailed research has shown that light intensity mainly influences herbicide translocation. Schultz and Burnside (1980a), using *Apocynum cannabinum*, showed that absorption of ^{14}C-glyphosate was unaffected by light intensity 7 days after treatment. However, more ^{14}C was translocated into untreated areas of the treated leaf at higher compared with lower light intensities after 7 days. Kells and Rieck (1979) found that in *S. halepense* more ^{14}C was translocated in 'full' light (42 W m^{-2}) than in shade or darkness. Accumulation of ^{14}C was greatest in areas of high metabolic activity and it was thought that the increased translocation was due to increased rates of photosynthesis and greater photosynthate movement. They suggested that practical use could be made of this by delaying tillage of *S. halepense* after spraying on overcast days to compensate for the reduced translocation.

Temperature

Temperature conditions influence plant growth and development by directly affecting the rate of chemical, physical and biochemical reactions. This is manifested in the following: plant shape, size and habit; leaf shape, size, area and morphology (e.g. pubescence and stomatal frequency); and cuticle development. Temperature also influences transpiration which in turn affects the water status of the plant, cuticle hydration and mineral absorption, for example. All of these, either directly or indirectly, influence the response of the plant to glyphosate. Low temperatures can have pronounced effects on plant growth. Freezing temperatures alter cell membrane permeability, and severe conditions can cause extensive damage to plant tissues due to ice crystal formation (Levitt, 1980).

In general, absorption and translocation of foliage-applied herbicides increase with a rise in temperature. This is due to effects on the rate of diffusion through the plant cuticle, increased rates of transpiration and subsequent apoplastic movement, and an increase in the general metabolic activity of the plant providing suitable energy sources for the active loading of assimilates in the translocation stream. Efficient translocation of assimilates is probably essential for the optimum translocation of phloem-mobile herbicides such as glyphosate. At constant r.h., temperature directly influences the rate of spray droplet drying on the plant surface. In this way, glyphosate absorption may be restricted under warm dry conditions since it is thought that water-soluble herbicides need to be in solution to be efficiently absorbed (Sargent, 1965). Temperature will also influence the rate of herbicide metabolism within the plant. Again, in general, a rise in temperature usually results in increased metabolism. Thus, the final effect of temperature on herbicide performance will be a result of this complex interplay of all the factors outlined above.

LONG-TERM PRE-SPRAYING PERIOD

Baird and Begeman (1972) found that preconditioning *A. repens* at 13°, 24° or 32°C for 2 weeks had no effect on herbicide efficacy. Similar effects, again with *A. repens*, were reported by Upchurch, Baird and Begeman (1972). Pretreatment of *Cynodon dactylon* for 5 days at 20°C (relatively cool) did not decrease glyphosate performance (Whitwell and Santelmann, 1978). However, using the broad-leaved woody species *Betula verrucosa*, Lund-Høie (1979) showed a positive correlation between pre-spraying temperature and ^{14}C-glyphosate absorption. The warmer the pre-spraying conditions, the more ^{14}C-glyphosate was absorbed, irrespective of whether cool (12°C) or warm (24°C) temperatures followed herbicide application.

Similar results were obtained by Coupland and Caseley (1981). In their study, *A. repens* plants were grown in three contrasting temperature regimes (10°/6°, 16°/10° and 26°/16°C; day/night, respectively), where light and humidity levels were held constant. Plants were sprayed when they had reached the same growth stage and then kept in a common 'intermediate' environment until harvested. Although the plants were at the same growth stage, the three sets of plants were morphologically quite distinct. The hot-grown plants were taller and grew faster than those grown under cooler conditions. This affected the plan areas of the foliage considerably, and spray retention was found to increase with temperature approximately in the ratio 1 : 2 : 3. These differences in retention undoubtedly affected herbicide performance and an analysis of rhizome bud kill showed a positive correlation with temperature.

Further studies showed that the hot-grown plants absorbed and translocated more herbicide than did the other plants. An investigation of the leaf surfaces of the three sets of plants revealed differences in trichome length and epicuticular wax

(Holloway, Bowdler and Caseley, 1980). The length of the trichomes on the leaf adaxial surface were much shorter (mean 34 μm) in the hot environment than in the other two environments (mean 110–150 μm) and the hot-grown leaves had slightly more epicuticular wax. Thus the effects of relatively hot temperatures during the pre-spraying period were attributed to both morphological and physiological effects.

The effect on herbicide performance of cold temperatures or frost prior to spraying depends upon several factors including the severity of the cold treatment, when it occurs in relation to spraying, and plant species. The only report of frost effects during this period is that of Ivany (1981), who showed in field experiments that glyphosate application after severe frosts which caused foliage necrosis resulted in poor control.

SHORT-TERM PRE-SPRAYING PERIOD

Most of the reports of temperature effects during the short-term pre-spraying period deal with the influence of frost or cold temperatures on herbicide performance. Davis, Fawcett and Harvey (1978) found that glyphosate was most effective against *A. repens* when plants were treated during the morning following a frost. This effect was obtained in both field and controlled environment experiments. In the same study, differences in response to the frost treatments were found between *A. repens* and lucerne (*Medicago sativa*). Lucerne was injured most by glyphosate after being subjected to frosts of −2°C, whereas *A. repens* was slightly more frost-tolerant and maximum activity occurred after exposure to −3° to −4°C. In another report, Davis, Fawcett and Harvey (1979) studied the effects of low temperatures on non-hardened *A. repens* and lucerne plants. In this study, pretreatment of actively growing plants at −4°C 'partially protected' lucerne from injury by glyphosate, but *A. repens* was affected to the same extent as the no-frost treatment. Studies of ^{14}C-glyphosate uptake and translocation provided some explanation for the above effects. In the earlier study, increased foliar uptake and increased translocation to the rhizomes in *A. repens* were found when glyphosate was applied after the simulated frost treatments. In lucerne, frost treatment increased uptake, but translocation was not significantly affected. In the later study, frost pretreatment reduced translocation of glyphosate in lucerne, but not in *A. repens*.

In both of the above reports, herbicide application was made to plants that were not visually affected by the frost treatments. More severe frost pretreatments, however, have resulted in reduced glyphosate efficacy. Devine and Bandeen (1983) showed that in *A. repens* with visible foliage damage due to frost injury (one or two nights at −6° to −8°C before spraying), glyphosate treatments had less effect than when applied to plants having milder frost treatments. They suggested that this damage to the foliage reduced glyphosate translocation to the rhizomes in some way, but no specific mechanism was described.

SHORT-TERM POST-SPRAYING PERIOD

For post-emergence herbicides, such as glyphosate, the short-term post-spraying period plays a major part in determining herbicide performance. It is during this period that the herbicide is absorbed, translocated and beginning to exert its influence at the sites of action. Reports describing the effects of temperature on herbicide performance during this period can be divided into two groups: those investigating the effects of frosty conditions, and those in which higher temperatures were used. Davis, Fawcett and Harvey (1978) studied the effects of simulated frost on glyphosate activity. Frost occurring after herbicide treatment resulted in poor control of *A. repens* compared with those treatments in which frost occurred before spraying. With lucerne there was no difference between those treatments in which frost occurred before, or after, herbicide application. In an earlier study, Hurst, Arnold and Withers (1976) found 'ineffective' control of *S. halepense* when frost occurred the morning after glyphosate application.

With warmer conditions, Banks and Santelman (1976) found no differences in the amounts of ^{14}C-glyphosate translocated in *S. carolinense* 24 h after treatment at either 13°C or 32°C. Although 'significant amounts' of radioactivity had been absorbed and translocated to the roots and apical portions of the plant after 24 h, it would seem from other data presented in the report that, with this species, more time is required for a toxic amount to enter the plant. For example, clipping the treated plants 24 h after spraying glyphosate reduced overall control. Wills (1978), using cotton, also found very little effect of temperature within 48 h of treatment. At constant humidity, increasing the temperature from 22° to 32°C resulted in 'either no significant effect or less than a onefold increase in absorption or translocation of ^{14}C-glyphosate'.

However, significant effects of temperature on the performance and translocation of glyphosate were observed by Coupland and Caseley (1981) in *A. repens*. In this study, toxic amounts of glyphosate accumulated in more rhizome nodes in a shorter time under the warmest conditions. For example, with 1.2 kg ha^{-1}, complete kill of rhizome buds was achieved 3 h after spraying at 26°C, whereas at 16°C the same effect was not achieved until 6 h after spraying. At 10°C, complete kill was not achieved after 12 h, but bud viability was reduced to 8% of the control value. In the same experiment, a greater translocation of ^{14}C-glyphosate to the crowns and rhizomes was observed under the warmest temperature compared to the cooler ones.

Jordan (1977), using *C. dactylon*, also has reported effects of temperature on glyphosate activity soon after spraying. At a constant 40% r.h., plants treated at 32°C were affected more than those kept at 22°C (temperature differences were maintained for 24 h after spraying). At 100% r.h. there was no significant difference between the two temperatures. More ^{14}C-glyphosate was absorbed at 32° than 22°C (for each of the two humidities), and more ^{14}C-glyphosate was translocated at 32° than 22°C (at 40% r.h.). However, there were no differences in the amounts translocated at 100% r.h. This emphasizes the relative importance of humidity on glyphosate activity (see Humidity section, p. 109).

LONG-TERM POST-SPRAYING PERIOD

The majority of research published on the influence of temperature on glyphosate performance has concerned the long-term post-spraying period. Jordan (1977) showed a significant 15% reduction in regrowth fresh weight of *C. dactylon* kept at 32°C compared to 22°C for 6 days after treatment. Using seedlings of *Apocynum cannabinum*, Schultz and Burnside (1980a) found a significant effect of a 5°C difference in temperature maintained for 7 days after treatment with ^{14}C-glyphosate. Translocation appeared to be the main process affected, with 39% compared with 18% (of the total activity applied) being translocated within plants kept at 30°C compared with 25°C, respectively. Similar effects were reported in *S. halepense* by McWhorter, Jordan and Wills (1980). Absorption was approximately doubled and translocation slightly increased as the air temperature was raised from 24° to 35°C. Lund-Høie (1979) reported an 'exponential correlation' between temperature and ^{14}C-glyphosate translocation in *Betula verrucosa*. He also showed that herbicide absorption increased in a similar way and that these effects were observed irrespective of pre-spraying temperatures, although the warmer the pre-spraying temperature, the more glyphosate was absorbed and translocated. Conversely, cool conditions were thought to be responsible for the lack of glyphosate translocation in *A. repens* at temperatures below 7°C (Duke and Hunt, 1977).

The positive correlation between glyphosate performance and temperature does not apply to all the published reports. Banks and Santelmann (1976) found no significant difference in the amounts of ^{14}C-glyphosate translocated in *S. carolinense* 3 days after treatment at either 13° or 32°C. McWhorter, Jordan and Wills (1980) showed in soya bean (*Glycine max*) that there was a negative correlation with temperature. Three days after treatment, more glyphosate was absorbed and translocated at 24° than at 35°C. A similar effect was obtained in cotton by Wills (1978). In this study, a decrease in temperature from 35° to 25°C resulted in up to 40% greater injury. No explanations were given in the above two examples for this negative relationship between temperature and herbicide activity.

In experiments where the temperature difference is imposed after a lethal quantity of glyphosate has reached the sites of action, research has invariably shown that more effective control is achieved with cooler, but not freezing temperatures (Carlsson, 1980). McWhorter and Azlin (1978) found with soya bean grown in growth chambers that toxicity increased with decreasing temperature in the order of 35°, 29° and 24°C. They also reported that, under field conditions, cool temperatures resulted in severe soya bean injury even with low rates of glyphosate (0.4 kg ha^{-1}). *Agropyron repens* probably has been studied the most concerning the influence of temperature during the long-term post-spraying period and there is complete agreement in all of these studies that cool temperatures enhance herbicide performance. This has been shown with field studies (Behrens and Elakkad, 1972; Sprankle and Meggitt, 1972; Duke and Hunt, 1977), and in controlled environment rooms (Baird and Begeman, 1972; Baird, Upchurch and Selleck, 1972; Caseley, 1972; Upchurch, Baird and Begeman, 1972; Wallgren, 1979). The same response to temperature has been found with other species, for example, in *Cyperus esculentus* by Tharawanich and Linscott (1975) and in cotton (Wills, 1978).

Thus, cool conditions after treatment enhance herbicide performance. This is despite the fact that more glyphosate is absorbed and translocated under warmer conditions soon after spraying (see above and previous sections, pp. 105 and 106). One possible explanation is that plants usually grow faster under warmer conditions and this may effectively dilute the herbicide within the plant. A similar conclusion was made by McWhorter and Azlin (1978) to explain the lack of phytotoxicity of glyphosate to soya bean under high soil moisture and high temperature conditions. Recent research by Coupland (in press) has shown that, in rhizome fragments of *A. repens*, relatively warm temperatures during the post-spraying period lead to more metabolism of the herbicide and a greater degradation to carbon dioxide. The metabolism of glyphosate within the plant is the subject of a separate chapter (see Chapter 3).

Wind

Of all the environmental factors affecting plants, wind or air movement has been studied the least. The literature search for this chapter failed to retrieve any reference concerning the effects of wind on glyphosate performance, apart from a few describing spray drift problems (e.g. Yates, Akesson and Bayer, 1978). Wind imposes physical constraints on spraying and often determines whether or not application is possible. Wind interacts with radiation and humidity to affect plant temperature, evapotranspiration and carbon dioxide exchange rates. Thus, wind affects herbicide performance indirectly via its effects on plant growth as well as directly by influencing spray interception and retention and the drying of spray deposits. Herbicide absorption may also be affected by wind-blown abrasive particles damaging the plant cuticle, perhaps enabling an easier entry of herbicide. An excellent account of the response of plants to wind has been written by Grace (1977), and the interaction of wind and herbicide performance has been briefly discussed by Muzik (1976).

Humidity

The water content of the air is widely expressed as percent relative humidity (% r.h.), which is the amount of water present in a given volume of air relative to the amount the air can hold at the same temperature. Transpiration and to some extent spray drop drying are dynamic processes and a precise correlation between these and % r.h. can only be expected at a given temperature. Thus it is important to record % r.h. and the temperature, which allows the amount of water in the air to be expressed in other, often more useful ways, e.g. absolute humidity (a.h.), which is the weight of water per unit volume of the air:

$$\text{a.h.} = \frac{216.7 \times e}{t + 273}$$

where a.h. is the absolute humidity (in grams per cubic metre of air), t is the air temperature (in degrees Celsius) and e is the vapour pressure (in millibars).

Aerial humidity has relatively little effect on accumulation of dry weight in plants if adequate water is available from the soil, but it may affect leaf size and shape, the number of stomata and trichomes, the amount and composition of epicuticular wax, and cuticle thickness (Baker, 1974; Ford and Thorne, 1974). These plant characteristics may well alter glyphosate performance, but most studies in relation to humidity have concentrated on conditions around the time of spraying, when rate of spray drop drying, cuticle hydration and transpiration are the main processes affecting glyphosate efficacy.

Merritt (1982) has shown that glyphosate penetration was enhanced with increasing concentration of the herbicide, but entry is likely to cease if the deposit dries. A fully hydrated cuticle favours the uptake of foliage-applied herbicides, particularly water-soluble compounds such as glyphosate which are believed to enter the plant via a hydrophilic pathway. Transpiration is increased under low humidity regimes, and if adequate water is available from the soil, acropetal movement of glyphosate will be increased in the apoplast.

LONG- AND SHORT-TERM PRE-SPRAYING PERIOD

None of the work reviewed was designed to determine the role of humidity, specifically before spraying, on glyphosate activity. However, several experiments included contrasting humidities which were continued from the pre- to post-spraying period. Chase and Appleby (1979) grew *Cyperus rotundus* plants, at 29°/24°C (day/night) and at humidities of 50 and 90% r.h., for 26 days prior to and 1 day after glyphosate application, when the foliage was cut or the translocation of ^{14}C-glyphosate determined. Much less regrowth resulted from the herbicide-treated high-humidity plants, and the ^{14}C-glyphosate studies showed that three times more ^{14}C was translocated into underground parts under the high-humidity compared with low-humidity regime. While the difference in humidity during the weeks before spraying may have contributed to these results, papers discussed later indicate that humidity during the short-term pre- and particularly post-spraying period clearly have a major effect on glyphosate performance.

Lund-Høie (1979) kept *Betula verrucosa* seedlings at two contrasting humidities 1 week before and after treatment with ^{14}C-glyphosate. At 12°C, increasing the humidity from 50 to 70% r.h. approximately doubled the entry into and movement out of the treated leaf, while at 24°C increasing the humidity from 25 to 70% r.h. led to a fivefold increase in these processes. The same general trends were reported by Jordan (1977), who maintained *Cynodon dactylon* plants at 40 and 100% r.h. for 3 days before returning them to an intermediate environment until assessment. The fresh weights of the low-humidity compared to high-humidity plants were five and tenfold greater at 22° and 32°C, respectively. These and several of the following results, where contrasting temperature and humidities are included, illustrate the close interaction between these two environmental factors with regard to their effect on glyphosate entry, movement and performance.

SHORT-TERM POST-SPRAYING PERIOD

Several workers have demonstrated the importance of humidity during the short-term post-spraying period using whole plant response and ^{14}C-glyphosate studies. Immediately after spraying established *A. repens* with glyphosate, Coupland and Caseley (1981) placed them in 50 or 90% r.h. until the rhizomes were fragmented into single node pieces at 3–24 h after spraying, when node viability was determined (*Table 7.5*). These results indicate the marked effect that humidity may exert on glyphosate performance during the 24 h following treatment.

TABLE 7.5   **Effect of humidity on the viability of rhizome nodes from** *Agropyron repens* **plants treated with 0.8 kg ha^{-1} glyphosate (after Coupland and Caseley, 1981)**

Relative humidity (%)	Time between spraying and rhizome fragmentation (h)*			
	3	6	12	24
	% node viability			
90	41	14	0	0
50	89	81	41	6

*Light 170 W m^{-2}, daylength 14 h, temperature 15°C.

Application of ^{14}C-glyphosate to *C. dactylon* immediately before imposing the contrasting environments and assessment 48 h later, showed that 100 compared with 40% r.h. resulted in both uptake and movement being increased four- and sixfold at 22° and 32°C, respectively (Jordan, 1977). Whitwell *et al.* (1980) conducted a similar type of ^{14}C-glyphosate experiment using the same species, time course and broadly equivalent environmental regime. In this experiment, surfactant was omitted and far less ^{14}C was absorbed and translocated, but the trend for relatively greater uptake and movement at high compared to low humidity was maintained. Similar results were obtained following ^{14}C-glyphosate treatment of cotton (Wills, 1978).

Coupland (1983) treated *A. repens* with an overall spray of glyphosate and, as would be expected from previous experiments, over a 48 h period, high compared to low humidity enhanced performance. The application of ^{14}C-glyphosate to the adaxial leaf sheath surface, where the microclimate would be expected to remain saturated, resulted in very rapid uptake and high compared to low humidity around the plants had no effect on subsequent translocation of [14]C. In contrast, high compared to low temperature did increase translocation following this method of application. These results would suggest that the enhanced translocation of ^{14}C-glyphosate resulting from high humidity referred to in this review is a result of increased penetration raising the concentration of glyphosate in the mesophyll, where entry into the symplast is probably concentration dependent (see p. 94).

LONG-TERM POST-SPRAYING PERIOD

Extending the post-spraying period of controlled humidity tends to produce the same trend as described above, with high humidity resulting in the best performance; however, the differences are less pronounced.

Glasshouse-grown soya bean and *S. halepense* plants were treated with ^{14}C-glyphosate and transferred immediately to 45 and 100% r.h. regimes at 21° and 35°C. Following assessment at 72 h, transport of ^{14}C out of treated leaves was found to be marginally better at 100 compared with 45% r.h. In *S. halepense* autoradiographs showed that ^{14}C reached the rhizome only under the 100% r.h. regime (McWhorter, Jordan and Wills, 1980). Working with the same species and similar environmental regimes, McWhorter and Azlin (1978) found that the adverse effect of low humidity on glyphosate performance was partially overcome by the addition of surfactant, but with or without surfactant glyphosate activity was always best at high humidity.

Humidity appears to exert its major effect on glyphosate uptake and movement and is unlikely to be of importance in the long term unless these processes have been impeded (see section on Precipitation, p. 114). Some of the factors that may contribute to the considerable influence of humidity on glyphosate activity are set out in *Table 7.6*.

In all the papers reviewed, regardless of species and experimental methods, presence or absence of surfactants, high compared with low humidity always resulted in enhanced glyphosate performance and, where assessed, uptake and movement were increased. All the studies included the short-term post-spraying period and this seems to be of signal importance with regard to this environmental factor.

TABLE 7.6   Effects of humidity on glyphosate uptake and movement

Factor	High humidity	Low humidity
Spray drop	Glyphosate remains in solution	Dries
Cuticle	More hydrated	Less hydrated
Glyphosate diffusion	Enhanced	Decreased
Glyphosate concn. in mesophyll	Increased	Decreased due to movement in apoplast
Plasmalemma penetration	Increased due to higher glyphosate concn. gradient	Decreased due to lower glyphosate concn. gradient
Transport in symplast	Higher	Lower

Soil moisture

As the soil is not normally involved in glyphosate activity, soil water content is only of importance inasmuch as it influences the water status of the plant and the microclimate around the plant.

Soil moisture may be expressed as a percentage of soil weight or field capacity, but these do not necessarily indicate availability of water to the plant. Water potential of the plant in Pascals (Pa), formerly bars, is the preferred form of expression (Levitt, 1980).

Soil moisture stress may be due to an excess or deficit of water, but only the latter has been investigated in relation to glyphosate. Following the imposition of water stress, cell enlargement and division are inhibited and consequently overall plant growth is reduced. An increasing water deficit results in gradual stomatal closure and eventually a rapid fall in photosynthesis, accompanied by a gradual decline in respiration and eventual wilting. Concomitantly, there are changes in the level of endogenous plant growth regulators, enzymes, and alterations in membrane and cuticle characteristics, resulting in smaller plants with altered morphology.

LONG- AND SHORT-TERM PRE-SPRAYING PERIOD

None of the work reviewed was specifically designed to investigate the effects of pre-spraying moisture stress on glyphosate performance. Moosavi-Nia and Dore (1979a) subjected pot-grown mature plants of *Cyperus rotundus* and *Imperata cylindrica* to three levels of soil moisture: near field capacity, moderate and extreme stress (*Table 7.7*).

In both species, increasing stress resulted in fewer and smaller shoots and reduced propagule numbers, size and weight. The ratio of shoots to propagules

TABLE 7.7   Effect of 6 weeks of contrasting soil moistures on shoots and propagules of *Cyperus rotundus* and *Imperata cylindrica* (after Moosavi-Nia and Dore, 1979a)

	Imperata cylindrica		Cyperus rotundus	
	Shoot dry wt. (g)	Rhizome dry wt. (g)	Shoot dry wt. (g)	Tuber bulb (no.)
Field capacity	5.16	1.49	3.14	15.4
Moderate stress	1.60	0.97	0.99	7.6
Extreme stress	0.70	0.28	0.25	3.6

tended to decrease in stressed plants, with the probable consequence that less spray would be intercepted per propagule. After glyphosate treatment, the plants were maintained in the same soil moisture regimes, the foliage cut off 1 week later and regrowth assessed after 6 weeks. In both species, glyphosate performance was depressed with increasing moisture stress and halved at the lowest moisture level compared to field capacity. However, returning the most stressed plants to field capacity for 1 week before and after glyphosate application led to a level of control approaching that achieved with plants kept continually at field capacity. This suggests that the reduced glyphosate performance in stressed plants may be attributed primarily to physiological and biochemical processes that can recommence on the removal of the stress, rather than to irreversible developmental changes such as leaf size and form and cuticular wax deposition.

McIntyre and Hsiao (1982) placed the rhizomes of hydroponically grown *A. repens* plants in ventilated boxes at high or low humidity for 3, 6 and 14 days, before ^{14}C-glyphosate was applied to the foliage, which was kept in a standard environment. The ^{14}C in the nodes (assessed 24 h later) was doubled in the high-humidity compared with low-humidity rhizome environment. In pot experiments with soil, several days without watering may be required to achieve the required stress, and the combination of hydroponically raised plants in conjunction with controlled humidity boxes provides a useful means of rapidly altering the 'subsoil' plant environment.

Chase and Appleby (1979) reduced the application of water to *C. rotundus* for 4–5 days before treatment with glyphosate and until assessment. The shoots were excised 24 h after spraying and regrowth of scapes assessed after 2 and 4 days. A plant water potential of -0.8 MPa did not reduce glyphosate performance, but at -1.1 MPa it was half the value obtained with plants at field capacity. Translocation of ^{14}C to below ground parts 24 h after foliage application of ^{14}C-glyphosate was approximately halved at -1.1 compared with -0.2 MPa.

Ahmadi, Haderlie and Wicks (1980) grew plants of *Echinochloa crus-galli* with a soil moisture deficit for 3 days before and after the application of ^{14}C-glyphosate to the second and third leaves, respectively, of 7.5 and 15 cm high plants (*Table 7.8*).

In the younger plants, only the most severe stress reduced herbicide absorption, but in the older plants it was halved at -0.5 MPa. In the stressed older plants, more of the absorbed herbicide remained in the treated area and translocation out of the treated leaf was substantially reduced. This was probably due to a decline in movement in both the apoplast and symplast resulting from reduced transpiration

TABLE 7.8   Uptake and translocation of ^{14}C-glyphosate in *Echinochloa crus-galli* at two growth stages and three soil moisture regimes after 3 days (after Ahmadi, Haderlie and Wicks, 1980)

Plant height (cm)	7.5			15.0		
Soil water potential (MPa)	−0.01	−0.5	−3.7	−0.01	−0.5	−3.7
			(d.p.m, as % of applied)			
Total absorbed	62	67	16	63	30	21
Treated area	7	7	6	7	11	15
Translocated:						
(a) within treated leaf	45	59	7	45	12	5
(b) out of treated leaf	10	14	3	13	7	1

and sink strength, respectively. The stressed taller and older leaves may also possess a stronger binding capacity keeping more herbicide in the treated area.

LONG- AND SHORT-TERM POST-SPRAYING PERIOD

McWhorter, Jordan and Wills (1980) found that uptake and movement of ^{14}C-glyphosate after 72 h in *S. halepense* and soya bean were unaffected by soil moisture content when the aerial temperature and humidity were 24°C and 100% r.h., respectively. However, higher temperatures and lower humidities combined with a soil moisture content close to wilting point significantly reduced the uptake and translocation of ^{14}C in both species. These results indicate that plant water stress may reduce glyphosate entry within 72 h and that to some extent a high absolute humidity can compensate for low soil moisture.

Cotton plants were treated with glyphosate (without wetter) and kept either at just above wilting point or close to field capacity for 4 days, and then, for all plants, maintained close to field capacity for 4 weeks until assessment. The wet and dry soil plants sustained the same degree of damage at 40% r.h., but at 100% r.h. the dry soil plants were damaged more at 35° but not 25°C (Wills, 1978). A possible explanation for this effect could be that high humidity and low soil moisture favour basipetal movement of water/glyphosate in the plant. Such apoplastic movement of herbicide has been demonstrated by Headford and Douglas (1967), who found that conditions of dry soil and dew deposition led to extensive basipetal movement of diquat in potatoes, resulting in tuber end-rot.

After glyphosate treatment, without surfactant, pots of *S. halepense* were subjected to either low or high soil moisture regimes for 14 days when they were assessed. Less damage was sustained by plants kept near wilting point and at 45% r.h. than those in regimes with higher levels of atmospheric or soil moisture. In contrast, soya bean was least susceptible at field capacity combined with low humidity. The addition of surfactant substantially increased the damage to both species (McWhorter and Azlin, 1978).

Generally, conditions that lower the water status of the plant, such as low humidity and soil moisture, tend to reduce the activity of glyphosate. The stress required for this to occur may depend on whether the plant is a drought-resistant or drought-avoiding species and whether it has been 'drought stress' hardened. Most reports would be improved by the possession of data on the water potential of the plants. Although addition of water may rapidly increase the soil moisture content, reducing it by withholding watering may take several days. The difficulty of reducing soil moisture content rapidly probably accounts for the lack of short-term experiments, but the method of McIntyre and Hsiao (1982) (described earlier in this section) offers a useful solution to this problem.

Precipitation

Condensation of water vapour in the air takes place when the air temperature falls below the dew-point temperature. Fog and/or rain are precipitated in the atmosphere and dew is deposited on cool surfaces including leaves. Dew may accumulate on surfaces protected from rain impact as well as those parts exposed to rain. In addition to wetting the leaf surface and maintaining cuticle hydration, dew may be absorbed by the leaf which can be important in drought conditions (Levitt, 1980).

Raindrops possess energy related to their terminal velocity which increases their potential to dislodge epicuticular and non-plant material such as spray deposits. Rain splash may distribute material dissolved or suspended in water from one part of the plant to another and from the soil to the plant and vice versa. In the case of glyphosate we are concerned only with herbicide that remains on the plant; any active ingredient which reaches the soil may be regarded as lost.

Rain and dew are conducive to a fully hydrated cuticle and to water-soluble compounds such as glyphosate being in solution. Both these situations favour penetration of water-soluble herbicides (Sargent, 1965).

LONG-TERM PRE-SPRAYING PERIOD

Rainfall is important during the long-term pre-spraying period in relation to maintenance of the water status of the plant; the effects of moisture stress on glyphosate performance are discussed in the section on soil moisture. Rainfall may physically alter the structure of the leaf surface and may leach components from within the leaf. This aspect has not been investigated, but could be one of the factors which contributes to the difference between controlled environment and field-grown plants.

SHORT-TERM PRE-SPRAYING PERIOD

The constraints imposed by rainfall on conventional hydraulic nozzle spraying have been discussed by Tottman and Philipson (1974). They considered that for spring application of herbicides in cereals, 1 mm of rain in the previous 6 h, or more than 2 mm in the previous 18 h, could lead to problems with the passage of a conventional tractor and sprayer with concomitant risk of damage to soil structure. Low ground pressure vehicles and lower volume application could overcome some of these difficulties (Elliott, 1980).

Dew or rain deposited on the foliage before spraying has tended to be regarded as undesirable by many farmers and contractors, but the limited experimentation on this topic does not fully support this view. Caseley, Coupland and Simmons (1975) used a laboratory pot sprayer to load the foliage of *A. repens* with distilled water prior to herbicide application. A 'heavy dew' of between 554 and 864 μl g^{-1} fr. wt of foliage delayed drying of glyphosate spray deposits by 2.5 h. Herbicide performance was not diminished following application to wet compared with dry leaves. Some spray run-off was observed in the experiment, but this loss was compensated by increases in spray interception and retention. The presence of drops of water on the leaves increased the target area and the weight of water caused the leaves to bend, which increased the plan area of the plant. The retention of the herbicide was also greater, probably due to the cushioning effect of spray droplets by the water on the foliage. However, increasing the quantity of water on the foliage will ultimately lead to a situation where the addition of herbicide solution containing surfactant will induce excessive run-off. In the field, compared with the laboratory, this situation could be reached sooner due to wind disturbance. Behrens (1977) produced dew on an unspecified species in a germinator by filling the outer double wall with cold water, while warming water in a container on the floor. Heavy dew deposits at the time of herbicide application resulted in some run-off and diminished the performance of glyphosate. In field studies, Turner (1980) found that dew had no adverse effect on glyphosate performance against sugar cane.

SHORT-TERM POST-SPRAYING PERIOD

Behrens (1977) found that saturating plants with dew soon after application reduced glyphosate performance more than dew immediately before spraying. Dew and slight rain deposits on plants before and/or after glyphosate application may lead to decreased performance if substantial quantities of active ingredient are removed from the plant. Dew or rain can also redistribute herbicide on the plant surface. Several studies have shown that herbicides are more effective when deposited in the leaf sheaths of grass weeds (Caseley and Coupland, 1980). Glyphosate is also known to be more phytotoxic when applied to the lamina base compared with the tip of *A. repens* (Coupland, Taylor and Caseley, 1978) and most active when deposited in the sheath (Coupland, 1983).

It is very difficult to quantify the amount of precipitation on plants, and its effect on herbicide performance is likely to depend on plant age, species, other environmental conditions, and the formulation and form of application of the herbicide.

Glyphosate activity was increased when the foliage of *A. repens* was wetted without causing 'run-off' (Coupland and Caseley, 1981). A similar wetting treatment applied 6 h after spraying glyphosate and daily for the next 3 days, particularly enhanced herbicide performance against plants kept at low compared with high humidity (Caseley, Coupland and Simmons, 1975).

Glyphosate is particularly vulnerable to rainfall from time of application until a lethal quantity of active ingredient has penetrated the foliage. Of the many papers which mention post-application rainfall, relatively few adequately describe the rainfall treatment and omit one or more of the following: intensity, duration, and interval between herbicide application and rain.

The references in *Table 7.9* illustrate some important aspects of the interaction between rain and glyphosate. Low intensities of rain, up to 0.5 mm h^{-1} for periods of up to 3 h after spraying, even when they occurred very soon after application, tended not to reduce herbicide performance against *A. repens* (Caseley, 1972), but 1.0 mm h^{-1} severely reduced herbicide activity and 12.5 mm at 2 h after herbicide application resulted in complete loss of activity (Behrens and Elakkad, 1976).

TABLE 7.9   Influence of rain on glyphosate performance

Interval	'Rain' description	Performance*	Reference
5 min	0.5 mm h^{-1} for 2.5 h	*xxxx*	Caseley (1972)
5 min	1.0 mm	*x*	Behrens and Elakkad (1976)
2 h	12.5 mm	0	
8 h	12.5 mm	*xxx*	
2 h	600 ml in 30 s	*xxxx a* / *x b*	Caseley, Coupland and Simmons (1975)
6 h	600 ml in 30 s	*xxxx*	Coupland and Caseley (1981)
8 h	—	*xxx*	Baird and Upchurch (1972)

*Performance: least = 0, most = *xxxx* (= as no rain); *a* = 95% r.h., *b* = 48% r.h.

Several workers have reported that a 6–8 h rain-free period is required for penetration of sufficient active ingredient to give acceptable performance of glyphosate (Behrens and Elakkad, 1972; Baird and Upchurch, 1972; Coupland and Caseley, 1981). Factors affecting the rate of penetration and thus the minimum duration of this rain-free period will include the dose, concentration and formulation of active ingredient, and the physiological condition and size of species. The environmental conditions during the period between herbicide application and onset of rain are also critical. Thus, 2 h was sufficient for a lethal dose to enter the plant at 95% r.h., but plants kept at 48% r.h. after spraying substantially recovered after the rain treatment (Caseley, Coupland and Simmons, 1975). It is likely, then, that any plant or environmental factor that slows entry of glyphosate into the plant will prolong the vulnerability of the glyphosate treatment to rainfall in the post-application period. Manipulation of formulation and/or application may reduce the risk of diminished glyphosate activity. For example, Turner (1981) showed that adding 0.5% Ethomeen surfactant to Roundup increased performance about fourfold when 5.0 mm of rain was applied to *A. repens* 1 h after herbicide application. Again, applying glyphosate at 20 l ha^{-1} by spinning disc (CDA) compared with 78 l ha^{-1} by conventional hydraulic nozzle significantly increased the damage to *A. repens* plants 'washed' 2 h after application (Caseley, Coupland and Simmons, 1976). They considered that the higher concentration of active ingredient at 20 l ha^{-1} enhanced the rate of uptake and was a major factor in reducing the vulnerability of the treatment to rainfall.

There is a need to gain a better understanding of the effect of rainfall on glyphosate activity on a wider range of weed species and how formulation and application may be exploited to overcome the undesirable effects of rain.

Summary and conclusions

Under favourable conditions, glyphosate rapidly penetrates the cuticle, moves in the apoplast and probably enters the symplast passively. Although glyphosate is ambimobile, long-distance transport is primarily in the phloem and glyphosate, along with photosynthates, accumulates in the strongest sinks, often within a few hours of treatment.

Glyphosate penetration and transport may be divided into a rapid initial stage followed by a longer and slower phase. Immediately following application, a steep concentration gradient exists across the cuticle which enhances diffusion into the mesophyll, facilitating subsequent uptake in the symplast. Since glyphosate only slowly depresses photosynthesis and phloem transport, it is readily conveyed towards active sinks. As glyphosate exerts its phytotoxic effect on meristematic activity, initially strong sinks become weakened and other, smaller, meristems are released from apical dominance and become active, resulting in redistribution of both photosynthates and glyphosate. In the leaf this may be reflected in slower export of glyphosate and reduced absorption across the cuticle. Eventually, however, accumulation of glyphosate in the leaf leads to secondary damage revealed by yellowing.

In species such as *A. repens*, glyphosate commonly kills all the buds on the rhizomes of the plant, whereas other herbicides often allow some of the buds to escape. This ability of glyphosate to systematically control a succession of buds is probably due to the specificity of its mode of action in association with slow detrimental effects on membrane integrity, photosynthesis and phloem transport.

As a general rule, seedlings are more susceptible than are more mature plants, or plants arising from established underground propagules. This is related to the leaf area intercepting the spray and the number of meristems and underground propagules to be controlled. At comparable stages of growth, individual species differ widely in their response to glyphosate and this has been shown to be attributable to differences in one or more of the following: interception, retention, penetration, movement and activity of the herbicide.

The trends associated with the influence of individual environmental factors and glyphosate performance show a high degree of consistency. During the long-term pre-spraying period, conditions such as low light levels that result in a high ratio of foliage to propagules result in the best control. Nearer the time of application, good growing conditions (for example, warm temperatures and adequate water supply) produce foliage that readily intercepts, retains and absorbs the herbicide. At the time of application, high wind speed and rain should be avoided. During the short-term post-spraying period, high humidity, dew or slight rain maintains the herbicide deposit in solution and ensures a fully hydrated cuticle, both of which enhance herbicide penetration. Warm, bright conditions immediately thereafter facilitate phloem transport of the herbicide. In the case of *A. repens*, cool compared to warm conditions in the long-term post-spraying period lead to higher glyphosate activity due to less degradation of the herbicide within the plant tissues.

Information collected in controlled environment studies may be considered together with results from outside experiments and synthesized into a herbicide-environment profile (Caseley, 1980), illustrated in *Table 7.10*.

The information contained in the environment/herbicide performance profile may be used in several ways including:

(1) Interpreting results from different sites and seasons.
(2) Increasing the precision of field recommendations.
(3) Assisting in the development and evaluation of new formulations and application methods.
(4) Improving the criteria for choosing periods for spraying.

Under the favourable conditions for glyphosate performance outlined in *Table 7.10*, a lethal dose of glyphosate may enter the plant in a few hours, but under

TABLE 7.10   Individual environmental factors leading to maximum control of *Agropyron repens* **with glyphosate**

Period and duration of factor	Pre-application period		Time of application	Post-application period	
	Long-term	Short-term		Short-term	Long-term
Light	low**	low*	—	high**	—
Temperature	low**	high**	—	medium**	low**
Humidity	—	high*	—	high***	—
Rain	—	0.5 mm*	<0.5 mm***	0.5 mm***	—
Soil moisture	medium*	medium***	medium***	medium***	—
Wind	—	—	<12 km h^{-1}***	—	—

Relative importance of factor: *(least) to *** (most).

conditions of low water potential and humidity the period is increased several-fold. During the period between spraying and absorption of a lethal dose by the plant, glyphosate is vulnerable to removal from and/or redistribution on the plant by rain, dew and potentially, but to a far lesser extent, by wind-borne soil particles. In general, these adverse environmental effects can be overcome to some extent by the use of additional surfactant or other adjuvants which improve the rate of absorption. The same additives may also improve performance where retention and, perhaps less fully understood, symplast loading are limiting factors. However, there is a delicate balance between increasing the entry of glyphosate (and additives) into the leaf and damaging the mechanisms associated with the subsequent movement of glyphosate within the plant.

With an increasing array of synthetic plant growth regulators at our disposal, perhaps more attention should be paid to increasing sink strength, so affecting a stronger 'pull' of glyphosate to the desired targets. Such adjuvants might also allow an extension of the range of growth stages and environmental conditions when treatments could be made.

From the papers reviewed here it is apparent there is a good understanding of the time course of entry, movement and accumulation of glyphosate in relation to a range of environmental factors, plant development and species. However, there is a need for further understanding the mechanisms involved in these processes if we are to fully exploit the potential of glyphosate. For example, a more detailed knowledge of glyphosate entry into the symplast, and its association with photosynthates therein, could provide valuable clues on how to enhance the phloem loading of glyphosate and improve its translocation.

References

ABU-IRMAILEH, B.E. and JORDAN, L.S. (1977). Some aspects of the mechanism of action of glyphosate, *Proceedings of the Western Society of Weed Science*, **30**, 57–63.

AHMADI, M.S., HADERLIE, L.C. and WICKS, G.A. (1980). Effect of growth stage and water stress on barnyardgrass (*Echinochloa crusgalli*) control and on glyphosate absorption and translocation, *Weed Science*, **28**, 277–282.

ARIF, A. (1979). The use of Roundup herbicide and the prospect of its development in Indonesia, *Simposium herbicida Roundup 3*, Medan, Indonesia, 11pp.

BAIRD, D.D. and BEGEMAN, G.F. (1972). Post-emergence characterization of a new quackgrass herbicide, *Proceedings of the Northeast Weed Science Society*, **26**, 100–106.

BAIRD, D.D. and UPCHURCH, R.P. (1972). Post-emergence characteristics of a new herbicide, MON-0468, on Johnsongrass, *Proceedings of the 25th Annual Meeting of the Southern Weed Science Society*, 113pp.

BAIRD, D.D., UPCHURCH, R.P. and SELLECK, E.W. (1972). Phosphonomethyl glycine, a new broad spectrum, post-emergence herbicide, *Proceedings of the 24th Annual California Weed Conference*, pp. 94–98.

BAKER, E.A. (1974). The influence of environment on leaf wax development in *Brassica oleracea* var. *gemmifera*, *New Phytologist*, **73**, 955–966.

BANKS, P.A. and SANTELMANN, P.W. (1976). Carolina horsenettle suspceptibility to glyphosate at varying growth stages, *Proceedings of the 29th Annual Meeting of the Southern Weed Science Society*, p. 402.

BEHRENS, R. (1977). Influence of dew on the phytotoxicity of foliarly applied herbicides, *Proceedings of the North Central Weed Control Conference*, **32**, 116.

BEHRENS, R. and ELAKKAD, M. (1972). Quackgrass control with glyphosate, *Proceedings of the North Central Weed Control Conference*, **27**, 54.

BEHRENS, R. and ELAKKAD, M.A. (1976). Influence of rainfall on phytotoxicity of foliarly applied herbicides, *Proceedings of the North Central Weed Control Conference*, **31**, 141.

BICKFORD, E.D. and DUNN, S. (1972). In *Lighting for Plant Growth*. Kent State University Press, USA, 221pp.

BINGHAM, S.W., SEGURA, J. and FOY, C.L. (1980). Susceptibility of several grasses to glyphosate, *Weed Science*, **28**, 579–585.

BOLT, P.F. and SWEET, R.D. (1974). Glyphosate studies on yellow nutsedge, *Proceedings of the Northeastern Weed Science Society*, **28**, 197–204.

BRATTAIN, R.L. and FAY, P.K. (1980). Glyphosate for chemical fallow, *Proceedings of the Western Society of Weed Science*, **33**, 76–77.

BRECKE, B.J. and DUKE, W.B. (1980). Effect of glyphosate on intact bean plants (*Phaseolus vulgaris* L.) and isolated cells, *Plant Physiology*, **66**, 656–659.

CARLSSON, T. (1980). Roundup against *Agropyron repens*—different times of application in the autumn, *Proceedings of the 21st Swedish Weed Conference*, Uppsala, pp. 39–47.

CASELEY, J.C. (1972). The effect of environmental factors on the performance of glyphosate against *Agropyron repens*, *Proceedings of the 11th British Weed Control Conference*, pp. 641–647.

CASELEY, J.C. (1974). Possible approaches to the enhancement of herbicide efficiency, *Proceedings of the 12th British Weed Control Conference*, **3**, 977–985.

CASELEY, J.C. (1980). Investigating the effects of weather on foliage-applied herbicides, *Agricultural Research Council Weed Research Organization, 8th Report 1978–79*, pp. 68–75.

CASELEY, J.C. and COUPLAND, D. (1980). Effect of simulated rain on retention, distribution, uptake, movement and activity of difenzoquat applied to *Avena fatua*, *Annals of Applied Biology*, **96**, 111–118.

CASELEY, J.C., COUPLAND, D. and HOUGH, M. (1983). Day compared with night application of glyphosate for *Elymus repens* control in cereals, *Aspects of Applied Biology*, **4**, 301–307.

CASELEY, J.C., COUPLAND, D. and SIMMONS, R.C. (1975). The effect of precipitation on the control of *Agropyron repens* with glyphosate, *Symposium on Status, Biology and Control of Grass Weeds in Europe, EWRS & COLUMA Paris*, **1**, 124–130.

CASELEY, J.C., COUPLAND, D. and SIMMONS, R.C. (1976). Effect of formulation, volume rate and application method on performance and rainfastness of glyphosate on *Agropyron repens*, *Proceedings of the British Crop Protection Council—Weeds*, pp. 407–412.

CHASE, R.L. and APPLEBY, A.P. (1979). Effects of humidity and moisture stress on glyphosate control of *Cyperus rotundus* L., *Weed Research*, **19**, 241–246.

CLAUS, J.S. and BEHRENS, R. (1976). Glyphosate translocation and quackgrass rhizome bud kill, *Weed Science*, **24**, 149–152.

COUPLAND, D. (1983). The influence of light, temperature and humidity on the translocation and activity of glyphosate in *Elymus repens* (= *Agropyron repens*), *Weed Research*, **23**, 347–355.

COUPLAND, D. (in press). The effect of temperature on the activity and metabolism of glyphosate applied to rhizome fragments of *Elymus repens* (= *Agropyron repens*), *Pesticide Science* (in press).

COUPLAND, D. and CASELEY, J.C. (1979). Presence of ^{14}C activity in root exudates and guttation fluid from *Agropyron repens* treated with ^{14}C-labelled glyphosate, *New Phytologist*, **83**, 17–22.

COUPLAND, D. and CASELEY, J.C. (1981). Environmental influences on the effects of glyphosate on *Agropyron repens*, *Proceedings of the AAB Conference. Grass Weeds in Cereals in the United Kingdom*, pp. 109–114.

COUPLAND, D., TAYLOR, W.A. and CASELEY, J.C. (1978). The effect of site of application on the performance of glyphosate on *Agropyron repens* and barban, benzoylprop-ethyl and difenzoquat on *Avena fatua*, *Weed Research*, **18**, 123–128.

CROWLEY, J. and PRENDEVILLE, G.N. (1980). Effects of herbicides of different modes of action on leaf-cell membrane permeability in *Phaseolus vulgaris*, *Canadian Journal of Plant Science*, **60**, 613–620.

DAVIS, H.E. (1976). Effects of the environment on the herbicidal activity of glyphosate (*N*-(phosphonomethyl)glycine) on quackgrass (*Agropyron repens* (L.) Beauv.) and alfalfa (*Medicago sativa* L.), *Ph.D. thesis*, University of Wisconsin, 122pp.

DAVIS, H.E., FAWCETT, R.S. and HARVEY R.G. (1978). Effect of fall frost on the activity of glyphosate on alfalfa (*Medicago sativa*) and quackgrass (*Agropyron repens*), *Weed Science*, **26**, 41–45.

DAVIS, H.E., FAWCETT, R.S. and HARVEY, R.G. (1979). Effects of frost and maturity on glyphosate phytotoxicity, uptake and translocation, *Weed Science*, **27**, 110–114.

DEVINE, M.D. and BANDEEN, J.D. (1983). Fate of glyphosate in *Agropyron repens* (L.) Beauv. growing under low temperature conditions, *Weed Research*, **23**, 69–75.

DEWEY, S.A. (1982). Manipulation of assimilate transport patterns as a method of studying glyphosate translocation in tall morning-glory (*Ipomoea purpurea* (L) Roth), *Ph.D. thesis*, Oregon State University, USA, 116pp.

DUKE, W.B. and HUNT, J.F. (1977). Fall applications of glyphosate for quackgrass control, *Proceedings of the Northeastern Weed Science Society*, **31**, 91.

ELLIOTT, J.G. (1980). Low volume, low drift and high speed—a great new opportunity, *British Crop Protection Monograph No. 24*, pp. 175–183.

ERICKSON, C.G. and DUKE, W.B. (1981). The effect of glyphosate and surfactant concentrations on subsequent penetration and translocation in quackgrass, *Proceedings of the Northeastern Weed Science Society*, **35**, 33.

EVANS, D.M. (1972). Field performance of glyphosate derivatives in the control of *Agropyron repens* and other perennial weeds, *Proceedings of the 11th British Weed Control Conference*, **1**, 64–70.

FAWCETT, R.S. and DAVIS, H.E. (1976). Effect of environment on glyphosate activity in quackgrass, *Proceedings of the North Central Weed Control Conference*, **31**, 159–160.

FLETCHER, R.A., HILDERBRAND, P. and AKEY, W. (1980). Effect of glyphosate on membrane permeability in red beet (*Beta vulgaris*) root tissue, *Weed Science*, **28**, 671–673.

FORD, M.A. and THORNE, G.N. (1974). Effects of atmospheric humidity on plant growth, *Annals of Botany*, **38**, 441–452.

GOTTRUP, O., O'SULLIVAN, P.A., SCHRAA, R.J. and BORN, W.H. van den (1976). Uptake, translocation metabolism and selectivity of glyphosate in Canada thistle and leafy spurge, *Weed Research*, **16**, 197–201.

GOUGLER, J.A. and GEIGER, D.R. (1981). Uptake and distribution of N-phosphonomethyl glycine in sugar beet plants, *Plant Physiology*, **68**, 668–672.

GRACE, J. (1977). *Plant Response to Wind*. London; Academic Press, 204pp.

HADERLIE, L.C., SLIFE, F.W. and BUTLER, H.S. (1978). ^{14}C-glyphosate absorption and translocation in germinating maize (*Zea mays*) and soybean (*Glycine max*) seeds and in soybean plants, *Weed Research*, **18**, 269–273.

HANSON, C.L., RIECK, C.E. and HARGER, T.R. (1975). Effects of light reduction on the herbicidal effectiveness of glyphosate, Abstract, *Weed Science Society of America*, pp. 4–5.

HEADFORD, D.W.R. and DOUGLAS, G. (1967). Tuber necrosis following the desiccation of potato foliage with diquat, *Weed Research*, **7**, 131–144.

HO, L.C. (1976). The relationship between the rates of carbon transport and of photosynthesis in tomato leaves, *Journal of Experimental Botany*, **27**, 87–97.

HOLLOWAY, P.J., BOWDLER, D. and CASELEY, J.C. (1980). Effect of environment on the physicochemical properties of couch grass (*Agropyron repens*) leaves, *Long Ashton Report 1979*, pp. 100–102, Long Ashton Research Station, Bristol, UK, 242pp.

HURST, H.R., ARNOLD, B.L. and WITHERS, F.T., Jr. (1976). Evaluation of herbicides for johnsongrass control in corn, *Proceedings of the 29th Annual Meeting Southern Weed Science Society*, p.58.

IVANY, J.A. (1981). Quackgrass (*Agropyron repens*) control with fall-applied glyphosate and other herbicides, *Weed Science*, **29**, 382–386.

JORDAN, T.N. (1977). Effects of temperature and relative humidity on the toxicity of glyphosate to Bermudagrass (*Cynodon dactylon*), *Weed Science*, **25**, 448–451.

KELLS, J.J. and RIECK, C.E. (1979). Effects of illuminance and time on accumulation of glyphosate in johnsongrass (*Sorghum halepense*), *Weed Science*, **27**, 235–237.

LEE, G.A. (1973). Influence of time of application and tillage on the herbicide performance of glyphosate, *Proceedings of the Western Society of Weed Science*, **26**, 37–38.

LEE, T.T. (1980). Characteristics of glyphosate inhibition of growth in soybean and tobacco callus cultures, *Weed Research*, **20**, 365–369.

LEVITT, J. (1980). In *Responses of Plants to Environmental Stresses*, 2nd edn, vols. I and II. London; Academic Press, 1119pp.

LOLAS, P.C. and COBLE, H.D. (1980). Translocation of ^{14}C-glyphosate in johnsongrass (*Sorghum halepense* L. Pers.) as affected by growth stage and rhizome length, *Weed Research*, **20**, 267–270.

LUND-HØIE, K. (1979). The physiological fate of glyphosate-^{14}C in *Betula verrucosa* and *Fraxinus excelsior*. The effect of ammonium sulphate and the environment on the herbicide, *Meldinger fra Norges Landbrukshøiskole*, **58**, 1–24.

LUND-HØIE, K. (1983). The influence of light on the physiological behaviour of glyphosate in Scots pine (*Pinus sylvestris* L.) and temperature on the toxic effect of the herbicide on Norway spruce (*Picea abies* L.), *Crop Protection*, **2**, 409–416.

MAJEK, B.A. (1980). The effect of environmental factors on quackgrass *Agropyron repens* (L.) growth and glyphosate penetration and translocation, *Thesis*, Cornell Univ., Ithaca, New York, USA.

MARQUIS, L.Y., COMES, R.D. and YANG, C.P. (1979). Selectivity of glyphosate in creeping red fescue and reed canary grass, *Weed Research*, **19**, 335–342.

MCALLISTER, R.S. and HADERLIE, L.C. (1980). Techniques for treating plants with radio-labelled herbicides, *Proceedings of the North Central Weed Control Conference*, **34**, 5–6.

MCFARLANE, J.C. (1979). Radiation: guidelines, in *Controlled Environment Guidlines for Plant Research* (T.W. Tibbitts and T.T. Kozlowski, Eds.). London; Academic Press, 413pp.

MCINTYRE, G.I. and HSIAO, A.I. (1982). Influence of nitrogen and humidity on rhizome bud growth and glyphosate translocation in quackgrass (*Agropyron repens*), *Weed Science*, **30**, 655–660.

MCWHORTER, C.G. and AZLIN, W.R. (1978). Effects of environment on the toxicity of glyphosate to johnsongrass (*Sorghum halepense*) and soybeans (*Glycine max*), *Weed Science*, **26**, 605–608.

MCWHORTER, C.G., JORDAN, T.N. and WILLS, G.D.(1980). Translocation of ^{14}C-glyphosate in soybeans (*Glycine max*) and johnsongrass (*Sorghum halepense*), *Weed Science*, **28**, 113–118.

MERRITT, C.R. (1982). The influence of form of deposit on the phytotoxicity of MCPA, paraquat and glyphosate applied as individual drops, *Annals of Applied Biology*, **101**, 527–532.

MOOSAVI-NIA, H. and DORE, J. (1979a). Factors affecting glyphosate activity in *Imperata cylindrica* (L) Beau. and *Cyperus rotundus* L. I. Effect of soil moisture, *Weed Research*, **19**, 137–143.

MOOSAVI-NIA, H. and DORE, J. (1979b). Factors affecting glyphosate activity in *Imperata cylindrica* (L.) Beau. and *Cyperus rotundus* L. II. Effects of shade, *Weed Research*, **19**, 321–327.

MUZIK, T.J. (1976). Influence of environmental factors on toxicity to plants, in *Herbicides—Physiology, Biochemistry and Ecology*, 2nd edn (L.J. Audus, Ed.). London; Academic Press, 564pp.

O'KEEFFE, M.G. (1981). The control of perennial grasses by pre-harvest applications of glyphosate, *Proceedings of the AAB Conference Grass Weeds in Cereals in the United Kingdom*, pp. 137–144.

PENN, D.J. and LYNCH, J.M. (1982). Toxicity of glyphosate applied to roots of barley seedlings, *New Phytologist*, **90**, 51–55.

PETERSON, C.A., DE WILDT, P.P.Q. and EDGINGTON, L.V. (1978). A rationale for the ambimobile translocation of the nematicide oxyamyl in plants, *Pesticide Biochemistry and Physiology*, **8**, 1–9.

PRICE, C.E. (1982). A review of the factors influencing the penetration of pesticides through plant leaves, in *The Plant Cuticle* (D.F. Cutler, K.L. Alvin and C.E. Price, Eds.), Linnean Society Symposium Series 10. London; Academic Press, pp.237–252.

RICHARD, E.P. and SLIFE, F.W. (1979). *In vivo* and *in vitro* characterisation of the foliar entry of glyphosate in hemp dogbane (*Apocynum cannabinum*), *Weed Science*, **27**, 426–433.

RIOUX, R., BANDEEN, J.D. and ANDERSON, G.W. (1974). Effects of growth stage on translocation of glyphosate in quackgrass, *Canadian Journal of Plant Science*, **54**, 397–401.

SALAZAR, L.C. and APPLEBY, A.P. (1982). Herbicidal activity of glyphosate in soil, *Weed Science*, **30**, 463–466.

SANDBERG, C.L., MEGGITT, W.F. and PENNER, D. (1980). Absorption, translocation and metabolism of ^{14}C-glyphosate in several weed species, *Weed Research*, **20**, 195–200.

SARGENT, J.A. (1965). The penetration of growth regulators into leaves, *Annual Review of Plant Physiology*, **16**, 1–12.

SCHULTZ, M.E. and BURNSIDE, O.C. (1980a). Absorption, translocation, and metabolism of 2,4-D and glyphosate in hemp dogbane (*Apocynum cannabinum*), *Weed Science*, **28**, 13–20.

SCHULTZ, M.E. and BURNSIDE, O.C. (1980b). Effect of lanolin or lanolin + starch rings on absorption and translocation of 2,4-D or glyphosate in hemp dogbane (*Apocynum cannabinum*), *Weed Science*, **28**, 149–151.

SHANER, D.L. and LYON, J.L. (1980). Interaction of glyphosate with aromatic amino acids on transpiration in *Phaseolus vulgaris*, *Weed Science*, **28**, 31–35.

SMID, D. and HILLER, L.K. (1981). Phytotoxicity and translocation of glyphosate in the potato (*Solanum tuberosum*) prior to tuber initiation, *Weed Science*, **29**, 218–223.

SMITH, H. (1975). In *Phytochrome and Photomorphogenesis*. London; McGraw-Hill, 235pp.

SPRANKLE, P. and MEGGITT, W.F. (1972). Effective control of quackgrass with fall and spring applications of glyphosate. *Proceedings of the North Central Weed Control Conference*, **27**, 54.

SPRANKLE, P., MEGGITT, W.F. and PENNER, D. (1975). Absorption, action and translocation of glyphosate, *Weed Science*, **23**, 235–240.

SUWANKETNIKOM, R. and PENNER, D. (1976). Environmental influence on yellow nutsedge control with bentazon and glyphosate, *Proceedings of the North Central Weed Control Conference*, **31**, 141.

THARAWANICH, T. and LINSCOTT, D.L. (1975). Factors influencing the effect of glyphosate on yellow nutsedge, *Proceedings of the Northeastern Weed Science Society*, p. 132.

TOTTMAN, D.R. and PHILIPSON, A. (1974). Weather limitations on cereal spraying in the spring, *Proceedings of the 12th British Weed Control Conference*, pp. 171–176.

TURNER, D.J. (1981). The effect of additives on the control of *Agropyron repens* with glyphosate, *Proceedings of the AAB Conference Grass Weeds in Cereals in the UK*, pp. 167–175.

TURNER, D.J. and LOADER, M.P.C. (1974). Studies with solubilized herbicide formulations, *Proceedings of the 12th British Weed Control Conference*, pp. 177–184.

TURNER, P.E.T. (1980). The efficacy of Roundup for killing sugarcane, *Proceedings of the South African Sugar Technologists Association*, pp. 1–6.

UPCHURCH, R.P. and BAIRD, D.D. (1972). Herbicidal action of MON-0573 as influenced by light and soil, *Proceedings of the Western Society of Weed Science*, **25**, 41–44.

UPCHURCH, R.P., BAIRD, D.D. and BEGEMAN, G.F. (1972). Influence of temperature and diluent properties of MON-0468 performance, Abstracts, *1972 Meeting of the Weed Science Society of America*, p. 80.

WALLGREN, B. (1979). Effect of glyphosate on *Agropyron repens* at different temperatures—preliminary results, *Proceedings of the 20th Swedish Weed Conference*, **1**, 139–144.

WHITWELL, T., BANKS, P., BASLER, E. and SANTELMANN, P.W. (1980). Glyphosate absorption and translocation in bermudagrass (*Cynodon dactylon*) and activity in horsenettle (*Solanum carolinense*), *Weed Science*, **28**, 93–96.

WHITWELL, T. and SANTELMANN, P.W. (1978). Influence of growth stage and soil conditions on Bermudagrass susceptibility to glyphosate, *Agronomy Journal*, **70**, 653–656.

WILLS, G.D. (1978). Factors affecting toxicity and translocation of glyphosate in cotton (*Gossypium hirsutum*), *Weed Science*, **26**, 509–513.

WYRILL, III, J.B. and BURNSIDE, O.C. (1976). Absorption, translocation and metabolism of 2,4-D and glyphosate in common milkweed and hemp dogbane, *Weed Science*, **24**, 557–566.

WYRILL, III, J.B. and BURNSIDE, O.C. (1977). Glyphosate toxicity to common milkweed and hemp dogbane as influenced by surfactants, *Weed Science*, **25**, 275–287.

YATES, W.E., AKESSON, N.B. and BAYER, D.E. (1978). Drift of glyphosate sprays applied with aerial and ground equipment, *Weed Science*, **26**, 597–604.

Part III

Behaviour of Glyphosate: Toxicology

Chapter 8

Toxicological properties of glyphosate—a summary

D. Atkinson
East Malling Research Station, UK

Introduction

Glyphosate was first announced as a new herbicide in 1971 (Baird *et al.*, 1971) and marketed in the USA in 1974. By 1976, it had been approved by the Environmental Protection Agency (EPA) in the USA for use in major grain crop systems—maize (*Zea mays*), wheat (*Triticum aestivum*), barley (*Hordeum vulgare*) and soya beans (*Glycine max*)—and by 1980 in over 50 agricultural crops and industrial sites (Monsanto, 1980). Chapters in the present volume detail usage for a wide range of crops and indicate the situations which possibly could result in the introduction of glyphosate to the environment or into food chains. The effect of glyphosate on microorganisms, the aquatic environment, wildlife, soil macroorganisms, etc., are all dealt with in other chapters, while this chapter summarizes data on the probable effects of glyphosate on animal and human health and on the levels of glyphosate likely to be found in foods. Assessments of both the potential acute and chronic effects of the commercial formulation Roundup, i.e. its ability to produce adverse effects and the probability of these adverse effects occurring, are important, particularly as feeding studies seem to indicate no adverse effects of the compound on palatability. Sullivan and Sullivan (1979) (see also Chapter 12) found that black-tailed deer (*Odocoileus hemionus columbianus*), given a choice of control or glyphosate-treated alder or alfalfa browse, either showed no preference or ate more of the treated foliage. Ingestion of treated browse did not affect consumption. O'Keeffe (1980) found that glyphosate applied pre-harvest to wheat and barley had no effect on grain quality or on their subsequent uses for bread-making or malting. In the absence of such effects, the toxicological profile is important for assessing the safety of residue levels. In this chapter, the name glyphosate usually refers to *N*-(phosphonomethyl)glycine and Roundup to the commercial formulation of the isopropylamine salt.

Short-term toxicity

The results of short-term tests for acute toxicity, due to exposure to glyphosate, are summarized in *Table 8.1*. Testing on a very wide range of species has shown that the active ingredient, glyphosate, is relatively non-toxic. The relative toxicities of glyphosate (4.3 g kg^{-1}) and the isopropylamine salt (4.9 g kg^{-1}) for rats (*Rattus* spp.) are similar.

TABLE 8.1   Acute toxicological evaluation of glyphosate

Species	Test	Glyphosate dose/effects	Reference
Quail	Acute oral LD_{50}	> 3.8 g kg^{-1}	WSSA (1983)
Rabbit	Acute oral LD_{50}	3.8 g kg^{-1}	EPA (1981; 1982b)
Rat	Acute oral LD_{50}	4.3 g kg^{-1} Isopropylamine salt of glyphosate, 4.9 g kg^{-1}	EPA (1982a; 1982b)
Rat	Acute oral LD_{50}	5.6 g kg^{-1} Roundup, 5.4 g kg^{-1}	WSSA (1983)
Rabbit	Acute dermal LD_{50}	7.9 g kg^{-1} Roundup, > 5.0 kg^{-1}	Worthing (1979)
Rabbit	Eye irritation	6.9 on FHSA scale of 110 (slightly irritating) Roundup, moderately irritating	WSSA (1983)
Rabbit	Skin irritation	0.1 on FHSA scale of 8.0 (non-irritating) Roundup, 4.3, moderately irritating	WSSA (1983)
Rat	Acute vapour inhalation	Roundup, no effect 4 h at 12.2 l^{-1} air	WSSA (1983)
Atlantic oyster	96 h TL_{50}	>10 mg kg^{-1} (slightly toxic)	Monsanto (1982); Tooby (Chapter 14, this volume)
Blue gill	96 h LC_{50}	120 p.p.m. Roundup, 14 p.p.m. (almost non-toxic)	WSSA (1983)
Carp	96 h TL_{50}	115 p.p.m. (almost non-toxic)	WSSA (1983)
Daphnia	48 h LC_{50}	780 p.p.m. (almost non-toxic) Roundup, 5.3 p.p.m.	WSSA (1983)
Duck	8 d dietary LC_{50}	>4640 p.p.m. (almost non-toxic)	WSSA (1983)
Fiddler crab	96 h TL_{50}	934 mg l^{-1} (almost non-toxic)	Monsanto (1982)
Harlequin	96 h LC_{50}	163 p.p.m. (almost non-toxic)	Monsanto (1982)
Quail	8 d dietary LC_{50}	>4640 p.p.m. (almost non-toxic)	WSSA (1983)
Shrimp	96 h TL_{50}	281 p.p.m. (almost non-toxic)	Monsanto (1982)
Trout	96 h LC_{50}	86 p.p.m. (slightly toxic) Roundup, 11 p.p.m. (slightly toxic)	WSSA (1983)

The formulated commercial product, Roundup, seems to be rather more toxic than the parent compound. This point is detailed by Tooby (see *Tables 14.1–14.3*, pp. 210–212). In trout, the 24 h median lethal concentration (mg l^{-1}) was 17 times higher for glyphosate than Roundup and 32 times higher than for the surfactant alone. Similarly, in relation to eye irritation, whereas glyphosate is only slightly irritating, Roundup is moderately irritating (Spurrier, 1973). The situation with respect to skin is similar. This would seem to be due to the direct effects of the formulants or adjuvants. As far as ingestion is concerned, LD_{50} values approach 1% of body weight. On the basis of single-dose feeding studies, the acute toxicity of Roundup is less than table salt and half as much as aspirin. Chronic effects could be different. On this basis, a 12 stone (67 kg) person would have to drink approximately 11 gallons (50 l) of the commercial formulations, diluted as recommended for normal field application to cereals, to receive a dose similar to that assessed in the rat test (Monsanto, 1980). The importance of these potentially toxic concentrations to the consumer of farm produce, grown in systems where glyphosate has been used, depends upon the residues actually found or allowed. The levels permitted in the USA (see *Table 8.5*), are discussed in a later section.

Apart from effects on humans, widely applied chemicals can have a major impact upon naturally occurring microorganisms and macroorganisms. Values given in *Table 8.1* suggest that these effects are likely to be small and some of them are discussed in Chapters 9–14 of this volume. In a major environmental impact assessment (Northwest Ecological Animal Research Ltd, Allison Road, Vancouver, British Columbia, Canada; Hildebrand *et al.*, 1982; Sullivan *et al.*, 1980; 1981), it was found that Roundup had little effect on a number of plant and animal populations in coastal British Columbia. One hundred times the field dose had no effect on either zooplankton or rainbow trout (*Salmo gairdneri*) fingerlings. The 96 h LC_{50} for the trout, 52 mg l^{-1}, would mean that in the field a 100 m length of non-moving water 1 m wide and 1 m deep would need to receive the whole of a 5.2 kg application, several times the recommended rate for weed control in 1 ha of cereals, to reach this level. Moving water or wider streams would need even higher rates of application. The absence of large acute effects in animals may relate to glyphosate's prime mode of action on the shikimic acid pathway, which is absent in animals (see Chapter 5).

Long-term toxicity

The results of a number of tests on a range of species have shown (*Table 8.2*) that glyphosate has, at the range of concentrations normally used or found in treated products, little or no sub-acute, chronic or neurotoxic effects. The rates tested are many orders of magnitude higher than permissible residue levels.

All compounds likely to enter the food chain need to be assessed not only for acute and chronic toxic effects, but also for their potential as teratogenic (*Table 8.3*), mutagenic and carcinogenic agents (*Table 8.4*). With respect to teratogenic

TABLE 8.2   **Sub-acute and chronic toxicology of glyphosate**

Species	Test	Glyphosate dose/effects	Reference
Rat, dog	Sub-acute toxicity: body weight food consumption behaviour mortality haematology blood chemistry urinalyses gross pathology histopathology	Dietary level of 2000 p.p.m. for 90 d, no difference from control	WSSA (1983); Monsanto (1977)
Rat, dog	Chronic toxicity; 2 year feeding study	300 p.p.m., no adverse effect	WSSA (1983)
Hen	Neurotoxicity test	No effect 15 g kg^{-1} (1.25 g twice daily for 3 d), with dosage regime repeated 21 days later)	EPA (1982a)

TABLE 8.3　Teratogenic and reproductive effects of glyphosate

Species	Test	Glyphosate dose/effects	Reference
Rabbit	*Oral* Bodyweight gain Death Administration day 6–27 of gestation	Negative effect 350 mg kg^{-1} d^{-1} (highest dose tested) NOEL* for fetotoxicity 175 mg kg^{-1} d^{-1}	EPA (1981; 1982a)
Rat	*Effects on fetal toxicity and birth defects* 3-generation reproductive study: parental and pup bodyweight gain, behaviour, survival	NOEL 10 mg kg^{-1} d^{-1}	EPA (1981; 1982a)
	Teratology study day 6–19 of gestation	Negative 3.5 g kg^{-1} d^{-1} (highest dose tested)	EPA (1981; 1982a)
	Fetotoxic study	NOEL 100 mg kg^{-1} d^{-1} for fetotoxicity	

*NOEL, no observable effect level.

effects, the levels which have been tested are high relative to rates of application $\simeq$ 200 mg m^{-2}, normal for weed control. A similar situation seems to exist in relation to both carcinogenic and mutagenic potential (*Table 8.4*). Although carcinogenesis and the role of oncogenes in relation to it are not completely understood, a large number of tests suggest glyphosate does not have obvious adverse effects. For example, the highest dose of glyphosate tested in a 26-month chronic toxicity rat study, 31 mg kg^{-1} d^{-1}, gave no observable oncogenic effects (EPA, 1982a). This rate of intake would correspond to a 60 kg man consuming 1.9 g d^{-1} glyphosate. On the basis of the current residue levels which are permitted, this would allow a 60 kg man to consume 19 t of cereal daily before exceeding the maximum permitted level. Several mutagenicity studies have also been conducted (*Table 8.4*). All of these were negative. One study by Vigfusson and Vyse (1980) examined the effect of

TABLE 8.4　Carcinogenic and mutagenic potential of glyphosate

Species	Test	Glyphosate dose/effects	Reference
Mouse	18-month feeding study	NCP* 300 p.p.m. (highest dose tested)	EPA (1981)
	Dominant lethal	negative 2 g kg^{-1}	EPA (1981)
	Host-mediated mutagenicity test	negative	EPA (1982a)
Salmonella sp.	Ames test	negative	EPA (1982a)
Bacillus subtilis Cohn, Prazmowski	Rec-assay mutagenicity test	negative up to 2 mg per disk	EPA (1982a)
Rat	Dominant lethal test	negative 2 g kg^{-1}	EPA (1982a)
	26-month feeding study	NOEL† (31 mg kg^{-1} d^{-1}) (no oncogenic effects, highest dose tested)	EPA (1982a)

*NCP, no carcinogenic potential.
†NOEL, no observable effect level.

Roundup, and of the fungicides Captan (*cis-N-*((trichloromethyl)thio)-4-cyclohexene-1,2-dicarboximide) and Dexon (sodium (4-(dimethylamino)phenyl) diazene sulphonate), on the induction of sister-chromatid exchanges (SCE) in human lymphocytes *in vitro*. An increase in SCE frequency is claimed to be related to the potential mutagenicity of materials (Vigfusson and Vyse, 1980). Using a test system where Dexon, which is known to be mutagenic in prokaryotic and eukaryotic test systems, caused an increase in SCE frequency, Roundup had no effect except at high rates. The rate of glyphosate (6.5×10^{-4} mol l^{-1}) which gave an effect was much higher than that of Dexon (10^{-5} mol l^{-1}). Vigfusson and Vyse concluded that the results suggested that 'glyphosate was, at the most, only weakly mutagenic'. Their study, however, used only two donors of blood cells. Lymphocyte SCE values vary significantly between human subjects (Whorton and Tice, 1981), so the use of at least 10 donors would have been preferable.

Glyphosate in the diet

Maximum permissible levels in foods and crop commodities have been laid down by the Environmental Protection Agency (EPA, 1982b) in the USA (*Table 8.5*). Maximum residue tolerances in most foods for direct consumption, whether meat, fruit or vegetable, are around 0.2 p.p.m, although those in grain products, normally eaten in larger quantities, are lower (0.1 p.p.m.). Actual residues in these

TABLE 8.5   **Maximum permissible levels of glyphosate in crops established by the U.S. Environmental Protection Agency (1982b)**

Commodity	Residue level (p.p.m.)	Commodity	Residue level (p.p.m.)
Alfalfa, fresh and hay	0.2	Pistachio nuts	0.2
Almonds, hulls	1	Pome fruits	0.2
Asparagus	0.2	Root crop vegetables	0.2
Avocados	0.2	Seed and pod vegetables	0.2
Citrus fruits	0.2	Seed and pod vegetables, forage	0.2
Coffee beans	1	Seed and pod vegetables, hay	0.2
Cotton, forage	15	Soya beans	6.0
Cotton, hay	15	Soya beans, forage	15
Cottonseed	15	Soya beans, hay	15
Cranberries	0.2	Stone fruit	0.2
Forage grasses	0.2	Sugarcane	2.0
Forage legumes (except soya beans and peanuts)	0.4	Fish	0.25
Grain crops	0.1	Beef, kidney	0.5
Grapes	0.2	Beef, liver	0.5
Grasses, forage	0.2	Chicken, kidney	0.5
Guavas	0.2	Chicken, liver	0.5
Leafy vegetables	0.2	Goat, kidney	0.5
Mangoes	0.2	Goat, liver	0.5
Nuts	0.2	Horse, kidney	0.5
Papayas	0.2	Horse, liver	0.5
Peanuts	0.1	Pig, kidney	0.5
Peanuts, forage	0.5	Pig, liver	0.5
Peanuts, hay	0.5	Sheep, kidney	0.5
Peanuts, hulls	0.5	Sheep, liver	0.5
Pineapple	0.1		

commodities are usually found to be much lower. Residue studies in animals have shown no detectable levels (< 0.05 p.p.m.) of glyphosate or its metabolite to be present in meat tissue, fat, eggs or milk. Low levels were found in liver and kidney and, therefore, a tolerance of 0.5 p.p.m. has been set. An evaluation of the safety of residues in raw agricultural commodities, even if they should occur at the permitted tolerance levels, has been described in detail (EPA, 1982a).

For new tolerances on various crop groupings at 0.1 p.p.m., resulting from the use of irrigation water following applications on or around aquatic sites and fish at 0.25 p.p.m., the case was as follows (EPA, 1982a): 'The acceptable daily intake (ADI) of glyphosate is 0.10 mg kg^{-1} day^{-1} based on a no observable effect level (NOEL) of 10 mg kg^{-1} day^{-1} (rat reproduction study) and a safety factor of 100. On this basis, the maximum permitted intake (MPI) for a 60 kg man is calculated at 6.0 mg day^{-1}. With the addition of these new tolerances, the theoretical maximum residue contribution (TMRC) has been calculated at 1.39 mg day^{-1} for a 1.5 kg daily diet. All approved tolerances thus utilize about 23 percent of the ADI. These calculations suggest risks to be small relative to amounts of residue in the diet.'

Although glyphosate is relatively non-toxic when administered orally (LD_{50} > 4 g kg^{-1}), it is more toxic if given intraperitoneally (LD_{50} 190–280 mg kg^{-1} for the isopropylamine salt) (Olorunsogo, Bababunmi and Bassir, 1977). The acute effects, elevated temperature, asphyxial convulsion, etc., seem similar to those caused by materials which alter mitochondrial energy transformations. Olorunsogo, Bababunmi and Bassir (1979) found that the isopropylamine salt of glyphosate enhanced oxygen consumption (220 nano-atoms O_2 min^{-1} compared with 132 in control) in the absence of ADP in mitochondria extracted from rat liver 5 h after intraperitoneal dosing. An application of 60 mg kg^{-1} glyphosate reduced the respiratory control ratio (ratio of ADP-stimulated respiration to ADP-less respiration) by 40%. Uncoupling of mitochondrial oxidative phosphorylation may be a major component in this type of glyphosate toxicity. The rates used in this study (60–120 mg kg^{-1} were, however, high even relative to levels normally expected to be found in diets (TMRC = 1.39 mg d^{-1}).

Conclusions

Assessments of both the short- and long-term toxic properties of glyphosate suggest that the levels indicated as causing adverse effects are outside those which would seem to be encountered in normal diets, on the basis of permitted maximum residue tolerances, and with the residue levels caused by the use of glyphosate for weed control at rates of the order of 1.5 kg ha^{-1}.

Acknowledgements

I am grateful to Mr J.F. Hebblethwaite of Monsanto for valuable advice and to Drs E. Grossbard, G.J. Levinskas and R.W. Street for their comments on the manuscript.

References

BAIRD, D.D., UPCHURCH R.P., HOMESLEY, W.B. and FRANZ, J.E. (1971). Introduction of a new broad spectrum postemergence herbicide class with utility for herbaceous perennial weed control. *Proceedings of the 26th North Central Weed Control Conference*, pp. 64–68.

ENVIRONMENTAL PROTECTION AGENCY (1981). Glyphosate; proposed tolerance. *Federal Register*, **46**(70), 21631.

ENVIRONMENTAL PROTECTION AGENCY (1982a). Glyphosate; tolerances and exemptions from tolerances for pesticide chemicals in or on raw agricultural commodities. *Federal Register*, **47**(241), 56136–56138.

ENVIRONMENTAL PROTECTION AGENCY (1982b). Code of Federal Regulations: Protection of Environment, *40 CFR*, pp. 180–364.

HILDEBRAND, L.D., SULLIVAN, D.S. and SULLIVAN, T.P. (1982). Experimental studies of rainbow trout populations exposed to field applications of Roundup herbicide. *Archives of Environmental Contamination and Toxicology*, **11**, 93–98.

MONSANTO (1977). Toxicity of the isopropylamine salts of glyphosate. *Monsanto Technical Bulletin*, **86**.

MONSANTO (1980). Toxicology and environmental review. *Roundup Herbicide Bulletin*, **1**, 1–3.

MONSANTO (1982). Glyphosate technical. *Monsanto Material Safety Data Sheet*, 1–4.

O'KEEFFE, M.G. (1980). The control of *Agropyron repens* and broad-leaved weeds pre-harvest of wheat and barley with the isopropylamine salt of glyphosate. *Proceedings of the 1980 British Crop Protection Conference—Weeds*, pp. 53–60.

OLORUNSOGO, O.O., BABABUNMI, E.A. and BASSIR, O. (1977). Proceedings of the 1st International Congress of Toxicology, Toronto, Canada, p. 34.

OLORUNSOGO, O.O., BABABUNMI, E.A. and BASSIR, O. (1979). Effect of glyphosate on rat liver mitochondria *in vivo*. *Bulletin of Environmental Contamination and Toxicology*, **22**, 357–364.

SPURRIER, E.C. (1973). Glyphosate—a new broad spectrum herbicide. *PANS*, **19**, 607–608.

SULLIVAN, D.S., SULLIVAN, T.P. and BISALPUTRA, T. (1981). Effects of Roundup herbicide on diatom populations in the aquatic environment of a coastal forest. *Bulletin of Environmental Contamination and Toxicology*, **26**, 91–96.

SULLIVAN, T.P. and SULLIVAN, D.S. (1979). The effects of glyphosate herbicide on food preference and consumption in black tailed deer. *Canadian Journal of Zoology*, **57**, 1406–1412.

SULLIVAN, L.D., SULLIVAN, D.S. and SULLIVAN, T.P. (1980). Effects of Roundup herbicide on population of *Daphnia magna* in a forest pond. *Bulletin of Environmental Contamination and Toxicology*, **25**, 353–357.

VIGFUSSON, N.V. and VYSE, E.R. (1980). The effect of the pesticides Dexon, Captan and Roundup on inter-chromatid exchanges in human lymphocytes *in vitro*. *Mutation Research*, **79**, 53–57.

WHORTON, E.B. and TICE, R.R. (1981). Sister chromatid exchanges: a statistical assessment. *Environmental Mutagenesis*, **3**, 369.

WORTHING, C.R. (1979). Glyphosate, in *The Pesticide Manual*, p. 292. British Crop Protection Council, Croydon, UK.

WSSA (1983). Glyphosate, *N*-(phosphonomethyl)glycine, in *Handbook of the Weed Science Society of America*. WSSA.

Part IV

Behaviour of Glyphosate: Environmental Impact

Chapter 9

Behaviour of glyphosate in soils and its degradation

L. Torstensson
Swedish University of Agricultural Sciences, Uppsala, Sweden

Introduction

When using herbicides, it is necessary to know how the chemicals behave in soils. This is important to optimize performance of the herbicide, to ensure that no damage is caused to subsequent crops and to avoid unwanted side-effects within or outside the area of use. Before dealing with the behaviour of glyphosate in soils, some general aspects of herbicide–soil interactions will be considered.

Following post-emergence treatment with herbicides, a large proportion of the amount applied reaches the soil. On entering the soil, herbicides may be bound in different ways to soil constituents, they may be transported from the target area, and they will be subjected to degradation by different mechanisms. A recent review of the behaviour of herbicides in the soil can be found in Hance (1980a).

Herbicides in the soil are bound through adsorption to clay minerals, organic materials, metallic oxides or to humic substances. Adsorption is often an equilibrium process and binding is therefore reversible. Adsorption–desorption phenomena are reviewed by Calvet (1980).

Transport of herbicides occurs in different ways. Movement away from the soil by evaporation is dependent on the vapour pressure of the herbicide and varies with temperature, water solubility, adsorption and wind speed. Movement within the soil is through diffusion or mass transport, in the latter case by means of water movement or transport of soil particles. Movement of a herbicide in the soil profile is generally by water and thus water solubility and adsorption characteristics of a herbicide are of great importance for its rate of transport. Reviews of herbicide transport in soil have been given by Leistra (1980) and Hance (1980b).

Decomposition of herbicides occurs through photochemical, chemical and biological processes. Ultraviolet light is the active component in photochemical decomposition and occurs in the atmosphere, on leaf surfaces and on the soil surface. Chemical transformations in soil include hydrolytic and oxidation processes. Reactions with free radicals in soil are also possible. Biological decomposition is generally considered to be of the greatest importance for most herbicides and is carried out by soil microorganisms.

Specific microorganisms are able to use certain herbicides, e.g. 2,4-D, MCPA and TCA, as a substrate for growth. They become adapted to utilize these substances, which means that repeated application of the same herbicide to the

137

same field results in decomposition occurring somewhat faster than following the first application. However, co-metabolism is the most frequent process involved in herbicide degradation by microorganisms. This does not result in adaptation and the microorganisms do not benefit by the reaction in the form of energy. A description of the role of microorganisms in decomposition of herbicides is given by Torstensson (1980).

The rate of decomposition of herbicides in soil is influenced by the properties of the herbicide, the climate, the soil type and the cultivation. The chemical structure of the herbicide, as well as its physical properties such as vapour pressure, solubility and affinity for adsorption, may directly and indirectly influence the rate of decomposition. The most favourable climatic conditions for high rates of herbicide decomposition are optimal temperature and uniform precipitation during the time of decomposition. Soil properties, such as content of organic matter and clay, pH, temperature, moisture content, composition of soil gases and amount of nutrients, are both directly and indirectly involved in regulating activity of soil microorganisms, and hence may influence their capacity to degrade herbicides.

It is clear that prediction of persistence of a chemical in soil is a difficult task. Persistence is not a fixed property of a herbicide, but is influenced by all the factors previously mentioned. These vary from site to site and many of them also from year to year. In order to predict persistence in soil in different situations, we must know how the rate of degradation is affected by soil conditions, climatic variations, cultivation, etc. Knowledge of the rates of herbicide dissipation from soil is important for both agronomic and environmental reasons. A review on prediction of herbicide persistence in soil is given by Hurle and Walker (1980).

In the light of these general considerations, the behaviour of glyphosate in the soil will be examined. The name glyphosate in this chapter refers to the free acid form of N-(phosphonomethyl)glycine. Where authors have used the isopropylamine salt as the commercial formulation Roundup, this will be stated clearly.

Adsorption

A characteristic of glyphosate is that its herbicidal activity through soil is low. This has been ascribed to its adsorption to the soil constituents (Sprankle, 1974). Sprankle, Meggitt and Penner (1975a) showed that 56 kg ha^{-1} did not reduce the dry weight of wheat (*Triticum aestivum*) plants grown on a clay loam or a muck soil. Glyphosate was rapidly inactivated in the soil (at rates 25 times those proposed for normal use). Several studies support this general view (Sprankle, Meggitt and Penner, 1975b; Moshier, Turgeon and Penner, 1976; 1978; Hensley, Beuerman and Carpenter, 1978). However, other investigations have pointed at obvious herbicidal activity of glyphosate through soil. Rodrigues and Worsham (1980) found that glyphosate, applied to wheat foliage, was exuded from the roots into the soil and caused root inhibition and foliar injury symptoms in maize (*Zea mays*) seedlings growing in the same soil. Salazar and Appleby (1982) have carried out experiments which indicate that glyphosate, in doses of 1–3.4 kg ha^{-1}, can injure some plant species by uptake from soil. The herbicide remained available for a sufficiently long period of time, 1–5 days, to cause growth reduction in common bentgrass (*Agrostis tenuis* Sibth 'Highland'), lucerne (*Medicago sativa* L. 'Vernal') and red clover (*Trifolium pratense* L. 'Kenstar'). However, these experiments were carried out under a set of conditions designed to maximize possible soil activity.

Investigating adsorption of glyphosate, Sprankle, Meggitt and Penner (1975b) found that it is bound to the soil through the phosphonic acid moiety. Inorganic phosphates compete for adsorption sites. Binding of glyphosate to organic matter saturated with various cations increased as follows:

$$Na^+ = Mg^{2+} < Zn^{2+} < Ca^{2+} = Mn^{2+} = Fe^{3+} = Al^{3+}$$

Cation-saturated clays showed great differences in adsorption of glyphosate (Sprankle, Meggitt and Penner, 1975b) and the binding to clays increased as follows:

$$Ca^{2+} < Mn^{2+} < Zn^{2+} < Mg^{2+} < Fe^{3+} < Al^{3+}$$

The strong adsorption to Al^{3+} and Fe^{3+} indicated that phosphate might be involved in adsorption. At lower concentrations, phosphate binds to clay minerals through exchangeable iron and aluminium. Glyphosate may form an adsorbent–cation– herbicide complex. At higher concentrations, phosphate may be precipitated. Iron and aluminium form colloidal phosphates. Hensley, Beuerman and Carpenter (1978) showed that when glyphosate was allowed to stand in solution with $FeCl_3$ a precipitate was formed and the herbicidal activity was reduced.

In comparing several types of clays and adsorbents, Sprankle, Meggitt and Penner (1975b) found that more glyphosate was adsorbed on kaolinite than on illite or Na^+-saturated bentonite. The iron and aluminium hydroxide also adsorbed small quantities of glyphosate. The cation exchange capacities decrease as follows:

bentonite > illite > kaolinite > iron and aluminium hydroxides

Therefore, binding did not seem to be related to the cation exchange capacity of clay, but rather to the cations on the clay, a finding later supported by Hensley, Beuerman and Carpenter (1978).

Glyphosate adsorption to the soil occurs rapidly within the first hour and increases slowly thereafter (Sprankle, Meggitt and Penner, 1975b). There is little effect of soil pH on adsorption (Sprankle, Meggitt and Penner 1975a; 1975b; Hance, 1976). Addition of phosphate decreases glyphosate adsorption (Sprankle, Meggitt and Penner, 1975a; 1975b) and Hance (1976) concluded that inorganic phosphate excludes glyphosate from sorption sites. Glyphosate sorption is not correlated with the total phosphate sorption capacity of a soil, but with its unoccupied phosphate sorption capacity (Hance, 1976).

Adsorption of glyphosate to soil has been described by using the Freundlich equation (Hance, 1976). When using this equation, $x/m = kc^{l/n}$, logarithmic plots of equilibrium solution concentrations (c) against quantities adsorbed by unit weight of adsorbent (x/m) were linear. The slopes l/n were all close to, but slightly below unity. Values for the constant k range for nine soils from 18 to 377 (H.W. Frazier, personal communication). Hance (1976) compared k-constants for glyphosate with those for diuron in the same soils and found for the latter herbicide a range of 10–270. Hence, glyphosate is not adsorbed much more extensively than diuron, a representative soil-acting herbicide. Hance (1976) concluded that it was unlikely that inactivation through adsorption was solely responsible for the low phytotoxicity of soil-applied glyphosate. Evolution of $^{14}CO_2$ from ^{14}C-labelled glyphosate does not suggest a particularly rapid rate of degradation in some soils (see *Tables 9.1* and *9.2*), which is also supported by field experiments (*Table 9.3*), and does not encourage a hypothesis for inactivation based on rapid disappearance of the herbicide. Since the herbicide has to be applied in relatively large concentrations to plant roots in culture solution to produce toxicity, Hance (1976) concluded that the low activity of glyphosate in soil is a consequence of the combination of moderate adsorption and low intrinsic toxicity when applied to the root.

Mobility

Glyphosate has been found to be fairly immobile in soil. The herbicide moves only slightly on soil thin-layer plates according to Helling (1971). Sprankle, Meggitt and Penner (1975b) found R_F values of 0.04–0.20. The R_F values increase as pH increases. Mobility also becomes greater with an increase in the phosphate level of the soil. Rueppel *et al.* (1977) also found low R_F values of 0.09–0.18 for glyphosate in soil thin-layer studies and classified the herbicide as immobile and thereby possessing no tendency for leaching. H.W. Frazier (personal communication) also classifies glyphosate as immobile and its main metabolite aminomethylphosphonic acid (AMPA) as slightly mobile.

Some run-off studies of glyphosate have also been carried out by Damanakis (1976), Rueppel *et al.* (1977) and Edwards, Triplett and Kramer (1980). These have been dealt with by Brønstad and Friestad in Chapter 13 of this book. Their results also support the finding that the mobility of glyphosate in soil is low (see also Chapter 14).

Degradation

Mechanism of degradation

Decomposition of a herbicide may occur photochemically, chemically or biologically. Glyphosate does not undergo chemical hydrolysis (H.W. Frazier, personal communication). The potential for chemical degradation of glyphosate in soil and water was examined by Rueppel *et al.* (1977) using sterile soil shake flasks. The result shows that chemical degradation with any of the three possible ^{14}C labels of glyphosate (see *Figure 9.1*) is not a major pathway of degradation. In soil treated with sodium azide, Sprankle, Meggitt and Penner (1975b) found that $^{14}CO_2$ was evolved at a slow rate only from ^{14}C-methyl-labelled glyphosate. In autoclaved soil, Torstensson and Aamisepp (1977) found slowly diminishing glyphosate effects on test plants (*Figure 9.2*). Slow chemical degradation of glyphosate may therefore occur, but it is not a major process of degradation of this compound.

The results of all investigations prove that the degradation of glyphosate is brought about by the microflora (Sprankle, Meggitt and Penner, 1975b; Quilty and Geoghegan, 1976; Rueppel *et al.*, 1977; Torstensson and Aamisepp, 1977). The dominant process is co-metabolism, thus microorganisms do not use the herbicide for growth (Sprankle, Meggitt and Penner, 1975b; Nomura and Hilton, 1977; Torstensson and Aamisepp, 1977; see also Chapter 11).

Glyphosate is difficult to analyse chemically, with respect to residual amounts in the soil (see also Chapter 17). It is very easy, however, to measure liberated ^{14}C from ^{14}C-labelled glyphosate as $^{14}CO_2$ evolved when the herbicide is decomposed

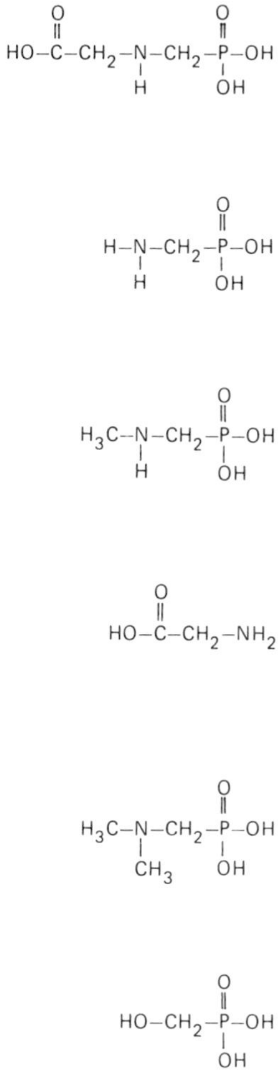

$$HO-\overset{\overset{\displaystyle O}{\|}}{C}-CH_2-\underset{\underset{\displaystyle H}{|}}{N}-CH_2-\overset{\overset{\displaystyle O}{\|}}{\underset{\underset{\displaystyle OH}{|}}{P}}-OH \qquad (1)$$

$$H-\underset{\underset{\displaystyle H}{|}}{N}-CH_2-\overset{\overset{\displaystyle O}{\|}}{\underset{\underset{\displaystyle OH}{|}}{P}}-OH \qquad (2)$$

$$H_3C-\underset{\underset{\displaystyle H}{|}}{N}-CH_2-\overset{\overset{\displaystyle O}{\|}}{\underset{\underset{\displaystyle OH}{|}}{P}}-OH \qquad (3)$$

$$HO-\overset{\overset{\displaystyle O}{\|}}{C}-CH_2-NH_2 \qquad (4)$$

$$H_3C-\underset{\underset{\displaystyle CH_3}{|}}{N}-CH_2-\overset{\overset{\displaystyle O}{\|}}{\underset{\underset{\displaystyle OH}{|}}{P}}-OH \qquad (5)$$

$$HO-CH_2-\overset{\overset{\displaystyle O}{\|}}{\underset{\underset{\displaystyle OH}{|}}{P}}-OH \qquad (6)$$

Figure 9.1. Glyphosate and metabolites identified at degradation in soil. (1) N-(phosphonomethyl)glycine; (2) aminomethylphosphonic acid (AMPA); (3) N-methylaminomethylphosphonic acid; (4) glycine; (5) N, N-dimethylaminomethylphosphonic acid; (6) hydroxymethylphosphonic acid

in laboratory experiments. One disadvantage of the ^{14}C-method is that the primary substance, in this case glyphosate, is not analysed, but a decomposition product from it, i.e. $^{14}CO_2$. In order for liberated ^{14}C to reflect correctly the decomposition of the herbicide, $^{14}CO_2$ must be liberated concurrently with the decomposition. This seems also to be the case for glyphosate. If cumulative amounts of $^{14}CO_2$, released during decomposition, are plotted against the square root of time, the data show a linear relationship (*Figure 9.3*), apart from the very first points which do not fall on the straight line. This is an indication of glyphosate being co-metabolically degraded (Stenström and Torstensson, 1983).

Quilty and Geoghegan (1976) suggest that one, or possibly several, fungal species are responsible for the degradation of glyphosate (as Roundup) in peat. Degradation was inhibited by application to the peat of antifungal antibiotics, i.e. nystatin or griseofulvin, and stimulated by the antibacterial chloramphenicol. Moore, Braymer and Larson (1983) have isolated a strain of the bacterium *Pseudomonas* sp. able to utilize the phosphonate moiety of glyphosate as the sole source of phosphorus (see also Chapter 11).

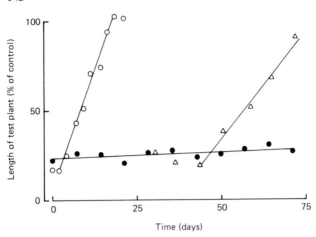

Figure 9.2. Bioassay of glyphosate (as Roundup) in soil with wheat (*Triticum aestivum*) after treatment with 0.09 mg a.i. g^{-1} soil. Un-autoclaved soil (●); autoclaved soil (○); autoclaved soil, incubated 1 month and then re-inoculated with un-autoclaved soil suspension (△) (from Torstensson and Aamisepp, 1977, by courtesy of Blackwell Scientific Publications Ltd)

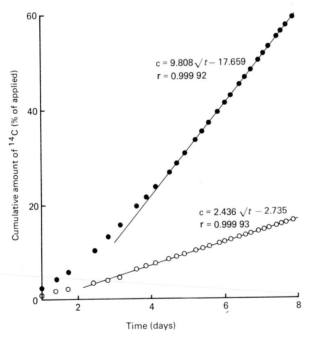

Figure 9.3. Cumulative evolution of $^{14}CO_2$ from ^{14}C-labelled glyphosate [*N*-(phosphonomethyl)glycine] in two soils. Agricultural soil, clay loam (○); forest soil, iron podsol (●) (after Stenström and Torstensson, 1983)

Quilty and Geoghegan (1976) suggested that the surfactant in Roundup, the formulation of the isopropylamine salt of glyphosate, stimulated degradation possibly because it enhanced microbial activity. The microbial activity of soil, as measured by the rate of respiration, is correlated with the degradation rate of glyphosate (*Figure 9.4*) (Torstenssen and Stark, 1979; 1981; Lönsjö *et al.*, 1980; Müller *et al.*, 1981; Stark, 1982). As degradation is by co-metabolism, the rate of decomposition should depend on the general microbial activity in the soil. This creates the necessary enzymic potential for decomposition.

Upon degradation of glyphosate in soil, the principal metabolite formed is aminomethylphosphonic acid (AMPA) (Rueppel *et al.*, 1977) (see *Figure 9.1*). In some instances several other metabolites have also been detected in small amounts. These minor metabolites included (*Figure 9.1*) *N*-methylaminomethylphosphonic acid, glycine, *N,N*-dimethylaminomethylphosphonic acid, hydroxymethylphosphonic acid and two unidentified metabolites. These minor metabolites were

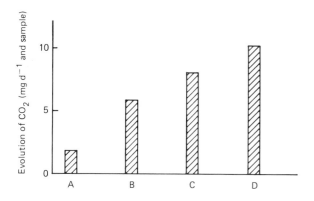

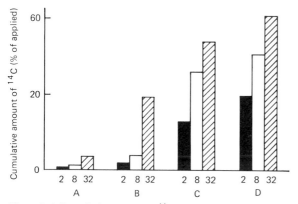

Figure 9.4. Cumulative release of $^{14}CO_2$ after 2, 8 and 32 days from ^{14}C-labelled glyphosate [*N*-(phosphonomethyl)glycine] in four soils (A–D) with different biological activity, measured as evolution of carbon dioxide per day (after Lönsjö *et al.*, 1980)

normally present in amounts less than 1% of applied glyphosate. Rueppel *et al.* (1977) found no metabolic products containing an intact *N*-phosphono-methylglycine grouping.

AMPA is also biologically degradable (Rueppel *et al.*, 1977). However, it can accumulate in certain soils (Comes, Bruns and Kelly, 1976; Nomura and Hilton, 1977; Rueppel *et al.*, 1977). The slower degradation of AMPA than glyphosate may reflect tighter binding of the metabolite to soil as compared with the parent compound.

Glyphosate is degraded under both aerobic and anaerobic conditions (Rueppel *et al.*, 1977). The metabolite distribution was similar for both the aerobic and anaerobic processes.

The potential formation of *N*-nitrosoglyphosate in soil has been investigated because it was suspected that *N*-nitrosoamines may be formed from certain agricultural chemicals. These may cause carcinogenic, mutagenic, teratogenic and acutely toxic effects in low concentrations. Tate and Alexander (1974) were unable to detect any *N*-nitrosoamines in soil treated with sodium nitrite and glyphosate. Later, Khan and Young (1977) could not demonstrate the formation of *N*-nitrosoglyphosate in soil samples that were incubated with glyphosate only. However, when different soils were treated with sodium nitrite and glyphosate at high rates (20 and 740 μg g^{-1}, respectively) formation of *N*-nitrosoglyphosate was observed. The highest yield was noted in soil low in organic matter and clay content. Nitrosation was not affected by soil pH. At low levels of glyphosate (5 μg g^{-1}) and nitrite nitrogen (2 μg g^{-1}), the formation of *N*-nitrosoglyphosate in soil was not observed.

Factors influencing rate of degradation

Most studies of rate of degradation of glyphosate in soil have been carried out in the laboratory using ^{14}C-labelled compound. The evolution of ^{14}CO$_2$ has been measured. In many cases, a fast evolution of ^{14}CO$_2$ has been recorded during the first few days after application of the herbicide (*Figure 9.5*). When the daily ^{14}CO$_2$ output from each experimental soil was plotted semilogarithmically against time it was found in some soils that ^{14}CO$_2$ evolution was not a continuous process (Nomura and Hilton, 1977; Hance, 1976; Torstensson and Stark, 1981) (see also *Figure 9.5*).

Nomura and Hilton (1977) suggested that the initial steep part of the curve represented the degradation of free or easily available glyphosate and the second part the degradation of what they called 'bound glyphosate'. They suggested that, during the steady state, the bound glyphosate became available at a constant rate by whatever mechanism of degradation. However, two of their five soils did not attain a steady state nor did three soils investigated by R.J. Hance (personal communication). Only two of the 15 soils examined by Torstensson and Stark (1981) showed a steady state of carbon dioxide evolution. Therefore, it does not seem as if the adsorption of glyphosate, which is a relatively fast process (Sprankle, Meggitt and Penner, 1975b), is a main regulatory mechanism for the rate of degradation of the herbicide.

The rate of evolution of ^{14}CO$_2$ from ^{14}C-labelled glyphosate incubated with different soils (*Tables 9.1* and *9.2*) suggests, in some cases, a fast decomposition of the herbicide with half-lives of less than a week. In other cases, half-lives are several months or years. The variation in the degradation rate of glyphosate

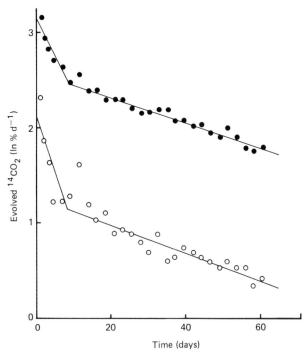

Figure 9.5. Daily rate of evolution of $^{14}CO_2$ from ^{14}C-labelled glyphosate [N-(phosphonomethyl)glycine] in two soils. Agricultural soil, clay loam (○) (after Torstensson, 1982); forest soil, iron podsol (●) (after Stark, 1982).

between different soils is large and does not seem to be easily explained by variation in soil factors, such as pH and organic matter (Stark, 1982). As glyphosate is degraded microbiologically, the variation in degradation rate may be due either to the level of microbial activity in the soil or the strength of adsorption that regulates the availability for degradation of the herbicide in the soil environment.

The general microbial activity of a soil is often fairly well correlated with the degradation rate of glyphosate (Torstensson and Stark, 1979; 1981; Lönsjö *et al.*, 1980; Müller *et al.*, 1981; Stark, 1982) (see *Figure 9.4*). However, there are discrepancies (Torstensson and Stark, 1981) that might be explained by differing availability of the herbicide to microbial degradation. Only minor effects on glyphosate degradation were observed when microbial activity was increased by addition to the soil of substrates such as glucose, sarcosine, glycine or lucerne (*Medicago sativa*) (Moshier and Penner, 1978). Apparently, only microorganisms incapable of degrading glyphosate are stimulated under these conditions.

The influence of soil pH on the degradation rate of glyphosate seems to be small (Moshier and Penner, 1978; Torstensson and Stark, 1981; Stark, 1982). The same applies to the content of organic matter of the soil (Torstensson and Stark, 1981; Stark, 1982). Addition of phosphate to some soils significantly stimulated degradation of glyphosate (Sprankle, Meggitt and Penner, 1975b; Moshier and Penner, 1978), but did not have such an effect on all soils. Degradation of

TABLE 9.1   Laboratory experiments on degradation in agricultural soils of ^{14}C-labelled glyphosate. Percentage of ^{14}C lost, estimated as $^{14}CO_2$ evolved

Soil type*		Time of observation (days)	^{14}C (%)	Half-life (days)	Reference
Sandy clay loam		28	45		Sprankle, Meggitt and Penner (1975b)
Clay loam	(3.8; 7.4)	28	14		
		40	50	40	Hance (1976)
		63	3		
		63	18		
Silt loam	(1.0; 6.5)	112	76.6	3	Rueppel *et al.* (1977)
Silty clay	(6.0; 7.0)	112	64.2	27	
Sandy loam	(1.0; 5.7)	112	43	130†	
	(2.1; 6.9)	60	66	18	Nomura and Hilton (1977)
	(3.1; 7.9)	60	58	43	
	(4.9; 6.1)	60	35		
	(9.5; 5.7)	60	1.2	11.2 years†	
	(9.7; 5.5)	60	0.8	22.8 years†	
Silt loam	(3.7; 5.6)	32	9.5		Moshier and Penner (1978)
Loamy sand	(1.2; 4.4)	32	3.0		
Sandy loam	(3.8; 6.6)	32	40		
Loam	(3.0; 7.5)	32	50.6	31	Lönsjö *et al.* (1980)
Clay loam	(5.2; 6.4)	32	5.1	270†	
Sandy loam	(4.0; 6.3)	48	17.3	175†	Torstensson (1982)
Clay loam	(4.8; 6.5)	48	32.9	90†	

*Within brackets: organic matter (%) and pH.
†Extrapolated values.

^{14}C-glyphosate to $^{14}CO_2$ is drastically reduced after addition of Fe^{3+} or Al^{3+} to the soil. Ca^{2+} and Na^+ additions have no effect, whereas Mn^{2+} increases the degradation rate (Moshier and Penner, 1978).

It appears probable that a certain soil has a specific capacity to degrade glyphosate, which depends on the naturally occurring microbial population producing the right types of enzymes necessary for catalysing the degradation of the herbicide. The degradation rate may not be changed by an increase in the general microbial activity if production of these enzymes is not induced. However, the rate of degradation is influenced by the addition of ions such as phosphate, Fe^{3+} or Al^{3+}, all of which influence adsorption and thus the availability of the herbicide for degradation.

The available literature contains relatively few investigations of glyphosate persistence under field conditions (*Table 9.3*). Both laboratory data and field data show a great variability in the rate of glyphosate decomposition between different soils (Torstensson and Stark, 1979; Stark, 1982). In some cases, comparative studies have been made of glyphosate degradation in the laboratory and the field. Results show good agreement between laboratory and field data (*Table 9.4*).

Many authors (Nomura and Hilton, 1977; Rueppel *et al.*, 1977; Lönsjö *et al.*, 1980; Stark, 1982; R.J. Hance, personal communication) mention the considerable variation in the rates at which different soils can degrade glyphosate. However, in some cases the rate of degradation is not very rapid and therefore the fast

TABLE 9.2   Laboratory experiments on degradation in forest soils of ^{14}C-labelled glyphosate. Percentage of ^{14}C lost, estimated as ^{14}CO$_2$ evolved. Time of observation was 32 days (from Torstensson and Stark, 1981)

Soil type*		^{14}C (%)	Half-life (days)
Clay loam	(12; 6.6)	52	28
Moraine, weak podsol formation	(17; 5.4)	31	70†
Iron podsol	(45; 4.6)	59	16
Brown soil	(30; 4.7)	56	22
Iron podsol	(32; 4.2)	69	13
Iron podsol	(27; 4.8)	81	6
Moraine	(11; 5.5)	59	17
Mull/brown soil	(26; 4.9)	44	45†
Iron podsol	(51; 4.5)	80	11
Iron humus podsol	(65; 4.5)	46	38†
Iron podsol	(28; 4.9)	41	43†
Iron podsol	(30; 4.5)	43	43†
Weakly formed iron podsol	(24; 4.6)	29	65†
Podsol with ashes	(30; 4.7)	8	200†
Iron podsol	(35; 4.5)	14	140†

*Within brackets: loss on ignition (%) and pH.
†Extrapolated values.

inactivation of glyphosate, observed in soil, is only partly dependent on its removal through decomposition. Inactivation of glyphosate through the soil is due to a combination of factors. This may be seen as an advantage, because the safe use of glyphosate may not depend on any single mechanism. However, it may also sometimes lead to difficulties in predicting the behaviour of the herbicide in soil.

Conclusions

Data found in the literature concerning adsorption, mobility and degradation of glyphosate in soils give a relatively clear indication of the behaviour and persistence of the herbicide in the soil environment. However, there are still questions about the mechanism of both adsorption and degradation of the herbicide that have to be answered. However, from current knowledge the following conclusions can be drawn:

(1) Glyphosate is rapidly adsorbed on soil. Adsorption occurs through the phosphoric acid moiety that competes for binding sites with inorganic phosphates. The extent of adsorption is therefore correlated with the unoccupied phosphate sorption capacity of the soil. Content of organic matter and soil pH have little effect on adsorption, but addition of phosphate decreases adsorption on soils with unoccupied phosphate sorption capacity. Adsorption of glyphosate is reversible.
(2) Glyphosate is practically immobile in soils. The mobility is slightly increased at high pH and at high levels of inorganic phosphate in the soil.
(3) Glyphosate may, to a minor extent, be degraded by chemical reactions, but the

TABLE 9.3   Field experiments on glyphosate persistence in soil

Soil type	Dose (kg ha^{-1})	Time of observation (days)	Residues in the soil Glyphosate	AMPA	Reference
Irrigation ditchbank:					
A	5.6	158	0.37 μg g^{-1}	0.74 μg g^{-1}	Comes, Bruns and Kelly (1976)
B	5.6	172	0.33 μg g^{-1}	0.82 μg g^{-1}	
Forest soils:					
clay loam	2.0	92	0.08 kg ha^{-1}	0.09 kg ha^{-1}	Torstensson and Stark (1979)
mull/brown soil	2.0	92	0.06 kg ha^{-1}	0.02 kg ha^{-1}	
brown soil—weak podsol	2.0	92	0.22 kg ha^{-1}	0.11 kg ha^{-1}	
mull/brown soil—weak podsol	2.0	92	0.15 kg ha^{-1}	0.08 kg ha^{-1}	
weakly formed iron podsol	2.0	98	0.27 kg ha^{-1}	0.03 kg ha^{-1}	
	4.0	98	0.38 kg ha^{-1}	0.05 kg ha^{-1}	
iron podsol	2.0	104	0.05 kg ha^{-1}	0.02 kg ha^{-1}	
	4.0	104	0.13 kg ha^{-1}	0.05 kg ha^{-1}	
Agricultural soils:					
loam	2.6	249	0.9 μg g^{-1}	0.3 μg g^{-1}	Müller et al. (1981)
fine silt	2.6	249	1.0 μg g^{-1}	0.2 μg g^{-1}	
sandy loam	4.0	103	1.1 μg g^{-1}	n.d.	Torstensson (1982)
clay loam	2.0	15	0.8 μg g^{-1}	n.d.	
	4.0	15	1.5 μg g^{-1}	n.d.	
	6.0	15	2.4 μg g^{-1}	n.d.	

n.d. = not determined.

TABLE 9.4   Comparison of degradation of glyphosate in the laboratory (from Torstensson and Stark, 1981) and field (from Torstensson and Stark, 1979) studies in the same forest soil. In the laboratory experiments ^{14}C-labelled glyphosate was used

Soil type	Laboratory experiment Time (days) for evolution of 50% ^{14}C	Field experiment Time (weeks) until 10% of applied glyphosate remained in the soil
Iron podsol	16	3
Moraine	17	7
Clay loam	28	9
Mull/brown soil	45	13
Moraine—weak podsol formation	70	13
Weakly formed iron podsol	65	>45

main route of degradation is by microbial activities. Degradation occurs without any lag phase and seems to be a co-metabolic process. It occurs under both aerobic and anaerobic conditions.

(4) The principal degradation product of glyphosate is aminomethylphosphonic acid (AMPA). AMPA is also biologically degradable. The rate of degradation of AMPA is often slower than for glyphosate, probably because of stronger

adsorption. At normal application rates of glyphosate, N-nitrosoglyphosate is not found in the soil.

(5) Rates of glyphosate degradation vary considerably between different soils. Half-lives, ranging from a few days to several months or years, have been detected. The rate of degradation cannot be correlated with a single soil factor, but with the general microbial activity of soils. This activity is an expression of the influence of all soil factors on the microorganisms and is often fairly well correlated with mineralization of the herbicide.

(6) The rapid disappearance of herbicidal activity when glyphosate is applied to soil is not due to a single factor. Inactivation through adsorption is of importance. Volatilization does not occur and leaching is practically negligible. Disappearance through degradation is often slow. When applied to plant roots, glyphosate has a low intrinsic toxicity, which is of importance. All factors together create the behaviour of glyphosate in soil.

(7) Our present knowledge of glyphosate behaviour and degradation gives no reason to suppose that the herbicide may cause any unexpected damage after application to the soil or elsewhere in the environment.

References

CALVET, R. (1980). Adsorption–desorption phenomena, in *Interactions Between Herbicides and the Soil*, pp. 1–30 (Ed. R.J. Hance). London; Academic Press.

COMES, R.D., BRUNS, V.F. and KELLY, A.D. (1976). Residues and persistence of glyphosate in irrigation water, *Weed Science*, **24**, 47–50.

DAMANAKIS, M.E. (1976). Behaviour of glyphosate in the soil (adsorption, leaching, degradation), *Annales de l'Institut Phytopathologique Benaki*, **11**, 153–167.

EDWARDS, W.M., TRIPLETT, G.B. JR. and KRAMER, R.M. (1980). A watershed study of glyphosate transport in runoff, *Journal of Environmental Quality*, **9**, 661–665.

HANCE, R.J. (1976). Adsorption of glyphosate by soils, *Pesticide Science*, **7**, 363–366.

HANCE, R.J. (1980a). *Interactions Between Herbicides and the Soil*. London; Academic Press.

HANCE, R.J. (1980b). Transport in the vapour phase, in *Interactions Between Herbicides and the Soil*, pp. 59–81 (Ed. R.J. Hance). London; Academic Press.

HELLING, C.S. (1971). Pesticide mobility in soils. I. Parameters of soil thin-layer chromatography, *Proceedings of the Soil Science Society of America*, **35**, 732–737.

HENSLEY, D.L., BEUERMAN, D.S.N. and CARPENTER, P.L. (1978). The inactivation of glyphosate by various soils and metal salts, *Weed Research*, **18**, 293–297.

HURLE, K. and WALKER, A. (1980). Persistence and its prediction, in *Interactions Between Herbicides and the Soil*, pp. 83–122 (Ed. R.J. Hance). London; Academic Press.

KHAN, S.U. and YOUNG, J.C. (1977). N-nitrosoamine formation in soil from the herbicide glyphosate, *Journal of Agricultural and Food Chemistry*, **25**, 1430–1432.

LEISTRA, M. (1980). Transport in solution, in *Interactions Between Herbicides and the Soil*, pp. 31–58 (Ed. R.J. Hance). London; Academic Press.

LÖNSJÖ, H., STARK, J., TORSTENSSON, L. and WESSÉN, B. (1980). Glyphosate: decomposition and effects on biological processes in soil, *Weeds and Weed Control, 21st Swedish Weed Conference*, pp. 140–146.

MOORE, F.K., BRAYMER, H.D. and LARSON, A.D. (1983). Isolation of a *Pseudomonas* sp. which utilizes the phosphonate herbicide glyphosate, *Applied and Environmental Microbiology*, **46**, 316–320.

MOSHIER, L.J. and PENNER, D. (1978). Factors influencing microbial degradation of ^{14}C-glyphosate to $^{14}CO_2$ in soil, *Weed Science*, **26**, 686–691.

MOSHIER, L., TURGEON, A.J. and PENNER, D. (1976). Effects of glyphosate and siduron on turfgrass establishment, *Weed Science*, **24**, 445–448.

MOSHIER, L., TURGEON, A.J. and PENNER, D. (1978). Use of glyphosate in sod seeding alfalfa (*Medicago sativa*) establishment, *Weed Science*, **26**, 163–166.

MÜLLER, M.M., ROSENBERG, C., SILTANEN, H. and WARTIOVAARA, T. (1981). Fate of glyphosate and its influence on nitrogen-cycling in two Finnish agricultural soils, *Bulletin of Environmental Contamination and Toxicology*, **27**, 724–730.

NOMURA, N.S. and HILTON, H.W. (1977). The adsorption and degradation of glyphosate in five Hawaiian sugarcane soils, *Weed Research*, **17**, 113–121.

QUILTY, S.P. and GEOGHEGAN, M.J. (1976). The degradation of glyphosate in peat, *Proceedings of the Society for General Microbiology*, **3**, 129.

RODRIGUES, J.J. and WORSHAM, A.D. (1980). Exudation of glyphosate from treated vegetation and its implication in increasing yields of no-till corn and soybeans, Abstracts, *Weed Science Society of America*, p. 92.

RUEPPEL, M.L., BRIGHTWELL, B.B., SCHAEFER, J. and MARVEL, J.T. (1977). Metabolism and degradation of glyphosate in soil and water, *Journal of Agricultural and Food Chemistry*, **25**, 517–528.

SALAZAR, L.C. and APPLEBY, A.P. (1982). Herbicidal activity of glyphosate in soil, *Weed Science*, **30**, 463–466.

SPRANKLE, P.L. (1974). Factors affecting the herbicidal activity of *N*-(phosphonomethyl)glycine (glyphosate) on quackgrass (*Agropyron repens* (L.) Beauv.) and in the soil, *Dissertation Abstracts International, B. The Sciences and Engineering*, **35**, 1144-B.

SPRANKLE, P., MEGGITT, W.F. and PENNER, D. (1975a). Rapid inactivation of glyphosate in the soil, *Weed Science*, **23**, 224–228.

SPRANKLE, P., MEGGITT, W.F. and PENNER, D. (1975b). Adsorption, mobility, and microbial degradation of glyphosate in the soil, *Weed Science*, **23**, 229–234.

STARK, J. (1982). Persistence of herbicides in forest soils, *Dissertation*, Swedish University of Agricultural Sciences, Uppsala Department of Microbiology, Report 15.

STENSTRÖM, J. and TORSTENSSON, L. (1983). Rate formulae for decomposition of pesticides in soil, *Weeds and Weed Control—24th Swedish Weed Conference*, Uppsala, 26–27 January 1983 (in press).

TATE, R.L. and ALEXANDER, M. (1974). Formation of dimethylamine and diethylamine in soil treated with pesticides, *Soil Science*, **118**, 317–321.

TORSTENSSON, L. (1980). Role of microorganisms in decomposition, in *Interactions Between Herbicides and the Soil*, pp. 159–178 (Ed. R.J. Hance). London; Academic Press.

TORSTENSSON, L. (1982). Decomposition of glyphosate in agricultural soils, *Weeds and Weed Control—23rd Swedish Weed Conference*, pp. 385–392.

TORSTENSSON, N.T.L. and AAMISEPP, A. (1977). Detoxification of glyphosate in soil, *Weed Research*, **17**, 209–212.

TORSTENSSON, L. and STARK, J. (1979). Persistence of glyphosate in forest soils, *Weeds and Weed Control—20th Swedish Weed Conference*, pp. 145–149.

TORSTENSSON, N.T.L. and STARK, J. (1981). Decomposition of ^{14}C-labelled glyphosate in Swedish forest soils, *Proceedings of the EWRS Symposium on Theory and Practice of the Use of Soil Applied Herbicides*, pp. 72–79.

Chapter 10

Effects of glyphosate on the soil fauna

H. Eijsackers
Research Institute for Nature Management, Arnhem, The Netherlands

Introduction

It is quite remarkable that so little is known about the side-effects on the soil fauna of a commonly used herbicide such as glyphosate (Roundup). The soil fauna plays an essential role in nutrient cycling of terrestrial ecosystems. The activity of the soil fauna includes fragmentation of litter to prepare it for microbial attack and incorporation with the soil, thus improving soil structure. The soil fauna comprises all organisms which stay—at least during one period of their life-cycle—in the soil. They range from mites to moles, but consist mainly of invertebrata. They are classified according to body size, food or duration of existence in the soil (*Table 10.1*).

Soil pollutants and herbicides may influence the soil fauna either by direct contact, or through litter fragmentation or reduced organic matter inputs due to weed control, or through plant–animal interactions (many soil animals are facultatively phytophagous). The mobility of soil fauna organisms enables escape or avoidance of polluted areas. Data on the precise distribution of herbicides in the soil and on the soil surface are important in assessing side-effects (Eijsackers and Van de Bund, 1980).

The name glyphosate in this chapter refers, in most instances, to the commercial formulation Roundup. This is the isopropylamine salt of *N*-(phosphonomethyl) glycine, to which non-herbicidal (n.h.) constituents have been added. Where authors have used the isopropylamine salt alone, or the n.h. ingredients, this will be stated clearly.

Effects by direct contact

Laboratory experiments

PHYTOFAUNA

References to the effects of herbicides on plant-inhabiting fauna are limited to two studies. Hislop and Prokopy (1981) tested 40 chemicals, used in orchards, for toxicity to the predatory mite *Amblyseius fallacis*, the most important predator of

151

TABLE 10.1   Classification of soil fauna according to size or food or degree of presence in the soil

	Basis of classification	
(A) Size	(B) Food	(C) Degree of presence
(1) Microfauna, <0.2 mm	(1) Saprophagous (consumption of dead organic matter)	(1) Transient (only adults stay part of life-cycle in the soil; oviposition and juveniles above the soil)
(2) Mesofauna, 0.2–2.0 mm, including microarthropods	(2) Coprophagous (consumption of excrements)	
(3) Macrofauna,	(3) Xylophagous (consumption of wood)	(2) Temporary (oviposition and juveniles in the soil; adults stay above the soil)
(a) 2–20 mm (mesoarthropods)	(4) Necrophagous (consumption of dead relatives)	(3) Periodic (only adults stay for short periods above the soil)
(b) > 20 mm (macroarthropods)	(5) Phytophagous (consumption of living plant parts)	(4) Permanent (adults, oviposition and juveniles stay always in the soil)
	(6) Microphagous (consumption of fungi and bacteria)	

the spider mites *Panonychus ulmi* and *Tetranychus urticae*. Glyphosate (10 ml l^{-1}) produced maximum mortality of 100% after 48 h using a slide-dipping technique (immersion for 5 s in a water solution). Application of glyphosate during the spring could therefore have detrimental effects when the mite is still in ground cover.

Robinson, Orr and Abernathy (1977) found with the foliar-feeding nematode *Nothanguina phyllobia* that a high dose (30 g l^{-1}) of glyphosate prolonged larval survival by 50%, thereby possibly increasing the incidence of this nematode on *Solanum elaeagnifolium*.

From these observations on the phytofauna and additional information on the aquatic fauna by Roorda, Schulten and Pieterse (1978) with Acari; Folmar, Sanders and Julin (1979) with Crustaceae, Gammaridae, Nematocera and Plecoptera; R. Kickuth (personal communication) with Gammaridae; and Hildebrand, Sullivan and Sullivan (1980) with Crustaceae—it may be concluded that for some invertebrate groups glyphosate (Roundup) is potentially toxic. However, under semi-field conditions (experimental ponds) no drastic effects have been observed (see also Chapter 14).

SOIL FAUNA

Permanent exposure

Table 10.2 summarizes the results of a number of toxicity tests carried out at our laboratory. Glass dishes (9 cm diam.), containing a substrate of moist, compacted sandy soil, were sprayed in a Potter tower with 1% and 4% glyphosate (1.49 and 5.96 ml m^{-2}, respectively). Observations on numbers of organisms of specific soil fauna species were made daily until the last specimen had died; then, from individual survival periods, mean longevity was calculated. Experiments were carried out at 15°C, 90% r.h., in darkness. The reactions of the organisms to glyphosate were very variable. For instance, the differences between the two experiments with the isopod *Philoscia muscorum* could be attributed to a difference in condition between different seasons; the experiments were started in June and December, respectively. Nevertheless, all isopods showed a consistent decrease in longevity after being sprayed with the highest dose, 5.96 ml m^{-2}, glyphosate. There were slight toxic effects to the springtail (*Onychiurus quadriocellatus*) which were

TABLE 10.2   Mean longevity (in days) of springtails, isopods and carabids after spraying with glyphosate

	Control	0.37	1.49	5.96	23.84 ml m^{-2}
Springtails					
Onychiurus quadriocellatus (N† = 40)	58.8	50.9	50.2	48.9*	—
Tomocerus flavescens (N = 30)	18.3	11.4	12.6	16.3	—
Isopods					
Philoscia muscorum (N = 5)	17.8	19.2	20.0*	13.0*	—
Philoscia muscorum (N = 5)	28.0	—	20.3*	20.4*	—
Oniscus asellus (N = 9)	49.3	44.8	44.1	30.8	—
Carabids					
Pterostichus oblongopunctatus (N = 5)	22.3	23.7	38.3	24.5	—
Abax ater (N = 10)	76.7	50.5	51.8	42.4*	66.3

*Statistically significant from control at 5% level.
†N = number of animals.

statistically significant at the dose of 5.96 ml m^{-2}. In a few tests the highest concentrations of glyphosate gave the smallest decrease in longevity. Recently, Martin (1982) tested glyphosate for its toxicity to the earthworm (*Allolobophora caliginosa*). In laboratory experiments, glyphosate (1, 10 and 100 mg g^{-1}) added to the soil did not affect significantly the mortality or growth of juvenile earthworms.

Choice experiments

An experimental design was developed (Eijsackers, 1978) in which animals were given a free choice between herbicide-treated and untreated parts of a substrate, thus enabling them to avoid contact with the herbicide. By comparing the mortality in a choice experiment with that in a simultaneous experiment, in which animals were permanently exposed to the herbicide, the ability of the animals to avoid the herbicide, possibly resulting in a reduced effect, can be assessed. Hoy, Dahlsten and Shea (1982) tested the isopod *Porcellio formosus* and the acarine *Pergalumna* sp. No deleterious effects on the mite were observed after exposure for 12 days to 0.336 g m^{-2} glyphosate, but the isopod had a decreased mortality (22%) in the free choice experiment compared with permanent exposure (39%) after 12 days. The isopod seems able to avoid the herbicide. Another approach is to observe the distribution of the animals and to correlate the possible avoidance with their mortality or mean longevity. In a series of experiments with the carabid *Notiophilus biguttatus*, neither a distinct avoidance of the treated part of the substrate nor a decreased longevity was found after treatment with 1.49 or 5.96 ml m^{-2} glyphosate (*Table 10.3*).

TABLE 10.3   Longevity and distribution of carabids on a substrate partially treated with glyphosate

	Percentage of total experimental period staying on the untreated part of the substrate			Mean longevity (days)		
	Control	1.49	5.96 ml m^{-2}	Control	1.49	5.96 ml m^{-2}
Notiophilus biguttatus						
(N† = 15)	58	60	69	32.9	43.7	31.0
(N = 5× 3)	52	51	52	34.9	23.5	29.8
(N = 3× 3)	50	55	53	19.1	17.9	25.1

†N = Number of animals per experimental unit.

Mobility

Tests in which the behaviour of the test animals is observed directly can give rapid indications of toxic and sub-lethal effects. Hoy, Dahlsten and Shea (1982) measured speed of movement for four acarine species using an electronic tracking and recording system. From their results (*Table 10.4*) it may be concluded that the glyphosate solvent significantly activated two acarine species (see also Chapter 11). The decrease in locomotion with *T. urticae* was not significant. Nevertheless, sub-lethal effects may occur when there is no or little mortality, comparing results for *Pergalumna* sp. (*Table 10.4*) with those in the preceding choice experiments. In the carabid choice experiments with *N. biguttatus*, an activity index was constructed, based on the number of days an animal had moved from the treated to the untreated substrate parts and vice versa, compared with the total number of observation days. The data showed a slight but non-significant decrease, with 5.96 ml m^{-2} glyphosate(37% vs. 42% in control experiments).

These experiments concerning direct contact toxicity suggest that effects of glyphosate are slight and seem limited to a few species.

TABLE 10.4   **Mean rates of locomotion of Acarina species after exposure to glyphosate or solvent for 20–24 h (rates stated in 0.08 mm s^{-1}) (from Hoy, Dahlsten and Shea, 1982)**

	Control	*Glyphosate*	*Glyphosate solvent*
Pergalumna sp.	1.54	1.51	3.25*
Ceratoppia bipilis	1.63	1.73	4.75*
Metaseiulus occidentalis	6.42	5.46	7.36
Tetranychus urticae	8.11	4.82	4.75

*Statistically significant at 5% level.

Field experiments

The only field experiment reported using glyphosate was by Hoy, Dahlsten and Shea (1982). In a uniform stand of *Arctostaphylos patula*, glyphosate was applied at 0.336 and 3.36 g m^{-2} in a randomized plot design. Microarthropods were extracted and counted 5 days before and 15 and 60 days after spraying. Collemboles numbers were reduced with both rates 15 days after spraying, but not significantly with the highest rate, and had increased until they reached control numbers after 60 days (*Figure 10.1*). Oribatid mites showed a similar response after 15 days. After 60 days, numbers were slightly (but not significantly) higher than in the control plots. In the plots sprayed with the lower glyphosate rate, the numbers of oribatid mites were lower both before and after spraying. Two other acarine groups (Actinedidae and Gamasidae) changed little in numbers. Nevertheless, the slight decrease in numbers of predatory gamasid mites after 15 days could have improved the survival for prey species (collemboles and oribatid mites).

Effects on litter consumption

Litter fragmentation

One of the primary roles of the soil fauna is the breakdown of litter by chewing it, followed by intimate mixing with their gut microflora which improves microbial

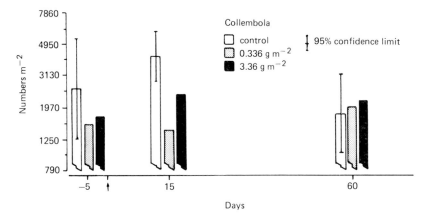

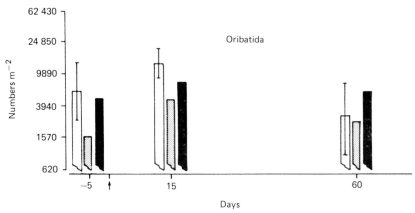

Figure 10.1. Mean numbers of Collembola and Oribatida
before and after spraying (↑) (after Hoy, Dahlsten and Shea,
1982)

decomposition. Experiments on litter fragmentation have been carried out by
sampling litter in the field and offering it in the laboratory to groups of soil
organisms. In this way, adverse effects on the consumers caused by the
consumption of the treated litter can also be seen. For field experiments, litter in
nylon bags or cloth boxes was buried in the litter. Mesh sizes were chosen so as to
allow selective entrance of soil fauna groups and prevent the loss of litter
fragments. *Figure 10.2* shows the results of a series of laboratory experiments with
birch (*Betula verrucosa*) litter treated with 6 l ha^{-1} glyphosate, sampled monthly
for 7 months, and offered as disks for 3-week periods to groups of 20 individual
isopods (*Philoscia muscorum*). In addition, 5 litter disks were treated in the same
way, but stored without exposure to consumers so as to measure weight loss due to
direct microbial breakdown.

From 1 to 5 months after spraying, more of the treated litter was consumed than
of the untreated. Only in October were the differences statistically non-significant.
Consumption of the treated litter was relatively constant over the period

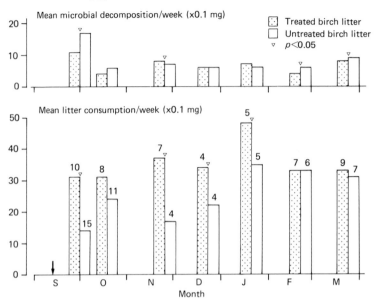

Figure 10.2. Mean weight loss due to consumption by isopods or microbial decomposition of birch litter disks untreated or treated with glyphosate and sampled 2, 5, 10, 14, 18, 23 and 27 weeks after spraying (↓). Consumption and decomposition are estimated during 3 successive weeks. Above each column the numbers of isopods that died during these 3 weeks are given. Significant differences in consumption between treated and untreated litter are marked (Wilcoxon signed rank test *p*<0.05)

September to March. The January sample, taken just after a frost period, showed higher consumption than those of previous months. Consumption of the untreated litter increased gradually, probably because of the weathering of the litter in the field. In contrast, microbial decomposition of the untreated litter disks was usually slightly, but significantly, better on most occasions than the treated (see Chapter 11). The total consumption for all isopods and samples, including mean weekly litter consumption per isopod and the period each isopod fed on the disks (depending on the survival period), resulted in a significantly higher rate of fragmentation of the treated birch litter (1.597 7 g) compared with untreated birch litter (1.236 2 g). Hoy, Dahlsten and Shea (1982) reported a statistically significant decrease in rates of decomposition of *Arctostaphylos patula* leaves in litter boxes after spraying with 0.336 g m^{-2} glyphosate (*Table 10.5*). However, they attributed this to fewer microarthropods in these plots prior to spraying. Moreover, there was no effect in plots sprayed with a tenfold dose (3.36 g m^{-2}) glyphosate. In addition, they doubt whether such a small difference in consumption (amounting to only 6%) was biologically meaningful.

Mortality by consumption of treated food

Mortality of the isopods fed on treated or untreated birch litter differed (*Figure 10.2*), but in one instance only (1 month after spraying) was mortality significantly lower with the treated food than the untreated.

TABLE 10.5   Mean weight of *Arctostaphylos patula* **leaves in litter boxes after 230 days (after Hoy, Dahlsten and Shea, 1982)**

	Mean total weight/plot (g)	Standard deviation
Control	15.39	1.27
Glyphosate, 0.336 g m^{-2}	16.31*	1.11
Glyphosate, 3.36 g m^{-2}	15.36	0.68

*Statistically significant at 5% level.

Plant–animal interactions

Faunal interference in plant–herbicide interactions was observed with the weevils *Notaris puncticollis* and *N. bimaculatus* by Westra and Wyse (1978) and Westra, Wyse and Cooke (1981). These species feed on *Agropyron repens*, the adults on culms and the larvae on rhizomes. In experiments with *N. puncticollis*, reduction of the insect population with chlordane (0.672 g m^{-2}) improved the effectiveness of a glyphosate application (0.112 and 0.168 g m^{-2}) in control of *A. repens* (Westra and Wyse, 1978).

The effectiveness of treatment of dense sods of *A. repens* with 0.17 g m^{-2} glyphosate interfered with feeding damage on the rhizomes of *A. repens* by *N. bimaculatus*, because this disrupted the translocation of glyphosate into the rhizomes. The negative influence of feeding on the effectiveness of glyphosate was quantified by spraying weevil-free and weevil-infested plots, which resulted in 26 and 15 shoots m^{-2}, respectively, vs. 298 and 611 shoots m^{-2} (Westra, Wyse and Cooke, 1981).

Conclusions

Summing up the results, it must be concluded that experiments carried out in the field so far indicate that the side-effects of glyphosate on the soil fauna are small or absent.

Nevertheless, there are some results of laboratory experiments which need confirmation. The 100% mortality in the experiments with *Amblyseius fallacis*, for instance, should be verified under more realistic conditions because of the less drastic effects found with related Acarina such as Gamasida. For the two isopod species *Philoscia muscorum* and *Oniscus asellus*, there was a distinct decrease in longevity compared with the control animals (31 and 38%, respectively) with application of recommended amounts of glyphosate (5.96 ml m^{-2}). However, the first species was not affected by glyphosate if offered by means of litter from sprayed shrubs.

Although, in both experiments, changes in litter fragmentation through spraying of glyphosate were observed, it is difficult to evaluate effects of this herbicide on litter breakdown. The 30% increase in birch litter fragmentation (*Figure 10.2*) occurring over the period of 6 months after spraying is well within the range of normal fluctuations in litter breakdown in Mull and Mor soil profiles with a high and low biological activity, respectively. Between 1957, with optimal conditions, and 1959, with dry conditions, the weight loss from December to September differed considerably; in the Mor profile between 30 and 65% weight loss and in the Mull profile between 20 and 90% weight loss occurred. However, these differences might also add to the increased litter fragmentation resulting from herbicide application, leading to increased differences in litter breakdown between treated and untreated plots. Moreover, an evaluation of the differences is connected intimately with the total change in vegetation cover caused by the herbicide. Long-term field trials could elucidate this problem. At present, glyphosate does not seem to be very toxic for the soil fauna, although adverse effects have been observed in studies with a number of representatives of the soil fauna. The limited number of observations, however, does not permit generalizations of these conclusions.

Acknowledgements

I am indebted to Mr G.J.S.M. Heijmans, who carried out the experiments in our laboratory, and to Dr J.B. Hoy for sending me the final report of his research and improving the manuscript. The drawings were prepared by Mr H. Dekker and the manuscript was typed by Mrs B. Soplanit and Mrs M. Lenselink.

References

EIJSACKERS, H. (1978). Side effects of the herbicide 2,4,5-T affecting mobility and mortality of the springtail *Onychiurus quadriocellatus* Gisin (Collembola), *Zeitschrift für angewandte Entomologie*, **86**, 349–372.

EIJSACKERS, H. and VAN DE BUND, C.F. (1980). Effects on the soil fauna, in *Interactions Between Herbicides and The Soil*, pp. 255–305 (Ed. R.J. Hance). London; Academic Press.

FOLMAR, L.C., SANDERS, H.O. and JULIN, A.M. (1979). Toxicity of the herbicide glyphosate and several of its formulations to fish and aquatic invertebrates, *Archives of Environmental Contamination and Toxicology*, **8**, 269–278.

HILDEBRAND, L.D., SULLIVAN, D.S. and SULLIVAN, T.P. (1980). Effects of Roundup herbicide on populations of *Daphnia magna* in a forest pond, *Bulletin of Environmental Contamination and Toxicology*, **25**, 353–357.

HISLOP, R.L. and PROKOPY, R.J. (1981). Integrated management of phytophagous mites in Massachusetts (USA) apple orchards. 2. Influence of pesticides on the predator *Amblyseius fallacis* (Acarina: Phytoseiidae) under laboratory and field conditions, *Protection Ecology*, **3**, 157–172.

HOY, J.B., DAHLSTEN, D.L. and SHEA, P.J. (1982). The effects of 2,4-D and an alternative material (glyphosate) used for brushfield rehabilitation on soil arthropod community and litter decomposition rate, *Final Report USA-UCB, Research Agreement No. PSW-81-0026*, 34 pp.

MARTIN, N.A. (1982). The effects of herbicides used on asparagus on the growth rate of the earthworm *Allolobophora caliginosa*, *Proceedings of the 35th New Zealand Weed and Pest Control Conference*, pp. 328–331.

ROBINSON, A.F., ORR, C.C. and ABERNATHY, J.R. (1977). Influence of *Nothanguina phyllobia* on silverleaf nightshade. *Proceedings of the 30th Annual Meeting of the Southern Weed Science Society*, p. 142.

ROORDA, F.A., SCHULTEN, G.G.M. and PIETERSE, A.H. (1978). The susceptibility of *Orthogabunna terebrantis* Wallwork (Acarina: Galumnidae) to various pesticides, *Proceedings of the 5th EWRS International Symposium on Aquatic Weeds*, Amsterdam, pp. 375–381.

WESTRA, P.H. and WYSE, D.L. (1978). Observations of *Notaris puncticollis* on quackgrass, *Proceedings of the North Central Weed Control Conference*, pp. 43–44.

WESTRA, P.H., WYSE, D.L. and COOKE, E.F. (1981). Weevil Notaris bimaculates feeding reduces effectiveness of glyphosate on quackgrass *Agropyron repens*, *Weed Science*, **29**, 540–547.

Chapter 11

Effects of glyphosate on the microflora: with reference to the decomposition of treated vegetation and interaction with some plant pathogens

E. Grossbard
Hatfield Polytechnic, UK

Introduction

The interaction between glyphosate and microorganisms is twofold. Members of the microflora are responsible predominantly for the degradation of this herbicide in soil (reviewed by Torstensson, see Chapter 9) and to a large extent also in water (reviewed by Brønstad and Friestad, see Chapter 13). On the other hand, glyphosate may either inhibit or stimulate the growth and activity of microorganisms. Some herbicides have been shown to have adverse effects, albeit at concentrations above those used in agricultural practice (Audus, 1964; Greaves *et al.*, 1976; Grossbard, 1976; Anderson, 1978).

Microbial activity is believed to determine soil fertility, especially by contributing to the recycling of nutrients. Thus a study of microbial responses to glyphosate will provide information on its effect on soil fertility.

There are two approaches to investigations on the influence of a herbicide on the soil microflora. First, an academic study to establish the magnitude and type of any response. Metabolic changes of the organisms should be examined. Here, every result would be of 'importance'. Alternatively, it may be ascertained whether or not a herbicide constitutes a 'hazard' to the soil microflora and consequently to soil fertility. Here, evaluation of results is concerned with the validity and importance of herbicides to agricultural practice. Both types of investigation are rendered difficult by the inadequacy of existing techniques and unsatisfactory methods of interpretation, especially in the context of agricultural practice (reviewed by Greaves, 1979; Greaves and Malkomes, 1980).

Soil microbiologists and agronomists are unable to quantify the microbial contribution to soil fertility, if only because the latter is difficult to define and measure. Consequently, the impact of biocides on soil fertility cannot be measured precisely. Natural fluctuations in microbial activities are considerable. Logically, the inhibitory effect of a herbicide should be regarded as relevant only if it exceeds the level of natural changes (reviewed by Domsch, Jagnow and Anderson, 1983). Such extreme effects of herbicides have been observed rarely. Nevertheless, regulatory bodies, such as the Environmental Protection Agency (EPA) in the USA, the Council of Europe and other bodies, have required, for purposes of registration, the submission of data on potential antimicrobial effects of herbicides (reviewed by Greaves and Malkomes, 1980). The EPA has, at present, deferred

159

this requirement. It can be resuscitated at any time, especially with the introduction of more toxic chemicals (Anon., 1981).

With glyphosate, a specific aspect has to be examined which does not apply to many other herbicides. Glyphosate is used in cereals, both pre- and post-harvest. Residues may be retained in the straw, albeit for a short time only. The subsequent utilization and/or disposal of the straw may be influenced by the interaction of residual glyphosate with the microflora. Also, overwintering of pathogens on straw, weeds or volunteer plants may be affected by glyphosate. However, often it has an adverse effect on the growth of plant pathogens in pure culture (Grossbard and Harris, 1976; Harris and Grossbard, 1978; 1979).

Soon after the introduction of glyphosate, in 1971 (Baird et al., 1971), research was initiated to examine its effect on the soil microflora (Grossbard, 1974; 1976; Quilty and Geoghegan, 1975; 1976). However, considering the importance of this herbicide, in the intervening years, surprisingly little work has been published since then. This chapter reviews the effects of glyphosate on microbial growth in pure culture and on physiological activities, with special reference to recycling of nutrients in the soil. The influence on decomposition of treated vegetation and interactions with some plant diseases will be examined.

The name glyphosate in this chapter refers, in most instances, to the commercial formulation Roundup. This is the isopropylamine salt of N-(phosphonomethyl) glycine to which non-herbicidal (n.h.) constituents, of undisclosed chemical composition and concentration, have been added. Where authors have used the isopropylamine salt of glyphosate alone, or the n.h. ingredients, this will be stated clearly. The concentrations cited are those given by the authors quoted.

Effects on the microflora

Pure cultures

Examination of the influence of herbicides on microorganisms by pure culture techniques is widely criticized. In their 'recommended tests for assessing side-effects of pesticides on the soil microflora', which were designed to give data for registration authorities, Greaves et al. (1980) have discounted pure culture studies. The reasons they gave are:

(1) Isolated organisms may be atypical of their form in the soil.
(2) 'They are normally stimulated to artificially high metabolic rates by growth in normal laboratory media.
(3) They are removed from their normal ecological associations.
(4) Interpretation of results is difficult and extrapolation to field situations impossible.'

Such is the complexity of the discipline of soil microbiology that almost every criticism of techniques and resulting data is justified, to some extent. However, occasionally the behaviour of microorganisms in pure culture does agree with that in soil or on vegetation, even though the herbicide concentrations used in pure culture experiments are not strictly comparable to those in the natural habitat. Moreover, pure culture techniques are useful for the rapid screening of large numbers of herbicides, and the data obtained may aid the design of field experiments. Furthermore, most published research on the effects of glyphosate on the soil microflora refers to data from monoculture studies. For these reasons, pure culture studies are reported here. Moreover, this review is not intended just as a discussion of whether or not glyphosate constitutes a hazard to the soil microflora and thus to soil fertility; it aims to contribute to an understanding of the glyphosate–microflora interaction in the widest sense.

The principal groups of soil microorganisms are actinomycetes, algae, bacteria and fungi, including yeasts.

Fungi

This group has been studied more extensively than any other. The fungi examined fall into two groups. Saprophytes, colonizing and decomposing dead plant material (weeds and straw), have been examined in detail (*Table 11.1*). Fungi which are

TABLE 11.1   The effect of glyphosate on the growth of some fungi on agar media

Fungus	Inhibition		Reference
	Control (%)	Conc. ($\mu g\ g^{-1}$)	
Alternaria sp.	18–63	100	Lönsjö *et al.* (1980)
Alternaria tenuis*	100	500	Cooper (pers. comm.)
Aspergillus niger*	Partial	20 a.e.	Grossbard and Wingfield (1978)
	100	500	Cooper (pers. comm.)
Cephalosporium sp.*	19–52	100	Lönsjö *et al.* (1980)
Chaetomium globosum*	Stim.	1–10	Lönsjö *et al.* (1980)
	19–63	100	Lönsjö *et al.* (1980)
	x_{50}‡	219	Grossbard and Harris (unpubl.)
	x_{50}§	306	Grossbard and Harris (1979).
	100	50	Cooper (pers. comm.)
C. indicum*	27–50	100	Lönsjö *et al.* (1980)
Cladosporium herbarum*	x_{50}	160	Grossbard (unpubl.)
	100	500	Cooper (unpubl.)
Doratomyces nanus*†	x_{50}	>240	Grossbard and Harris (1979)
Fusarium lateritium*	33–73	100	Lönsjö *et al.* (1980)
F. nivale	x_{50}	17	Harris (1981)
Gliocladium roseum*	x_{50}	17	Harris (1981)
	100	500	Cooper (pers. comm.)
Neurospora crassa	0	2 mmol l^{-1}	Roisch and Lingens (1980)
Penicillium sp.*	37–67	100	Lönsjö *et al.* (1980)
Pleurotus astreatus†	x_{50}	>320	Grossbard and Harris (1979)
Polystictus versicolor†	x_{50}	80	Grossbard and Harris (1979)
Schizophyllum commune†	x_{50}	100	Grossbard and Harris (1979)
Stachybotrys chartarum*	x_{50}	25	Grossbard (1976)
	100	50	Cooper (pers. comm.)
Trichoderm polysporum*	27–68	100	Lönsjö *et al.* (1980)
T. viride*	0	20	Grossbard and Wingfield (1978)
	100	500	Cooper (pers. comm.)
Trichurus spiralis*†	x_{50}	>320	Grossbard and Harris (1979)

*Cellulolytic fungi.
†Lignolytic fungi.
‡Incubation at 17°C.
§Incubation at 22°C.

x = expressed as ED$_{50}$, the dose which causes a reduction of the colony diameter to 50% of that of the control.

Concentrations given by various authors as p.p.m., parts 10^{-6} or $\mu g\ ml^{-1}$ are expressed here as $\mu g\ g^{-1}$ a.i. (active ingredient) or a.e. (acid equivalent).

The range given in % control by Lönsjö *et al.* (1980) refers to the inhibition observed on different media. Incubation temperature was 12°C.

powerful cellulose decomposers have been selected for these tests. The second group consists of pathogens, primarily litter-borne, attacking mainly cereals (*Table 11.2*).

RESPONSES IN PURE CULTURE

The earliest reports came from Grossbard (1974; 1976) and Quilty and Geoghegan (1975; 1976). *Tables 11.1* and *11.2* show that glyphosate may exert an inhibitory effect on the development of many of the fungi tested. The degree of growth reduction varied widely from the sensitive *Fusarium nivale* (Ces. Fr.) and *Stachybotrys chartarum* (Ehrenbex Link) Hughes to the fairly resistant *Chaetomium globosum* Kunze and *Gliocladium roseum* Bainier.

The data in *Tables 11.1* and *11.2* are expressed as ED_{50}. This is the median effective dose which will produce a 50% response. In the case of measurements of colony diameters, it is the dose required to produce a colony diameter 50% of that of the control.

Results from different laboratories may differ, even if the same species and concentration of herbicide was used (*Table 11.1*). Incubation temperature, composition of the nutrient medium, the method of culture, the age and type of isolate, all affect the response to the herbicide. Even similar experiments in the same laboratory, using the same technique, may convey different impressions of the relative sensitivity of fungi to glyphosate. Recently, S.L. Cooper (personal communication) tested 46 named cultures by a very sensitive microtitre technique (Cooper *et al.*, 1978), in which mycelium fragments or spores were inoculated into a liquid medium containing a range of glyphosate concentrations. A severe effect occurred only at 500 μg ml^{-1}, where 43% of isolates were killed, whereas at 100 and 50 μg ml^{-1} only 21 and 17%, respectively, of isolates failed to grow. These data fit in with those quoted in *Tables 11.1* and *11.2*. In contrast, in an earlier test (Cooper *et al.*, 1978), 91% of the fungi tested were inhibited to a varying extent by 50 μg ml^{-1}.

TABLE 11.2   A comparison between the effect of Roundup, the isopropylamine salt of glyphosate (IPSG) and the non-herbicidal ingredients of the formulation on the growth of some fungi

Fungus	Isolate	Roundup	IPSG	Non-herbicidal ingredients
		(ED_{50} as μg a.i. g^{-1})		
Fusarium nivale	1	12	81	17
Pseudocercosporella herpotrichoides Fron	—	49	344	n.d.
Rhizoctonia solani	—	56	91	n.d.
Septoria nodorum	R1	64	320	n.d.
	HG2	111	750	149
S. tritici	—	52	3211	n.d.
Chaetomium globosum*†	—	219	1012	123
Gliocladium roseum*		320	1046	n.d.
Trichurus spiralis†‡		250	1020	n.d.

*After Grossbard and Harris (unpublished). Data on pathogens after Harris (1981).
†Incubation at 17°C.
‡After Grossbard (unpublished).
Data for *S. nodorum*, isolate HG2, are for linear growth rate. This strain was tested soon after isolation from the host, i.e. wheat (*Triticum aestivum*); note the high ED_{50}. All other data refer to the colony diameter.
IPSG = isopropylamine salt of glyphosate.
n.d. = not determined.

However, these fungi were isolated randomly from soil and were unidentified. Thus, several isolates may have been of the same species.

Interpretation of data from pure culture experiments requires a sense of proportion. If, for instance, high glyphosate concentrations (e.g. 100 µg g^{-1} of soil) are required for 50% inhibition, the practical implications are unlikely to be serious, as the herbicide is applied to vegetation and a proportion only may reach the soil.

Herbicides, including glyphosate, are rarely fungicidal, although they may extend the lag phase and/or reduce the growth rate. Thus, while fungicides may suppress completely growth of some fungi at a concentration as low as 1 µg g^{-1} (Smith and Long, 1980), 500 µg g^{-1} of glyphosate are required for a similar effect (*Table 11.1*).

Comparing other herbicides with glyphosate, S.L. Cooper (personal communication) has shown that while dalapon was less inhibitory than glyphosate, dinoseb was much more so.

Differential effect of ingredients of formulation of glyphosate as Roundup

The antifungal effects of glyphosate, formulated as Roundup, may be due largely to the n.h. ingredients (Quilty and Geoghegan, 1975; Grossbard and Harris, 1976). Test fungi, growing in the presence of the active herbicidal ingredient, the isopropylamine salt of glyphosate, showed normal development. However, when treated with the equivalent dose of glyphosate as Roundup, inhibition of growth, sporulation and of other responses occurred. By implication, it is concluded that the n.h. ingredients are largely responsible for the antifungal effects.

The n.h. ingredients themselves have been tested only on a few occasions, as they are not readily available. As shown in *Table 11.2*, their effects, at concentrations equivalent to those present in Roundup, on the growth of fungi were similar to those of the complete formulation. Bizarre outlines and sectoring of colonies can be caused in the same way by the n.h. ingredients as it is by Roundup at high concentrations. The differential activity of n.h. ingredients has been observed also with other herbicides such as paraquat, formulated as Gramoxone W (Wilkinson and Lucas, 1969). These authors believed that the surfactant facilitated the entry of paraquat through the fungal cell wall, although Smith and Lyon (1976) do not support this hypothesis. Changed permeability in fungi, resulting from the use of n.h. ingredients, has not been studied with glyphosate as Roundup. The phenomenon has, however, been examined in higher plants (see also Chapters 7 and 15).

Plant pathogens

A comparison of *Table 11.1* with *Table 11.2* may suggest that the pathogens are more sensitive to glyphosate than saprophytes. Growth inhibition of a pathogen by a herbicide may be desirable, as this may suppress over-wintering of pathogens (see p. 180) or their development on new plant tissues, such as volunteer plants. However, data are available for a few species only, which may not represent realistically the two populations.

Glyphosate is sometimes more active against specific pathogens than paraquat. Examples are *S. nodorum* (Beck), glume blotch of wheat, *Rhynchosporium secalis* (Oud) Davies, leaf blotch of barley and especially *F. nivale*, an important pathogen, which interferes with the successful establishment of grass seedlings (Grossbard and Harris, 1976; Harris, 1981).

Sporulation

Spore formation and subsequent germination were greatly inhibited in *S. nodorum* and *R. secalis* by glyphosate more than by paraquat (Grossbard and Harris, 1976; Harris and Grossbard, 1979). The herbicidal ingredients of both herbicides were inactive. Occasionally, glyphosate induced spore formation in cultures of *S. nodorum* when this property had been lost. Quilty and Geoghegan (1975) observed a reduction in the length of germ tubes of *Botrytis allii* Nunn, but after a brief lag normal growth was resumed.

Uptake of ^{14}C-labelled glyphosate by spores of S. nodorum

This uptake was studied by Harris and Grossbard (1979) and Harris (1981), who observed that spores of *S. nodorum* transferred apparently residual herbicide onto agar media containing no glyphosate. Subsequently, these spores, although previously washed, failed to germinate. Spores of *S. nodorum*, grown in a medium containing ^{14}C-labelled *N*-(phosphonomethyl)glycine, were radioactive even after repeated washing. Autoradiography of such spores revealed the presence of ^{14}C (*Figure 11.1*). It is, however, uncertain if the labelled material had been

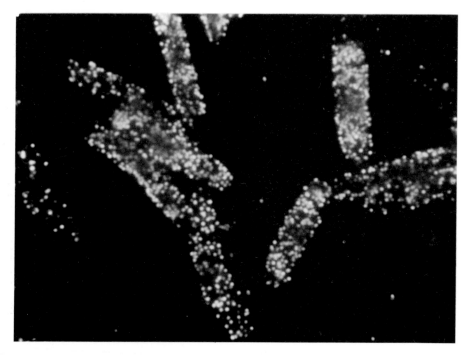

Figure 11.1. Autoradiographs of spores of *Septoria nodorum* from cultures grown in an agar medium, containing 160 μg g^{-1} glyphosate and 0.005 μCi ml l^{-1} ^{14}C-glyphosate, as *N*-(phosphonomethyl)glycine, using liquid emulsion. Group of strongly labelled spores from a coverslip pressed on to the surface of the agar culture, photographed in dark field. Magnification ×3215. The bright spots are images of silver grains and their density an indication of the radioactivity of the spores (by courtesy of D. Harris, 1981)

incorporated into the spores or if it was merely adsorbed onto the spore surface. The spores are contained in a cirrhus, a structure which consists of a mucilagenous substance. Glyphosate may have been adsorbed onto these mucilage residues, adhering to the surface of the spores, even after washing.

In these experiments, the labelled *N*-(phosphonomethyl)glycine was diluted with glyphosate as Roundup. Whether the n.h. ingredients also were transferred by the spores was not proven by this technique, but as they failed to germinate on media in the absence of herbicide, this is a possibility (Grossbard and Harris, 1976; Harris and Grossbard, 1979; Harris, 1981; see also p. 179).

RESPONSES IN SOIL

These responses differed greatly from those in pure culture. Counts of propagules were considerably higher in treated soil than in controls (Roslycky, 1982). In peat, even at 500 μg a.e. g^{-1} (Quilty and Geoghegan, 1976) a marked increase was observed. These authors believed that the n.h. ingredients are degraded in the soil and the products utilized by the microflora. The increase in propagule numbers may also result from enhanced spore formation by glyphosate, as observed occasionally in pure culture.

Yeasts

Few reports have been published. Cooper *et al.* (1978) tested 15 unidentified isolates at 50 μg ml^{-1} of glyphosate. Of these, 14 were inhibited. Roisch and Lingens (1980) used *Saccharomyces cerevisiae* (Meyen ex Hansen) as a test organism in their study on the biosynthesis of aromatic amino acids. A concentration of 2 mmol l^{-1} had no effect.

Actinomycetes and bacteria

These two groups have been studied to a lesser extent than the fungi.

RESPONSES IN PURE CULTURE

Few named cultures have been investigated. One early study was made by Jaworski (1972), who used *Rhizobium japonicum* (Kirchner) Buchanan as a test organism to investigate the biosynthesis of aromatic amino acids. The bacterium was inhibited by 10^{-5} mol l^{-1} glyphosate. Roisch and Lingens (1980) investigated *Escherichia coli* (Migula) Castellani and Chalmers, and *Pseudomonas aureofaciens* Klyver; the lag phase was extended and growth inhibited by 2 mmol l^{-1} glyphosate (*Table 11.3*)

Cooper *et al.* (1978) and Roslycky (1982) screened large numbers of unidentified soil isolates against a range of concentrations of glyphosate. Cooper *et al.* (1978), using liquid medium, observed a greater sensitivity of isolates of actinomycetes than of bacteria. Of the 40 isolates of actinomycetes tested, 94% were inhibited by 50 μg ml^{-1} glyphosate. The data do not distinguish between growth reduction and complete growth prevention, which renders difficult an assessment of the relative significance of these figures. In contrast, the results of Roslycky (1982) suggest actinomycetes isolates were more tolerant of glyphosate than were bacteria. At 50 μg a.e. ml^{-1}, all actinomycetes grew, but 52% of the bacteria failed to develop on agar medium at this concentration.

TABLE 11.3 The effect of glyphosate on the growth of bacteria

Named species	Substrate	Inhibition (% control)[*]	Conc. (μg g^{-1})	Reference
(a) Individual species				
Rhizobium japonicum		n.g.	10^{-5} mol l^{-1}	Jaworski (1972)
Salmonella typhimurium	Nutrient	n.g.	2 mmol l^{-1}	Roisch and Lingens (1980)
Escherichia coli	solution	n.g.	2 mmol l^{-1}	Roisch and Lingens (1980)
Pseudomonas aureofaciens		n.g.	2 mmol l^{-1}	Roisch and Lingens (1980)
Pseudomonas sp., glyphosate degrading	Soil	Stim.	80 μl kg^{-1}	Cérol and Seguin (1982)
(b) Unidentified isolates				
NUMBERS TESTED				
50	Nutrient solution	68[†]	50	Cooper *et al.* (1978)
349	Nutrient agar	9[*]	10	Roslycky (1982)
		52[*]	50	
		63[*]	100	
		98[*]	1000	
(c) Total propagules and physiological groups				
TOTAL PROPAGULES				
	Peat	Stim., T	300 a.e.	Quilty and Geoghegan (1976)
	Soil	Stim.	n.g.	Anon. (1979)
	Soil	Stim., T	100	Roslycky (1982)
	Soil	Stim.	1000	
	Soil	0	1–100	
PHYSIOL. GROUPS				
Cellulolytic	Peat	T, Stim.	300 a.e.	Quilty and Geoghegan (1976)
	Soil	Stim.	2660 a.e.	Grossbard and Wingfield (1978)
	Soil	LD$_{50}$	625	Kruglov, Gersh and Shtal'berg (1980)
Nitrifier	Peat	0	300 a.e.	Quilty and Geoghegan (1976)
	Soil	0	6.7	Fisichella, Tropea and Belligno (1979)
Saprophytes	Soil	LD$_{50}$	625	Kruglov, Gersh and Shtal'berg (1980)

[*]Percentage of isolates which failed to grow.
[†]Percentage of isolates inhibited to varying degree.
Conc. = concentration in μg a.i. g^{-1} unless otherwise stated; includes p.p.m., parts 10^{-6} and μg ml^{-1}.
n.g. = extent of inhibition not given.
Stim. = stimulation.
T = transient effect.

Comparison and interpretation of these data is difficult since different methods have been used and the isolates were not identified. Therefore, neither the spectrum of sensitivity nor the potential influence of the effects on soil fertility can be gauged. However, the identification of over 300 colonies, as were tested by Roslycky (1982), especially of actinomycetes, is a task few laboratories can attempt.

RESPONSES IN SOIL

These responses were similar to those of fungi in that propagule numbers, especially of actinomycetes, were greater in glyphosate-treated soil than in controls (Anon., 1979; Kruglov, Gersh and Shtal'berg, 1980). Increases in total propagules and those of physiological groups of bacteria are shown in *Table 11.3*. Roslycky (1982), who observed marked increases in actinomycetes and bacteria at concentrations as high as 1000 µg a.i. g^{-1}, states 'that this might reflect utilisation of glyphosate as a substrate . . .'. However, glyphosate is thought to be degraded co-metabolically (Sprankle, Meggitt and Penner, 1975; see also Chapter 9). Cérol and Seguin (1982) isolated a species of *Pseudomonas* from soil which they believe degrades glyphosate. They reported that this species multiplied profusely in treated soil. In peat, transient increases have been recorded of celluloytic and proteolytic bacteria, whereas nitrifying bacteria were little affected (Quilty and Geoghegan, 1976; Kruglov, Gersh and Shtal'berg, 1980; see also *Table 11.3*). However, nothing is known about the diversity of the species when counts of total propagules are made.

Algae

Few reports are available on the effect of glyphosate on this important group. Algae are a vital component of the aquatic and soil environments and can be exposed to glyphosate in both situations (see also Chapters 13, 14 and 18). The paucity of data is surprising, in view of the influence of glyphosate on photosynthesis (see also Chapter 5). This process was studied by Van Rensen (1974) using *Scenedesmus* sp. and oxygen release to measure effects on photosynthesis. Glyphosate, as the isopropylamine salt of *N*-(phosphonomethyl) glycine, without a surfactant, reduced this process, the effect increasing with time of incubation, light intensity and temperature (see also Chapters 5 and 18). However, washing of the cells after exposure, reduced the inhibitory effect.

Photosynthesis was also studied by Richardson, Frans and Talbert (1979) with *Euglena gracilis* Klebs. Changes in populations and chlorophyll production were recorded and compared with the effects of known photosynthesis inhibitors, fluometuron and metribuzin and with monosodium methane arsonate (MSMA), with special emphasis on time of exposure.

Biocidal effects on algae are often influenced by the size of the initial inoculum as well as by the duration of exposure. The first factor was not considered by the authors quoted here. However, the importance of inoculum density has been emphasized in recently developed guidelines of the Organisation for Economic Co-operation and Development (OECD) for assessing the growth inhibitory effects of chemicals on algae. A preference for small inocula (10^3–10^4 cells ml^{-1}) is stated, in order to avoid the problems associated with high biomass found towards the end of the test period (72 h or a × 16 increase in cell numbers in controls) (M.P. Greaves, personal communication).

Interaction between herbicide concentration and exposure time was investigated by Richardson, Frans and Talbert (1979). This varied between herbicides. *Euglena* was relatively tolerant of glyphosate, but at 1.2 × 10^{-3} mol l^{-1} severe reduction of cell numbers occurred. This reached a maximum after 76 h and then declined (see also Chapter 18). In contrast to fluometuron and metribuzin, glyphosate stimulated photosynthesis at higher concentrations (6 × 10^{-4} mol l^{-1}), especially after long exposure (96 h), but reduced it markedly at lower concentrations and shorter exposures (100 min). The authors suggested that decreased severity, after long exposure, may be due to a detoxification mechanism.

Although glyphosate reduced chlorophyll production, it stimulated slightly respiration. A dose-related reduction in cell numbers and growth rates was caused by glyphosate, applied as an aqueous solution of the isopropylamine salt in *Chlorella sorokiniana* Shihira. Cell destruction was observed at $23 \times 7 \times 10^{-6}$ mol l^{-1} a.e., but filtration through kaolinite removed these inhibitory effects (Christy, Karlander and Parochetti, 1981). The three above-mentioned algal species are used as bioassay organisms, as discussed by Richardson (see Chapter 18), who also gives figures on dose-related responses.

The effect of glyphosate on diatoms was studied by Sullivan, Sullivan and Bisalputra (1981). In the aquatic environment of a coastal forest, observed changes in population density were ascribed to habitat differences and seasonal variations and not to the activity of the herbicide (see also Chapter 14).

Although the algae tested in pure culture were sensitive to glyphosate, adverse effects in soil may be prevented by adsorption, as may be deduced from the kaolin effect on *Chlorella*, or by degradation. In the aquatic environment, if rapid water exchange takes place, recovery may occur, as suggested by laboratory experiments with fluometuron and metribuzin (Richardson, Frans and Talbert, 1979).

Total microflora

Rueppel *et al.* (1977) attempted to estimate the effects of glyphosate on all microorganisms in soil. Counts were made of progagules in soil samples 1 month after the application of 4 and 8 µg g^{-1} of glyphosate, which are low concentrations even in terms of field applications.

Counts of all colonies (fungi, bacteria and, presumably, actinomycetes) on each plate showed no adverse effects of glyphosate. Indeed, microbial development was enhanced in one of three soils. This agrees with other reports quoted earlier, where much higher glyphosate concentrations were used and where the three microbial groups were counted separately on selective media.

The functional approach

RESPIRATION

Physiological activities of microorganisms are investigated frequently in the context of side-effects of herbicides. This 'functional approach', as recommended in the EPA guidelines (Anon., 1978), is intended to reflect the microbial contribution to soil fertility. Respiration, expressed as carbon dioxide evolution or oxygen uptake, is a principal criterion, although it is not confined to the soil microflora; all living soil organisms respire.

Evolution of carbon dioxide

Evolution of CO_2 is widely regarded as a measure of the mineralization of organic matter. In unamended soils, CO_2 output from other sources is relatively small. Glyphosate, like other herbicides, is degraded in soil to CO_2. This contributes to the increase in CO_2 output above that of the control and which frequently follows application of the chemical. The use of glyphosate labelled with C-14 allows precise measurement of the contribution from the degradation of the herbicide and that of its metabolite aminomethylphosphonic acid (AMPA) (reviewed by Torstensson, see Chapter 9). Increased CO_2 output may be due also to enhanced biological activity. This, in turn, could accelerate microbial degradation of glyphosate (also reviewed in Chapter 9). Such increases are usually transient and CO_2 output quickly returns to control soil levels. However, in some soils reduction in CO_2 output has been observed. Its extent and duration was small, even when glyphosate was used at high (100 µg g^{-1}) concentrations (Marsh, Davies and Grossbard, 1977). The inhibition was less than caused by bentazone, at similar concentration in the same soil (Grossbard and Davies, 1976; Marsh *et al.*, 1978) or 2,4,5-T (Marsh and Davies, 1978).

Kruglov, Gersh and Stahl'berg (1980), applying much greater concentrations, up to 500 µg g^{-1}, found that, after an initial peak, CO_2 output in glyphosate-treated soil was still greater than in controls. However, Cérol and Seguin (1982) observed, in one soil out of four, reduced CO_2 output despite using field rates only.

Transient stimulations and inhibitions of CO_2 output may reflect interactions between natural fluctuations and glyphosate-induced changes in growth and activities of soil microorganisms. However, at present, these phenomena cannot be defined clearly or quantified.

Oxygen uptake

Uptake of oxygen was measured by Roslycky (1982) by the total 'microbiota', consisting of all propagules in the supernatant of a soil suspension (Roslycky, 1977), in the presence of various concentrations of glyphosate. In addition, the author estimated oxygen consumption by each of the three microbial groups—actinomycetes, bacteria and fungi—numerous unidentified soil isolates of each group being bulked together. Oxygen uptake of the total 'microbiota' was stimulated by low amounts (1–10 µg ml^{-1}), but inhibited by high concentrations of glyphosate (*Table 11.4*). The criterion for inhibition was the time required for oxygen uptake to begin and to utilize a given amount, i.e. 250 µl of oxygen.

Inhibition was greatest with actinomycetes, where oxygen uptake was almost arrested at 1000 µg ml^{-1}. The response of bacteria was slightly less severe and the fungi were least affected. Very high concentrations reduced the rate of oxygen uptake also. These results contrast with the enumeration data from soil samples, which show that numbers of propagules of all three groups had increased in glyphosate-treated soil.

The effect of glyphosate treatment may be due to the suppression of germination, and subsequent growth, of numerous spores in the respiration flasks. Unchecked germination in controls may lead to high oxygen uptake. This is especially true for the genus *Streptomyces*. Furthermore, the isolates were respiring

TABLE 11.4   The effect of glyphosate on oxygen uptake by three microbial groups and the total microbiota (after Roslycky, 1982)

Microbial group		*Significant inhibitory concentrations* (µg ml^{-1})*			
	Control	50	100	500	1000
		(hours required to consume 250 µl O_2)			
Total microbiota	9.4	11.30	11.9	13.40	14.4
Actinomycetes	8.7	9.50	9.7	23.25	C
Bacteria	4.65	7.10	23.5	C	C
Fungi	3.0	—	—	—	3.39

*Concentrations at which significant differences from control occurred at the times quoted at the 95% level.
C = O_2 uptake 'below the 250 µl level due to inhibitions'.
— = no figures quoted by author because 'response inconsistent'.

in a very artificial system, a liquid medium in close contact with the dissolved herbicide. Such intimate contact would not occur in field conditions nor would the very high concentrations at which inhibition was recorded. This artificiality and the unknown species diversity, make it difficult to assess the significance of the data. Thus, while Roslycky's observations are of academic interest, they do not necessarily indicate a severe impact on the agricultural environment.

The contribution of actinomycetes to overall soil respiration and their role in soil fertility has not been quantified. However, they are powerful decomposers of cellulose, protein and other complex organic molecules. More research is required to ascertain whether this observed inhibition of actinomycete respiration in the laboratory has any relevance to field conditions.

TRANSFORMATION OF NITROGEN

Mineralization of nitrogenous compounds in soil is an important microbial activity of undisputed relevance to soil fertility. Some herbicides have an adverse influence on the process, especially on its final stage, the conversion of NO_2^- to NO_3^- (Audus, 1964; Debona and Audus, 1970; Grossbard and Marsh, 1974; Greaves et al., 1976; Anderson, 1978). This inhibition occurs frequently at concentrations well above those used in agricultural practice, although occasionally it was recorded when field rates were applied (reviewed by Grossbard and Davies, 1976). No inhibitory effects of glyphosate on nitrate formation were observed at concentrations up to 25 μg g^{-1} (H.W. Frazier, personal communication). Even a high concentration of 100 μg g^{-1} failed to inhibit ammonification or nitrification. In fact, mineralization of nitrogen, expressed as the sum of NH_4^+ and NO_3^-, was increased in glyphosate-treated soil (Marsh, Davis and Grossbard, 1977; see also *Figure 11.2*).

Quilty and Geoghegan (1976), applying an even higher concentration, i.e. 300 μg a.e. g^{-1}, to cultivated peat observed a slight delay in nitrification. Glyphosate did not affect nitrification in situations where other herbicides were inhibitory. Working with the same soil and concentrations, as used with glyphosate by Marsh, Davies and Grossbard (1977), dalapon and pyrazone (Davies and Marsh, 1977), 2,4,5-T (Marsh and Davies, 1978) and bentazone (Marsh et al., 1978) all inhibited nitrification temporarily. Furthermore, accumulation of nitrates in glyphosate-treated soil was reported by Kruglov, Gersh and Stahl'berg (1980). The amount of total nitrogen was not affected significantly by treatment with glyphosate, not even at 20 kg ha^{-1} (Bliev and Martynov, 1981).

The reasons for stimulation of nitrate formation may be twofold. An appreciable amount of nitrogen may become available on the degradation of the glyphosate molecule, especially when a high rate is used and nitrates may be formed (H.W. Frazier, personal communication). However, it is more likely that the increase in nitrate may be due to proliferation of nitrifying bacteria (*Table 11.3c*).

NITROGEN FIXATION

Interactions between glyphosate and legumes are important, not only when legumes are the sole crop, but also in renovation of pastures and in intensively managed grassland (see also Chapter 26). It is thus essential that this herbicide should not reduce the numbers and nodulation efficiency of indigenous or inoculated rhizobia.

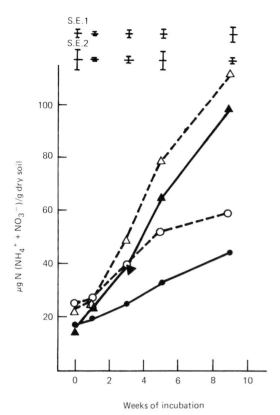

Figure 11.2. Effect of 100 p.p.m. glyphosate on nitrogen mineralization (continuous aeration after first week of incubation). Triangle soil: ▲———▲, control; △----△, glyphosate. S.E.1 shows standard errors. Boddington Barn soil: ●———●, control; ○-----○, glyphosate. S.E.2 shows standard errors (from Marsh, Davies and Grossbard, 1977, by courtesy of Blackwell Scientific Publications Ltd)

Baltazar and Brontonegro (1979) observed curtailed nodulation of soya beans by glyphosate at 0–2 kg ha^{-1}. They ascribed this to herbicide injury to the root *per se* and not to inhibition of the nitrogen-fixing ability of rhizobia. This greater sensitivity of the legume, than the rhizobium, to herbicides occurs with other compounds, such as linuron and asulam (Grossbard 1970; Grossbard and Davies, 1976). On the other hand, growth inhibition of *Rhizobium japonicum* in liquid culture by as little as 10^{-5} mol l^{-1} glyphosate has been reported (Jaworski, 1972).

DENITRIFICATION

Only one account on denitrification could be found in the literature. Glyphosate at 2.6 kg ha^{-1} had no effect on this process (Müller *et al.*, 1981).

CELLULOSE DECOMPOSITION

The potential influence of glyphosate on microbial degradation of cellulose is of special practical importance. The herbicide is applied in reduced cultivation and direct drilling (see also Chapter 27), coming into close contact with straw, one of the most important sources of cellulose. Although celluloytic fungi show varying degrees of sensitivity to glyphosate (Grossbard 1974; 1976; Grossbard and Wingfield, 1978; Lönsjö *et al.*, 1980, see also *Table 11.1*), many species tolerate amounts of glyphosate likely to be found under field conditions. Furthermore, numbers of cellulolytic bacteria were increased in glyphosate-treated soil (*Table 11.3c*).

There is evidence that the ability of cellulolytic microorganisms to degrade cellulose is not impaired by glyphosate. H.W. Frazier (personal communication) reported that ^{14}C-labelled cellulose, treated with 6 and 28 kg ha^{-1} of glyphosate, was degraded in soil at the same rate as untreated controls over a 12-week incubation period. Calico, a cellulose substrate sprayed with glyphosate and either buried or placed on the surface of soil, decomposed slightly faster than if untreated or treated with aminotriazole, another herbicide used in direct drilling (Grossbard and Wingfield, 1978). E.B. Roslycky (personal communication) also reported stimulation of cellulose decomposition by glyphosate. Bliev and Martynov (1981) observed no adverse effects on cellulose (filter paper) decomposition in forest nursery soil. Stimulation occurred at some sampling dates, even at 20 kg a.i. ha^{-1}.

ENZYMIC ACTIVITIES

In soil

Although the precise relationship between soil enzymes and soil fertility has yet to be defined (Davies and Greaves, 1981), accumulated enzymes may play an important role in nutrient cycling (Lethbridge, Bull and Burns, 1981). These activities are not confined to the microflora, as many other soil organisms excrete enzymes. Consequently, it has been questioned whether enzyme activities are valid criteria for assessing side-effects of herbicides on the soil microflora (Greaves *et al.*, 1980). Although methods have been developed for estimating enzyme activities in soil, they are open to criticism and interpretation of results is fraught with difficulties (Anderson, 1978; Greaves *et al.*, 1980; Davies and Greaves, 1981). Nevertheless, attempts have been made to elucidate potential interactions between soil enzymes and herbicides (reviewed by Grossbard, 1976; Grossbard and Davies, 1976; Anderson, 1978; Davies and Greaves, 1981).

Urease has received most attention because of its involvement in nitrogen transformation. Glyphosate, at rates up to 5.4 kg a.e. ha^{-1}, had no effect on urease, phosphatase and dehydrogenase (*Figure 11.3*). Only at the high rate of 21 kg a.e. ha^{-1} was a reduction of urease activity observed, but the effect was not statistically significant (Davies and Greaves, 1981). In contrast, soil dehydrogenase activity was significantly increased. The effect, however, was transient and smaller than could be accounted for by natural variation.

While the addition of lucerne (*Medicago sativa*) meal increased the activity of all enzymes, a significant interaction with the herbicide was not observed. Lethbridge,

Figure 11.3. The effect of 21.6 kg ha^{-1} glyphosate on (a) phosphatase, (b) dehydrogenase and (c) urease activities in soil. (○) Control, (△) glyphosate; open symbols, soil plus lucerne meal; closed symbols, unsupplemented soil. Bars show standard errors (from Davies and Greaves, 1981, by courtesy of Blackwell Scientific Publications Ltd)

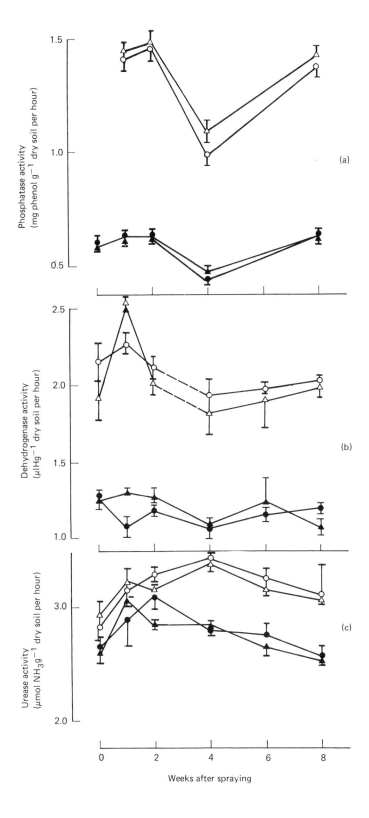

Weeks after spraying

Bull and Burns (1981) compared effects on urease and 1,3-β-glucanase of 2,4-D, di-allate, benzoylprop-ethyl, malathion and glyphosate. At five times the recommended field rates, both enzymes were unaffected. At 0.1-1.0 kg ha^{-1} glyphosate, as well as 2,4-D, enhanced activity of 1,3-β-glucanase, while di-allate curtailed it. Urease activity was not influenced.

Nitrogenase

This is the most important enzyme involved in nitrogen fixation. Interaction with glyphosate in soils has been studied only by Müller *et al.* (1981). Nitrogenase activity was lower in one of two soils, treated with 2.6 kg ha^{-1} of glyphosate, 28 days after application. However, Müller *et al.* (1981) believe that the difference in the response of the two soils was due to different density of the vegetation cover removed by the herbicide. The variation in the response may be related to differences in the C/N ratio in the two soils.

In pure culture

Extensive research has been done on the effect of glyphosate on the enzymes involved in the biosynthesis of aromatic amino acids in higher plants. Bacteria were also used, as they too have an aromatic amino acid pathway (Jaworski, 1972). Glyphosate inhibited the growth of the test bacteria (*Table 11.3a*) by interfering with this important biosynthesis. Among the enzymes inhibited were phospho-2-oxo-3-deoxyheptonate aldolase and 3-dehydroquinate synthase. These effects could be eliminated by the addition of Co^{2+}. Anthranilate synthase was also inhibited. In this case, addition of Mg^{2+} restored its activity (Roisch and Lingens, 1980). The subject is reviewed by Cole (see Chapter 5) and Duke and Hoagland (see Chapter 6). As only a few enzymes of considerable diversity and specificity have been examined, either in pure culture or soil, a generalization as to the effect of glyphosate on the enzymic activities of the microflora is not possible.

Decomposition of treated vegetation

Straw

The success of reduced cultivation or direct drilling relies, to some extent, on the rapid disposal of surface litter after harvest or chemical sward destruction (see also Chapters 26 and 27). While burning is the most efficient way of disposal, considerable difficulties are encountered (reviewed by Elliott, 1975; Ellis, 1979). The most desirable method is natural decomposition *in situ*. This, however, is a slow process, especially for straw. If herbicides were to delay this further, repercussions might be serious. Where glyphosate is applied, either pre-harvest or post-harvest, for weed control in cereals, residues may remain in the straw, at least for a short period. The manufacturers recommend that straw sprayed with glyphosate pre-harvest must not be used in horticulture (Anon., 1982). Precise data on this subject are scarce and more research is needed. Such residues of glyphosate may affect the rate of straw decomposition and therefore interfere with digestibility for animals, ease of composting and numerous other uses.

Glyphosate residues from post-harvest applications are those most likely to influence decomposition of stubbles and straw remains in the field. Lönsjö *et al.*

(1980) demonstrated that 10% of the initial amount of ^{14}C-glyphosate applied to barley (*Hordeum vulgare*) stubble were detected 1 day after application. This was equivalent to 120 p.p.m. of ^{14}C-glyphosate in the straw. One month later, after the straw had been incorporated with soil, 25% had been evolved as [14]CO_2. The ^{14}C-glyphosate as *N*-(phosphonomethyl)glycine, was diluted with the formulated compound, Roundup. It is not known how much of this was retained by the straw, although this may be important. Thus, in pure culture, the growth of the fungus *Chaetomium globosum*, while tolerating relatively large concentrations of glyphosate, is reduced to some extent by Roundup and by the n.h. ingredients, but barely by the isopropylamine salt of glyphosate. Thus, although residues of the labelled glyphosate in straw would not affect it (*Table 11.2*), the n.h. ingredients, if still present in straw, might exert an influence. This applies to other celluloytic fungi such as fusaria, which are fairly sensitive to glyphosate.

Grossbard and collaborators have shown, in laboratory and field experiments, that glyphosate rarely affects straw decomposition (Grossbard and Cooper 1974; Grossbard and Davies, 1976; Grossbard and Harris, 1979; 1981). Comparisons were made with other herbicides, used in non-ploughing techniques, such as aminotriazole (as Weedazol TL) and paraquat (as Gramoxone W). Criteria used were loss in weight of straw and oxygen uptake by the microflora on the straw.

LABORATORY EXPERIMENTS

Loss in weight

This was not affected by glyphosate in most experiments, although variable transitory inhibitions were sometimes recorded. *Figure 11.4* illustrates the effect of glyphosate and paraquat at six and nine times greater than the recommended field rate, on the decomposition of stems and leaves of treated straw, incubated on the soil surface in the laboratory. Glyphosate-sprayed straw behaved like the controls, with leaves decomposing faster than stems. Addition of urea accelerated decomposition of glyphosate-treated straw more than that of the paraquat treatment.

FIELD EXPERIMENTS

Trials, using agricultural rates, gave variable results. In one experiment, three herbicides—aminotriazole, glyphosate and paraquat—enhanced decomposition, but the overall rate was very slow (Grossbard and Harris, 1979). In a second trial, glyphosate had no effect, but paraquat delayed decomposition to a small, but statistically significant, extent (Grossbard, unpublished). However, Pollard (1979) showed that 5 months after spraying with paraquat and glyphosate, the smallest amount of recoverable straw was on plots sprayed with paraquat, while a similar quantity was recorded on both control and glyphosate-treated plots (*Table 11.5*). The discrepancies between these data may be due to large differences between the experimental methods used by these authors and perhaps also to differences in microflora composition and environmental conditions. However, Grossbard and Harris (1981) also showed that, occasionally, paraquat enhanced straw decay and glyphosate caused small transient reductions. Effects of these herbicides on straw decay were normally too small to be of agricultural importance, as straw decay *in situ* is already very slow.

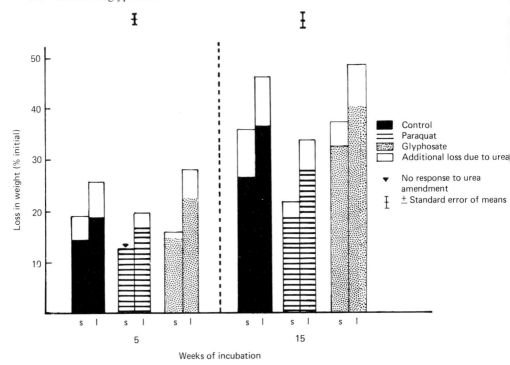

Figure 11.4. The effect of herbicides and of urea on the loss in weight of wheat straw, stems (s) and leaves (l), incubated on the soil surface. Rates: paraquat, stems 4.7 kg a.i. ha^{-1}, leaves 21 kg a.i. ha^{-1} to allow for larger surface area; glyphosate, stems 9.4 kg a.i. ha^{-1}, leaves 42.3 kg a.i. ha^{-1} (Grossbard and Harris, unpublished)

TABLE 11.5   Effect of paraquat and glyphosate on straw decomposition in the field (after Pollard, 1979).

| | Amount of straw recovered (g d.m. m^{-2})* | | | | |
| | Days after application | | | | |
	8	42	76	105	154
Paraquat	534	473	405	433	374
Glyphosate	502	550	464	438	434
No herbicide	476	440	439	428	458
S.E.±	20.1	16.6	15.7	15.1	17.0

*Initial amount applied, 500 g d.m. m^{-2}.
d.m. = dry matter.

Respiration of straw microflora

Respiration of straw microflora is regarded as an indirect estimate of the rate and extent of degradation of straw, but must be distinguished from soil respiration, where total biological activity is measured. A straw-colonizing microflora, respiring actively, is more likely to decompose the substrate faster than one with a low rate of respiration. Both oxygen uptake and CO_2 evolution may be measured.

OXYGEN UPTAKE

Glyphosate exerted either no effect or stimulated oxygen uptake (Grossbard and Harris, 1979; 1981). Only in one of four experiments was oxygen uptake reduced. The tolerance of straw-decomposing microflora to glyphosate was apparent when urea-treated wheat straw, sprayed at 9.4 kg a.i. ha^{-1}, was incubated in soil for 21 weeks. The weight loss from both treatment and control was 42%. Addition of a second dose of urea produced a rise in oxygen uptake of more than 200 μl O_2 h^{-1} g^{-1}. This implies that, despite glyphosate treatment, the straw microflora was still in a sufficiently active state to continue straw degradation after replenishing the nitrogen supply (Grossbard and Harris, 1981).

CARBON DIOXIDE EVOLUTION

This was examined with ^{14}C-labelled rye (*Secale cereale*) straw, sprayed with either paraquat or glyphosate and incubated on the soil surface in a continuous gas flow system (Grossbard, 1979). Decomposition of the straw progressed at a fast rate. Neither herbicide influenced it significantly. In another experiment, where decay was very slow, due to a static system being used with inadequate supply of moisture, both herbicides curtailed $^{14}CO_2$ evolution (Grossbard, 1979). This difference suggests that the effects of these two herbicides may perhaps depend on the rate of straw degradation, possibly because the microflora, when under stress, is more susceptible to glyphosate than in more favourable conditions.

Interaction between fungi, herbicides and straw decay

Chaetomium globosum, the efficient cellulose-degrading fungus, when grown in pure culture on agar or autoclaved straw, tolerates large amounts of glyphosate (*Tables 11.1* and *11.2*), but is sensitive to low concentrations of aminotriazole or paraquat (Grossbard and Harris, 1979). *C. globosum*, commonly present on untreated straw, was also readily isolated from glyphosate-treated material, but not from that sprayed with paraquat. While large fruiting bodies, perithecia, were present in straw sprayed with up to 42 kg ha^{-1} of glyphosate, they were absent in straw treated with paraquat at 4.7 kg ha^{-1}. Thus, the tolerance of glyphosate shown by *C. globosum*, in pure culture, was confirmed in its normal habitat—decaying straw. This is one occasion where it is legitimate to draw analogies from the behaviour of a fungus in pure culture to field conditions.

Similar observations have been made with other straw-decomposing fungi such as *Doratomyces nanus* Corda and *Trichurus spiralis* Clem and Shear (Grossbard and Harris, 1979). On the other hand, some cellulose-decomposing fungi, such as some *Fusarium* spp., are susceptible to glyphosate but are fairly resistant to paraquat. This may be one reason why straw decomposition, following paraquat treatment, is sometimes stimulated (Pollard, 1979). Thus, microbial species composition may influence the effect of a herbicide on straw decay. In addition environmental conditions, such as temperature, moisture of soil and atmosphere, nutrient levels in the decaying straw and the soil, are important factors affecting straw decay directly and indirectly by changing species composition.

Decomposition of dead vegetation other than straw

Techniques such as direct drilling and reseeding or renovation of grasslands (see also Chapter 26) produce much dead plant material. Little work has been done on the effects of glyphosate on the decay of dead weeds. H.W. Frazier (personal communication) studied its effects on the decomposition of ^{14}C-labelled leaf litter in soil. He did not observe any inhibitory effects during 6 weeks following the applications of 5 and 25 µg g^{-1} (see also Chapter 10). The decomposition of rye grass (*Lolium perenne*) was investigated by Grossbard (unpublished). Neither glyphosate nor paraquat inhibited decomposition of rye grass in laboratory and field experiments.

Table 11.6 compares weight loss of rye grass and straw treated with field rates of

TABLE 11.6   The effect of glyphosate and paraquat on loss in weight of straw and rye grass (*Lolium perenne*), decomposing in the field for 8 weeks (Grossbard, unpublished).

Treatment	Straw	Rye grass
	(loss in weight, % initial)	
Control	11	46
Glyphosate	12	46
Paraquat	8	48
SEM±	0.72	2.–

Rates: glyphosate 1.5 kg ha^{-1}; paraquat 0.5 kg ha^{-1}.

herbicide. Straw weight loss was inhibited by paraquat only, glyphosate being ineffective. This difference, which was absent with grass, may reflect differences in the cell wall composition. Grossbard and Morrison (unpublished) showed that, during decomposition over 15 weeks, paraquat-treated leaves of wheat (*Triticum aestivum*) straw retained a greater percentage of cellulose and hemi-cellulose than those of untreated straw. There is much less cellulose in the cell walls of rye grass than in straw. Therefore, the curtailment of decomposition of a small amount of initial cellulose or hemi-cellulose by paraquat was not sufficiently marked for significant differences from the glyphosate treatment to become apparent. With very young rye grass, decomposition was accelerated by both herbicides, but especially by glyphosate resulting, after several weeks, in less residual cellulose and hemi-cellulose in glyphosate-treated grass than in that sprayed with paraquat or in controls.

Effects on plant diseases

Interrelations between herbicides and plant disease incidence are very complex. Despite extensive investigation, full understanding requires further research. The topic has been reviewed by Heitefuss (1972), Katan and Eshel (1973), Altman and Campbell (1979) and Papavizas and Lewis (1979).

Many herbicides, including glyphosate, may inhibit growth, spore formation, germination and the aggressiveness of plant pathogens, properties which might be utilized for disease control. Cereal pathogens, especially those infecting the leaf and ear, over-winter on straw residues and stubble. Thus, direct drilling and reduced cultivation enhance their survival and ability to serve as inoculum for the succeeding crop. They also spread to seedlings arising from shed grains. This subject has been discussed by Yarham and Hirst (1975), Hornby (1975), Stedman (1977; 1982), Harris and Grossbard (1978; 1979), Harris (1981) and Yarham and Norton (1981). Examples of such fungi are *Rhynchosporium secalis,* causing leaf blotch of barley (Stedman, 1977; 1982); *Septoria nodorum,* causing glume blotch of wheat (Harrower, 1974; Holmes and Colhoun, 1975; Harris and Grossbard, 1978; reviewed by Harris, 1981) and *S. tritici,* causing leaf blotch of wheat (Holmes and Colhoun, 1975). Furthermore, over-wintering of those cereal pathogens which are primarily soil borne, is also enhanced by straw debris remaining on or just below the soil surface (Hornby, 1975; reviewed by Harris, 1981).

Pathogens, colonizing straw remains, will be exposed to residual herbicide for some time and glyphosate may inhibit their growth and/or sporulation. In contrast, pathogen development may be enhanced by the additional nutrient supply provided from decomposing straw. Thus, disease severity will be the resultant of these two factors.

Laboratory and greenhouse experiments

Detailed experiments have been carried out, both in the laboratory and in the field, with *S. nodorum.* In pure culture, the fungus was susceptible to concentrations of glyphosate which are likely to be applied in the field (*Table 11.2*). In tests of fungal aggressiveness on detached wheat leaves, spores, from cultures, treated with glyphosate, and then washed, produced fewer lesions than untreated spores, possibly due to a carry-over of residues by spores which may have curtailed infection. Also, the number of pycnidia, asexual reproductive bodies, was reduced, especially at high inoculum when the detached leaves became moribund (*Table 11.7*) (Harris and Grossbard, 1979; Harris, 1981). Certain inconsistencies in results between experiments were probably due to interactions of inoculum density and the state of senescence of the detached leaves.

Field experiments

The effects of glyphosate on survival and sporulation of the cereal pathogens *S. nodorum* (Harris and Grossbard, 1978; Harris, 1981) and *R. secalis* (Stedman, 1982) have been examined. In both experiments, the cereals (wheat and barley, respectively) were sprayed pre- or post-harvest with glyphosate and paraquat at recommended rates. Volunteer plants were included in the *R. secalis* trials. Monthly counts showed that spores of *S. nodorum* survived and proliferated for at

TABLE 11.7   **Effect of glyphosate on the production of pycnidia by** *Septoria nodorum* **on detached wheat** (*Triticum aestivum*) **leaves after 23 days incubation at 18°C (after Harris and Grossbard, 1979)**

Treatment	Herbicide concentration (μg a.i. g^{-1})	Mean nos. of pycnidia/leaf* Inoculum density (spores ml^{-1})						
		$5 \times 10^6 \pm$ S.E.		$1 \times 10^6 \pm$ S.E.		$5 \times 10^4 \pm$ S.E.		$1 \times 10^4 \pm$ S.E.
No herbicide (control)	0	7.4	1.99	6.1	1.91	12.2	5.89	12.6	5.42
Roundup***	160	2.6	0.84	1.9	0.79	9.8	3.71	7.1	1.66

*Means of 18 replicates, ± S.E. of mean number of pycnidia per leaf.
***Herbicide treatment significantly different from control at $P = 0.001$.

least 6 months, indicating the stimulating effect of accumulated straw residues on pathogen survival. Variation in numbers between sampling times was great and no significant differences were found between herbicide treatment and control (Harris and Grossbard, 1978; Harris, 1981). In *R. secalis,* Stedman (1982) observed reduction in spore numbers on barley stubbles by both chemicals, but this was not consistent. Glyphosate reduced spore numbers on volunteer plants, as did paraquat, after a transient rise. Spore viability of *R. secalis* was not influenced by either herbicide as found also for *S. nodorum* (Harris, 1981).

These results contrast with those from experiments using agar cultures and detached leaves. Here, glyphosate inhibited markedly vegetative growth, spore formation and subsequent development (*Tables 11.2* and *11.7*). This discrepancy between laboratory and field experiments with *S. nodorum* may be due to differential activity of the ingredients of the formulation. The antifungal activity of the formulation is due to the complex of n.h. constituents (*Table 11.2*) and not the isopropylamine salt of glyphosate, which is relatively ineffective. The fate of these n.h. ingredients on the straw and in the soil is unknown. It is possible that they are degraded rapidly in the field and so are ineffective. In laboratory experiments with *R. secalis* (Grossbard and Harris, 1976; Harris, 1981), only the formulated compound has been tested. By analogy with *S. nodorum*, it is possible that a marked decrease in spore formation could occur also in *R. secalis* due to the influence of ingredients other than the isopropylamine salt of glyphosate.

Effect of recolonization

Glyphosate is frequently applied as a desiccant, serving as a harvest aid (Whigham and Stoller, 1978). The desiccated plant remains may provide a suitable substrate for competitive, saprophytic colonization by pathogens and, consequently, may furnish inoculum for re-infection or further primary invasion.

Cerkauskus, Dhingra and Sinclair (1982) investigated the effect of herbicides on the pathogen *Macrophomina phaseolina* Petrak, which colonizes dead soya bean (*Glycine max*) stems after desiccation. Sclerotia—resting, reproductive structures—are formed on these stems, serving as the principal source of inoculum for further infection. These authors compared glyphosate, paraquat, sodium chlorate and sodium borate in a field trial to ascertain whether they would prevent colonization of soya bean stems by the fungus because other herbicides have been shown to reduce survival of *M. phaseolina* (Filho and Dhingra, 1980). Glyphosate and the other herbicides, reduced colonization in one soil only, which had a high content of organic matter. A significant difference between herbicides was not observed.

Other effects

Glyphosate could also influence re-infection by controlling weeds and volunteer plants. Eradication of such plants might be beneficial if they act as alternate hosts. Conversely, it could be harmful by providing plant residues as substrate for colonization. Thus, Stedman (1982) showed that volunteer plants of barley, killed by paraquat or glyphosate, served as a source of inoculum for *R. secalis*. Another indirect effect is the enhancement of the development of *Fusarium culmorum* by acetic acid, exuded by dead or dying rhizomes, of *Agropyron repens* killed with glyphosate (Penn and Lynch, 1982). These authors suggest that an interval of about

7 weeks, between spraying *A. repens* and sowing the new barley crop, may prevent damage to barley seedlings (Penn and Lynch, 1981).

This is an interesting aspect of the interaction of herbicides with plant disease incidence. Glyphosate blocks the production of the phytoalexin glyceollin in soya beans, inoculated with an incompatible strain (race) of either the fungal pathogen *Phytophthora megasperma* f.c. *glycinea* Drechsl (Keen, Holliday and Yoshikawa, 1982) or with the bacterium *Pseudomonas syringae*, p.v. *glycinea* van Hall (Holliday and Keen, 1982). The authors demonstrated that the inhibition of glyceollin production rendered soya beans susceptible even to incompatible strains. The production of this phytoalexin is associated with the biosynthesis of phenylalanine and tyrosine. Pre-feeding glyphosate-treated soya beans with these two aromatic amino acids restored glyceollin production and total expression of resistance to the fungus. It only restored partially resistance to the bacterium (see also Chapter 6).

Conclusions

Although more research is required to clarify the interactions of glyphosate with the microflora a few common threads lead through the labyrinth of observations.

In pure culture, many microbial species are inhibited by glyphosate. This effect is selective, variable in magnitude and frequently dose related. In terms of agricultural practice, inhibitory effects, especially of the celluloytic fungi, occur at concentrations well above those normally used in agriculture. Moreover, the amount of herbicide which reaches the soil is smaller than that applied, because a certain proportion of glyphosate, which is foliar applied, is retained by the vegetation. Also glyphosate is adsorbed and degraded in soil; one reason why the microorganisms examined tolerate generally the glyphosate in soil much better than in pure culture in laboratory media. Furthermore, the numbers of propagules of all microbial groups in soil increased following glyphosate treatment. Despite the shortcomings of techniques for enumerating microbial propagules in soil, this observation implies utilization by soil microflora of either glyphosate itself or its degradation products.

Little is known about the effect of the metabolite of glyphosate, AMPA, on soil microorganisms. This represents another useful area of future research, as is the fate of the n.h. ingredients of the formulation. The inhibitory effect of glyphosate on some of the fungi tested may be due largely to the n.h. constituents of the formulation. The phenomenon has been investigated in fungi only, but may occur in other microbial groups also. The cereal pathogens investigated here were clearly inhibited by formulated glyphosate in laboratory experiments. However, in field trials no effects occurred. It is possible that the n.h. constituents had been degraded long before the active ingredient, which would have no effect on the fungi. On the other hand, it is feasible that under field conditions, pathogens may exhibit enhanced resistance to a herbicide.

A great gap in our knowledge, of the response of soil microorganisms to glyphosate, is the lack of data on the behaviour of the microflora of the rhizosphere. Glyphosate is exuded by the roots and, therefore, will be in close contact with the rhizosphere population before the chemical becomes adsorbed. Perhaps it is the rhizosphere microflora which is responsible for the rapid degradation of glyphosate.

In the rare instances when glyphosate delayed decomposition of straw, the extent was too small to be of significant practical implication. However, the discrepancies in the behaviour of paraquat and glyphosate, in both laboratory and field experiments, call for an enquiry into the environmental conditions which determine the interaction of herbicides and straw decay, and finally of over-wintering of pathogens on the herbicide-treated vegetation remains. An important area of research is the determination of the persistence of residues in straw and other dead vegetation; few data are available in this field.

A reassuring aspect of the behaviour of glyphosate is that it does not curtail nitrification in the soil, an activity affected adversely by some other herbicides. Mineralization of nitrogen, even at high concentrations of glyphosate, is enhanced, as is another important function—cellulose decomposition.

Investigations on microbial responses to herbicides must continue, even though EPA and other regulatory bodies no longer require data of such investigations for registration purposes. More intensive research eventually may prove, unequivocally, the claim made by Rueppel et al. (1977) that glyphosate 'has also been shown to have minimal effect on microflora'. On present evidence, however, it may be concluded that soil fertility per se is unlikely to be impaired by the agricultural use of glyphosate.

Acknowledgements

I wish to thank the members of the Information Department of the Weed Research Organization (WRO), Mrs Barbara Burton and Mr J. Mayall, for their help in the literature search, and Dr K. Goulding of Hatfield Polytechnic and Mr M. Greaves of WRO for critical discussion of this review. My thanks are also due to Mr B.O. Bartlett of WRO for statistical advice on the data of the work by Grossbard and Harris, and Grossbard, quoted here, to Mrs S. Cooper of WRO for permission to quote some of her unpublished data and to Mrs D. Rogers and Mrs M. Locke for typing this chapter.

References

ALTMAN, J. and CAMPBELL, C.L. (1979). Herbicides and environment: a review on stimulating and inhibiting interactions with plant diseases, Zeitschrift für Pflanzenkrankheiten und Pflanzenschutz, **86**, 290–302.
ANDERSON, J.R. (1978). Pesticide effects on non-target soil microorganisms, in Pesticide Microbiology, pp. 247–312 (Eds. I.R. Hill and S.J.L. Wright). London and New York; Academic Press.
ANON. (1978).Environmental Protection Agency, Registration of pesticides in the United States, Federal Register, **43**(132), II, 29696–29741.
ANON. (1979). Environmental toxicology; effect of pesticides on non-target organisms, in Research Branch Report, 1976–78, Agriculture Canada (1979), pp. 250–251.
ANON. (1981). Environmental Protection Agency, Guidelines for registering pesticides in the United States, subpart N, in Chemistry Requirements: Environmental Fate, draft June 15, 1981, pp. 38–39.
ANON. (1982). Pre-harvest use of Roundup herbicide, in Product Information Guide, Monsanto Agricultural Division, 1982/83.

AUDUS, L.J. (1964). Herbicide behaviour in soil. II. Interactions with soil microorganisms, in *The Physiology and Biochemistry of Herbicides*, pp. 190–203 (Ed. L.J. Audus). London and New York; Academic Press.

BAIRD, D.D., UPCHURCH, R.P., HOMESLEY, W.P. and FRANZ, J.E. (1971). Introduction of a new broad spectrum, post emergence herbicide with utility for herbaceous perennial weed control, *Proceedings of the 26th North Central Weed Conference*, pp. 64–68.

BALTAZAR, A.M. and BRONTONEGRO, S. (1979). Effects of trifluralin, glyphosate and U-44, 078 on nodulation and nitrogen fixation of soybeans (*Glycine max* (L) Merr.) *Philippine Journal of Weed Science*, **6,** 69–80.

BLIEV, YU,K. and MARTYNOV, A.N. (1981). The influence of glyphosate on the fertility of a sodpodsolic soil, *Khimiya v Sel'skom Khozyaistive*, **19,** 51–54.

CERKAUSKAS, R.F., DHINGRA, O.D. and SINCLAIR, J.B. (1982). Effect of herbicides on competitive saprophytic colonization by *Macrophomina phaseolina* of soybean stems, *Transactions of the British Mycological Society*, **79,** 201–205.

CÉROL, E. and SEGUIN, G. (1982). The influence of herbicides on the microflora of soils of vineyards in Bordeaux, *Comptes Rendues des Séances Academie d'Agriculture*, **68,** 804–807.

CHRISTY, S.L., KARLANDER, E.P. and PAROCHETTI, J.V. (1981). Effects of glyphosate on the growth rate of *Chlorella*, *Weed Science*, **29,** 5–7.

COOPER, S.L., WINGFIELD, G.I., LAWLEY, R. and GREAVES, M.P. (1978). Miniaturized methods for testing the toxicity of pesticides to microorganisms, *Weed Research*, **18,** 105–107.

DAVIES, H.A. and GREAVES, M.P. (1981). Effects of some herbicides on soil enzyme activities, *Weed Research* **21,** 205–209.

DAVIES, H.A. and MARSH, J.A.P. (1977). The effect of herbicides on respiration and transformation of nitrogen in two soils. II. Dalapon, pyrazone and trifluralin, *Weed Research*, **17,** 373–378.

DEBONA, A.C. and AUDUS, L.J. (1970). Studies on the effects of herbicides on soil nitrification, *Weed Research*, **10,** 250–263.

DOMSCH, K.H., JAGNOW, G. and ANDERSON, T.-H. (1983). An ecological concept for the assessment of side-effects of agrochemicals on soil microorganisms, *Residue Reviews*, **86,** 65–105.

ELLIOTT, J.G. (1975). Reduced cultivation and direct drilling in farming systems, *Outlook on Agriculture*, **8,** 250–253.

ELLIS, F.B. (1979). Agronomic problems from straw residues with particular reference to reduced cultivation and direct drilling in Britain, in *Straw Decay and its Effect on Disposal and Utilization*, pp. 11–20 (Ed. E. Grossbard). Chichester; Wiley.

FILHO, E.S. and DHINGRA, O.D. (1980). Effect of herbicides on survival of *Macrophomina phaseolina* in soil, *Transactions of the British Mycological Society*, **74,** 61–64.

FISICHELLA, G., TROPEA, M. and BELLIGNO, A. (1979). Biochemical fertility of soils in eastern Sicily. VIII. Influence of herbicides on the nitrifying quality of the soils, *Tecnica Agricola*, **33,** 10–20.

GREAVES, M.P. (1979). Measurement and interpretation of side-effects of pesticides on microbial processes, *Proceedings of the British Crop Protection Conference—Pests and Diseases*, **2,** 469–477.

GREAVES, M.P., COOPER, S.L., DAVIES, H.A., MARSH, J.A.P. and WINGFIELD, G.I. (1976). Herbicides and soil microorganisms, *CRC Critical Reviews in Microbiology*, **5,** 1–38.

GREAVES, M.P. and MALKOMES, H.P. (1980). Effects on soil microflora, in *Interactions between Herbicides and the Soil*, pp. 223–253 (Ed. R.J. Hance). London and New York; Academic Press.

GREAVES, M.P., POOLE, N.J., DOMSCH, K.H., JAGNOW, G. and VERSTRAETE, W. (1980). Recommended tests for assessing the side-effects of pesticides on the soil microflora, *Technical Report, Agricultural Research Council, Weed Research Organization*, no. 59.

GROSSBARD, E. (1970). Effect of herbicides on the symbiotic relationship between *Rhizobium trifolii* and white clover, in *White Clover Research Occasional Symposium No. 6.*, pp. 47–59 (Ed. J. Lowe). British Grassland Society.

GROSSBARD, E. (1974). The effect of herbicides on the decay of pure cellulose and vegetation in Weed Research Organization: Research and Development at Begbroke. *Chemistry and Industry*, **15,** 611.

GROSSBARD, E. (1976). Effects on the soil microflora, in *Herbicides, Physiology, Biochemistry, Ecology*, vol. 2, pp. 99–147 (Ed. L.J. Audus). London and New York; Academic Press.

GROSSBARD, E. (1979). The continuous monitoring of the evolution of $^{14}CO_2$ from ^{14}C labelled rye straw, treated with herbicides, incubating undisturbed on the soil surface, in *Straw Decay and its Effect on Disposal and Utilization*, pp. 299–305 (Ed. E. Grossbard). Chichester; Wiley.

GROSSBARD, E. and COOPER, S.L. (1974). The decay of cereal straw after spraying with paraquat and glyphosate, *Proceedings of the 12th British Weed Control Conference*, **2,** 337–344.

GROSSBARD, E. and DAVIES, H.A. (1976). Specific microbial responses to herbicides, *Weed Research*, **16,** 163–169.

GROSSBARD, E. and HARRIS, D. (1976). The action of Gramoxone W and Roundup on cereal pathogens, *Mededelingen van de Faculteit Landbouwwetenschappen Rijksuniversiteit Gent*, **41**, 693–702.

GROSSBARD, E. and HARRIS, D. (1977). The selective action of the herbicides Gramoxone W and Roundup on *Chaetomium globosum* in relation to straw decay, *Transactions of the British Mycological Society*, **69**, 141–146.

GROSSBARD, E. and HARRIS, D. (1979). Effects of herbicides on the decay of straw, in *Straw Decay and its Effect on Disposal and Utilization*, pp. 167–176. (Ed. E. Grossbard). Chichester; Wiley.

GROSSBARD, E. and HARRIS, D. (1981). Effects on straw decay of the herbicides paraquat and glyphosate in combination with nitrogen amendments, *Annals of Applied Biology*, **98**, 277–288.

GROSSBARD, E. and MARSH, J.A.P. (1974). The effect of seven substituted urea herbicides on the soil microflora, *Pesticides Science*, **5**, 609–623.

GROSSBARD, E. and WINGFIELD, G.I. (1975). Techniques for the assay of effects of herbicides on the soil microflora. II. The effect of herbicides on cellulose decomposition, in *Some Methods for Microbiological Assay*, pp. 236–256 (Eds. R.G. Bond and D.W. Lovelock). London and New York; Academic Press.

GROSSBARD, E. and WINGFIELD, G.I. (1978). Effects of paraquat, aminotriazole and glyphosate on cellulose decomposition, *Weed Research*, **18**, 347–353.

HARRIS, D. (1981). Effects of herbicides used in reduced cultivation and direct drilling on some fungal cereal pathogens, particularly *Septoria nodorum*, Berk, *Ph.D. thesis*, Hatfield Polytechnic.

HARRIS, D. and GROSSBARD, E. (1978). Survival of the glume blotch fungus on straw treated with herbicides, *Proceedings of the 1978 British Crop Protection Conference—Weeds*, **2**, 603–608.

HARRIS, D. and GROSSBARD, E. (1979). Effects of the herbicides Gramoxone W and Roundup on *Septoria nodorum*, *Transactions of the British Mycological Society*, **73**, 27–33.

HARROWER, K.M. (1974). Survival and regeneration of *Leptosphaeria nodorum* in wheat debris, *Transactions of the British Mycological Society*, **63**, 527–533.

HEITEFUSS, R. (1972). Causes of side-effects of herbicides on plant diseases, *Zeitschrift für Pflanzenkrankheiten, Pflanzenpathologie und Pflanzenschutz*, Sonderheft VI, 79–87.

HOLLIDAY, M.J. and KEEN, N.T. (1982). The role of the phytoalexins in the resistance of soybean leaves to bacteria. Effect of glyphosate on glyceollin accumulation, *Phytopathology*, **72**, 1470–1474.

HOLMES, S.J.I. and COLHOUN, J. (1975). Straw-borne inoculum of *Septoria nodorum* and *S. tritici* in relation to incidence of disease on wheat plants, *Plant Pathology*, **24**, 63–66.

HORNBY, D. (1975). Inoculum of the Take-all fungus: nature, measurement distribution and survival, *EPPO Bulletin*, **5**, 319–333.

JAWORSKI, E.G. (1972). Mode of action of *N*-phosphonomethylglycine: inhibition of aromatic amino acid biosynthesis, *Journal of Agricultural and Food Chemistry*, **20**, 1195–1198.

KATAN, J. and ESHEL, Y. (1973). Interactions between herbicides and plant pathogens, *Residue Reviews* **45**, 145–177.

KEEN, N.T., HOLLIDAY, M.J. and YOSHIKAWA, M. (1982). Effects of glyphosate on glyceollin production and the expression of resistance to *Phytophthora megasperma* f. sp. *glycinea* in soybean, *Phytopathology*, **72**, 1467–1470.

KRUGLOV, YU.V., GERSH, N.B. and SHTAL'BERG, M. (1980). The influence of glyphosate on the soil microflora, *Khimiya v Sel'skom Khozayisteve*, **18**, 42–44.

LETHBRIDGE, G., BULL, A.T. and BURNS, R.G. (1981). Effects of pesticides on 1,3-β-glucanase and urease activities in soil in the presence and absence of fertilisers, live and organic materials, *Pesticide Science*, **12**, 147–155.

LÖNSJÖ, H., STARK, J., TORSTENSSON, L. and WESSEN, B. (1980). Glyphosate: decomposition and effects on biological processes in soil, *Weeds and Weed Control, 21st Swedish Weed Conference*, 2. Report, pp. 140–146.

MARSH, J.A.P. and DAVIES, H.A. (1978). The effect of herbicides on respiration and transformation of nitrogen in two soils. III. Lenacil, terbacil, chlorthiamid and 2,4,5-T, *Weed Research*, **18**, 57–62.

MARSH, J.A.P., DAVIES, H.A. and GROSSBARD, E. (1977). The effect of herbicides on respiration and transformation of nitrogen in two soils I. Metribuzin and glyphosate, *Weed Research*, **17**, 77–82.

MARSH, J.A.P., WINGFIELD, G.I., DAVIES, H.A. and GROSSBARD, E. (1978). Simultaneous assessment of various responses of the soil microflora to bentazone, *Weed Research*, **18**, 293–300.

MÜLLER, M.M., ROSENBERG, C., SILTANEN, H. and WARTIOVAARA, T. (1981). Fate of glyphosate and its influence on nitrogen-cycling in two Finnish agricultural soils, *Bulletin of Environmental Contamination and Toxicology*, **27**, 724–730.

PAPAVIZAS, G.C.L. and LEWIS, J.A. (1979). Side effects of pesticides on soil-borne plant pathogens, in *Soil-borne Plant Pathogens*, pp. 483–505. (Eds. B. Schippers and W. Gams). London and New York; Academic Press.

PENN, D.J. and LYNCH, J.M. (1981). Effect of decaying couch grass rhizomes on the growth of barley, *Journal of Applied Ecology*, **18**, 669–674.

PENN, D.J. and LYNCH, J.M. (1982). The effect of bacterial fermentation of couch grass rhizomes and *Fusarium culmorum* on the growth of barley seedlings, *Plant Pathology*, **31**, 39–43.

POLLARD, F. (1979). The decay of straw on the surface of undisturbed soil in the field and the effect of herbicides, in *Straw Decay and its Effect on Disposal and Utilization*, pp. 177–184. (Ed. E. Grossbard). Chichester; Wiley.

QUILTY, S.P. and GEOGHEGAN, M.J. (1975). Effects of glyphosate on fungi, *Proceedings of the Society for General Microbiology*, **II**, 87.

QUILTY, S.P. and GEOGHEGAN, M.J. (1976). Effects of 'Round-up' on microbial populations in cultivated peat, *Proceedings of the Society for General Microbiology*, **III**, 128.

RENSEN, J.J.S. VAN (1974). Effects of *N*-(phosphonomethyl)glycine on photosynthetic reactions in *Scenedesmus* and in isolated spinach chloroplasts, I, *Proceedings of the 3rd International Congress on Photosynthesis in Rehovot, Israel*, pp. 683–687.

RICHARDSON, J.T., FRANS, R.E. and TALBERT, R.E. (1979). Reactions of *Euglena gracilis* to fluometuron, MSMA, metribuzin and glyphosate, *Weed Science*, **27**, 619–624.

ROISCH, U. and LINGENS, F. (1980). The mode of action of the herbicide *N*-(phosphonomethyl)glycine: its effect on the growth and the enzymes of aromatic amino acid biosynthesis of *Escherichia coli*, *Hoppe-Seyler's Zeitschrift für Physiologische Chemie*, **361**, 1049–1058.

ROSLYCKY, E.B. (1977). Response of soil microbiota to selected herbicide treatments, *Canadian Journal of Microbiology*, **23**, 426–433.

ROSLYCKY, E.B. (1982). Glyphosate and the response of the soil microbiota, *Soil Biology and Biochemistry*, **14**, 87–92.

RUEPPEL, M.L., BRIGHTWELL, B.B., SCHAEFER, J. and MARVEL, J.T. (1977). Metabolism and degradation of glyphosate in soil and water, *Journal of Agricultural and Food Chemistry*, **25**, 517–527.

SMITH, R.N. and LONG, P.A. (1980). The effect of two fungicides, benlate and phenyl mercury acetate, on a population of cellolytic fungi in soil and in pure culture, *International Biodeterioration Bulletin*, ISSN 0200-6164, **16**, 119–125.

SMITH, S.N. and LYON, A.J.E. (1976). The uptake of paraquat by soil fungi, *New Phytologist*, **76**, 479–484.

SPRANKLE, P., MEGGITT, W.F. and PENNER, D. (1975). Adsorption, mobility, and microbial degradation of glyphosate in soil, *Weed Science*, **23**, 229–234.

STEDMAN, O.J. (1977). Effect of paraquat on the number of spores of *Rhynchosporium secalis* on barley stubbles and volunteers, *Plant Pathology*, **26**, 112–120.

STEDMAN, O.J. (1982). The effect of three herbicides on the number of spores of *Rhynchosporium secalis* on barley stubble and volunteer plants, *Annals of Applied Biology*, **100**, 271–279.

SULLIVAN, D.S., SULLIVAN, T.P. and BISALPUTRA, T. (1981). Effects of Roundup herbicide on diatom populations in the aquatic environment of a coastal forest, *Bulletin of Environmental Contamination and Toxicology*, **26**, 91–96.

TROPEA, M., FISICHELLA, G. and LONGO, A. (1979). Influence of glyphosate on CO_2 evolution in some typical soils of eastern Sicily, *Tecnica Agricola*, **31**(1–3), 11 pp.

WHIGHAM, D.K. and STOLLER, E.W. (1978). Soybean desiccation by paraquat, glyphosate and ametryn to accelerate harvest, *Agronomy Journal*, **71**, 630–633.

WILKINSON, V. and LUCAS, R.L. (1969). Effects of constituents of Gramoxone W on rates of respiration of soil fungi, *Weed Research*, **9**, 288–295.

YARHAM, D.J. and HIRST, J.M. (1975). Diseases in reduced cultivation and direct drilling systems, *EPPO Bulletin*, **5**, 287–295.

YARHAM, D.J. and NORTON, J. (1981). Effects of cultivation methods on disease, in *Strategies for the Control of Cereal Disease*, pp. 157–166. (Eds. J.F. Jenkyn and R.T. Plumb). Oxford; Blackwell.

Chapter 12

Effects of glyphosate on selected species of wildlife

T.P. Sullivan
Applied Mammal Research Institute, Langley, Canada

Introduction

Glyphosate is used for weed control in both agricultural and forest environments. Most studies on glyphosate have been agriculturally oriented with little emphasis on forests or their associated wildlife. In the coastal coniferous forests of western North America, intensive reforestation programmes must reduce or eliminate deciduous shrubs and weeds which compete with newly planted or established coniferous trees. The deciduous species *Alnus rubra, Rubus spectabilis* and *Acer circinatum* greatly hamper the regeneration of these forests. Glyphosate is one of the most effective means of controlling deciduous brush in forest stands (Sutton, 1978; Newton and Roberts, 1979).

Most studies, to date, concerning the effects of glyphosate on terrestrial wildlife have been conducted in the coastal forests of the Pacific Northwest of North America. Many of the wildlife species of forested areas are associated with early stages of forest succession. These initial stages of forest growth are characterized by a variety of plants that provide food and cover for wildlife. The use of herbicides such as glyphosate for forestry weed control (see also Chapter 21) may alter the habitat, making it unsuitable for wildlife. This herbicide-induced habitat conversion has an indirect effect on wildlife populations, whereas direct effects of a herbicide on a given population would be observed in demographic parameters such as reproduction, growth and survival.

This chapter will discuss the effects of glyphosate on selected species of wildlife in terms of habitat manipulation and demographic variables. Studies have been conducted concerning the impact of glyphosate on feeding preferences and habitat use by black-tailed deer (*Odocoileus hemionus columbianus*) (Sullivan and Sullivan, 1979; Sullivan and Sullivan, 1980, unpublished; Campbell *et al.*, 1981). Effects of glyphosate-induced habitat alteration on small mammal populations have been reported by Sullivan and Sullivan (1982) and on bird community structure as outlined by Morrison and Meslow (in press). Direct effects of glyphosate on several demographic parameters in a deer mouse (*Peromyscus maniculatus*) population have been reported by Sullivan and Sullivan (1981). These glyphosate studies will be compared with those describing the effects of other herbicides on wildlife species.

The name glyphosate in this chapter refers to the isopropylamine salt of *N*-(phosphonomethyl)glycine used as the commercial formulation Roundup.

Black-tailed deer

Black-tailed deer are abundant in the coastal forests of the Pacific Northwest of North America. These animals forage largely on herbaceous and woody plant species, which are abundant in the early successional stages of cutover forest land. For maximum effectiveness, in releasing conifers from deciduous competition, glyphosate should be applied in late summer after the current year's growth of conifers has hardened off (Sutton, 1978). This pre-winter browse reduction could be critical to survival of deer, particularly where spraying has covered large areas. Deer could either leave the affected area in search of food or remain and feed on the dying and dead vegetation. In addition, effects on their food preferences by deer consuming treated foliage and the possible conveyance of herbicide residues to humans are of particular concern (Thilenius and Brown, 1976; Leng, 1977; Dost, 1978; Newton and Snyder, 1978; Sjöden and Söderberg, 1978).

Food preference and consumption

A study conducted by Sullivan and Sullivan (1979) determined the preference of black-tailed deer (in a pen situation) for glyphosate-treated and untreated browse. Effects on consumption of other foods (commercial chow) by deer feeding on the treated browse were also monitored. *Alnus rubra* was the natural forage chosen for this study because its foliage is available well into autumn, is readily eaten by deer and is one of the main deciduous target species for control with herbicides in the Pacific Northwest (Lauterbach, 1967). Glyphosate-treated (dosage rate of 2.2 kg ha^{-1}) and untreated browse samples were collected from the field and fed to deer. Browse and chow consumption were measured every 4–5 d in a simulated field situation.

There was no significant difference (analysis of variance $p=0.08$) between the amounts of control and treated *A. rubra* eaten by the deer during five trials (*Figure 12.1*). However, overall average values were higher for treated (46.3) than control (36.3) browse. Significantly (analysis of variance $p=0.008$; Duncan's multiple range test), more *A. rubra* was eaten in trial 5 than in the other trials, probably as a result of preference for treated browse which was composed of dead leaves. In general, deer did not show an aversion to the glyphosate-treated browse and, in some instances, actually preferred it over the untreated browse. Animals fed control and treated *A. rubra* browse did not show any significant (analysis of variance) variation in their consumption of chow. Similar results were obtained for chow consumption in association with the presence of control and glyphosate-treated lucerne (*Medicago sativa*) hay. In this second experiment, deer ate significantly (analysis of variance $p=0.02$) more treated lucerne. The deer seemed to prefer the lucerne sprayed with glyphosate and did not avoid eating it at any time.

According to Monsanto, glyphosate may be a mild skin irritant. However, since the glyphosate-treated *A. rubra* and lucerne did not affect chow consumption, any irritation to the buccal cavity of the deer was insufficient to affect normal feeding. In addition, preference results indicated that sprayed browse was as acceptable as unsprayed browse.

A similar study by Campbell *et al.* (1981) reported on the acceptance by black-tailed deer of foliage treated with glyphosate and several other herbicides. Douglas fir (*Pseudotsuga menziesii*) seedlings were sprayed with glyphosate (Roundup) at rates of 1.1, 2.2, 3.4 and 4.5 kg ha^{-1} and, along with control

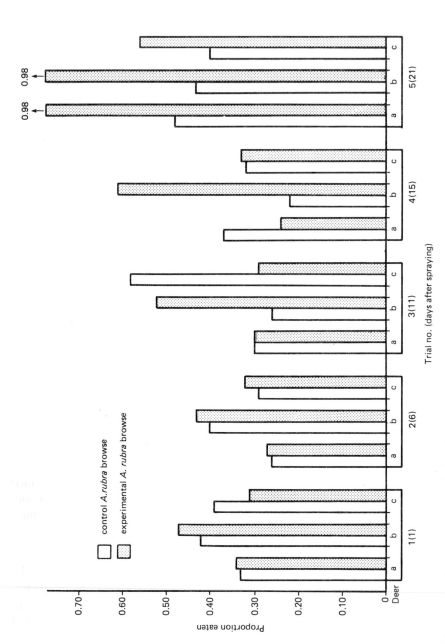

Figure 12.1. Preference by black-tailed deer (*Odocoileus hemionus columbianus*) for control red alder (*Alnus rubra*) browse and experimental *A. rubra* treated with glyphosate (2.2 kg ha^{-1}). Histograms represent proportion of *A. rubra* eaten per 24-hour day at each of 5 consecutive time intervals after field spraying of the herbicide (from Sullivan and Sullivan, 1979, by courtesy of the National Research Council, Canada)

seedlings, were placed in a 1 ha area enclosure with several deer. Measurements of browsing were made several times each day during a given test.

Deer readily browsed Douglas fir seedlings during all herbicide tests in this study (Campbell *et al.*, 1981). Browsing was significantly lower (analysis of variance; Duncan's multiple range test $p=0.05$) for glyphosate at 2.2, 3.4 and 4.5 kg ha^{-1} than for controls. In addition, browsing was significantly higher for 1.1 kg ha^{-1} glyphosate than for 3.4 and 4.5 kg ha^{-1}. At 1.9 d after spraying, nearly all seedlings were browsed. However, treatments with glyphosate at 3.4 and 4.5 kg ha^{-1} were still browsed least (88 and 89%, respectively). Mid-February applications of glyphosate resulted in reduced growth of seedlings, 28% mortality at 1.2 kg ha^{-1}, and 88% total mortality at 2.2, 3.4 and 4.5 kg ha^{-1}. Thus, the reduced acceptance of seedlings treated with glyphosate at phytotoxic rates, indicated possible sensitivity by deer to either the herbicide or the physiological changes in Douglas fir. Campbell *et al.* (1981) suspected that the latter explanation was more likely and, therefore, that proper timing and application of glyphosate are critical to minimizing toxicity to Douglas fir seedlings. Deer showed no obvious adverse effects from the glyphosate or other herbicides used. However, only general observations were made on the health of the test animals.

Habitat use

In terms of deer habitat use, following herbicide treatment, the deciduous trees normally remain defoliated until at least the next growing season, as with a burned area. In successive years, the habitat may provide better forage as herbs and low shrubs initiate vegetative succession and enhance deer use (Krefting and Hansen, 1969; Borrecco, Black and Hooven, 1972). This is the basis of habitat manipulation with herbicides which attempts to improve food and cover for wildlife. A preliminary study of deer habitat use in several control and glyphosate-treated coniferous plantations has been conducted by Sullivan and Sullivan (1980, unpublished).

In ten (five control and five treated) Douglas fir plantations in British Columbia, deer habitat use was estimated by systematic counting of pellet-groups. Circular sampling plots (5 m^2) located at 15.2 m intervals along two or three parallel lines covered each habitat. Plots were examined monthly during the year after manual and machine application of glyphosate for weed and shrub control in the plantations. All pellet-groups were counted and removed and only groups containing 30 pellets were recorded. In addition, deer counts were made for 2–3 nights per month in plantation habitats with suitable visibility between the rows of trees. A hand-held 12 V auto spotlight was shone from a vehicle moving very slowly along adjacent roads. Startled deer would look towards the light which was then clearly reflected in their eyes. Night-count data were used to supplement information on relative plantation use by deer, rather than as an index of population density (Harestad and Jones, 1981).

The number of pellet-groups per hectare for black-tailed deer in plantation habitats is given in *Table 12.1*. The data for the May sampling time were the cumulative number of pellet-groups deposited over at least the previous year. However, this May index may be considered an indication of deer habitat use since the previous summer, if we assume that deer pellets deteriorate beyond recognition within a year of deposition. In areas of heavy rain (coastal forest), pellet-groups frequently disappear within a year of deposition (Neff, 1968; Fisch, 1979). In the

TABLE 12.1   Number of pellet-groups per ha for black-tailed deer (*Odocoileus hemionus columbianus*) **in plantation habitats during the fall and winter period of 1979–80 (May sampling time) and the summer of 1980 (June to August sampling times)**

		May	June	July	August
5–8-year-old plantations	(area, ha)				
Control sites					
A	(17.1)	176.5	25.9	0.0	0.0
B	(17.0)	194.7	53.1	0.0	0.0
C	(1.7)	378.4	83.3	0.0	54.1
Herbicide sites					
D	(18.6)	419.8	0.0	24.7	24.7
E	(4.0)	523.8	0.0	0.0	0.0
10–20-year-old plantations					
Control sites					
F	(8.9)	120.0	100.0	0.0	0.0
G	(4.5)	175.4	0.0	0.0	0.0
Herbicide sites					
H	(6.2)	303.0	0.0	0.0	60.6
Manual cutting with herbicide on roadsides					
I	(3.8)	666.7	111.1	111.1	0.0
J	(10.0)	290.3	0.0	193.5	64.5

5–8-year-old plantations in May, up to twice as many pellet-groups were counted in the herbicide sites than at the control areas. However, in June, pellet-groups were recorded in the control plantation but not in the herbicide areas. There was little difference between areas in July and August. A similar relationship occurred in the 10–20-year-old plantations in May with up to twice as many pellet-groups at site H compared with control sites F and G. Sites I and J also had more deer pellets, this difference persisting throughout the summer. Night-counts of deer indicated little difference between control and glyphosate-treated plantations.

This study was concerned with the distribution and trend of habitat usage by deer in several areas. Therefore, an index value (number of pellet-groups per hectare) seemed adequate in evaluating differences as influenced by habitat manipulation with glyphosate. No attempt was made to relate pellet-group data to the actual number of deer in each habitat.

Sullivan and Sullivan (1980, unpublished) assumed that the majority of pellet-groups, counted in May 1980, gave a fairly accurate measure of deer activity the previous year. If this is the case, then weed control with glyphosate (June-July 1979) did not reduce the incidence of deer in treated plantations during 1979–80. A comparable result was reported by Borrecco, Black and Hooven (1972), where deer use of areas treated with atrazine and 2,4-D actually increased during the period of vegetation recovery after herbicide application. Several studies have outlined the role of herbicides in obtaining this positive habitat response for wildlife (Jenkins, 1955; Krefting, Hansen and Stenlund, 1956; Mueggler, 1966; Lawrence, 1967; Bramble and Byrnes, 1976; Landes, 1976).

This general premise was supported by the pellet-group counts in plantations I and J which had manual cutting of deciduous shrubs and roadside use of glyphosate (*Table 12.1*). Cutting resulted in widespread sprouting of deciduous stems which presumably increased the available food for deer. Similar results were obtained at sites D and E which also had a return of vegetative growth in the first growing season after spraying. Sullivan and Sullivan (1980, unpublished) concluded, from this preliminary study, that for at least the first year after treatment, glyphosate-induced weed and shrub control did not adversely affect deer use of these conifer plantations.

Small mammals

The forest habitats in which herbicides, such as glyphosate, are mainly used represent early successional stages after logging and/or burning. Associated with these young forests, and forming an integral part of the community, are several species of small mammals. The members (mice, voles, chipmunks, shrews) of this ubiquitous faunal group are dependent on the plant products (e.g. seeds, fruits, vegetative parts) of the deciduous and coniferous components of the vegetation. In turn, small mammals are a vital food source for avian and terrestrial predators such as hawks, owls, weasels, martens and many others.

Habitat manipulation

Habitat manipulation or conversion with herbicides may have profound effects on the abundance and composition of small mammal populations. In western North America, studies have reported that 2,4-D reduced vegetation and the abundance of pocket gophers (*Thomomys talpoides*) (Keith, Hansen and Ward, 1959; Tietjen *et al.*, 1967; Johnson and Hansen, 1969). Black and Hooven (1974) found that the application of several herbicides altered the species composition of small mammal communities. Borrecco (1976) reported that removal of herbaceous vegetation with a combination of herbicides reduced snowshoe hare (*Lepus americanus*) activity. Populations of small mammals showed either neutral or positive responses to herbicide (2,4,5-T) treatment in West Virginia (Kirkland, 1978).

With respect to glyphosate, Sullivan and Sullivan (1982) provided an intensive demographic analysis of small mammal populations on control and treated areas in coastal coniferous forest before and after herbicide application. These populations included the deer mouse, Oregon vole (*Microtus oregoni*), Townsend's chipmunk (*Eutamias townsendii*) and shrews (*Sorex* spp.). Populations were monitored (mark and recapture) on 1 ha checkerboard grids at 2- or 3-week intervals in control and treated habitats. The treatment grid had trap (drift) lines on three sides in adjacent forest during the period immediately before and after glyphosate application. These lines measured potential movement of animals to and from the treated area. Glyphosate was applied to the 20-year-old conifer plantation (4.9 ha), at the rate of 2.2 kg ha^{-1} of active ingredient, in September 1979.

After the herbicide application and subsequent leaf-fall, small mammals did not, initially, show a negative response with respect to their distribution and movements on the experimental area. Herbicide-induced leaf-fall was approximately 3–4 weeks earlier than the normal autumn senescence of deciduous plants in surrounding forest areas. Had this early leaf-fall temporarily affected the distribution of animals, then some movement to and from the treated area should be expected. However, there was neither an influx of new animals from surrounding regions onto the treatment grid (or drift lines), or significant movement of marked animals from the sprayed area out to the drift lines.

By early summer of 1980 the majority of target hardwood trees and some understorey shrubs had been killed by the herbicide. This resulted in conifer release, but decreased the cover or sheltering capacity of the habitat. Most rodents have a very strong negative reaction to disturbance or decrease in their shelter (Eadie, 1953; Mossman, 1955; Powell, 1968; Hansson, 1971). This effect can be very evident in early successional stages (grass-shrub) of coniferous forest which are subjected to herbicide treatment. Such areas do not have older plantation trees to offset, at least partly, the loss of deciduous vegetation. In general, the plantation had greater amounts of light penetration and herbaceous growth than prior to treatment.

The responses of small mammal populations, in terms of average densities, to this glyphosate-induced habitat alteration are listed in *Table 12.2*. The population of deer mice, on the treated area in this study, remained comparable to the control population. The average abundance of mice in the herbicide area declined in 1980 (13.6) relative to the previous year (19.2). This decline was somewhat greater than that on control areas, from 1979 (12.3) to 1980 (10.2). This difference was mainly due to a pulse of recruitment on the control area at the end of breeding (Sullivan and Sullivan, 1982).

The trend in populations of Oregon vole on control and treated areas are not as clear as for the deer mouse. This species of vole has a 3- or possibly 4-year cycle in abundance (Sullivan and Krebs, 1981). There was evidence of cycling behaviour on both study areas when average densities were examined (*Table 12.2*). These data indicated the existence of at least a 3-year cycle with 3–4 times as many voles on the control in both 1978 and 1980 than on the treated grid. Although the abundance of voles was quite different between areas, the cyclic pattern of numbers was similar. Thus, it would appear that the Oregon vole was not adversely affected by the habitat alteration. If the flush of grasses and herbs persists in the treated plantation, then this habitat might become more suitable for voles in future years.

In studies with other herbicides used in grass–shrub successional stages, some changes in small mammal community composition have occurred when the effects of habitat disturbance were measured one or more years after treatment (Black and Hooven, 1974; Kirkland, 1978). Such changes in community composition reflect

TABLE 12.2 Responses of small mammal populations to application (September 1979) of glyphosate herbicide in a 20–year-old conifer plantation. Values represent average densities per hectare per trapping period during each year of the study (after Sullivan and Sullivan, 1982)

Species	Area*	1978	1979	1980
Deer mouse	Con.	22.7	12.3	10.2
(*Peromyscus maniculatus*)	Gly.	24.2	19.2	13.6
Oregon vole	Con.	25.1	5.6	11.9
(*Microtus oregoni*)	Gly.	7.8	0.7	3.0
Townsend's chipmunk	Con.	9.3	7.8	5.4
(*Eutamias townsendii*)	Gly.	3.4	2.0	2.1
Shrews	Con.	1.6	3.3	3.1
(*Sorex* spp.)	Gly.	2.8	3.5	2.6

*Con. = control; Gly. = glyphosate.

shifts in the relative abundance of the different species. In particular, some species of microtines may respond negatively to habitat alteration if the grass–herb component is removed. Black and Hooven (1974) found Oregon voles less abundant and deer mice more abundant on treated areas. Similarly, Kirkland (1978) reported microtines declining slightly and deer mice increasing after herbicide application.

Populations of chipmunks and shrews were not adversely affected by the habitat change (*Table 12.2*). This result is consistent with that reported by Black and Hooven (1974). Kirkland (1978) and Sullivan and Sullivan (1982) found that shrews increased on treated areas. This may be due to an increase in invertebrates, associated with decomposing vegetation (on a treated area), and hence more food for shrews. Potential herbicide residues in invertebrates may concentrate in the food chain since various small mammals, particularly shrews, and many avian species utilize this important food source. Studies are needed to assess the possible transmittance of glyphosate residues to terrestrial vertebrates from their consumption of invertebrate prey. There was a higher abundance of chipmunks on the control than the experimental grid in our study. However, the small population of chipmunks on the treated grid persisted with little response to the habitat alteration.

Thus, treatment of a 20–year-old Douglas fir plantation with glyphosate had no adverse effects on the distribution and abundance of small mammals, at least during the first year after habitat alteration. Future changes in the composition of the small mammal community may occur as a result of successional stages following the original habitat alteration.

Effects on reproduction, growth and survival

The indirect effects of glyphosate herbicide on small mammal populations through ecological changes in vegetative cover and composition have been discussed. Few studies have been concerned with the more direct effects of herbicides on demographic parameters in small mammal populations. Wahlgren (1979) reported that Roundup had no adverse effects on reproductive parameters in laboratory mice. Sullivan and Sullivan (1981), in an intensive field study, reported the potential effects of this herbicide on reproduction, growth and survival in control and treatment populations of the deer mouse, which is a ubiquitous member of the small mammal fauna in coastal coniferous forest environments in western North America. Thus, it is a suitable species for analysis of any direct effects of glyphosate.

Deer mouse populations were monitored (mark and recapture) on 1 ha checkerboard grids in control and treatment habitats (Sullivan and Sullivan, 1982). Population densities and recruitment patterns on these areas were similar throughout the study, 1978–80 (Sullivan and Sullivan, 1982). Assessment of reproduction included length of breeding seasons, proportion of breeding animals, number of successful pregnancies and number of juvenile animals recruited into population.

There was little variation between areas in the length of reproductive periods, although the post-treatment population in 1980 started breeding 6 weeks before the control. There were no statistically significant differences between areas in proportions of males and females in breeding condition. The control population had more successful pregnancies than the treated in 1978, a trend reversed in 1979 and 1980 (*Table 12.3*). Recruitment of juveniles was similar for both populations until 1980 when the control had a much higher number (29/31.6) than the treated (23/40.7).

Minimum survival rates for all males and females in the deer mouse populations for breeding (summer) and non-breeding (winter) seasons are given in *Table 12.4* Both male and female deer mice in the experimental population survived better than their counterparts in the control during each summer. This difference was statistically significant for both sexes in the summer of 1979. Overwinter survival was also higher among experimental animals, particularly for males in 1978–79 and winter 1980. On both grids, survival was generally better in the summer of 1978 than in either of the subsequent years.

TABLE 12.3   Number of successful pregnancies during breeding seasons and observed and expected numbers of juveniles recruiting into populations up to 6 weeks after breeding (from Sullivan and Sullivan, 1981, by courtesy of the National Research Council, Canada)

| | Control | | Treatment* | |
	Total	$N*$	Total	$N\dagger$
Number of successful pregnancies				
1978	10	(7)	6	(4)
1979	8	(7)	10	(7)
1980	7	(7)	9	(7)
Expected number of juveniles				
1978	45.2		27.1	
1979	36.2		45.2	
1980	31.6		40.7	
Observed number of juveniles				
1978	32 (70.8%)		20 (73.8%)‡	
1979	21 (58.0%)		22 (48.7%)	
1980	29 (91.8%)		23 (56.5%)	

*A box indicates post-treatment data for 1980; 1978/79 are pre-treatment data.
†N = number of trapping periods (1978: 2-week interval; 1979–80: 3-week interval).
‡Observed number as percentage of expected number of juveniles.

Growth rates were used as another index of conditions within populations of deer mice. In terms of body weight, there was little variation between males in either population. Female body weights were not compared because undetected pregnancies result in variable data. The growth rates of juveniles are vital to population maintenance. Instantaneous relative growth rates were determined for individual juvenile mice during periods of weight gain. There was no difference in growth rates of animals in 1978 (*Figure 12.2*). Young male mice on the treatment grid grew slightly faster in 1979, but less fast in 1980 than those on the control. Female juveniles on the treatment grid grew slower than control females in 1979 and 1980.

Any adverse effects of glyphosate on deer mouse reproduction should have appeared in the breeding season after treatment (Sullivan and Sullivan, 1981). Following application, glyphosate, or its breakdown products, would be present in falling leaves from affected deciduous trees. A total of eight animals (5 males and 3 females) survived the 1979–80 overwinter period on the treated grid and so were exposed during that time. No animals (0/14) persisted on the control grid from autumn 1979 to spring 1980. Of the 8 mice, 7 continued to live on the treated grid and breed during part or all of the 1980 season.

TABLE 12.4 Minimum survival rates per 14 days (1978) and 21 days (1979–80) of deer mice (*Peromyscus maniculatus*) for the study areas. Sample size in parentheses (from Sullivan and Sullivan, 1981, by courtesy of the National Research Council, Canada)

| | Control | | Treatment* | |
	Males	Females	Males	Females
Summer 1978				
Total	0.75 (32)	0.92 (36)[f]	0.95 (19)[g]	1.00 (16)
Adults	0.69 (13)	0.89 (27)	0.93 (14)	1.00 (13)
Juveniles	0.79 (19)	1.00 (9)	1.00 (5)	1.00 (3)
Winter 1978–79				
Total	0.67 (51)[a]	0.74 (81)	0.83 (110)[a]	0.82 (89)
Summer 1979				
Total	0.63 (30)[b]	0.67 (21)[cf]	0.86 (37)[b]	0.90 (30)[c]
Adults	0.67 (27)	0.63 (19)[d]	0.78 (23)	0.92 (26)[d]
Juveniles	0.33 (3)	1.00 (2)	1.00 (14)	0.75 (4)
Winter 1979–80				
Total	0.66 (41)	0.62 (37)	0.77 (57)	0.75 (52)
Summer 1980				
Total	0.56 (18)	0.72 (18)	0.73 (51)[g]	0.81 (31)
Adults	0.50 (14)[e]	0.73 (15)	0.78 (45)[e]	0.80 (30)
Juveniles	0.75 (4)	0.67 (3)	0.33 (6)	1.00 (1)
Winter 1980				
Total	0.58 (19)**	0.75 (28)	0.90 (31)**	0.73 (22)

*A box indicates post-treatment data after herbicide application in autumn 1979.
Note: a–a, b–b, c–c, d–d, e–e, f–f, g–g, $p < 0.05$; **, $p < 0.01$; significant difference by chi-square.

These results are consistent with those obtained for laboratory mice fed Roundup herbicide in their food (Wahlgren, 1979). Parameters such as litter size, weight at weaning and survival rate of litters were assessed in this laboratory study. These parameters are difficult, if not impossible, to measure in a live field population. However, the consistent frequency of lactation in females captured in consecutive trapping periods during 1980 suggests that litters survived to at least the weaning stage. Johnson and Hansen (1969) found litter size little affected by 2,4-D in field populations of deer mice.

The generally higher survival of experimental animals in this study may be attributable to lack of competition from Oregon voles and a more forest-like habitat (Sullivan and Sullivan, 1982). A 20–year–old conifer plantation would provide more cover and insulation during the overwinter period than the shrub habitat in the control area. This may have been particularly relevant during the winter of 1979–80 when no control animals survived compared with 42% on the treatment grid.

Bird community structure

The structure of forest bird communities is strongly influenced by the successional stage of the vegetation. Herbicides can alter the successional stage of a given habitat, and so affect nesting birds. Several studies, on effects of phenoxy (2,4-D

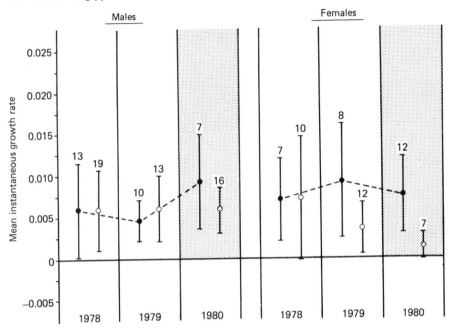

Figure 12.2. Mean growth rates with 95% confidence limits for juvenile males and female deer mice (*Peromyscus manicula-tus*) during 1978–80. Control population (●), treatment population (○); shaded periods represent 1 year after application of glyphosate (2.2 kg ha^{-1}). Sample size above upper confidence limits (from Sullivan and Sullivan, 1981, by courtesy of the National Research Council, Canada)

and 2,4,5-T) herbicides on bird communities, have reported densities altered by spray treatment (Beaver, 1976; Slagsvold, 1977; Savidge, 1978). Until recently, there were no studies of the effects of glyphosate-induced habitat alteration on forest birds.

Morrison and Meslow (in press), in cutover forest land in Oregon, studied typical habitats used by nesting birds before and after treatment with glyphosate. The main objectives were to determine if any shifts in habitat use, foraging behaviour and density by given species could be related to glyphosate-induced habitat modification. Glyphosate was applied at the rate of 2.2 kg ha^{-1} in October 1979. Results from the preceding field season served as pretreatment data, while those for 1980 and 1981 provided 1- and 2-year post-treatment data (Morrison and Meslow, in press).

There was little difference in total density of nesting birds between treated and untreated sites during all years of the study. Several species of birds decreased use of shrub cover and increased use of deciduous trees, 1 year after treatment. Many species returned to pre-spray use of most measured habitat components 2 years after treatment. The MacGillivray's warbler (*Oporornis tolmiei*), rufous-sided towhee (*Pipilo erythrophthalmus*), rufous hummingbird (*Selaphorus rufus*) and Wilson's warbler (*Wilsonia pusilla*) increased vertical foraging diversity after glyphosate treatment. These species were not able to maintain pre-spray densities even with shifts in habitat use and foraging behaviour (Morrison and Meslow, in press). Most species had returned to near pre-spray foraging behaviour 2 years after treatment.

Conclusions

Studies on food preference and habitat use by black-tailed deer indicate that these animals will consume glyphosate-treated foliage and occupy treated habitats. If the nutritional content of dying foliage is not greatly reduced, and there are no adverse effects of glyphosate on the physiology of deer, then these animals should be able to feed successfully within a sprayed area. This is particularly relevant in treated areas used as winter range. Spraying with glyphosate, hence accelerating leaf fall, should not make the foliage unattractive as a food supply for these animals. The long-term effects of glyphosate on deer and related ungulates are not known. Thus, more studies on seasonal and annual variation in deer browsing, related to use of herbicides such as glyphosate, are needed. The general acceptance of glyphosate-treated foliage suggests that field evaluations to determine long-term beneficial and harmful effects of glyphosate on deer and deer habitat use are necessary.

Glyphosate did not have any negative effects on the distribution and abundance of small mammal populations, at least during the first year after habitat alteration. Future changes in composition of small mammal communities after glyphosate application may occur in association with vegetative succession and interactions among animal species. For example, intolerant species such as voles (*Microtus* spp.) are particularly sensitive to perturbation of their preferred habitat, whereas mice (*Peromyscus* spp.) are more tolerant of habitat change. Presumed competition between species of these two genera has been recorded by several authors. Therefore, the length of time that a treated area maintains a grass–herb community, in association with the cyclic phases of voles, may determine the distribution and abundance of *Peromyscus* spp. during the years following herbicide treatment.

Evaluation of the direct effects of glyphosate was conducted on a population of deer mice, a common inhabitant of target areas. Roundup apparently had no adverse effects on reproduction, growth or survival in field populations of deer mice 1 year after treatment. Inconsistencies in growth rates and juvenile survival between control and experimental deer mice in the year after treatment could be due to the herbicide or internal demographic factors. Field dose applications of this herbicide should not have a direct effect on the dynamics of deer mouse and perhaps related rodent populations. Further direct and indirect effects of glyphosate on forest small mammals may become apparent in long-term studies covering 3–5 years after treatment.

Herbicides such as glyphosate, through alteration of vegetation, can modify the density, habitat use and foraging behaviour of nesting birds. The preliminary study outlined concluded that at least four species were unable to maintain pre-spray densities even with shifts in habitat use and foraging behaviour. Most avian species had returned to pre-spray foraging behaviour 2 years after treatment. At this time, the vegetation was similar to conditions present prior to glyphosate application. However, only 23% of total plant cover was damaged by the herbicide. Thus, further studies are needed to assess the response of plant and bird communities to the full range of effects typical of glyphosate.

References

BEAVER, D.L. (1976). Avian populations in herbicide treated brush fields, *Auk*, **93**, 543–553.

BLACK, H.C. and HOOVEN, E.F. (1974). Response of small mammal communities to habitat changes in western Oregon, in *Wildlife and Forest Management in the Pacific Northwest*, pp. 177–186 (Ed. H.C. Black). School of Forestry, Oregon State University, Corvallis.

BORRECCO, J.E. (1976). Controlling damage by forest rodents and lagomorphs through habitat manipulation, *Proceedings of the Vertebrate Pest Control Conference*, **7**, 203–210.

BORRECCO, J.E., BLACK, H.C. and HOOVEN, E.F. (1972). Response of black-tailed deer to herbicide-induced habitat changes, *Western Proceedings of the 52nd Annual Conference of the Western Association State Game and Fish Commission*, Portland, Oregon, pp. 437–451.

BRAMBLE, W.C. and BYRNES, W.R. (1976). Impact of brush control on wildlife food and cover, in *Herbicides in Forestry*, pp. 136–155 (Eds. W.R. Byrnes and H.A. Holt). Proceedings of the J.S. Wright Forestry Conference, Purdue University, West Lafayette, Indiana.

CAMPBELL, D.L., EVANS, J., LINDSEY, G.D. and DUSENBERRY, W.E. (1981). Acceptance by black-tailed deer of foliage treated with herbicides, *Research Paper PNW – 290*. United States Department of Agriculture, Forest Service, Pacific Northwest Forest and Range Experiment Station, p. 31.

DOST, F.N. (1978). Toxicology of phenoxy herbicides and hazard assessment of their use in reforestation. United States Department of Agriculture. Forest Service, California Reg. R–5.

EADIE, W.R. (1953). Response of *Microtus* to vegetative cover, *Journal of Mammalogy*, **34**, 253–264.

FISCH, G. (1979). Deer pellet deterioration, in *Sitka Black-tailed Deer*, pp. 209–218 (Eds. O.C. Wallmo and J.W. Schoen). U.S.D.A. Forest Service, Juneau, Alaska.

HANSSON, L. (1971). Habitat, food and population dynamics of the field vole *Microtus agrestis* in south Sweden, *Viltrevy*, **8**, 267–378.

HARESTAD, A.S. and JONES, G.W. (1981). Use of night counts for censusing black-tailed deer on Vancouver Island, in *Proceedings of Symposium on Census and Inventory Methods for Populations and Habitats*, pp. 83–96 (Eds. F.L. Miller and A. Gunne). The Wildlife Society, April 10, 1980, Banff, Alberta.

JENKINS, B.C. (1955). Wildlife habitat development with herbicides in Michigan, *Proceedings of the North Central Weed Control Conference*, **12**, 58.

JOHNSON, D.R. and HANSEN, R.M. (1969). Effect of range treatment with 2,4-D on rodent populations, *Journal of Wildlife Management*, **33**, 125–132.

KEITH, J.O., HANSEN, R.M. and WARD, A.L. (1959). Effects of 2,4-D on abundance and foods of pocket gophers, *Journal of Wildlife Management*, **23**, 137–145.

KIRKLAND, G.L. (1978). Population and community responses of small mammals to 2,4,5-T, *Research Note PNW–314*. United States Department of Agriculture Forest Service, Pacific Northwest Forest and Range Experiment Station. 61 pp.

KREFTING, L.W. and HANSEN, H.L. (1969). Increasing browse for deer by aerial application of 2,4-D, *Journal of Wildlife Management*, **33**, 784–790.

KREFTING, L.W., HANSEN, H.L. and STENLUND, M.H. (1956). Stimulating regrowth of mountain maple for deer browse by herbicides, cutting, and fire, *Journal of Wildlife Management*, **20**, 434–441.

LANDES, R.K. (1976). Herbicides for wildlife habitat manipulation, in *Herbicides in Forestry*, pp. 113–127 (Eds. W.R. Byrnes and H.A. Holt). Proceedings of the J.S. Wright Forestry Conference, Purdue University, West Lafayette, Indiana.

LAUTERBACH, P.G. (1967). Chemical weeding and release of conifers in western Oregon and Washington, in *Herbicides and Vegetation Management in Forests, Range, and Noncrop Lands*, pp. 148–151 (Ed. M.A. Newton). School of Forestry, Oregon State University, Corvallis.

LAWRENCE, W.H. (1967). Effects of vegetation management on wildlife, in *Herbicides and Vegetation Management in Forests, Ranges, and Noncrop Lands*, pp. 88–93 (Ed. M.A. Newton). School of Forestry, Oregon State University, Corvallis.

LENG, M.L. (1977). Comparative metabolism of phenoxy herbicides in animals, in *Fate of Pesticides in the Large Animal*, pp. 53–76. New York; Academic Press.

LOBUE, J. and DARNELL, R.M. (1959). Effect of habitat disturbance on a small mammal population, *Journal of Mammalogy*, **40**, 425–437.

MORRISON, M.L. and MESLOW, E.C. (in press). Effects of the herbicide glyphosate on bird community structure, western Oregon, *Forest Science*.

MOSSMAN, A.S. (1955). Light penetration in relation to small mammal abundance, *Journal of Mammalogy*, **36**, 564–566.

MUEGGLER, W.F. (1966). Herbicide treatment of browse on a big-game winter range in northern Idaho, *Journal of Wildlife Management*, **30**, 141–151.

NEFF, D.J. (1968). The pellet-group count technique for big game trend, census, and distribution: a review, *Journal of Wildlife Management*, **32**, 597–614.

NEWTON, M. and ROBERTS, C.A. (1979). Brush control alternative for forest site preparation, *Proceedings of the 28th Annual Oregon Weed Control Conference*. Salem, Oregon.

NEWTON, M. and SNYDER, S.P. (1978). Exposure of forest herbivores to 2,3,7,8-tetrachlorodibenzo-p-dioxin (TCDD) in areas sprayed with 2,4,5-T, *Bulletin of Environmental Contamination and Toxicology*, **20**, 743–750.

POWELL, J. (1968). Rodent numbers on different brush control treatments in South Texas, *Texas Journal of Science*, **20**, 69–76.

SAVIDGE, J.A. (1978). Wildlife in a herbicide-treated Jeffery pine plantation in eastern California, *Journal of Forestry*, **76**, 476–478.

SJÖDEN, P.O. and SÖDERBERG, U. (1978). Phenoxy-acetic acids: sublethal effects, in *Chlorinated Phenoxy Acids and their Dioxins*, vol. 27, pp. 149–164 (Ed. C. Ramel). Ecological Bulletin, Stockholm.

SLAGSVOLD, T. (1977). Bird population changes after clearance of deciduous scrub, *Biological Conservation*, **12**, 229–244.

SULLIVAN, T.P. and KREBS, C.J. (1981). *Microtus* population biology: demography of *M. oregoni* in southwestern British Columbia, *Canadian Journal of Zoology*, **59**, 2092–2102.

SULLIVAN, T.P. and SULLIVAN, D.S. (1979). The effects of glyphosate herbicide on food preference and consumption in black-tailed deer, *Canadian Journal of Zoology*, **57**, 1406–1412.

SULLIVAN, T.P. and SULLIVAN, D.S. (1980). The effects of Roundup herbicide on habitat use by black-tailed deer in coastal British Columbia, in *The Effects of Roundup Herbicide on Forest Animals in Coastal British Columbia*, pp. 37–48. Monsanto Canada Inc. Final Report.

SULLIVAN, T.P. and SULLIVAN, D.S. (1981). Responses of a deer mouse population to a forest herbicide application: reproduction, growth, and survival, *Canadian Journal of Zoology*, **59**, 1148–1154.

SULLIVAN, T.P. and SULLIVAN, D.S. (1982). Responses of small mammal populations to a forest herbicide application in a 20–year old conifer plantation, *Journal of Applied Ecology*, **19**, 95–106.

SUTTON, R.F. (1978). Glyphosate herbicide: an assessment of forestry potential, *Forestry Chronicle*, **54**, 24–28.

THILENIUS, J.F. and BROWN, G.R. (1976). Effects of 2,4-D on digestability and production of subalpine herbage, *Journal of Range Management*, **29**(1), 63–65.

TIETJEN, H.P., HALVORSEN, C.H., HEGDAL, P.L. and JOHNSON, A.M. (1967). 2,4-D herbicide, vegetation, and pocket gopher relationships, Black Mesa, Colorado, *Ecology*, **48**, 634–643.

WAHLGREN, J.R. (1979). The effects of the herbicide Roundup[R] on reproduction in mice, *B.Sc. Agriculture thesis*, University of British Columbia, Vancouver, B.C., Canada. 37 pp.

Chapter 13

Behaviour of glyphosate in the aquatic environment

J.O. Brønstad* and H.O. Friestad
Agricultural University of Norway, Ås-NLH, Norway

Introduction

With regard to the solubility of glyphosate, one might say that water is its right element. Water dissolves approximately 1% of glyphosate at ambient temperature, whereas the solubility of the compound in organic solvents is far less. This preference for water is not reflected, however, by the number of behavioural studies of glyphosate in aquatic environments. Thus, a search in the literature, resulted in just a handful of references. Many of these originated from work of the manufacturer, Monsanto, who may also be in possession of further information not normally accessible, and valuable information may be interspersed among other literature topics or exist as unpublished raw data.

This chapter reviews the result of the literature search mentioned above. The name glyphosate in this chapter refers to the free acid form of *N*-(phosphono-methyl)glycine. Where authors have used this term for the isopropylamine salt, as the commercial formulation Roundup, this will be stated clearly.

Entry of glyphosate into the aquatic environment

Except when used to control water weeds, as described for example by Riemer and Welker (1974; see also Chapter 24), glyphosate will rarely reach water sources directly. Consequently, the effects on the environment at the time of application are important. These will be very briefly discussed in the following paragraphs.

It can be ascertained that losses of glyphosate to the atmosphere by evaporation will be negligible due to the low vapour pressure of the compound. In fact, fortified water samples can be concentrated from 1 l to less than 50 ml without loss of glyphosate when heated in an open beaker on a hot plate (Brønstad and Friestad, 1976).

When applied as a spray in forestry or agriculture, glyphosate (as Roundup) will be distributed primarily on surfaces of vegetation and soil. If not washed off by rain, a part of the portion reaching the plant material may penetrate into the plant, but will eventually become a soil residue as the weeds decay (see also Chapter 7). The initial binding to plants varies from species to species. The 'wash-off' effect of

*Present address: Grong videregaende skole, 7870 Grong, Norway.

rain also varies and is dependent on the time lapse between spraying and rainfall. As an example, raspberries (*Rubus idaeus*), with initial high residues (9 mg kg^{-1}), were not affected by 35 mm of rain on the 7th day after application (Lund-Høie and Friestad, unpublished data), whereas rain a few hours after spraying generally washed off so much glyphosate that its herbicidal effect was clearly reduced.

Glyphosate is strongly adsorbed to soils, and the binding has been found to be strongest in soils with the highest capacity for phosphates, the highest content of organic matter and the lowest pH (Ching *et al.*, 1975).

As a result of this strong binding to soils, the leachability of glyphosate is very low. Using a bioassay technique for the analysis, Damanakis (1976) found that 110 mm of rainfall could leach glyphosate (as Roundup) down to 15 cm soil depth. In this case, glyphosate representing 150 times the usual dosage was deposited on the top of soil-filled columns approximately 5 cm in diameter. Based on studies of labelled glyphosate on soil thin-layer plates, Rueppel *et al.* (1977) classify glyphosate as an immobile compound. The metabolite, aminomethylphosphonic acid (AMPA), is considered to be slightly mobile (H.W. Frazier, personal communication).

There are several studies showing that glyphosate is not sensitive to movement in run-off. Edwards, Triplett and Kramer (1980) measured the transport of glyphosate (as Roundup), as run-off from a field under no-tillage, in a watershed which was sprayed in early spring at rates of 1.12 to 8.96 kg ha^{-1}, and found 1.85% of the amount applied to be the maximum loss. This occurred as a result of heavy rainfall on the day following application. The three-year study also showed that 99% of the total run-off took place during the first rainfall after each application. Extremely low run-off values of 0.001% were observed by Rueppel *et al.* (1977) in laboratory experiments using artificial rainfall and soil beds inclined at 7.5°.

In line with these observations are results described by Comes, Bruns and Kelley (1976). They found that water entering dry irrigation canals, which had been sprayed 23 weeks before with 5.6 kg ha^{-1} of glyphosate (as Roundup), did contain, in the upper 10 cm layer of the canal banks, 0.35 p.p.m. of glyphosate and 0.78 p.p.m. of AMPA.

Behaviour and fate of glyphosate in water

If glyphosate should enter what, in the strictest sense, is usually understood as the 'aquatic environment', it may have an immediate effect and/or dissipate. Since the former aspect is covered by later chapters of this book, only dissipation is discussed here.

Pure glyphosate is stable for many years at room temperature when dissolved in distilled water or in 1 N hydrochloric acid. Spray solutions of the formulated product Roundup, stored in glass bottles at room temperature, do not change noticeably in 7 months (Friestad, 1978). The tendency to hydrolytic decomposition is also low or non-existent. Thus, concentrating standard solutions from 1 l to 10 ml from 0.1 N hydrochloric acid or from 0.1 N ammonium hydroxide on a hot plate, did not result in loss of glyphosate (Friestad, 1978).

Despite such observations, glyphosate is considered to dissipate rapidly from natural waters. According to H.W. Frazier (personal communication) 'at least three pathways of dissipation are possible: (1) microbial to yield AMPA and CO_2; (2) photolytic to yield AMPA; and (3) adsorption to sediment, giving bound residues which can slowly break down microbially under anaerobic conditions.'

Microbial degradation

The investigation reported by Rueppel *et al.* (1977) probably is the most pertinent in this connection. Their degradation and metabolism studies were performed under aerobic as well as anaerobic conditions, in shake flasks containing 1 mg of ^{14}C-labelled glyphosate in a water–soil mixture (20:1,w/w). The evolution of $^{14}CO_2$ was measured and possible metabolites (*Table 13.1*) examined by TLC/beta camera technique.

The studies involved use of glyphosate having a ^{14}C label either in the position closest to the phosporus atom (*N*-phosphono-^{14}C-methyl), in the carboxyl position (glycine-1-^{14}C), or in the methylene position (glycine-2-^{14}C). Under sterile conditions, practically no ^{14}C-labelled carbon dioxide evolved during 7 days and the composition of the supernatants in the shake flasks remained unaltered. These facts led to the conclusion that chemical degradation is of little importance in the elimination of glyphosate. Under non-sterile conditions, however, glyphosate was degraded and in 28 days up to 55% of the compound was transformed into carbon dioxide (i.e. total decomposition) at a rate more or less independently of label site (*Table 13.2*).

The only metabolite of any significance was found to be AMPA. Metabolites 3, 6, 7 and 8 were detected in the soil. However, their contribution to the total radioactivity never exceeded 1%. Metabolites with intact *N*-(phosphonomethyl)glycine grouping were not detected.

The release of labelled carbon dioxide shows that microorganisms present in soil are able to degrade glyphosate. The concentration of such organisms in natural waters will, however, rarely reach those of the shake flasks discussed above. Studies more closely related to conditions in natural waters would be interesting, but very few have been published.

Two reports (Sacher, 1978; H.W. Frazier, personal communication) refer to dissipation studies in more or less natural water. In the former study, the loss of

TABLE 13.1   Structures of glyphosate (1) and potential metabolites identifiable in the studies of Rueppel *et al.* (1977)

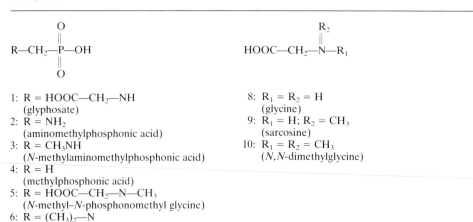

$$R\!-\!CH_2\!-\!\underset{\underset{O}{\|}}{\overset{\overset{O}{\|}}{P}}\!-\!OH \qquad\qquad HOOC\!-\!CH_2\!-\!\underset{}{\overset{\overset{R_2}{\|}}{N}}\!-\!R_1$$

1: R = HOOC—CH₂—NH
    (glyphosate)
2: R = NH₂
    (aminomethylphosphonic acid)
3: R = CH₃NH
    (*N*-methylaminomethylphosphonic acid)
4: R = H
    (methylphosphonic acid)
5: R = HOOC—CH₂—N—CH₃
    (*N*-methyl–*N*-phosphonomethyl glycine)
6: R = (CH₃)₂—N
    (*N,N*-dimethylaminomethylphosphonic acid)
7: R = HO
    (hydroxymethylphosphonic acid)

8: R₁ = R₂ = H
    (glycine)
9: R₁ = H; R₂ = CH₃
    (sarcosine)
10: R₁ = R₂ = CH₃
    (*N,N*-dimethylglycine)

TABLE 13.2   Decomposition of glyphosate in presence of soil microflora

Label position	Metabolism	Percentage of ^{14}C released as $^{14}CO_2$	Percentage of ^{14}C activity in supernatant
N-phosphono-^{14}C-methyl	Aerobic	46.8	5.4
	Anaerobic	37.3	2.6
Glycine-1-^{14}C	Aerobic	55.3	0.3
	Anaerobic	51.4	0.2
Glycine-2-^{14}C	Aerobic	55.3	1.4
	Anaerobic	33.5	4.8

glyphosate was followed in a non-flowing model pond of 2 m diameter and approximately 0.5 m height. Glyphosate was introduced into the system through soil treated with ^{14}C-labelled glyphosate at a rate, corresponding to 4.4 kg ha^{-1}, which was spread out at the bottom of the pond 3 days before the introduction of the water. In this system, an initial concentration of 460 p.p.b. was decreased at a rate which followed a first-order kinetics. The half-life was found to be approximately 12 days.

The other report shows that aerobic metabolism in sphagnum bog water led to 63% breakdown, primarily to carbon dioxide and AMPA, after 63 days at 30°C. There seem to be differences in both the mechanism and rate of disappearance in these studies, but without better knowledge of experimental conditions, speculative comparisons would be of dubious value. However, both authors conclude that glyphosate dissipates readily in water.

Using considerably higher concentrations than those mentioned in the reports discussed, the dissipation of glyphosate (as Roundup) from water from a small forest pond has also been followed by chemical analysis in this laboratory (Friestad, 1978). The model pond was in this case a 10 l plastic bucket containing 7 l of water and about 1 kg mud from the pond. Roundup, corresponding to 1400 mg of glyphosate, was added to the bucket, which was kept outdoors partly shielded by a large tree to avoid flooding by rain. The water level was kept constant by covering the bucket with a lid during heavy rain and by addition of water to compensate for evaporation loss. Despite low average temperatures (9.1–3.8°C) during this period, the glyphosate content sank to about 30% of its theoretical starting value of 200 p.p.m. after 50 days. At this point the bucket was taken in and stored at 4°C over the winter. On continuation of the experiment next year, the glyphosate concentration declined to less than 3% 1 year after the start. Interestingly, analysis of the sediment at the end of the study showed that more than 50% of the originally introduced herbicide still was extractable in an unchanged form from the clay-like material at the end of the study. This is qualitatively in good agreement with the observations of H.W. Frazier (personal communication), where binding to sediments was found to make a major contribution to the dissipation in lake water, studied under anaerobic conditions.

Photolysis

The extensive investigations by Rueppel *et al.* (1977) also include examination of glyphosate solutions in a photoreactor. It was found that less than 2% of the radioactivity of the N-phosphono-^{14}C-methyl-labelled compound had disappeared as volatile degradation products after irradiation in a Crosby reactor for a period equivalent to 16 days each with 8 h of sunlight. No alteration was observed in the composition of the aqueous solutions with respect to their content of glyphosate, which was originally 170 p.p.m., AMPA, and the N-methyl derivative of the latter. In view of the considerably faster microbial degradation seen in shake flasks studies, these authors concluded that photodecomposition would play a very minor role in environmental breakdown of glyphosate.

This conclusion has later been qualified (H.W. Frazier, personal communication). When sterile, de-ionized water was replaced with sterile, natural water, photo-irrigation of a 1 p.p.m. solution resulted in 18.4% and 86.7% transformation to AMPA in 1 and 14 days, respectively. Dark controls showed glyphosate to be stable. This latter work suggested that glyphosate might be photolabile in natural waters. The photolability was believed to be catalysed by calcium or other metal ions.

A Norwegian study (Lund-Høie and Friestad, unpublished) of possible photodecomposition was undertaken after preliminary outdoor experiments with relatively low glyphosate concentrations (1 p.p.m.) had led to a dissipation pattern thought to be influenced by sunlight. In a laboratory degradation study performed at a constant temperature of 22°C, 40 l of Roundup solution, corresponding to 2000 p.p.m. of glyphosate in de-ionized water, was irradiated by u.v. lamps (254 nm) placed 15 cm above the water. After irradiation by 2.4 mW cm^{-2} for 10 weeks, the glyphosate content was reduced to 300 p.p.m., whereas the non-irradiated controls showed practically no change in the glyphosate concentration. Since the analytical method in this laboratory could determine only glyphosate, a sample of the irradiated solution was sent to Monsanto for additional analysis and found to contain 256 p.p.m. of glyphosate and 1610 p.p.m. of AMPA (J.M. Malik, personal communication). This demonstrates that AMPA is the dominant, perhaps the only, conversion product and that photolysis can occur in de-ionized water. Whether this has any bearing on the conclusion that photodecomposition is of minor importance in the dissipation of glyphosate is unclear.

Fate of AMPA

From the experiment just described, aminomethylphosphonic acid is photolytically more stable than its precursor. In the shake flask studies, AMPA was degraded consistently slower than glyphosate. As an explanation, Rueppel et al. (1977) suggest stronger adsorption to soil or lower permeability through the cell walls of microorganisms. However, they also point to the fact that several aminomethylphosphonates have been reported to be naturally occurring compounds and that AMPA may be utilized as the only phosphorus source by some organisms. It therefore seems unlikely that this metabolite constitutes any threat to our aquatic environment (see also Chapter 9).

Conclusions

Glyphosate may enter aquatic environments when applied as a herbicide against water weeds, by spills, possible waste water disposal at production or packing sites, or by similar, more accidental, types of discharge. By regular usage in agriculture or forestry, chances of contamination seem very remote. For this reason, and probably also due to analytical difficulties, few studies of the fate of glyphosate in the aquatic environment have been published. The available literature indicates that the compound dissipates by microbial degradation, adsorption to sediments, and by photolysis. To decide the order of importance of these processes as well as their rates, more research work is needed. Since the compound carries many of the features of an ideal herbicide and therefore may ultimately reach considerable production figures, a better elucidation also of these aspects of the herbicide should be encouraged.

References

BRØNSTAD, J.O. and FRIESTAD, H.O. (1976). Method for determination of glyphosate residues in natural waters based on polarography of the *N*-nitroso derivative, *Analyst*, **101**, 820–824.

CHING, S., NOMURA, N., YAUGER, W., UYEHARA, G. and HILTON, H.W. (1975). *Annual Report of the Experimental Station of the Hawaiian Sugar Planters Association*, pp. 38–40.

COMES, R.D., BRUNS, V.F. and KELLEY, A.D. (1976). Residues and persistence of glyphosate in irrigation water, *Weed Science*, **24**, 47–50.

DAMANAKIS, M.E. (1976). Behaviour of glyphosate in the soil, *Annales de l'Institut Phytopathologique Benaki*, **11**, 153–167.

EDWARDS, W.M., TRIPLETT JR., G.B. and KRAMER, R.M. (1980). A watershed study of glyphosate transport in runoff, *Journal of Environmental Quality*, **9**, 661–665.

FRIESTAD, H.O. (1978). Determination of glyphosate in water, soil, and plant material by means of differential pulse polarography, *Nordic Plant Protection Conference 1978*, Ruissalo, Finland, pp. 83–85.

RIEMER, D.N. and WELKER JR., W.V. (1974). Control of fragrant waterlily and spatterdock with glyphosate, *Journal of Aquatic Plant Management*, **12**, 40–41.

RUEPPEL, M.L., BRIGHTWELL, B.B., SCHAEFER, J. and MARVEL, J.T. (1977). Metabolism and degradation of glyphosate in soil and water, *Journal of Agricultural and Food Chemistry*, **25**, 517–528.

SACHER, R.M. (1978). Safety of Roundup in the aquatic environment, *Proceedings of the EWRS 5th Symposium on Aquatic Weeds*, **5**, 315–322.

Chapter 14

Fate and biological consequences of glyphosate in the aquatic environment

T.E. Tooby
MAFF, Harpenden, UK

Introduction

The aquatic environment has a capacity to receive toxic materials of all kinds, but the problem is defining that capacity in quantitative terms (Preston, 1979). However, critical pathways and targets can be identified and used to provide a means of evaluating the potential hazard to the aquatic environment from the use of chemicals, especially pesticides.

In any attempt to protect the aquatic environment from detrimental effects of pesticides, two important facts must be taken into consideration: one is that the natural community structure is dynamic and is characterized by a continual succession of species; the other is that the community is often highly site specific (Cairns, 1975). Therefore, any hazard evaluation must consider the use to which the body of water is put and should recognize that not all waters support the most sensitive organisms or the same wide variety of taxa for good biological or geographical reasons.

Most chemicals, if in low enough concentrations, can be detoxified or excreted by aquatic organisms without adverse effects to either the individual's internal homeostatic mechanism or the community to which it belongs. It will be impossible, at times, to interpret the data from some studies because the 'end-point' between the adaptive response and the detrimental effect is difficult to define. Measurements made on community structure in the aquatic environment are even more difficult to interpret because of the large perturbations or deviations recorded in natural populations (Odum, Finn and Franz, 1979). For these reasons, most biologists have been dissuaded from field studies and very few scientific papers have dealt with the activity of a given pesticide at the population or community level (Livingston, 1977).

The data published on glyphosate for aquatic hazard evaluation have been prepared for pesticide registration purposes. Such information required by registration authorities covers the methods of application, the main areas of usage, the routes of entry into water and the chemical, physical and biological properties of both the active ingredient and formulation (Tooby, 1981). As is to be expected, most of the studies undertaken have measured the effects of relatively high concentrations of glyphosate which have caused death or large and obvious behavioural changes. These studies can be divided into two categories—laboratory and field investigations—and refer mainly to experiments with fish and macro-invertebrates.

The effects on macroflora and microorganisms are dealt with elsewhere (see also Chapters 11, 13 and 24). Similarly, the full details of the degradation pathways of glyphosate in soil, hydrosoil and water are reported elsewhere and will be presented briefly in this chapter, where relevant (see also Chapters 9 and 13).

Routes of entry into water

The isopropylamine salt of glyphosate, N-(phosphonomethyl)glycine, is a broad-spectrum herbicide used to control most annual weeds and perennial grasses. The commercial formulation, Roundup, can be applied up to 8 l ha^{-1} (2.9 kg a.i. ha^{-1}) from ground machinery to control weeds in a variety of agricultural, horticultural and forestry situations. Therefore, it could be used adjacent to a wide variety of aquatic ecosystems. As the solubility of glyphosate in water is 1.2% and the partition coefficient P, between n-octanol and water, is 0.0006 (at a concentration of 20 mg glyphosate per litre), data on the mobility of this chemical in soil will be relevant in the aquatic hazard evaluation. In this paper, because the biological effects of the active ingredient and the formulation are different, it will be important to differentiate between them; therefore, the term glyphosate will be used to refer to N-(phosphonomethyl)glycine and the term Roundup will be used for the commercial formulation containing 36% glyphosate acid equivalent.

Glyphosate (in the formulation Roundup) is extremely effective against emergent and bankside weeds (Evans, 1978) which could result in the direct contamination of watercourses. Roundup can be applied up to 6 l ha^{-1} (2.2 kg a.i. ha^{-1}) to emergent vegetation; however, in such situations the watercourse would have been drained before application or would be severely choked by the vegetation. This herbicide can be effective also in controlling water lilies, but although application is made directly on to the leaves, some contamination of the body of water could occur.

Glyphosate, therefore, could enter the aquatic environment by direct application, in the case of use in or near water, or by run-off or leaching from land use. Clearly, one of the most important aspects of the evaluation of the potential risk will be the rate of degradation of glyphosate in the soil and water and its potential for binding onto particles (see also Chapters 9, 13 and 28).

Degradation in soil and water

Laboratory studies

METABOLISM AND DEGRADATION IN SOIL

The fate and persistence of glyphosate in the soil is discussed in detail by Torstensson (Chapter 9). However, certain information will be presented here briefly to provide relevant data with which to evaluate the potential hazard.

Chemical degradation was studied in soil (Ray silt loam) and water, rendered sterile by repetitive autoclaving (Rueppel et al., 1977). No degradation was recorded, indicating that purely chemical factors are not involved in a major pathway of breakdown for glyphosate. However, in the presence of a rich soil microflora, glyphosate was biodegradable in both aerobic and anaerobic conditions. Between 47% and 55% of the activity of ^{14}C-labelled glyphosate was degraded to ^{14}CO$_2$ within 4 weeks in Ray silt loam under aerobic conditions. This was nearly the same extent and rate as sucrose–^{14}C, used as a reference standard. Rapid degradation of ^{14}C-methyl-labelled glyphosate occurred in other soils (Lintonia sandy loam and Drummer silty clay) which had high microbial populations. The influence of microorganisms on the rate of degradation was demonstrated in two soils: one which had a small natural microbial population (Norfolk sandy loam) and the other which had been stored and dried (Drummer silty clay), reducing the population. In both soils the rate of degradation was slow (see also Chapters 9 and 13).

The rates of degradation of glyphosate vary between different soils and can only be correlated with the general microbial activity which is an expression of many soil factors. Degradation occurs without any lag phase and seems to be a co-metabolic process under both aerobic and anaerobic conditions. Disappearance of any biological activity of glyphosate in soils is primarily due to a rapid inactivation by adsorption. As adsorption occurs through the phosphoric acid moiety and competes for binding sites with inorganic phosphates, the extent or capacity of adsorption is correlated with the unoccupied sites on the soil (see also Chapter 9).

The principal soil metabolite observed in the experiment of Rueppel et al. (1977) was aminomethylphosphonic acid (AMPA), which indicates that the glycine methylene and carboxyl groups may be lost as glyoxylate which, in turn, can be readily metabolized by the glyoxylate and citric acid cycles. These products can become precursors of complex, insoluble, non-extractable natural constituents in the soil organic matter. Other metabolities have been characterized, but comprise less than 1% of the total applied radio-labelled compound.

The degradation of the major metabolite was observed in Ray silt loam and Drummer silty clay soils; 34.8% and 16.1%, respectively, of the applied radio-labelled glyphosate was degraded to ^{14}CO$_2$ in 63 days. The slower rate, compared with glyphosate, reflects the tighter binding of the metabolite to soil.

Rueppel et al. (1977) also studied the potential run-off and mobility through soils and the rate of photodecomposition. In an experiment using a tray inclined at 7.5 degrees, containing Ray, Drummer and Norfolk soils and applying glyphosate at a rate of 1.12 kg a.i. ha^{-1} to the upper one-third of the soil surfaces, followed by three artificial rainfalls, less than 1% of the applied chemical was found in the run-off water and sediment. In soil mobility studies, 97–100% of the ^{14}C-activity was adsorbed onto soil columns containing the same three soils. Therefore, the lack of run-off is not surprising, due to the potential for adsorption on to soil particles. It was found that there was little loss of ^{14}C-activity through volatile degradation products following u.v. irradiation and this would be a minor route for degradation in the environment (see also Chapters 13 and 28).

METABOLISM AND DEGRADATION IN WATER AND HYDROSOIL

A full description of the fate of glyphosate in water is given by Brønstad and Friestad (Chapter 13). Residues did not decline in sterile water, but degradation did occur in natural waters with a high microbial population.

The metabolic pathways in hydrosoils are similar to those found in the soil, with the same metabolites and a similar proportion of ^{14}C activity bound to the silt particles. These points are particularly well illustrated by the following studies. A.

Henshall and B. Brightwell (personal communication) followed the degradation of methane–[14]C-labelled glyphosate in samples of water (pH 8.2–8.6) and mud (water content 26–38%) taken from the Mississippi, Illinois and Missouri rivers and from Springfield Lake, Illinois. It was noticeable that the degradation was markedly reduced in water alone. Only 1.5–5.8% of the ^{14}C-activity was found as [14]CO_2 in 45 days. However, as this was similar to the rate of degradation of the sucrose–[14]C reference compound, the slow rate was considered to be due to the low microbial population. The rate of degradation in the muds was similar to that found in soil with a rich microflora.

In another series of experiments, using natural waters high in particulate matter and a rich microflora from Ballard farm pond, Missouri (pH 7.3), Cattail swamp, Wisconsin (pH 6.2) and a sphagnum bog, Wisconsin (pH 4.2), J. Malik (personal communication) found that the most rapid rate of degradation of labelled glyphosate was in water at the lowest pH. The time taken to reach 50% degradation to the primary metabolite and [14]CO_2 in aerobic conditions at pH 4.2 was 7 weeks. The breakdown rate was similar in aerobic conditions and the rates of elimination did not follow simple first-order rate kinetics, which probably reflects the rapid adsorption onto particulate matter and a biphasic degradation.

Field studies

Several studies have been reported in which glyphosate residues were measured, following a variety of applications of Roundup to both static and flowing water. In static water, glyphosate was reported to be lost from the water body fairly rapidly. Following the application of Roundup (3.6 kg a.i. ha^{-1}) to a body of water 30 cm deep, the maximum residue concentration was found to be 1.7 mg a.i. l^{-1} after 4 h (P. Mestdagh, personal communication). Thereafter, the time taken to reach 50% of this maximum level was 12 h and the residues declined to the limit of determination, 8 days after treatment. During this time, the concentration of glyphosate in the hydrosoil followed a similar decline, which remained less than one-tenth of the concentration in the water. The metabolite aminomethylphosphonic acid was found in water 1 day after treatment and reached a maximum level of 0.07 mg a.i. l^{-1}, 4 days after treatment; however, residues of this metabolite were not found in the hydrosoil. The fairly rapid loss of glyphosate from water was reported also by Sacher (1978a) in a pond treated with glyphosate. No treatment concentration was given in this paper, but the decline of residues from a maximum of 460 µg a.i. l^{-1} followed a first-order rate and can be expressed in the equation $C_w = 374e^{-0.05t}$, where C_w is the concentration of glyphosate in µg l^{-1} at any time t.

These results are somewhat surprising, in view of the poor degradation found in laboratory studies, and most probably reflect the influence of suspended solids in adsorbing and removing residues from the water body. However, other factors such as water chemistry may have influenced the rate of loss, but such details were not reported.

In flowing water, the rate of elimination from the point of application will depend on the flow rate of the water body. In one study, Roundup was metered into each of two flowing canals to give an estimated concentration in the water of 150 µg a.i. l^{-1} (Comes, Bruns and Kelley, 1976). Samples were taken at points several kilometres downstream, so the extent of the movement of the herbicide in flowing water could be measured. Of the applied dose, 79–91% was accounted for at a sampling point 0.3 km downstream from the point of application, 70% at a point 1.6 km downstream and 58% at the end of the two canals 8 and 14.4 km downstream. This clearly demonstrates that, in certain conditions, glyphosate as Roundup could be transported a long distance downstream from the point of application. It is possible in this study that the glyphosate was bound to suspended solids, but the biological significance is unknown.

The same authors reported the results of a field study in more realistic conditions, in which they applied Roundup at a rate of 5.6 kg a.i. ha^{-1} to a ditch and its banks after draining the irrigation system. The ditch was flooded again 23 weeks after treatment and neither glyphosate nor the primary metabolite were found in the first flow of water. This confirms the results from the laboratory leaching and run-off tests. Samples of soil, taken from the top 10 cm of the ditch bottom 1 day before the flooding, contained 0.35 mg glyphosate per kilogram and 0.78 mg primary metabolite per kilogram.

Effects of glyphosate on aquatic organisms

Laboratory studies

ACUTE TOXICITY

Both the formulation Roundup and the isopropylamine salt of glyphosate alone have been tested for acute lethal toxicity to a number of fish and invertebrate

TABLE 14.1   The acute lethal toxicity of glyphosate (isopropylamine salt) to aquatic organisms

Species	Test conditions	Temp (°C)	Water hardness (mg CaCO$_3$ l^{-1} or salinity $^0/_{00}$)	pH	Median lethal concentration (mg l^{-1}) 24 h	48 h	96 h	Reference
Rainbow trout (*Salmo gairdneri*)								
fingerlings	static	—*	—	—	—	50	—	Folmar (1976)
fingerlings	static	12	40	7.2	97	—	97	Folmar *et al.* (1979)
fingerlings	static	—	—	—	—	—	38	Sacher (1978a)
fingerlings	static	—	—	—	—	—	50	Sacher (1978b)
Bluegill sunfish (*Lepomis macro-chirus*)	static	22	40	7.2	150	—	140	Folmar *et al.* (1979)
fingerlings	—	—	—	—	—	—	78	Sacher (1978b)
fingerlings	—	—	—	—	—	—	>24	Sacher (1978b)
Channel catfish (*Ictalurus punctatus*)								
fingerlings	static	22	40	7.2	130	—	130	Folmar *et al.* (1979)
Fathead minnows (*Pimephales promelas*)								
fingerlings	static	22	40	7.2	97	—	97	Folmar *et al.* (1979)
Carp fingerlings (*Cyprinus carpio*)	static	—	—	—	—	—	125	Sacher (1978b)
Atlantic oyster embryos (*Crassostrea virginica*)	—	—	—	—	—	>10†	—	Sacher (1978b)
Fiddler crab (*Uca pugilator*)	—	—	—	—	—	—	934	Sacher (1978b)
Grass shrimp (*Palaemonetes vulgaris*)	—	—	—	—	—	—	281	Sacher (1978b)
Chironomus plumosus	static	22	40	7.2	55	—	—	Folmar *et al.* (1979)

*—=not reported. †Measured response = failure to survive to D-shaped veliger larva.

TABLE 14.2   The acute lethal toxicity of Roundup to freshwater aquatic organisms

Species	Test conditions	Temp. (°C)	Water hardness (mg CaCO$_3$ l^{-1})	pH	Median lethal concentration (mg l^{-1}) 24 h	48 h	96 h	Reference
Rainbow trout (*Salmo gairdneri*)								
fingerlings	static	12	—*	6.2	—	—	54.8	Hildebrand *et al.* (1982)
fingerlings	static field bioassay	11	—	6.7	—	—	52	Hildebrand *et al.* (1982)
fingerlings	static	12	40	7.2	8.3	—	8.3	Folmar *et al.* (1979)
fingerlings	—	—	—	—	—	—	48	Sacher (1978b)
Channel catfish (*Ictalurus punctatus*)								
fingerlings	static	22	40	7.2	13	—	13	Folmar *et al.* (1979)
fingerlings	—	—	—	—	—	—	19.5	Sacher (1978b)
Bluegill sunfish (*Lepomis macrochirus*)								
fingerlings	static	22	40	7.2	6.4	—	5.0	Folmar *et al.*(1979)
fingerlings	—	—	—	—	—	—	24	Sacher (1978b)
Fathead minnows (*Pimephales promelas*)								
fingerlings	static	22	40	7.2	2.4	—	2.3	Folmar *et al.* (1979)
Harlequin fish	continuous flow	23	20	7.9	21	16	12	Tooby (1976)
Grass carp (*Ctenopharyngodon idella* Val.) yearlings	continuous flow	18	270	8.1	26	24	15	Tooby *et al.* (1980)
Major carp (*Cirrhina mrigala*)	static	15–18	—	—	—	—	5–10	Singh and Yadav (1978)
Crayfish	—	—	—	—	—	—	>1000	Sacher (1978b)
Gammarus pseudolimnaeus	static	12	40	7.2	>100	62	43	Folmar *et al.* (1979)
Daphnia magna	static	22	40	7.2	—	3.0†	—	Folmar *et al.* (1979)
D. pulex	—	—	—	—	—	192†	—	Sacher (1978b)
Chironomus plumosus	static	22	40	7.2	—	18†	—	Folmar *et al.* (1979)

*—= not reported. †Measured response = immobility.

species. The results of the studies on glyphosate are summarized in *Table 14.1* and those for Roundup in *Table 14.2*.

Lloyd (1977) stated that the shape and slope of the acute lethal toxicity curve was extremely valuable for identifying potential risk of a chemical. In many of the studies there was no difference between the 24 h and 96 h LC$_{50}$ values. The probable reason for this was that, in the static test conditions used, the test concentrations of glyphosate declined during the test period to levels which were no longer biologically active. Despite the obvious variety of test conditions, there does not appear to be a great difference between the sensitivities of the species of fish used. The relationship between the 24 h and 96 h LC$_{50}$ values indicates that survival time increases by a factor of 4 with a decrease of 50% in the test concentration (see concentration–response data of Tooby, 1976, and Tooby, Lucey and Stott, 1980). There does not appear to be an obvious difference between the sensitivity of fish and macro-invertebrates, although the larger crustacea appear to be slightly less sensitive than fish.

Roundup is more toxic than glyphosate alone, which indicates that the chemicals

TABLE 14.3 **Comparison of the acute lethal toxicities of glyphosate (isopropylamine salt), Roundup and the surfactant to rainbow trout (*Salmo gairdneri*) and bluegill sunfish (*Lepomis macrochirus*) tested in static conditions at pH 6.5 (after Folmar, Sanders and Julin, 1979)**

| Fish | Chemical | Median lethal concentration (mg l^{-1}) | |
		24 h	96 h
Rainbow trout fingerlings	Roundup	14	7.6
	glyphosate	240	140.0
	surfactant	7.4	7.4
Bluegill sunfish fingerlings	Roundup	7.6	4.2
	glyphosate	240	140.0
	surfactant	4.2	1.3

formulated with glyphosate significantly modify the toxicity (see also Chapters 11 and 15). Folmar, Sander and Julin (1979) examined the toxicity of Roundup, glyphosate and the surfactant to rainbow trout (*Salmo gairderi*) and bluegill sunfish (*Lepomis macrochirus*) fingerlings (*Table 14.3*). The surfactant alone is more toxic than glyphosate, which explains the increase in toxicity of Roundup.

To put these acute toxicity data in perspective, the safety factor, based on the ratio of the 96 h LC$_{50}$ for rainbow trout (Folmar, Sanders and Julin, 1979) of 8.3 mg Roundup per litre and a predicted maximum environmental concentration of 0.6 mg Roundup per litre, is 14. The environmental concentration for this purpose was calculated from the maximum recommended treatment rate for aquatic use applied to water 1 m deep.

The toxicity of Roundup is affected by temperature and water pH. An excellent series of experiments was reported by Folmar, Sanders and Julin (1979), in which the effect of temperature, pH and the stage of development of the test organism on the acute lethal toxicity of Roundup were studied. Some of these data are presented in *Table 14.4*. An increase in both temperature and pH caused an increase in the toxicity of Roundup. The same authors reported that the toxicity of the surfactant increased with an increase in pH; however, glyphosate decreased in toxicity with an increase in pH, but the reason was unknown. In *Table 14.2*, the wide variation between the 48 h LC$_{50}$ values quoted for the two species of *Daphnia* cannot be explained by species variation alone. It is probable that the experimental conditions, such as pH or temperature, were different in the two studies.

The early life-stages of fish species are the most sensitive to aquatic pollutants (McKim, 1977), and in this respect glyphosate is no exception. The 'yolk-sac' and early 'swim-up' fry were the most sensitive to Roundup and the eggs were the least sensitive (*Table 14.4*). Folmar, Sanders and Julin (1979) also reported that, following exposure to Roundup for 4 h, followed by a transfer to flowing clean water, to observe post-treatment effects, survival of eggs and yolk-sac fry were reduced at 10 and 5 mg Roundup per litre, respectively.

The same authors studied the impact of 12 h exposure of either Roundup or glyphosate on the drift of the midge larva (*Chironomus plumosus*), along an artificial stream. The results were interesting in that there was a significant increase in the drift observed after an exposure to Roundup at a concentration of 2.0 mg l^{-1}, but not after exposure to glyphosate alone at 2.0 mg glyphosate per litre. In addition, solutions of Roundup were 'aged' at 12°C and 22°C for a period of 7 days prior to testing for acute toxicity. There was no difference between the toxicity of aged and fresh solutions of Roundup to fish, which was to be expected in waters with a low microflora.

TABLE 14.4   The effect of temperature, pH and the stage of development of the test organism on the acute toxicity of Roundup to fish (after Folmar, Sanders and Julin, 1979).

Fish	Stage of development	Temp. (°C)	pH	Median lethal concentration (mg l^{-1}) 24 h	96 h
Rainbow trout	fingerling	7	7.2	14	14
(*Salmo gairdneri*)	fingerling	12	7.2	14	7.5
	fingerling	17	7.2	7.5	7.4
	fingerling	12	6.5	14	7.6
	fingerling	12	7.5	2.4	1.6
	fingerling	12	8.5	2.4	1.4
	fingerling	12	9.5	2.4	1.4
	eyed eggs	12	7.2	46	16
	sac fry	12	7.2	11	3.4
	swim-up fry	12	7.2	2.4	2.4
	alevin	12	7.2	2.2	1.3
Bluegill sunfish	fingerling	17	7.2	9.6	7.5
(*Lepomis macro-*	fingerling	22	7.2	6.4	5.0
chirus)	fingerling	27	7.2	4.3	4.0
	fingerling	22	6.5	7.6	4.2
	fingerling	22	7.5	40	2.4
	fingerling	22	8.5	3.9	2.4
	fingerling	22	9.5	2.4	1.8
Channel catfish	eyed eggs	22	7.2	43	—*
(*Ictalurus punctatus*)	sac fry	22	7.2	4.3	4.3
	swim-up fry	22	7.2	3.7	3.3
	fingerling	22	7.2	13	13

*— = not determined

SUB-LETHAL TOXICITY

Rainbow trout in spawning condition were exposed to both Roundup and glyphosate for a period of 12 h at concentrations of 0.02, 0.2 and 2.0 mg l^{-1} (Folmar, Sanders and Julin, 1979). This was followed by a 30-day period in clean flowing water, after which time the fecundity, measured as the number of eggs per female, and the gonadosomatic index, measured as the ratio of gonad weight to total body weight, were determined. No detectable changes were recorded when compared with a control group. No residues of glyphosate or the primary metabolite were found above the limits of determination in eggs or muscle tissue from the fish exposed to glyphosate, but fish exposed to Roundup accumulated 60 µg glyphosate per kilogram in the eggs and 80 mg glyphosate per kilogram in the muscle tissue, although there must be some considerable doubt about the validity of the latter figure, in view of the data on the accumulation of glyphosate residues in fish.

During an earlier study on the acute toxicity of a range of herbicides to grass carp (*Ctenopharyngodon idella* Val.) (Tooby, Lucey and Stott, 1980), the fish were observed to refuse food when exposed to sub-lethal concentrations of many of the herbicides, including Roundup. A further experiment (Tooby, in preparation) showed that a continuous exposure of 10 mg Roundup per litre caused complete feeding inhibition. However, at the next lowest concentration of 3.2 mg Roundup per litre, there was no significant loss of feeding compared with a control group and a pre-test observation.

A recent interesting attempt at understanding the interrelationships between macro-invertebrates and the possible use of chemical stimuli to communicate has been developed by R. Kickuth (personal communication). The main hypothesis is that some chemicals could alter the behaviour of certain aquatic organisms by confusing chemical signals. For example, such chemicals could be amino acids and the structure of glyphosate is close to that of sarcosine. In order to test this hypothesis, two species of shrimp, *Rivulogammarus* sp. and *Carcinogammarus* sp., were placed in avoidance chambers and exposed to extremely low levels of glyphosate. At levels between 17 and 23 μg glyphosate per litre neither of the species avoided or were attracted to the chemical, nor were they killed by it. However, the mating behaviour of one of the species, which would have been regarded as the more sensitive species, from a clean, upland, fast-flowing stream, was slightly impaired, compared with a control group. This response was measured as the frequency of the two sexes being found coupled together. It is doubtful at this stage whether these effects would be significant in the natural environment. Also, there is no evidence to support the use of chemical stimuli by organisms inhabiting fast-flowing streams.

TISSUE RESIDUE ACCUMULATION AND ELIMINATION

The results of several studies on the accumulation potential of glyphosate in fish have been published by Sacher (1978a; 1978b), but no experimental details were given which reduces their usefulness in this review. Bluegill sunfish were exposed for 28 days to 0.6 mg glyphosate per litre. Although no residues data were given, the maximum bio-concentration factor was 1.6. However, in another three species of fish, much lower bioaccumulation factors were found, which might be explained by different experimental conditions. The three species of fish—rainbow trout, largemouth bass (*Micropterus salmoides*) and channel catfish (*Ictalurus punctatus*)—were exposed for a 14-day period to four concentrations of glyphosate, 0.1, 1.0, 3.0 and 10.0 mg l^{-1}, followed by a 35-day period in clean water. The results for the highest exposure concentration only were presented in graphical form. The bio-accumulation factors for rainbow trout, largemouth bass and channel catfish exposed to 10 mg glyphosate per litre were 0.03, 0.04 and 0.18, respectively. From the graph it appeared that an equilibrium concentration between fish and the water was reached by the end of 7 days of exposure, in both rainbow trout and largemouth bass. However, the tissue analysed was not specified. In channel catfish, an equilibrium concentration was not reached in the fish and the graph showed a variable accumulation which might have been a reflection of the experimental conditions. In clean water, the rainbow trout and channel catfish eliminated residues fairly rapidly, reaching about 50% of the initial concentration within 4–6 days.

It has been proposed (Hamelink, Waybrant and Ball, 1971; Neely, Branson and Blau, 1974) that partition coefficients indicate the amounts of organic chemical to be found in animals. Therefore, glyphosate would not be expected to accumulate in high quantities. However, the uptake and retention of molecules depends not only on passive diffusion but also on processes of active transport, metabolism and excretion, which vary with different species (Walker, 1975). Nevertheless, although the published data on glyphosate accumulation are minimal, the bio-accumulation potential is low in the species tested.

AVOIDANCE BEHAVIOUR

It has been shown that rainbow trout show a preference to avoid high concentrations of Roundup. Folmar (1976) found that rainbow trout did not avoid concentrations of up to 10 mg Roundup per litre during a 1 h exposure in a classic Y-shaped channel experiment. However, concentrations of 40 and 50 mg Roundup per litre were avoided during a 1 h exposure and the highest concentration was avoided during a 20 min exposure in a similar experiment (Hildebrand, Sullivan and Sullivan, 1982), but no explanation for this is given.

In a similar series of experiments, mayfly nymphs (*Ephemerella walkeri*) (older than 4th instar) were shown to avoid a concentration of 10 mg Roundup per litre (Folmar, Sanders and Julin, 1979). Although these results are interesting, they demonstrate that the concentrations at which there is a statistically significant avoidance reaction are very close to the acutely lethal concentration and are unlikely to be found in the environment following recommended application practices.

Field studies

The only studies reported on the effects of glyphosate on microflora were those published by Sullivan, Sullivan and Bisalputra (1981). The effects of Roundup application on the diatom populations in each of two streams and a pond were studied, as a measure of the effect of this chemical on primary production. In each case, Roundup was applied to the water body at a rate of 2.2 kg a.i. ha^{-1}. It was found that the variation in abundance of the diatoms was determined mainly by habitat and season. However, some diatom species, notably *Tabellaria* spp., *Navicula* spp. and *Cymbella* spp., in the sediment increased in numbers in a treated pond compared with that of a control site. This was probably due to the change in habitat following the eradication of emergent vegetation and the consequent change in nutrient status, incident light and temperature (see also Chapter 11).

The results of most of the other field studies emphasize the limitations of laboratory experiments and the difficulty in predicting risks. In common with many chemicals, effects are not seen in the field at levels which would be detrimental in the laboratory because of the rapid loss of chemical from the water. In the short term, adsorption onto suspended solids and hydrosoil rapidly reduces the biologically available soluble glyphosate. This effect has been clearly demonstrated with a synthetic pyrethroid (Crossland, 1982) and an algicide (Tooby, Thompson and Rycroft, 1982), and glyphosate could be regarded as being very similar.

Applications of Roundup at 2.2 kg a.i. ha^{-1}, and at 10 and 100 times this rate, were made directly to a stream (Hildebrand, Sullivan and Sullivan, 1982) and no overt signs of stress were observed in rainbow trout caged downstream of the application. For 15 min, during and shortly after the application, the trout increased swimming activity. Unfortunately, no chemical analyses were carried out on the river water and, therefore, the value of this study may be limited. Roundup applications directly onto water in experimental ponds at rates up to 100 times that recommended, caused negligible effects on *Daphnia magna* populations (Buikema, Benfield and Niederlehner, 1981). To some extent this can be explained by the presence of suspended solids in the water body. The toxicity of glyphosate to daphnids can be reduced by about one-third in the presence of 50 mg l^{-1} suspended solids (USDI, 1981). It is of interest to note that daphnids were unable to prevent accretion of small particles onto their limbs and carapace when exposed to sub-lethal concentrations of the insecticide permethrin (Stratton and Corke, 1981). However, glyphosate is unlikely to have the same toxic action as the insecticide on this physiological function.

Conclusions

Glyphosate, when used as recommended by the manufacturer, is unlikely to enter watercourses through run-off or leaching following terrestrial application. Clearly, significant residues could enter water when Roundup is used as an aquatic herbicide. In static water, residues decline fairly rapidly due mainly to adsorption onto particulate matter. In some flowing water the conditions could be such that glyphosate could remain in solution or adsorbed onto particulate matter in suspension, for some distance downstream from the point of application.

Although the rate of degradation of residues depends on pH, temperature and the presence of microorganisms, most aquatic environments likely to receive Roundup treatment will provide the most ideal conditions for degradation. The field experience seems to support the laboratory predictions that residues will be adsorbed and will eventually break down. Therefore, it is unlikely that glyphosate will affect aquatic organisms at the concentrations found in the environment after use at the recommended rates. It is also unlikely that residues will be accumulated in fish tissues.

The only evidence which suggests a potentially harmful effect at glyphosate concentrations likely to be found after aquatic herbicide use, refers to a species of shrimp which would normally inhabit an ecological niche which would not receive glyphosate treatment.

Waters requiring weed control will have a management strategy dictated by the use to which that water is put. In land drainage areas, the main consideration would be for complete weed eradication. In an amenity area, wildlife or fishing may dictate that certain areas of emergent weed should remain. Loss of some of the weed habitat increases the open-water areas and consequently increases the predation; for example, the numbers of some macro-invertebrates will be reduced by predatory fish. Any weed loss alters the habitat and the balance of species, so the weed removal itself is likely to be of greater significance than glyphosate residues. In most cases, however, the problem weed will have rendered the watercourse unusable as a drainage channel, navigable waterway or fishery because of the encroachment of emergent weed to cover all or a major part of the surface. This excessive weed growth would not provide the best habitat for aquatic organisms and would represent an ecosystem that has become unbalanced and in need of management.

References

BUIKEMA, A.L., BENFIELD, E.F. and NIEDERLEHNER, B.R. (1981). Effects of pollution on freshwater invertebrates, *Journal of the Water Pollution Control Federation*, **53**(6), 1007–1015.
CAIRNS, J., JNR. (1975). Quantification of biological integrity. Proceedings of the Symposium on

Integrity of Water, Washington D.C., 10–12 March (Eds. R.K. Ballentine and L.J. Guarria), Washington, Environmental Protection Agency.

COMES, R.D., BRUNS, V.F. and KELLEY, A.D. (1976). Residues and persistence of glyphosate in irrigation water, *Weed Science*, **24**(1), 47–50.

CROSSLAND, N.O. (1982). Aquatic toxicology of cypermethrin. II. Fate and biological effects in pond experiments, *Aquatic Toxicology*, **2**, 205–222.

EVANS, D.M. (1978). Aquatic weed control with the isopropylamine salt of *N*-phosphonomethyl glycine, *Proceedings of the European Weed Research Society 5th Symposium on Aquatic Weeds*, Amsterdam, pp. 171–178.

FOLMAR, L.C. (1976). Overt avoidance reaction of rainbow trout fry to nine herbicides, *Bulletin of Environmental Contamination and Toxicology*, **15**(5), 509–514.

FOLMAR, L.C., SANDERS, H.O. and JULIN, A.M. (1979). Toxicity of the herbicide glyphosate and several of its formulations to fish and aquatic invertebrates, *Archives of Environmental Contamination and Toxicology*, **8**(3), 269–278.

HAMELINK, J.L., WAYBRANT, R.C. and BALL, R.C. (1971). A proposal: exchange equilibria control the degree chlorinated hydrocarbons are biologically magnified in lentic environments, *Transactions of the American Fisheries Society*, **100**, 207–214.

HILDEBRAND, L.D., SULLIVAN, D.S. and SULLIVAN, T.P. (1982). Experimental studies of rainbow trout populations exposed to field applications of Roundup herbicide, *Archives of Environmental Contamination and Toxicology*, **11**(1), 93–98.

LIVINGSTON, R.J. (1977). Review of current literature concerning the acute and chronic effects of pesticides on aquatic organisms, *CRC Critical Reviews in Environmental Contamination*, **7**, 325.

LLOYD, R. (1977). Are short term fish toxicity tests a dead end? Paper presented to the British Association for the Advancement of Science, Aston University, Birmingham, UK.

MCKIM, J.M. (1977). Evaluation of tests with early-life stages of fish for predicting long-term toxicity, *Journal of the Fisheries Research Board of Canada*, **34**(8), 1148–1154.

NEELY, W.B., BRANSON, D.R. and BLAU, G.E. (1974). Partition coefficients to measure bioconcentration potential of organic chemicals in fish, *Environmental Science and Technology*, **8**, 1113–1115.

ODUM, E.P., FINN, J.T. and FRANZ, E.H. (1979). Perturbation theory and the subsidy-stress gradient, *Biological Science*, **29**(6), 349–352.

PRESTON, A. (1979). Standards and environmental criteria: the practical application of the results of laboratory experiments and field trials to pollution control, *Philosophical Transactions of the Royal Society of London*, Ser. B, **286**, 611–624.

RUEPPEL, M.L., BRIGHTWELL, B.B., SCHAEFER, J. and MARVEL, J.T. (1977). Metabolism and degradation of glyphosate in soil and water, *Journal of Agricultural and Food Chemistry*, **25**(3), 517–528.

SACHER, R.M. (1978a). Safety of Roundup in aquatic environment, *Proceedings of the European Weed Research Society 5th Symposium on Aquatic Weeds*, Amsterdam, pp. 315–322.

SACHER, R.M. (1978b). Roundup, Seminar, Madrid, March 1978, pp. 3–23.

SINGH, S.P. and YADAV, N.K. (1978). Toxicity of some herbicides to major carp fingerlings, *Indian Journal of Ecology*, **5**(2), 141–147.

STRATTON, G.W. and CORKE, C.T. (1981). Interaction of permethrin with *Daphnia magna* in the presence and absence of particulate material, *Environmental Pollution*, Ser (A), **24**, 135–144.

SULLIVAN, D.S., SULLIVAN, T.P. and BISALPUTRA, T. (1981). Effects of Roundup herbicide and diatom populations in the aquatic environment of a coastal forest, *Bulletin of Environmental Contamination and Toxicology*, **26**(1), 91–96.

TOOBY, T.E. (1976). Effects of aquatic herbicides on fisheries, in Proceedings of a Symposium on Aquatic Herbicides, Oxford. British Crop Protection Council, Monograph No. 16, pp. 62–77.

TOOBY, T.E. (1981). Predicting the direct toxic effects of aquatic herbicides to non-target organisms, Proceedings of a Symposium on Aquatic Weeds and their Control, Christ Church, Oxford, 7–8 April 1981, pp. 265–274.

TOOBY, T.E., LUCEY, J. and STOTT, B. (1980). The tolerance of grass carp, *Ctenopharyngodon idella* Val., to aquatic herbicides, *Journal of Fish Biology*, **16**(4), 591–597.

TOOBY, T.E., THOMPSON, A.N. and RYCROFT, R.J. (1982). The effects of an experimental algicide PH 40:62 on aquatic macroinvertebrates, *Proceedings of the European Weed Research Society 6th Symposium on Aquatic Weeds*, Novi Sad, pp. 235–243.

USDI (1981). *Fisheries and Wildlife Research, 1980*, US Department of the Interior, Fish and Wildlife Service.

WALKER, C.H. (1975). Variations in the intake and elimination of pollutants, in *Organochlorine Insecticides: Persisent Organic Pollutants* (Ed. F. Moriarty), London, Academic Press, pp. 73–130.

Part V

Application of Glyphosate

Chapter 15

Effects on glyphosate performance of formulation, additives and mixing with other herbicides

D.J. Turner
Weed Research Organization, Oxford, UK

Introduction

Herbicides can be applied in a variety of ways, but liquid sprays are the commonest method. These are usually water based, and contain the herbicide in solution or as an emulsion or suspension. Some compounds can be used directly as the unamended active ingredient, but usually they must be formulated to be usable and effective. Material intended for spray application must disperse readily in water and be at least reasonably active against target weeds. Some formulated products contain a derivative of the herbicide, which retains the phytotoxicity of the parent compound but has more suitable physical properties. Water-soluble derivatives, if they can be made, often are the first choice. Oil-soluble materials are almost as common: with these products an oil-based concentrate is dispersed as an emulsion in a much larger volume of water. Wettable powders, which consist of finely ground solid material mixed with dispersing and suspending agents, are another standard type of formulation. Strictly speaking, the term 'formulation' refers to a product prepared for practical use. However the term is also applied to the derivative used in making the formulation, for example acid, ester or amine salt formulations of 2,4-D.

As well as the herbicide or its derivative, formulated products usually contain other non-herbicidal ingredients, to facilitate mixing or improve herbicidal efficacy. Thus an oil-based formulation will usually contain a surfactant which assists the formation of a stable emulsion of the oil in water. Other surfactants may be added to improve the wetting and spreading properties of sprays. Sequestrants may be included, to help counteract the effects of hard water. Some commercial formulations contain other ingredients, such as dyes or materials which retard evaporation. The exact constitution is often undisclosed because formulations are difficult to patent.

There are limitations as to what can be mixed with a herbicide at the factory. Some chemicals are unstable or react with other ingredients to reduce the storage life of the product; others are bulky or require special packaging. Some ingredients are only useful in special circumstances, for example when the herbicide is used against a particular weed. Materials which for such reasons are not included in the manufacturer's formulation are sometimes added to the spray just before use. These materials are termed additives or adjuvants. Some are similar or identical to the formulation ingredients which are used by the chemical companies, for example surfactants, whereas others, such as urea or ammonium salts, are rarely found in commercial formulations. Another herbicide may be used as an additive; for example, where there is need to widen the spectrum of herbicidal activity or to combine rapid contact with longer lasting residual effects. Additives can be used or left out of the spray as desired, but when formulation ingredients are incorporated at the factory there is no such choice.

It is against this background that glyphosate formulation and additives will be discussed.

Derivatives of glyphosate

Glyphosate acid, N-(phosphonomethyl)glycine, is strongly herbicidal and was used in early field trials under the code MON 0573 (Baird et al., 1971). However, low water solubility—about 1% at 25°C (Anon., 1971)—makes the free acid inconvenient to use. At an early stage of development, salts with higher water solubility were introduced. These include the monosodium salt (Mon 0459), the monodimethylamine salt (MON 0468) and the monoisopropylamine salt (MON 0139) (Anon., 1971). Shaner (1978) mentions the use of a potassium salt. However, for many years Monsanto have concentrated on glyphosate isopropylamine. A mixture of MON 0139 with a wetter of undisclosed type, MON 0818, was issued first as MON 2139, later as the commercial formulation Roundup (Baird, Brown and Photak, 1974). Why the isopropylamine salt was chosen in preference to other formulations has not been disclosed; however, according to Franz (1979), many hundreds of derivatives including esters, hydrazides and amides were made and tested. The isopropylamine salt is active, convenient to use and in most circumstances probably as effective as any other derivative. In laboratory studies, Shaner (1978) observed little difference in the effect on transpiration rate of isopropylamine and potassium salts. It is possible that less polar glyphosate derivatives might give better results where the herbicide must pass through lipophilic barriers such as bark or thick leaf cuticle. In general, esters are more suitable than salts under such circumstances. Glyphosate esters can be made without difficulty, esterification being an essential step in a commonly used method for determining residues (Worthing, 1979).

Unfortunately, many esters of glyphosate are relatively insoluble in the lipophilic solvents used in formulation (E.G. Cotterill, personal communication). An effective but expensive method of obtaining a lipophilic type of glyphosate formulation is to solubilize unformulated aqueous glyphosate isopropylamine, or Roundup, into oil with a large amount of surfactant (Turner and Loader, 1974). Solubilized oil-based glyphosate is a clear transparent liquid, which superficially resembles a true solution. However, solubilized preparations have a complex structure, the solute molecules remaining in aqueous solution within aggregations of surfactant molecules, termed micelles. A detailed account of solubilization of surfactants is given by Elworthy, Florence and Macfarlane (1968). A comparison of the activity of aqueous- and oil-based solubilized glyphosate solutions against a species with thick leaf cuticle, *Rhododendron ponticum,* is shown in *Figure 15.1.* After 64 days, plants treated with 3 kg a.i. ha^{-1} of glyphosate in water (as Roundup) were little affected, but plants treated with the same amount of glyphosate solubilized into oil were defoliated. As well as increasing the activity of

F 97   64 days
Control

3 kg ha⁻¹

Glyphosate,
aqueous

3 kg ha⁻¹

Glyphosate,
solubilized
(GMO)

3 kg ha⁻¹

Glyphosate,
solubilized
(PEG)

Figure 15.1. Effect of aqueous and solubilized glyphosate on
Rhododendron ponticum. Solubilized oil-based spray solutions were prepared by using a 1:2 mixture of glycerol mono-
oleate and Agral (3rd plant from left) or a 1:1 mixture of Ethomeen T13 and glycerol mono-oleate (4th plant from left)

glyphosate applied to leaves, solubilization can enhance the effects of bark
applications (Turner and Loader, 1974). In a glasshouse experiment carried out by
Parker, reported by Ivens (1976), solubilization increased glyphosate activity
against a grass, *Imperata cylindrica.* In general, however, results with herbaceous
species have been disappointing. Solubilized glyphosate as the isopropylamine salt
applied in 20 l ha⁻¹ of oil with a rotary atomizer had less effect on *Agropyron
repens* than aqueous glyphosate isopropylamine with a wetting agent, applied
similarly (Caseley, Coupland and Simmons, 1976). Solubilization may enhance
uptake, but overall have an adverse effect on herbicide activity, perhaps because
the herbicide molecules are immobilized within the micelles. When oil containing a
solubilized water-soluble dye is emulsified with water, movement of dye from the
micelle to the continuous aqueous phase is slow (D.J. Turner, unpublished results).

Another instance of re-formulating Roundup for a special purpose is for selective
application to tall weeds with a sponge-rubber roller. Oswald (1978; 1980)
incorporated Roundup, 1–10% glyphosate a.i., into a calcium alginate gel. This
performed well against *Rumex obtusifolius* in grassland (see p. 413).

Formulation ingredients and non-herbicidal additives

Surfactants

The addition of surfactants generally improves the activity of glyphosate
isopropylamine. This is recognized by Monsanto, whose commercial product
Roundup contains added wetter, the type and amount of which are undisclosed.
Early reports by Baird *et al.* (1971) mention the use of 1% 'Activate 107' wetter in
spray solutions containing MON 0459 (monosodium salt) and MON 0468
(dimethylamine salt). Evans (1972), working in Britain with dimethylamine and

isopropylamine salts, used only a 0.1% concentration of an undisclosed surfactant. Wyrill and Burnside (1977) evaluated a range of surfactants as additives for glyphosate isopropylamine applied to *Asclepias syriaca* and *Apocynum cannibinum*. Effects were variable and difficult to predict, but almost all surfactants enhanced phytotoxicity. In general, ethoxylated amine surfactants were better than non-ionic ones, performance tending to improve with increased ethylene oxide content. Surfactants with a hydrophile–lipophile balance (HLB) (Behrens, 1964) of 16–20, were particularly effective. Shaner (1978) found that addition of only 0.05% surfactant (MON 0818) to the spray solution increased the speed of action of technical glyphosate isopropylamine, as measured by effects on rates of transpiration from treated pea (*Pisum sativum*), bean (*Phaseolus vulgaris*) and sunflower (*Helianthus annuus*) leaves. Chykaliuk, Abernathy and Gipson (1979; 1980) found that the use of Roundup, in place of the technical isopropylamine salt, increased absorption of ^{14}C-glyphosate by leaves of *Helianthus ciliaris,* from 30% to 82% of the applied dose. However, with another surfactant, AG 98, absorption increased to 99%. In the field, the mixture of technical isopropylamine salt with AG 98 was more effective than an equivalent treatment with Roundup.

When no other additives were used, Turner and Loader (1980) found the hydrophilic type of non-ionic or cationic surfactant to be more effective. This result agrees with work by Wyrill and Burnside (1977). However, in the presence of ammonium sulphate the more lipophilic wetters gave better results.

Jordan (1981) demonstrated an interaction between the presence of surfactant (0.2% nonoxynol in the spray solution) and spray volume. With spray volumes of 47, 94 or 187 l ha^{-1} the surfactant enhanced phytotoxicity, but the effect almost disappeared at a volume of 374 l ha^{-1}.

So far, the addition of surfactants to technical glyphosate isopropylamine has been considered. There are many reports of effects of adding surfactants to formulated glyphosate. It is not always stated that Roundup was used, but in most cases this may be assumed. Selected results are summarized in *Table 15.1*.

It is clear that the addition of extra surfactant often improves the effects of Roundup, particularly when low doses are used against resistant weeds. This is perhaps to be expected, as Roundup is used for many and varied purposes. Doses may vary from 0.2 to 4 kg a.i. ha^{-1} or more, and spray volumes from perhaps 5 to 500 l ha^{-1}. The ratio of surfactant to herbicide in Roundup is fixed so that the use of a single formulation for such diverse treatments must involve compromise. If, as seems likely, the surfactant level in Roundup is intended for application of about 2 kg a.i. ha^{-1} of herbicide in 200–250 l ha^{-1}, it will be inadequate when only 0.2 kg a.i. ha^{-1} is applied in this spray volume. Conversely, when higher doses are applied in very low volumes, the surfactant concentration may be too high.

It is sometimes assumed that the main effect of surfactants in herbicide formulations is to reduce interfacial tension and so improve the wetting properties of sprays. Surfactants do promote wetting, of course, but the concentrations needed to achieve maximum reduction of interfacial tension of solution are low, often less than 0.02% (Durham, 1961). In the experiments discussed, enhancement of phytotoxicity was obtained with much higher concentrations, e.g. 0.5% or 2%. These amounts were present initially in the spray solution: as the spray deposit evaporated from leaves, surfactant concentration would have increased even further. It must be concluded that the effects of surfactants on glyphosate phytotoxicity are not entirely due to reduced surface tension, but at least partly to

TABLE 15.1   The effect of the addition of surfactants on the performance of Roundup

Species tested	Surfactant(s) and concentration in spray solution	Effect	Reference
Agropyron repens	Range of non-ionic and cationic surfactants, 0.1%–2.5%	Increased phytotoxicity particularly from more hydrophilic surfactants	Turner and Loader (1980)
A. repens	Atplus 411F, 1.5%	0.5 kg a.i. ha^{-1} had effect equal to 1 kg a.i. ha^{-1} without additives	Bhowmik and Doll (1981)
Allium spp.	'Spraytac' (mixture of resin, ethylene oxide surfactant and paraffinic ketones), 0.5%–1%	Enhanced activity	Hardcastle (1976)
Convolvulus arvensis	X-77 wetter, concentration unspecified	No effect	Lange et al. (1975)
C. arvensis	MON 0011 wetter, 1%	Improved control, particularly when spray solution made up with hard water	Selleck and Kline (1978)
Cotton (Gossypium hirsutum)	Nonoxynol wetter, 1%	Increased phytotoxicity, particularly in hot dry conditions	Wills (1978)
Cynodon dactylon	Z-77 wetter, concentration unspecified	Improved activity	Lange et al. (1975)
Cyperus rotundus	MON 0027 wetter, 0.25% or 2%	Greater activity in glasshouse and in the field	Wills (1973b)
C. rotundus	MON 0011 wetter, 0.5%	Improved control	Selleck (1980)
Digitaria sanguinalis, Panicum dichotomiflorum	MON 0011 wetter, 0.5%	Improved control	Ahrens (1980)
Equisetum arvense	Alkylaryl polyoxyethylene surfactant, 0.5%	Greatly improved control	Coupland and Peabody (1981)
E. arvense	Cationic surfactant, Ethomeen C25, 0.5%	Improved control	UK West of Scotland Agricultural College (1981)
Oat (Avena sativa), Radish (Raphanus sativus)	Cationic surfactant, Ethomeen T25, 0.5%	Enhanced activity	Davies and Taylor (1980)
Tropical grass and broad-leaved weeds	Triton AE wetter and sticker	Increased phytotoxicity when rain occurred soon after spraying	Rao et al. (1976; 1977)
Panicum dichotomiflorum	Unspecified surfactant, 0.5%–1%	Improved activity	Bundick and Mitchell (1979).
Phragmites communis	Unspecified surfactant, 1%	Increased effect of 2.24–4.48 kg a.i. ha^{-1} glyphosate	Riemer (1973)
Rosa multiflora	MON 0011 wetter, 0.5%	Increased phytotoxicity	Albaugh, Mitchell and Graham (1977)

other functions, perhaps solvent action or to the formation of micellar solutions (Price, 1977).

Oil adjuvants

By comparison with surfactants, little information is available about the effects on glyphosate performance of oil additives, even though proprietary products are on sale worldwide. It is emphasized that oils must be formulated with a surfactant if they are to give a stable sprayable emulsion with water, and in studies with other herbicides it is sometimes uncertain whether effects are due to the oil itself or to the emulsifier.

Preest (1975), working in New Zealand, found that glyphosate activity against *Pteridium aquilinum* was markedly improved by addition to the spray solution of 10% of diesel oil emulsified with Triton X-45. The emulsifier was present at 0.18% concentration in the spray solution. Ampong-Nyarko (1980) increased Roundup activity against *Cyperus rotundus* by adding to the spray solution 2% of an emulsifiable oil additive, 'Actipron'. Similar effects were obtained when 2% of a mixture of Agral and Ethylan A2 surfactants with domestic paraffin was added.

In Germany, an oil–surfactant mixture 'Oleo Rustica' had no effect on Roundup toxicity to *A. repens* (German Federal Republic: Biologische Bundesanstalt für Land- und Fortwirtschaft, 1978). However, activity against this species was increased by another oil adjuvant, 'Booster plus E' (Erickson and Duke, 1979).

Ammonium sulphate and related compounds

Under suitable conditions, ammonium salts, particularly ammonium sulphate, can increase the phytotoxicity of a variety of water-soluble leaf-applied herbicides, including DNOC (Harris and Hyslop, 1942; Crafts and Rieber, 1945), endothal (Tischler, Quimba and Bejuki, 1951), and 2,4-D (Sexsmith, 1953). The mode of action is not fully understood. Activation of glyphosate by ammonium sulphate was first reported by Wills (1973a). Many ammonium and alkali metal salts improved the effects of this herbicide against *Cyperus rotundus*. A surfactant was included in the spray solutions. There have been many other reports of activation, some of which are summarized in *Table 15.2*.

TABLE 15.2   The effect of ammonium salts on the performance of glyphosate

Species tested	Ammonium salt and rate or concentration in spray solution	Effect	Reference
Aegopodium podagraria	Ammonium sulphate, at 5 kg ha^{-1}	5 l ha^{-1} Roundup with additive as effective as 7.5 or 10 l ha^{-1} without	Schneider (1980)
Agropyron repens	Ammonium sulphate and nitrate at 1.25–10 kg ha^{-1} (0.5–4% w/v)	Increased activity	Blair (1975)
A. repens and other weeds	Ammonium sulphate and phosphate, both at 1% w/v	Increased effect	Zemanek (1978; 1979); Zemanek and Sterba (1979); Zemanek, Kubrova and Sterba (1979)
A. repens	Ammonium sulphate, 1.25 or 2.5 kg ha^{-1}	Increase in effect of 0.25 kg a.i. ha^{-1} glyphosate	Fiveland (1978)
Cynodon dactylon	Ammonium sulphate, 2.5 kg ha^{-1}	Use mentioned with low rates of glyphosate	Vernon (1980)
Cyperus rotundus	Ammonium sulphate, 5% w/v	Increase in effect of 0.33–1 kg a.i. ha^{-1} glyphosate, with wetting agent in spray volumes 26–480 l ha^{-1}	Ampong-Nyarko (1980)

TABLE 15.2 continued

Species tested	Ammonium salt and rate or concentration in spray solution	Effect	Reference
C. rotundus	Ammonium sulphate, phosphate, urea 0.6–2.5%	Large increase in effect, e.g. 0.25 kg a.i. ha^{-1} with additive equivalent to 0.5 kg a.i. ha^{-1} without	Suwannamek and Parker (1975)
C. rotundus	Ammonium sulphate, 5–20 kg ha^{-1}	Slight increase in activity	Terry (1975)
C. rotundus, Parthenium hysterophorus, Digitaria spp.	Ammonium sulphate, 1 kg ha^{-1}	Enhanced activity, 1 kg a.i. ha^{-1} of herbicide with additive had as much effect as 2 kg a.i. ha^{-1} without	Hammerton (1974)
C. rotundus	Ammonium sulphate, phosphate, chloride, 4.4 or 8.8 kg ha^{-1}	Significant increase in phytotoxicity of 1.1 kg a.i. ha^{-1}	Suwanketnikom and Penner (1978)
Digitaria scalarium	Ammonium sulphate, 5–20 kg ha^{-1}	Antagonism	Terry (1975)
Dwarf bean (Phaseolus sp.)	Ammonium sulphate, urea, 0.1–2.5 kg ha^{-1}	Activation of very low doses of glyphosate	Turner and Loader (1975)
Eichhornia crassipes	Ammonium sulphate, 1–2 kg ha^{-1}	Mixtures with glyphosate	Fernandes et al. (1978)
Imperata cylindrica	Ammonium sulphate, phosphate, urea, 0.6–2.5% w/v	Little effect	Suwannamek and Parker (1975)
I. cylindrica and other weeds of tea plantations	Ammonium sulphate, 0.5–1.5% w/v	Increased phytotoxicity	Rao et al. (1976; 1977); India Tea Research Assn (1978)
I. cylindrica	Ammonium sulphate, 1% w/v	Increased activity	Lee (1977)
Mixed annual weeds	Ammonium sulphate, 10 kg ha^{-1}	Improved control	Barbera (1978)
Mixed weed species	Ammonium sulphate, 1.25 kg ha^{-1}	Improved control under field conditions	Sharma, Satyanarayana and Ramachandran (1980)
Mixed weed species	Ammonium sulphate, 5 kg ha^{-1}	Increased Roundup activity	Zambia, Dept. of Agriculture (1980)
Potato (Solanum tuberosum)	Ammonium sulphate, 1.25–5% w/v	Improved control of volunteers by technical glyphosate isopropylamine salt with wetter	Lutman and Richardson (1978)
Stipa trichotoma	Ammonium sulphate, 2% w/v	Improved control by glyphosate	I'ons and Nel (1977)
Weeds of rubber plantations	Ammonium sulphate, 10 kg ha^{-1}	Increased effects of low doses (0.25–0.5 kg a.i. ha^{-1})	Yang Zu Nang (1978)
Weeds of vineyards	Ammonium sulphate, 10 kg ha^{-1}	6 l ha^{-1} of Roundup with additive as effective as 8 l ha^{-1}	Heras (1978)
Wheat (Triticum aestivum)	Ammonium sulphate, 25% w/v	Restoration of phytotoxicity lost when spray solution made up with hard water	Rajkomar and Ashford (1979)
Woody spp. (Betula and Fraxinus)	Ammonium sulphate, 0.5–5% w/v	Increased absorption and translocation of ^{14}C-glyphosate	Lund-Høie (1979)
Woody spp.	Ammonium sulphate, urea, 0.7–7% w/v	Increased phytotoxicity	Turner and Loader (1975)

In the UK, many field experiments testing glyphosate additives have been carried out by the Agricultural Development and Advisory Service (ADAS). Most of these examined effects on *A. repens*. In the earlier trials the recommended and one-half of the recommended dose of Roundup was used. In general, the half-dose (0.72 kg a.i. ha^{-1}) had almost as much effect as the full dose: overall, the level of control was so good that there was little opportunity for ammonium sulphate to give further improvement (O'Keeffe and Turner, 1977; Harvey and Potts, 1978; Harvey, Attwood and Potts, 1981). However, occasionally useful increases in activity were observed, as for example in the ADAS Northern Region 1977 trials, where the addition of 50 g l^{-1} ammonium sulphate to spray solutions containing the recommended dose of Roundup increased control at two different sites from 74% to 98% and from 61% to 85% (United Kingdom, Ministry of Agriculture, Fisheries and Food, Agricultural Development and Advisory Service, 1978).

In more detailed studies with *A. repens,* Turner and Loader (1980), as already mentioned, observed a marked interaction between ammonium sulphate and surfactant type. Hydrophilic surfactants, particularly cationics, were most effective in simple mixtures with glyphosate, but in the presence of ammonium sulphate the response was reversed, more lipophilic surfactants giving better results. The reasons for this are not yet understood. An example of the interaction is given in *Table 15.3*. The water-soluble surfactant, Ethylan TT15 (HLB 17), performed best on its own, but the more lipophilic wetter, Ethylan TF (HLB 6), was more effective in mixtures with ammonium sulphate. The addition of ammonium sulphate slightly reduced the effects of Ethylan TT15. The table shows results obtained with technical glyphosate salt, MON 0139, but effects with low doses of Roundup were similar.

In these experiments, ammonium sulphate concentrations from about 1% to 10% w/v had similar effects when an appropriate surfactant was present. Surfactant concentrations of between 0.1% and 2.5% in the spray solution were used. Higher concentrations of ammonium sulphate of above 10% often reduced the phytotoxicity of glyphosate. Glyphosate activation appeared to be regulated by the concentration of ammonium sulphate in the spray solution and not by the dose per hectare. Ammonium sulphate solution of 40% w/v concentration sprayed at 75 l ha^{-1} supplies the same dose of salt as solution containing 10% w/v ammonium sulphate applied at 300 l ha^{-1}. However, while the former treatment was antagonistic, the second increased phytotoxicity. These contrasting results are not readily explained. In both cases the sprays would have dried down within a few minutes, apparently leaving similar amounts of ammonium sulphate on the leaf surfaces. Distribution of the salt may possibly have been less even with the lower spray volume.

TABLE 15.3   *Agropyron repens:* **percentage of viable rhizome buds after 4 weeks (control = 100) (from Turner and Loader, 1980)**

Surfactant (used at 0.5% v/v concentration in spray solution)	Glyphosate (as MON 0139)			
	(0.1 kg a.i. ha^{-1})		(0.3 kg a.i. ha^{-1})	
	Ammonium sulphate, 5% concentration in spray solution*			
	absent	present	absent	present
None	96 a	73 a	46 a	77 a
Ethylan TT15 (HLB 17)	12 b	27 b	0 c	12 b
Ethylan TF (HLB 6)	77 a	8 c	50 a	0 c

*Entries followed by the same letter are not significantly different at the 5% level of probability.

Ammonium sulphate with a lipophilic cationic surfactant (Ethomeen C12) appears to have special advantages when rain falls shortly after spraying. This mixture also reduces antagonism between glyphosate and soil-acting herbicides such as simazine (Turner, 1981).

During 1980, mixtures of ammonium sulphate with a lipophilic cationic wetter were tested in ADAS field experiments to examine pre-harvest treatments in cereal crops (United Kingdom, Ministry of Agriculture, Fisheries and Food, 1981). As in the previous trials, remarkably good control of *A. repens* was obtained with all glyphosate treatments. This high activity made it difficult to demonstrate activation. However, with quarter-doses (0.36 kg a.i. ha^{-1}), phytotoxicity was increased by the additives at all sites. With this glyphosate dose, average bud kill in the absence of additives was 89%. When 5% ammonium sulphate and 0.5% Ethylan TF wetter were added to the spray solution bud kill rose to 96%.

Other ammonium salts and urea may also enhance phytotoxicity (*Table 15.2*), but are generally less effective than ammonium sulphate (Wills, 1973a; Blair, 1975; Suwannamek and Parker, 1975; Turner and Loader, 1975). Mangoensoekarjo (1981) observed that addition of 10–15 kg ha^{-1} urea slightly improved control of *C. rotundus* by glyphosate. Yeoh and Mat Taib (1979) successfully used urea in mixture with glyphosate against *Imperata cylindrica*. Parochetti (1978) reported that the addition of aqueous nitrogenous fertilizer containing ammonium nitrate and urea accelerated leaf necrosis in barley (*Hordeum vulgare*) and rye (*Secale cereale*). However, Jensen (1977) found that the addition of this type of fertilizer had little effect on glyphosate phytotoxicity to *A. repens*.

The precise mode of action of ammonium salts is unknown, but there is evidence that these materials modify membrane permeability. Thus, the addition of ammonium sulphate increases the rate of entry of ^{14}C-MCPA into poplar (*Populus* sp.) leaves by a factor of about ten (M.P.C. Loader, unpublished results). Poovaiah and Leopold (1974) suggest that ammonium sulphate modifies membrane permeability by 'salting out' constituent macromolecules such as proteins, and Smith and Walker (1978) found that low concentrations of it markedly increased membrane transport in an alga, *Chara corralina* (= *C. australis*). Influx of chloride ions and efflux of potassium ions increased, and changes in membrane conductance were recorded. Ammonium salts do not appear to affect translocation directly. In Loader's studies, increased movement of ^{14}C from site of entry occurred, but this appeared to reflect increased uptake rather than direct stimulus of translocation.

Polybasic acids and their salts and esters

Glyphosate can be inactivated by many divalent and trivalent cations (see also Chapter 4). This was first reported by Wills (1973a), who included calcium, iron and zinc salts among many inorganic compounds tested in trials with *C. rotundus*. Since this observation there have been other reports of inactivation, notably by calcium ions in hard water. Antagonistic effects of cations appear to occur within plants and in spray solutions; Nilsson (1979) found that glyphosate had less toxicity than expected against wheat grown in solutions containing high amounts of iron or manganese. The effects of metallic ions on performance is discussed in Chapter 4. However, from the purely formulation aspect, materials which immobilize or sequester polyvalent metals can sometimes remove this antagonism and increase phytotoxicity. Phosphates often do this (Wills, 1973a; Suwannamek and Parker, 1975; Suwanketnikom and Penner, 1978; Zemanek and Sterba, 1979). With the ammonium phosphates, the activation could be due to ammonium or the anion, but it is likely that both play a part. Many phosphate esters increase glyphosate activity (Turner, 1972; Blair, 1975; Turner and Loader, 1975). As the esters are readily hydrolysed, this effect may be due to the release of phosphoric acid. In experiments with a range of acids, Turner and Loader (1978) found that divalent and trivalent acids including oxalic, citric, tartaric, phosphoric and lactic acids enhanced glyphosate activity, but most monobasic acids of similar strength did not. Some monobasic acids reduced glyphosate activity. It was suggested that these different responses reflect the ability of the acids to sequester or immobilize metals, particularly calcium. An example of effects observed in a pot experiment with *A. repens* is shown in *Table 15.4.*

TABLE 15.4   *Agropyron repens:* **fresh weight of shoots after 12 weeks (control = 100) (from Turner and Loader, 1978)**

Additive (2% concentration in spray solution)	Glyphosate (as Roundup)*	
	(0.2 kg a.i. ha^{-1})	(0.4 kg a.i. ha^{-1})
None	84 a	10 b
Orthophosphoric acid	11 b	2 b
Citric acid	41 a	17 b
Oxalic acid	10 b	0 c
Tartaric acid	6 b	0 c
Acetic acid	92 a	51 a
Propionic acid	92 a	20 b

*Entries followed by the same letter are not significantly different at the 5% level of probability.

In the field, addition of phosphoric or oxalic acid increased the effects of low doses of Roundup against *A. repens* (Turner and Loader, 1978). Activation was of the same order as observed with ammonium sulphate: at one trial site 0.25 kg a.i. ha^{-1} of glyphosate with 2% w/v of phosphoric or oxalic acid in the spray solution had effects similar to 0.5 kg a.i. ha^{-1} without additive. Sequestrant additives have not been widely tested against other species, but divalent and trivalent cations have increased the effects on plants of glyphosate and the related plant growth regulator glyphosine (Anon., 1976a; 1977). The addition of 0.1 mol l^{-1} potassium dihydrogen phosphate increased phytotoxicity and translocation of ^{14}C-labelled glyphosate in soya bean (*Glycine max*) (McWhorter, Jordan and Wills, 1980). As with ammonium phosphate, it is not clear whether this was an effect of the anion or cation, or both. In Zambia, slight activation of glyphosate by oxalic acid has been recorded (Zambia, Department of Agriculture, 1980). In practice, these additives are difficult to use because they sometimes cause precipitation of glyphosate acid from concentrated spray solutions which can block spray nozzles.

Other non-herbicidal additives

Various other materials have been added to glyphosate spray solutions with the object of improving phytotoxicity, selectivity or reliability. Potassium and sodium salts are of interest. Wills (1973a; 1973b) found that addition of 0.2 mol l^{-1} potassium carbonate markedly increased glyphosate phytotoxicity to glasshouse-grown. *C. rotundus;* the control achieved with 0.5 kg a.i. ha^{-1} glyphosate increasing from 17% to 81%. The effects were most evident in hot, dry conditions.

No explanation was advanced. However, potassium carbonate is used to assist desiccation in haymaking and grape drying, apparently allowing water to seep through waxy cuticles and evaporate (Crocker and Lodge, 1981). An effect of this kind may well allow aqueous herbicides like glyphosate to enter leaves more readily.

Other work with non-herbicidal additives is summarized in *Table 15.5.*

TABLE 15.5   The effect of some other non-herbicidal additives on the performance of glyphosate

Species tested	Additive	Effect	Reference
Ampelamus albidus	Ethephon, 0.6 kg ha^{-1}	No synergistic effect	Moshier (1980)
Calystegia sepium	'Nalco' anti-drift agent	No marked effect	Kline and Selleck (1977)
Convolvulus arvensis	'Vistik' thickener	No marked effect	Lange *et al.* (1975)
Mixed tropical spp.	Kaolin, 3.6 kg ha^{-1}	Improved control	Sharma, Satyanarayana and Ramachandran (1980)
Sorghum halepense, *Amaranthus retroflexus,* *Sesbania exalta*	'Nalco' anti-drift agent, 0–1% v/v	No marked effect	McWhorter (1977)
Wheat (*Triticum aestivum*) Vine (*Vitis* sp.)	Viscoelastic high molecular weight thickener, 0.08–0.12%	No adverse effect	Yates, Akesson and Bayer (1978)
Pteridium aquilinum	Ethephon	No marked effect	UK West of Scotland Agricultural College (1978)

Mixtures with other herbicides

Residual herbicides

Tank mixing glyphosate with triazines, ureas, uracils and other soil-acting herbicides generally reduces its activity. This antagonism was first reported by Baird *et al.* (1971); mixing with alachlor, diuron, linuron or pronamide (propyzamide) reduced glyphosate phytotoxicity irrespective of the formulation of the residual herbicide. Many other workers have observed similar effects; for example, Worsham (1972) with linuron and simazine, and Stryckers and Himme (1974) with atrazine. Somabhi (1974) and Appleby and Somabhi (1978) investigated the antagonism with the triazine herbicides in detail. They found that the interaction occurred only in mixed sprays and not when simultaneous applications were made to different leaves or when the triazine was applied to the soil and glyphosate to the foliage. The non-herbicidal ingredients used to formulate simazine also reduced glyphosate phytotoxicity. *In vitro*, 10% of glyphosate was removed from aqueous solutions when these were shaken with simazine formulated as a wettable powder or the unspecified ingredients used in the formulation. More glyphosate was absorbed when more concentrated spray mixtures were used. The interaction was unaffected by the addition of extra surfactant. Pulver and Romero (1976) observed that an emulsifiable concentrate formulation of ametryne gave less reduction of glyphosate phytotoxicity than ametryne or atrazine as wettable powders. Technical (unformulated) atrazine had little effect. These results support the view that the antagonism is due to the formulation ingredients rather than to the residual herbicides themselves. However, Link *et al.* (1979) consider that antagonism is probably due to chemical bonding or physiological action, rather than glyphosate adsorption. Other studies in this field are summarized in *Table 15.6(a).*

TABLE 15.6   The effect of the addition of other herbicides on the performance of glyphosate

(a) RESIDUAL HERBICIDES			
Species tested	Residual herbicide(s)	Effect on glyphosate activity	Reference
Agropyron repens	Diuron Simazine	Tank mixing reduces glyphosate activity	Seddon (1974)
A. repens, Taraxacum officinale, Cirsium arvense	Chlorbromuron Cyanazine Bifenox Metribuzin Atrazine Linuron	Antagonistic in mixture with glyphosate	Selleck and Baird (1981)
Echinochloa crus-galli	Terbutryne	Reduced glyphosate translocation	Ahmadi, Haderlie and Wicks (1980)
Grass weeds	Methazole	Antagonism, which can be partly eliminated by separate application	Aitken (1977)
Several species	Terbuthylazine Simazine Diuron Terbacil	Antagonism	Schepens and Coomans (1975)
Several species	Diuron Terbacil Bromacil Simazine Aminotriazole	Antagonism in tank mixes, but not when separate applications are used	Selleck (1975)
Mixed weed association	Oryzalin Simazin	Antagonism	Ahrens (1981)
Weeds of maize in Nigeria	Atrazine Metalochlor	No loss of glyphosate activity	International Institute of Tropical Agriculture (1978)
Perennial weeds	Oryzalin	No antagonism	Link, Chappell and Hipkins (1980)
Maize (Zea mays)	Tebuthiuron		
Unspecified	Tebuthiuron	Said to be compatible with glyphosate	Ford (1974)

(b) HERBICIDES USED FOR CONTROLLING BROAD-LEAVED WEEDS			
Species tested	Broad-leaved weed herbicide(s)	Effect on glyphosate activity	Reference
Ampelamus albidus	2,4-D Dicamba	Mixtures more effective than glyphosate alone	Rao et al. (1977)
Ampelamus albidus	2,4-D 2,4-D/dicamba	Synergistic effect on young plants	Moshier and Russ (1978)
Asclepias syriaca	2,4-D	Antagonism	Cramer and Burnside (1980)
Brunnichia cirrhosa	Dicamba	Antagonism	Strachan and Duncan (1980)
Cirsium arvense	Dicamba	Mixtures more effective than glyphosate alone	Belles, Wattenbarger and Lee (1980)
Cereals Avena fatua	2,4-D Dicamba Bromoxynil MCPA	Antagonism, particularly with ester formulation	O'Sullivan (1979)
Cereals Avena fatua	2,4-D Dicamba Bromoxynil MCPA	Both technical herbicides and solvent blanks reduce glyphosate activity	O'Sullivan and O'Donovan (1980)

TABLE 15.6   continued

(b) HERBICIDES USED FOR CONTROLLING BROAD-LEAVED WEEDS			
Species tested	Broad-leaved weed herbicide(s)	Effect on glyphosate activity	Reference
Convolvulus arvensis	2,4-D Dicamba	Low doses as effective in mixtures as higher doses of glyphosate alone	Rieck and Schumacher (1978)
Eichornia crassipes	2,4-D	Mixtures give good results	Widyanto and Soerjani (1978)
Mixed weeds (Indonesia)	2,4-D	Synergistic with glyphosate in low doses; antagonistic at higher rates	Yang Zu Nang (1978)
Mixed weeds (S. America)	2,4-D	Possibly synergistic	Tollervey et al. (1979)
Mixed weeds (India)	2,4-D	Possibly synergistic	India Tea Research Assn. (1979)
Tamus communis	2,4-D	Apparently compatible with glyphosate	Proctor (1975)

(c) OTHER HERBICIDES			
Species tested	Herbicide	Effect on glyphosate activity	Reference
Annual grasses and broad-leaved weeds	Asulam	Mixtures promising	Fretz (1974)
Pteridium aquilinum	Asulam	Effects additive, but not synergistic	Williams (1977)
P. aquilinum	Asulam	Mixtures appear promising	UK West of Scotland Agric. College (1978)
P. aquilinum	Sodium chlorate	Activity reduced	Williams (1977)
Cyperus rotundus	Paraquat	Activity improved	Terry (1973)
C. rotundus	Paraquat	Activity reduced	Worsham (1972)
Sorghum halepense	Chlorflurecol	Activity unaffected	Banks and Santelmann (1977)
Imperata cylindrica	Dalapon	Activity reduced	Sharma (1977)

Despite these effects, mixtures with residual herbicides often have important practical advantages which outweigh the disadvantages. Glyphosate controls emerged weeds well, but has almost no effect on germinating seeds: the addition of even a small amount of residual herbicide can greatly extend the period of control provided by a glyphosate treatment. If necessary, the antagonism between residual herbicides and glyphosate can be eliminated by applying the compounds separately. However, double spraying can be expensive and in practice it may be better to use a higher glyphosate dose (Appleby and Somabhi, 1978; Selleck and Baird, 1981) or to increase glyphosate activity by the use of a suitable additive. For example, the adverse effects of mixing with bromacil can be reduced by adding an emulsifier (Anon., 1976b). Antagonistic effects of linuron and simazine can be countered by adding ammonium sulphate and surfactant (Turner, 1981).

The effects of mixing glyphosate with herbicides used for broad-leaved weed control are less clear cut. In some circumstances mixtures are antagonistic, but on other occasions additive effects or synergism have been reported. On balance, glyphosate appears to be reasonably compatible with salt formulations of 2,4-D or dicamba. The results of experiments with these herbicides, and others with similar types of activity, are summarized in *Table 15.6(b)*.

Mixtures with other herbicides have received less attention (*Table 15.6c*).

Practically, there appears to be little point in using mixtures of glyphosate and paraquat, although there is an interesting suggestion that small amounts of paraquat may increase glyphosate activity (Terry, 1973). Mixtures with asulam do not appear to be antagonistic and may be of practical use for clearing poor quality grassland infested with bracken, prior to reseeding.

These reports relate to experiments where it is possible to compare the effects of glyphosate used alone and in mixtures. However, many workers have used mixtures without testing at least the glyphosate component separately. References to some of the more unusual tank mixes which have been used are given in *Table 15.7*.

TABLE 15.7   Some other herbicides which have been used in tank mixes with glyphosate

Herbicide	Reference
Buthidazole	Alley and Humburg (1979)
Chloramben	Noll (1978)
Diphenamid	Liu and Acevedo-Borero (1980)
Hexazinone	Haramaki (1977); Chappell and Link (1977)
MSMA	Sharma, Haridas and Venkataramani (1973)
Methabenzthiazuron	Potter and Stalder (1981)
Napropamide	Arnold and Aldrich (1979)
Oxyfluorfen	Somody, Michieka and Ilnicki (1978); Chitapong, Ilnicki and Horng (1981)
Pendimethalin	Somody, Michieka and Ilnicki (1978)
Tetrapion	Mangoensoekarjo (1981)
Triclopyr	McCormack and Saviello (1981)

Conclusions

Although other derivatives and formulations have been tested, only Roundup, containing glyphosate isopropylamine and undisclosed formulation materials, is available at present. Studies with other types of formulation may be rewarding. In particular, there appears to be a need for oil-soluble formulations, for use against plants with bark or a thick leaf cuticle. Little information is available about alternatives to the isopropylamine salt, and it is unclear why this is used in preference to others. At present we have only a limited understanding of factors which limit phytotoxicity, particularly those influencing movement to sites of activity.

There is now ample evidence to show that formulation ingredients and additives can greatly influence activity and reliability. This is probably true of most herbicides, but with glyphosate the effects are particularly clear. More research, particularly with weeds which show some resistance to the herbicide, may yield useful results. Materials which improve the activity, selectivity or reliability of glyphosate treatments can be included in the formulated product at the factory, or added as a tank mix just before spraying. Surfactants are probably of most importance but other materials, notably ammonium sulphate, can also have large effects, particularly when low doses of Roundup are applied in medium or high spray volumes. In most instances, formulation ingredients increase phytotoxicity. However, it is worth pointing out that incorrect use of certain materials can reduce activity; for example, when excessive concentrations of ammonium sulphate are used (Turner and Loader, 1980). Even the ingredients which are present in

Roundup may have unwanted effects; for example, when very high concentrations of the formulation are applied with a rope-wick applicator (Dale, 1979) or similar equipment. A case can be made for making available glyphosate isopropylamine free from surfactants or other formulation ingredients, these being added by the user to suit the circumstances.

Mixing Roundup with other formulated herbicides or pesticides can be hazardous. In addition to the ingredients, mixtures will contain formulation ingredients contributed by both products. However, mixtures often have important advantages in reducing spraying time and cost. There is a clear need for more research in this field. When mixtures are needed, the use of glyphosate isopropylamine free from other materials may be essential.

References

AHMADI, M.S., HADERLIE, L.C. and WICKS, G.P. (1980). Effect of growth stage and water stress on barnyard grass (*Echinochloa crus-galli*) control and on glyphosate absorption and translocation, *Weed Science*, **28**, 277–282.

AHRENS, J.F. (1980). Effects of surfactants or pre-emergence herbicides on the selectivity of asulam and glyphosate in woody plants, *Proceedings of the 34th Annual Meeting of the North Eastern Weed Science Society*, pp. 330–333.

AHRENS, J.F. (1981). Chemical control of established weeds in field grown arborvitae, Abstract, *Proceedings of the 35th Annual Meeting of the North Eastern Weed Science Society*, pp. 248–252.

AITKEN, J.B. (1977). The potential of glyphosate in pecan weed control systems, *Proceedings of the 30th Annual Meeting Southern Weed Science Society*, pp. 190–196.

ALBAUGH, G.P., MITCHELL, W.N. and GRAHAM, J.C. (1977). Evaluation of glyphosate for multiflora rose control, *Proceedings of the 31st Annual Meeting of the North Eastern Weed Science Society*, pp. 283–291.

ALLEY, H.P. and HUMBURG, N.E. (1979). Research in weed science, *Research Journal of the Wyoming Agricultural Experimental Station*, no. 137, pp. 61–81.

AMPONG-NYARKO, K. (1980). The effects of ammonium sulphate, surfactants and spray volume on the activity of glyphosate on *Cyperus rotundus*, MSc. thesis, Department of Agricultural Botany, University of Reading.

ANON. (1971). Salts and derivatives of MON 0573 post-emergence herbicide, *Monsanto Agricultural Division Technical Bulletin 057-1-71*.

ANON. (1976a). Effect of di- and trivalent cations on the herbicidal activity of *N*-phosphonomethyl glycine, *Research Disclosure*, **148**, 10.

ANON. (1976b). *N*-phosphonomethyl glycine (glyphosate)-containing herbicidal mixtures, *Research Disclosure*, **148**, 15.

ANON. (1977). Treatment of sugarcane with compositions containing a dibasic acid, *Research Disclosure*, **160**, 5.

APPLEBY, A.P. and SOMABHI, M. (1978). Antagonistic effect of atrazine and simazine on glyphosate activity, *Weed Science*, **26**, 135–139.

ARNOLD, C.E. and ALDRICH, J.H. (1979). Weed control in immature pecan (*Carya illinoensis*) and peach (*Prunus persica*) plantings, *Weed Science*, **27**, 638–641.

BAIRD, D.D., BROWN, R.H. and PHOTAK, S.C. (1974). Influence of pre-emergence herbicides, nitrogen, soil density and mowing on post-em activity of glyphosate for quackgrass control, *Proceedings of the 28th Annual Meeting of the North Eastern Weed Science Society*, pp. 76–86.

BAIRD, D.D., UPCHURCH, R.P., HOMESLEY, W.P. and FRANZ, J.E. (1971). Introduction of a new broad spectrum post emergence herbicide class with utility for herbaceous perennial weed control, *Proceedings of the 26th North Central Weed Conference*, pp. 64–68.

BANKS, P.A. and SANTELMANN, P.W. (1977). Glyphosate as a post-emergence treatment for Johnsongrass control in cotton and soyabeans, *Agronomy Journal*, **69**, 579–582.

BARBERA, C. (1978). (Possible uses for glyphosate in controlling annual species), *Proceedings of the Roundup Seminar*, Madrid, 1978, pp. 123–127.

BEHRENS, R.W. (1964). The physical and chemical properties of surfactants and their effects on formulated herbicides, *Weeds*, **12**, 255–258.

BELLES, W.S., WATTENBARGER, D.W. and LEE, G.A. (1980). Herbicidal control of Canada thistle (Cirsium arvense L. Scop.), Abstract, Proceedings of the Annual Meeting of the 33rd Western Weed Science Society, p. 134.

BHOWMIK, P.C. and DOLL, J.D. (1981). Comparison of the flat fan nozzle and CDA applications, Proceedings of the North Central Weed Control Conference, 35, 46–47.

BLAIR, A.M. (1975). The addition of ammonium salts or a phosphate ester to herbicides to control Agropyron repens (L.) Beauv, Weed Research, 15, 101–105.

BUNDICK, E. and MITCHELL, W.H. (1979). Influence of surfactants on activity of glyphosate and paraquat in no-tillage soyabeans, Proceedings of the 33rd Annual Meeting of the North Eastern Weed Science Society, p. 75.

CASELEY, J.C., COUPLAND, D. and SIMMONS, R.C. (1976). Effect of formulation, volume rate and application method on performance and rainfastness of glyphosate on Agropyron repens, Proceedings of the 1976 British Crop Protection Conference—Weeds, pp. 407–412.

CHAPPELL, W.E. and LINK, M.L. (1977). Soil sterilants for maintaining electric substations, Proceedings of the 30th Annual Meeting of the Southern Weed Science Society, pp. 330–331.

CHITAPONG, P., ILNICKI, R.D. and HORNG, L.C. (1981). Establishing soya beans in a no-tillage double-crop system with several herbicide combinations, Abstract, Proceedings of the 35th Annual Meeting of the North-Eastern Weed Science Society, p. 4.

CHYKALIUK, P.B., ABERNATHY, J.R. and GIPSON, J. (1979). Additives for enhancing glyphosate activity on perennial weeds, Proceedings of the 32nd Annual Meeting of the Southern Weed Science Society, p, 66.

CHYKALIUK, P.B., ABERNATHY, J.R. and GIPSON, J.R. (1980). Effect of additives on herbicide uptake and control of Texas blueweed, woolly leaf bursage and silverleaf nightshade, Abstract, Proceedings of the 33rd Meeting of the American Weed Science Society, p. 236.

COUPLAND, D. and PEABODY, D.V. (1981). Effect of four foliage applied herbicides on field horsetail, Equisetum arvense, Weed Science, 29, 113–119.

CRAFTS, A.S. and RIEBER, M.G. (1945). Studies on the activation of herbicides, Hilgardia, 16, 487–500.

CRAMER, G.L. and BURNSIDE, O.C. (1980). Control of common milkweed, Proceedings of the 34th North Central Weed Control Conference, 1979, Abstract, pp. 12–13.

CROCKER, G.J. and LODGE, G.M. (1981). Potassium carbonate speeds up lucerne haymaking, Agricultural Gazette of New South Wales, June, 33–36.

DALE, J.E. (1979). A non mechanical system of herbicide application with a rope wick, PANS, 25, 431–436.

DAVIES, E.Ll.P. and TAYLOR, W.A. (1980). The biological activity of three herbicides when applied by differing hydraulic nozzle types, in Spraying Systems for the 1980's, British Crop Protection Council Monograph 24 (Ed. J.O. Walker), pp. 49–54.

DURHAM, K. (1961). Properties of detergent solutions—amphipathy and adsorption, in Surface Activity and Detergency (Ed. K. Durham). London; Macmillan.

ELWORTHY, P.H., FLORENCE, A.T. and MACFARLANE, C.B. (1968). Solubilization by Surface-Active Agents and its Applications in Chemistry and the Biological Sciences. London; Chapman and Hall, 335 pp.

ERICKSON, C.G. and DUKE, W.B. (1979). Comparison of the bicycle and Herbi sprayer applications, Proceedings of the 33rd Annual Meeting of the North Eastern Weed Science Society, pp. 134–136.

EVANS, D.M. (1972). Field performance of glyphosate derivatives in the control of Agropyron repens and other perennial weeds, Proceedings of the 11th British Weed Control Conference, pp. 64–70.

FERNANDES, J.D., GUERREIRO, A.R., VASCONCELOS, T. and MOREIRA, I. (1978). Trials on the controls of aquatic plants in Portugal, Proceedings of the 5th European Weed Science Society Symposium on Aquatic Weeds, Amsterdam, 1978, pp. 189–194.

FIVELAND, T.J. (1978). Addition of ammonium sulphate to glyphosate, in Weeds and Weeds Control, 19th Swedish Weed Conference, Uppsala, K5–K10.

FORD, D.H. (1974). Spike for total vegetation control, Proceedings of the 26th Annual Meeting of the California Weed Conference, pp. 25–27.

FRANZ, J.E. (1979). Glyphosate and related chemistry, in Advances in Pesticide Science, Symposium papers presented at the 4th International Congress of Pesticide Chemistry, Zurich, July 1978. (Ed. H. Geissbuhler), pp. 139–147.

FRETZ, T.P. (1974). Evaluation of herbicide combinations for use in shade tree nurseries, Research Summary, Ohio Agricultural Research and Development Centre, 1974, no. 79, pp. 65–70.

GERMAN FEDERAL REPUBLIC: Biologische Bundesanstalt für Land- und Forstwirtschaft (1978). (Annual Report of the German Plant Protection Service), 1977, p. 93.

HAMMERTON, J.L. (1974). Weed control work in progress at the University of the West Indies, part 4, *PANS*, **20**, 425–436.

HARAMAKI, C. (1977). Control of perennial and annual weeds in established plantings of narrowleaf evergreens, *Proceedings of the 31st Annual Meeting of the North Eastern Weed Science Society*, pp. 329–334.

HARDCASTLE, W.S. (1976). Chemical control of wild *Allium* species, *Agronomy Journal*, **68**, 144–145.

HARRIS, L.E. and HYSLOP, G.R. (1942). Selective sprays for weed control in crops, *Bulletin*, Oregon Experimental Station, no. 403.

HARVEY, J.J., ATTWOOD, P.J. and POTTS, M.J. (1981). The control of *Agropyron repens* in cereal stubbles with glyphosate, *Proceedings of the Conference on Grass Weeds in Cereals in the U.K.*, Reading, 1981, pp. 155–165.

HARVEY, J.J. and POTTS, M.J. (1978). A cost effective approach to the control of *Agropyron repens* in cereal stubbles with glyphosate, *Proceedings of the 1978 British Crop Protection Conference—Weeds*, pp. 49–55.

HERAS, J.J.G., LAS. (1978). (Roundup in the vineyards of Navarre), *Proceedings, Roundup Seminar*, Madrid, 1978, pp. 67–72.

INDIA TEA RESEARCH ASSOCIATION (1978). *Annual Scientific Report, 1977*, Tocklai Experimental Station, pp. 18–20.

INDIA TEA RESEARCH ASSOCIATION (1979). *Annual Scientific Report, 1977–78*, Tocklai Experimental Station, pp. 22–24.

INTERNATIONAL INSTITUTE OF TROPICAL AGRICULTURE (1978). *Annual Report, 1978*, p. 98.

I'ONS, J.H. and NEL, L.O. (1977). On the chemical control of Nassella tussock in the Eastern Cape Province, *Proceedings of the 2nd National Weeds Conference of South Africa*, 1977, pp. 185–192.

IVENS, G.W. (1976). *Imperata cylindrica* (L.) Beauv. in West African agriculture, *Proceedings of the Biotrop Workshop on Alang-Alang (Imperata cylindrica)*, Bogor, Indonesia, July 1976, pp. 149–156.

JENSEN, K.I.N. (1977). Quackgrass control in apple orchards with fall-applied pronamide and glyphosate, *Annual Report, 1977*, Research Station Kentville, Nova Scotia, Canada, pp. 46–47.

JORDAN, T.N. (1981). Effect of diluent volumes and surfactant on the phytotoxicity of glyphosate to bermudagrass (*Cynodon dactylon*), *Weed Science*, **29**, 79–83.

KLINE, W.L. and SELLECK, G.W. (1977). Effect of glyphosate applications on hedge bindweed, *Proceedings of the 31st Annual Meeting of the North Eastern Weed Science Society*, p. 98.

LANGE, A.H., FISCHER, B.B., ELMORE, C.L., KEMPEN, H.M. and SCHLESSELMAN, J. (1975). Roundup—the end of perennial weeds in tree and vine crops, *California Agriculture*, **29**(19), 6–7.

LEE, S.A. (1977). Germination, rhizome survival and control of *Imperata cylindrica* (L.) Beauv. on peat, *MARDI Research Bulletin*, **5**, 1–9.

LINK, M.L., CHAPPELL, W.E. and HIPKINS, P.L. (1980). Additional studies on the glyphosate-residual herbicide antagonism phenomenon (abstract), *Proceedings of the 33rd Annual Meeting of the Southern Weed Science Society*, p. 157.

LINK, M.L., COARTNEY, J.S., CHAPPELL, W.E. and HIPKINS, P.L. (1979). Antagonistic aspects of glyphosate-residual herbicide tank mixes, *Proceedings of the 32nd Annual Meeting of the Southern Weed Science Society*, p. 241.

LIU, L.C. and ACEVEDO-BORERO, E. (1980). Chemical weed control in taniers, *Journal of Agriculture of the University of Puerto Rico*, **64**, 442–449.

LUND-HØIE, K. (1979). The physiological fate of glyphosate ^{14}C in *Betula verrucosa* and *Fraxinus excelsior*. The effect of ammonium sulphate and the environment on the herbicide, *Meldinger fra Norges Landbrukshøiskole*, **58**, 24.

LUTMAN, P.J.W. and RICHARDSON, W.G. (1978). The activity of glyphosate and aminotriazole against volunteer potato plants and their daughter tubers, *Weed Research*, **18**, 65–70.

MCCORMACK, M.L. JR. and SAVIELLO, T.B. (1981). Glyphosate and triclopyr mixtures to control forest brush, Abstract, *Proceedings of the 35th Annual Meeting of the North Eastern Weed Science Society*, p. 218.

MCWHORTER, C.G. (1977). Weed control in soyabeans with glyphosate applied in the recirculating sprayer, *Weed Science*, **25**, 135–141.

MCWHORTER, C.G., JORDAN, T.N. and WILLS, G.D. (1980). Translocation of ^{14}C glyphosate in soybeans (*Glycine max.*) and Johnsongrass (*Sorghum halepense*), *Weed Science*, **28**, 113–118.

MANGOENSOEKARJO, S. (1981). *Cyperus rotundus* L. control with glyphosate: the influence of mixing urea and herbicides, *Proceedings of the 6th Conference of the Weed Science Society of Indonesia*, pp. 41–44.

238 Effects on glyphosate performance of formulation, additives and mixing

MOSHIER, L.J. (1980). Response of honeyvine milkweed (*Ampelamus albidus*) to herbicide applications, *Weed Science*, **28,** 722–724.

MOSHIER, L.J. and RUSS, O.G. (1978). Response of honeyvine milkweed to herbicides, *Proceedings of the North Central Weed Control Conference*, p. 108.

NILSSON, G. (1979). Reduced effect of glyphosate on wheat plants grown with excessive iron and manganese, in *Weeds and Weed Control*, Proceedings of the 20th Swedish Weed Conference, Uppsala, 1979, vol. 1, Reports, pp. 150–151.

NOLL, C.J. (1978). Chemical weeding of cucumber grown in a stale seedbed, *Proceedings of the 32nd Annual Meeting of the North Eastern Weed Science Society*, pp. 230–232.

O'KEEFFE, M.G. and TURNER, E.W. (1977). *Summary Report 1977*, United Kingdom Agricultural Development and Advisory Service, East Midland Region, p. 13.

O'SULLIVAN, P.A. (1979). Herbicide combinations for zero tillage weed control, *Abstracts of the 1979 Meeting of the Weed Science Society of America*, p. 20.

O'SULLIVAN, P.A. and O'DONOVAN, J.T. (1980). Interactions between glyphosate and various herbicides for broadleaf weed control, *Weed Research*, **20,** 255–260.

OSWALD, A.K. (1978). The control of *Rumex obtusifolius* in grassland by selective application of herbicides, *Proceedings of the 1978 British Crop Protection Conference—Weeds*, pp. 475–481.

OSWALD, A.K. (1980). Progress in the development of the selective application of herbicides to control *Rumex obtusifolius* in grassland, *Proceedings of the 1980 British Crop Protection Conference—Weeds*, pp. 209–215.

PAROCHETTI, J.U. (1978). Effect on no-tillage cover crops by paraquat, diquat or glyphosate applied in water or fertilizer solution, *Proceedings of the 32nd Annual Meeting of the North Eastern Weed Science Society*, pp. 36–43.

POOVAIAH, B.W. and LEOPOLD, A.C. (1974). Hormone–solute interactions in the lettuce hypocotyl hook, *Plant Physiology*, **54,** 289–293.

POTTER, C.A. and STALDER, L. (1981). (Tribunil, a soil herbicide for control of annual weeds in stone fruit orchards), *Schweizerische Zeitschrift für Obst-und Weinbau*, **17,** 194–198.

PREEST, D.S. (1975). Effect of additives on bracken control by asulam and glyphosate, *Proceedings of the 28th New Zealand Weed and Pest Control Conference*, pp. 49–52.

PRICE, C.E. (1977). Penetration and translocation of herbicides and fungicides in plants, *Proceedings of the Symposium Herbicides and Fungicides—Factors Affecting their Activity*, Bangor, Wales, 15–17 Sept., 1976 (special publication 29, Chemical Society, London, 1977), pp. 42–66.

PROCTOR, J.M. (1975). Weed control, black bryony on arable land, in *Experiments and Development in the Eastern Region*, United Kingdom Ministry of Agriculture, Fisheries and Food Agricultural Development and Advisory Service, p. 116.

PULVER, E.L. and ROMERO, C. (1976). (Foliar absorption and translocation of glyphosate in *Cyperus rotundus*), *Revista Comalfi*, **3,** 94–113.

RAJKOMAR, L. and ASHFORD, R. (1979). Effect of water quality on phytotoxicity of glyphosate, in *Abstracts of the 1979 Meeting of Weed Science Society of America*, pp. 33–34.

RAO, V.S., RAHMAN, F., SINGH, H.S., DUTTA, A.K., SAIKA, M.C., SHARMA, S.N. and PHUKAN, B.C. (1976). Effective weed control in tea by glyphosate, *India Journal of Weed Science*, **8,** 1–14.

RAO, V.S., RAHMAN, F., SINGH, H.S., DUTTA, A.K., SAIKA, M.C., SHARMA, S.N. and PHUKAN, B.C. (1977). Effective weed control in tea by glyphosate, *Programme and Abstracts of Papers, Weed Science Conference and Workshop in India*, paper no. 96, p. 58.

RIECK, W.L. and SCHUMACHER, R. (1978). Glyphosate performance on field bindweed in North Central United States, *Proceedings of the 33rd North Central Weed Control Conference*, p. 150.

RIEMER, D.N. (1973). Effect of rate, spray volume and surfactant on the control of *Phragmites communis* with glyphosate, *Proceedings of the 27th Annual Meeting of the North Eastern Weed Science Society*, pp. 101–104.

SCHEPENS, G.M. and COOMANS, W. (1975). (Results of two years' experiments with glyphosate in Belgium), *Proceedings of the 27th International Symposium on Crop Protection*, part II, Mededelingen van de Fakulteit Landbouwweten Schappen, Gent, 1975, **40**(2), 919–930.

SCHNEIDER, H. (1980). (Roundup for control of goatsfoot (*Aegopodium podagra*) in pasture renovation), *Mittelungen für die Schweizerische Landwirtschaft*, **28,** 37–39.

SEDDON, J.C. (1974). Field performance of the isopropylamine salt of glyphosate for the control of *Agropyron repens* and other weeds in top fruit orchards, *Proceedings of the 12th British Weed Control Conference*, pp. 595–602.

SELLECK, G.W. (1975). Antagonistic effects with glyphosate herbicide plus residual herbicide combinations, *Proceedings of the 29th Annual Meeting of the North Eastern Weed Science Society*, p. 327.

SELLECK, G.W. (1980). The influence of water quality, volume and surfactant on efficacy of glyphosate on perennial weeds, *Proceedings of the 34th Annual Meeting of the North Eastern Weed Science Society*, pp. 281–283.

SELLECK, G.W. and BAIRD, D.D. (1981). Antagonism with glyphosate and residual herbicide combinations, *Weed Science*, **29**, 185–190.

SELLECK, G.W. and KLINE, W.L. (1978). Factors affecting the efficacy of glyphosate for hedge bindweed (*Convolvulus sepium* L.) control on Long Island, *Abstracts, 1978 Meeting of Weed Science Society of America*, p. 34.

SEXSMITH, J.J. (1953). Nutrient element additives to 2,4-D sprays, *Research Report of the 10th North Central Weed Control Conference*, pp. 57–58.

SHANER, D.L. (1978). Effects of glyphosate on transpiration, *Weed Science*, **26**, 513–516.

SHARMA, V.A., SATYANARAYANA, N. and RAMACHANDRAN, K. (1980). Additives and herbicidal efficiency of glyphosate, *Pesticides*, **14**, 19–20.

SHARMA, V.S. (1977). Chemical control of *Imperata cylindrica* (L.) Beauv. (Lalang) in Malaysia, *Planters Bulletin (1976)*, no. 145, pp. 85–89.

SHARMA, V.S., HARIDAS, P., VENKATARAMANI, K.S. (1973). Roundup—a promising broad spectrum weedkiller, *Planters Chronicle*, **68**, 287–288.

SMITH, F.A. and WALKER, N.A. (1978). Entry of methylammonium and ammonium ions into *Chara* internodal cells, *Journal of Experimental Botany*, **29**, 107–120.

SOMABHI, M. (1974). Interaction between glyphosate and certain S–triazine herbicides, *Dissertation Abstracts International B*, **35**(7), 3130.

SOMODY, C.N., MICHIEKA, R.A. and ILNICKI, R.D. (1978). Glyphosate and paraquat in no-kill double crop soya beans, *Proceedings of the 32nd Annual Meeting of the North Eastern Weed Science Society*, pp. 52–55.

SOMODY, C.N., MICHIEKA, R.W., ILNICKI, R.D. and SOMODY, J. (1978). Paraquat and glyphosate in combination with herbicides for weed control in no-till corn, *Proceedings of the 32nd Annual Meeting of the North Eastern Weed Science Society*, pp. 44–48.

STRACHAN, W.F. and DUNCAN, R.G. (1980). Field performance of dicamba for redvine control, *Proceedings of the 33rd Annual Meeting Southern Weed Science Society*, p. 68.

STRYCKERS, J. and HIMME, M. VAN (1974). (Review of the results obtained for the cropping year 1972–1973 by the Centrum voor Onkruidonderzoek), **178**, 162–164.

SUWANKETNIKOM, R. and PENNER, D. (1978). Effect of ammonium salts on bentazone and glyphosate activity on yellow nutsedge (*Cyperus rotundus* L.), *Abstracts of the 1978 Meeting of Weed Science Society of America*, p. 73.

SUWANNAMEK, U. and PARKER, C. (1975). Control of *Cyperus rotundus* with glyphosate: the influence of ammonium sulphate and other additives, *Weed Research*, **15**, 13–19.

TERRY, P.J. (1973). *Third Progress Report of the East African Herbicide Research Project R 2557*, 1 Jan., 1973 to 30 June, 1973.

TERRY, P.J. (1975). *Seventh Progress Report of the East African Herbicide Research Project R 2557/R 2995*, 1 Jan., 1975 to 30 June, 1975.

TISCHLER, N., QUIMBA, G.P. and BEJUKI, W.M. (1951). Activators which considerably increase the defoliant and the phytotoxic properties of endothal, *Proceedings of the 5th Annual Meeting of the North Eastern Weed Science Society*, p. 35.

TOLLERVEY, F.E., FRANS, R., PANAIGUA, O. and LARA, R. (1979). Weed control investigations in Bolivian crops, 1977–1978, *Report, Centro de Investigacion Agricale Tropicale (CIAT)*, no. 2, 90 pp.

TURNER, D.J. (1972). The influence of additives on the penetration of foliar applied growth regulator herbicides, *Pesticide Science*, **3**, 323–333.

TURNER, D.J. (1981). The effect of additives on the control of *Agropyron repens* with glyphosate, *Proceedings of the Conference on Grass Weeds in Cereals in the U.K.*, Reading, 1981, pp. 167–175.

TURNER, D.J. and LOADER, M.P.C. (1974). Studies with solubilized herbicide formulations, *Proceedings of the 12th British Weed Control Conference*, pp. 177–184.

TURNER, D.J. and LOADER, M.P.C. (1975). Further studies with additives—effect of phosphate esters and ammonium salts on the activity of leaf-applied herbicides, *Pesticide Science*, **6**, 1–10.

TURNER, D.J. and LOADER, M.P.C. (1978). Complexing agents as herbicide additives, *Weed Research*, **18**, 199–207.

TURNER, D.J. and LOADER, M.P.C. (1980). Effect of ammonium sulphate and other additives on the phytotoxicity of glyphosate to *Agropyron repens* (L.) Beauv., *Weed Research*, **20**, 139–146.

UNITED KINGDOM, MINISTRY OF AGRICULTURE, FISHERIES AND FOOD (1981). *Research and Development Report, Booklet 2224 (80) Agricultural Service, Cereals, 1980*, pp. 343–346.

UNITED KINGDOM, MINISTRY OF AGRICULTURE, FISHERIES AND FOOD, AGRICULTURAL DEVELOPMENT AND ADVISORY SERVICE (1978). *1977 Research and Development Report, Northern Region Development Committee*, p. 19.

UNITED KINGDOM WEST OF SCOTLAND AGRICULTURAL COLLEGE (1978). *Annual Report 1977*, pp. 59–60.

UNITED KINGDOM WEST OF SCOTLAND AGRICULTURAL COLLEGE (1981). *Annual Report 1980*, **200**, 69–72.

VERNON, R. (1980). Weed control in Zambia's maize, *Proceedings of the 7th East African Weed Science Conference, 1979*, pp. 72–82.

WIDYANTO, L.S. and SOERJANI, K. (1978). Water hyacinth management in Indonesia, *Proceedings of the Plant Protection Conference*, Malaysia, pp. 342–352.

WILLIAMS, G.H. (1977). The effect of herbicide mixtures on the control of bracken (*Pteridium aquilinum* (L) Kuhn.), *Proceedings of the European Weed Science Society Symposium 'Different Methods of Weed Control and their Integration'*, Uppsala, 1977, **1**, 157–162.

WILLS, G.D. (1973a). Effect of inorganic salts on the toxicity of glyphosate to purple nutsedge, *Abstracts of the 1973 Meeting of the Weed Science Society of America*, p. 59.

WILLS, G.D. (1973b). Toxicity of glyphosate to purple nutsedge as affected by surfactant, *Proceedings of the 26th Annual Meeting of the Southern Weed Science Society*, pp. 408–412.

WILLS, G.D. (1978). Factors affecting the toxicity and translocation of glyphosate on cotton (*Gossypium hirsutum*), *Weed Science*, **26**, 509–513.

WORSHAM, A.D. (1972). MON 0468, a potential chemical control for perennial grass weeds in no-tillage crops, *Proceedings of the 25th Annual Meeting of the Southern Weed Science Society*, p. 175.

WORTHING, C.R. (Ed.) (1979). *The Pesticide Manual—a World Compendium*, British Crop Protection Council, 6th edition, 655 pp.

WYRILL, J.B. and BURNSIDE, O.C. (1977). Glyphosate toxicity to common milkweed and hemp dogbane as influenced by surfactants, *Weed Science*, **25**, 275–287.

YANG ZU NANG (1978). The use of mixtures of glyphosate with 2,4-D, linuron and ammonium sulphate to control weeds in rubber plantations, *Biotrop Newsletter*, **23**, 8.

YATES, W.E., AKESSON, N.B. and BAYER, D.E. (1978). Drift of glyphosate sprays applied with aerial and ground equipment, *Weed Science*, **26**, 597–604.

YEOH, C.H. and MAT TAIB, I. (1979). Weed control on Malaysian rubber smallholdings, *Proceedings of the 6th Asian Pacific Weed Science Society Conference*, Jakarta, Indonesia, **2**, 387–397.

ZAMBIA, DEPARTMENT OF AGRICULTURE (1980). *Mount Makulu Research Station Weed Control Research and Extension Team Annual Report, 1979*, pp. 37–40.

ZEMANEK, J. (1978). (The influence of ammonium sulphate on glyphosate activity), *Agrochemia*, **18**, 105–107.

ZEMANEK, J. (1979). (Inhibition of the regenerating ability of couch grass (*Agropyron repens* L.P. Beauv.) by the herbicide glyphosate), *Ochrana Rostlin*, **15**, 653–658.

ZEMANEK, J., KUBROVA, J. and STERBA, R. (1979). A study of the biological properties of glyphosate, *Proceedings of the 7th Czechoslovak Plant Protection Conference, 1978*, p. 302.

ZEMANEK, J. and STERBA, R. (1979). (Investigating the biological effects of the herbicide glyphosate), *Sbornik Vysoke Skoly Zemedelsi v Praze-Suchdole, Fakulta Agronomica, Rada A*, **30**, 109–123.

Chapter 16

Methods of application of glyphosate

C.G. McWhorter
USDA, Stoneville, USA

C.W. Derting
Monsanto Agricultural Products Company, USA

Introduction

Glyphosate, *N*-(phosphonomethyl)glycine, has caused the development of more innovative application techniques than any other herbicide. Conventional spray methods were initially used to apply glyphosate, but the effectiveness of the herbicide and the lack of crop selectivity soon fostered a new generation of application techniques not previously available. In addition to applications with conventional spray equipment, glyphosate is being applied with recirculating sprayers (RCS), numerous different types of rope-wick applicators (RWA), roller applicators, carpet applicators, wet apron hooded sprayers, mistblower aerial equipment, controlled droplet application (CDA) equipment, injectors, hand-operated sprayers, and hand-operated wipe-on devices.

Some of the advantages and disadvantages of the different methods used to apply glyphosate will be discussed. It is important, however, to summarize the precautions that should be exercised when applying glyphosate, regardless of the method of application.

The name glyphosate in this chapter refers to the isopropylamine salt of *N*-(phosphonoemethyl)glycine used as the commercial formulation Roundup.

Precautions in use

Spray solutions of glyphosate should be mixed, stored and applied only in containers of stainless steel, aluminium, fibreglass, plastic or plastic-lined steel. Herbicide solutions should not be stored or applied from containers or tanks made of galvanized steel or unlined steel (except stainless steel). A zinc coating will react with glyphosate and reduce its herbicidal activity. Glyphosate solutions may react with zinc, iron or steel to produce hydrogen gas which may give a highly combustible gas mixture when confined. Open flame, sparks or other ignition sources could cause this gas mixture to burn or explode, resulting in serious injury.

Glyphosate solutions should not be allowed to drift or splash onto desirable vegetation. Minute quantities of glyphosate may severely damage crops or other plants to which treatment was not intended. Drift of the herbicide should be avoided, regardless of the method of application. The likelihood of unintended injury from drift is greatest when wind velocity exceeds 8 km h^{-1}. The use of coarse spray droplets and drift control additives is beneficial in reducing the drift potential (see also p. 455).

Clean water should always by used in preparing glyphosate solutions. Water that is contaminated with soil and organic debris may cause reduced control. This is especially important with recirculating spray equipment. The addition of other herbicides to glyphosate solutions may reduce its activity (see also Chapter 15). No other herbicides or materials should be mixed with glyphosate unless specifically approved and recommended for tank mixture applications.

Selective methods of application

Glyphosate is highly toxic to most field and horticultural crops when applied post-emergence in foliar sprays at rates that provide good to excellent weed control. Adequate crop selectivity can be achieved mechanically by applying the herbicide solution to the weeds while minimizing contact with the crop plants. Unconventional devices which selectively place the herbicide solution only on the weeds include the roller applicator, recirculating sprayer, rope-wick applicator, shielded wiper, hooded wiper, shielded sprayer and the carpet applicator.

Early development of 'wipe-on' equipment in the USA

The use of selective wipe-on pesticide applicators in the USA originated in the early 1900s. Mahanay (1909) patented a horse-drawn device to apply insecticide solutions to plant foliage by means of wicks or other absorbent material. His device utilized capillary action to transport pesticide solution from a receptacle through wicks which brushed the pesticide onto the crop as the device moved through the field. Goode (1923) developed an improved method of application by mounting a rotating drum of insecticide solution on a horse-drawn plough. The drum contained lines of evenly spaced perforations covered by strips of felt. The drum, filled from a reservoir mounted higher up on the plough, rotated as it contacted the tops of crop plants and thus brought the absorbent strips into successive contact with leaves. Hay (1929) patented an improved wipe-on applicator with a tubular pesticide reservoir mounted horizontally between the plough handles and above the crop. Strands of absorbent material (wicks) extended from the liquid in the tube to a point below the device where, by capillary action, the pesticide solution was wiped onto the top of plants as the device travelled through the field. Related devices were patented by Corley and Salley (1937) and Segars and Lamar (1940).

Herbicides were not used with wipe-on applicators for selective weed control in crops until commercial development of 2,4-D [(2,4-dichlorophenoxy)acetic acid] and other phenoxy herbicides in the late 1940s. One of these methods, used by farmers in the USA for more than three decades, involved wrapping the sprayboom of a hydraulic sprayer with burlap, blankets or other absorbent material to apply 2,4-D as the sprayboom moved through the field. The boom was held a few centimetres above the crop and wiped herbicide onto weeds that were taller than the crop. These early wipe-on methods were of limited use, but the invention of the rope-wick applicator (Dale, 1980) in 1976 rapidly expanded the development of wipe-on technology.

Glyphosate rates used

For standard hydraulic-sprayer applications, the use of glyphosate can be reported in grams (acid equivalent) applied per hectare. It is impossible precisely to determine the amount of herbicide used per hectare with most wipe-on applications, thus only the herbicide concentration will be reported (in unit/unit, herbicide:water solutions). Unless otherwise specified, all herbicide dilutions are on a volume/volume (v/v) basis using the commercial formulation of glyphosate that contains 360 g glyphosate a.e. per litre (3 lb gal^{-1}).

Rope-wick applicators

Rope-wick applicators (RWAs) were first used by farmers in 1978 and since then have been used widely. RWAs appeal to farmers because of efficiency and simplicity of operation. They are efficient because they apply far less herbicide per hectare than any other method of application. The amount of herbicide used is proportional to the weed infestation. The materials to construct a RWA are easily available and cost about $100 US for a four-row applicator (about 4 m in length). The cost of commercially available RWAs varies from $300 to $2500 US depending on length and equipment mounting and elevation control.

The rapid initial acceptance of RWAs by farmers was unprecedented. Within 18 months of the first public disclosure (Dale, 1978), the inventor had received over 20 000 requests for his publication on how to construct RWAs (Dale, 1979). It was estimated that 26 manufacturers in the USA marketed 15–20 000 tractor-mounted RWAs in 1979 and that individual farmers probably constructed an equal number (Wills and McWhorter, 1981). A greater number have been built since that time. Additionally, an estimated 100 000 hand-held RWA devices have been sold in the USA. More than 4 million hectares of cropland were treated with glyphosate in RWAs in 1980 and this increased to over 8 million hectares in the USA in 1981. These devices are also manufactured in several other countries, where their acceptance has been widespread.

RWAs are usually constructed using either 7–8 cm PVC pipe or aluminium pipe. Two or more rows of braided rope are used to convey the herbicide solution to the weeds that contact the rope (*Figure 16.1*). Herbicide solution in the rope is replenished through capillary movement of the solution from the pipe that serves as a reservoir. The herbicide is wiped from the rope onto weeds.

Most widespread use of RWAs has been in soya bean (*Glycine max*), grain sorghum (*Sorghum bicolor*), cotton (*Gossypium hirsutum*), pastures and horticultural crops. Tall-growing weeds most frequently treated with glyphosate by rope-wick application (and other wipe-on devices) include *S. halepense, S. bicolor, Zea mays, Asclepias syriaca, Ambrosia* spp., *Amaranthus* spp. and *Helianthus annuus*. This technique has also been used for the control of many other weed species.

One treatment with a RWA applying a 33% glyphosate solution at 4–6 km h^{-1} will provide excellent (90–100%) control of *S. bicolor* or *Z. mays*, good (70–90%) control of *S. halepense*, but only poor to fair control (40–70%) of more tolerant weeds such as *A. syriaca, Amaranthus* spp. and *H. annuus*. The level of control can be increased by reducing the speed of application and by making a second application in the opposite direction.

The control of individual weeds following treatment with the RWA may be

Figure 16.1. A Stoneville-type rope-wick applicator mounted
on the front of a tractor to apply glyphosate to *Sorghum
halepense* growing taller than soya bean (*Glycine max*)

highly variable (Lutman, 1979), especially with weeds that tend to be more tolerant
to glyphosate such as *A. syriaca* and *H. annuus*. The variable control is probably
due to variable amounts of glyphosate deposited by the RWA. Lutman, Oswald
and Byast (1982) reported that the amount of glyphosate deposited on individual
plants varied from 0.37 mg g^{-1} to 3.34 mg g^{-1}. They also found that plants near the
front of a treatment line received more glyphosate than those treated soon after
treatment of other weeds.

There are many variations in the design and components used in RWAs. The
three basic designs of tractor-mounted RWAs in row-crop use are (a) the standard
Stoneville type with exposed rope segments 10–20 cm long (*Figure 16.1*), (b)
multiple RWAs with rope segments about 33 cm long, positioned horizontally
above the crop (*Figure 16.2*), and (c) pressurized RWAs with rope segments 50 cm
long, extending forward in a wedge shape and overlapping from a pipe-type
reservoir (*Figure 16.3*). Variations of all three types are available that utilize low air
pressure to force glyphosate solution through the ropes.

Several types and sizes of ropes have been used in RWAs, but most are about 13
mm in diameter. Those most frequently used include various types of nylon solid
braids and a rope made of a diamond-braided polyester exterior over an interior
filler of twisted acrylic yarn (Derting, 1981; Wu and Derting, 1981; Revelle, 1982).
The latter rope transports glyphosate solution much more rapidly and has greater
load capacity than other types. These are desirable properties when weed
infestations are severe. They allow faster travel speeds without using air pressure to
force solution through the wick. Excessive dripping of glyphosate from the rope

Figure 16.2. A multiple rope-wick applicator used to apply glyphosate to *Sorghum halepense* in soya bean (*Glycine max*). The rope segments are supplied with glyphosate solution from both ends. The direction of travel is from left to right

Figure 16.3. A pressurized rope-wick applicator mounted on the front of a tractor to apply glyphosate to *Sorghum halepense* growing taller than soya bean (*Glycine max*)

will injure crop plants, but can be regulated in several ways, including the use of solenoid valves in air vents (Dale, 1982).

Glyphosate solutions for use in the RWA are usually prepared by mixing 1 unit of formulated glyphosate product in 2 units of water. The degree of wetting and the resulting application rate can be controlled to some degree by varying the liquid level in the pipe. Normally, 4 l of herbicide will treat up to 40 ha, depending on the level of weed infestation and manner of operation. Ground speed of the applicator can also be used to vary the rates of the herbicide applied. The proper speed varies depending on weed density, weed species and the rate of wicking of the ropes. The rate of wicking can be regulated by venting the reservoir, adjusting the tightness-of-fit of the ropes and changing rope placement. The devices are usually operated at 6–8 km h^{-1} to permit the operator to make necessary height adjustments with minimum crop injury. Treatments usually need to be repeated for optimum control. Weed control is increased in areas with dense weed infestations by operating the device in opposite directions in the same day.

The most recent development in RWAs is a recirculating device (*Figure 16.4*). Low air pressure is used in the uppermost tube to force liquid through the rope sections into a lower mounted plastic tube that operates under a slight vacuum. Liquid caught in the lower tube is again pumped back into the original plastic tube to complete the recirculation cycle. The advantage of this system is that rope sections remain constantly wet without herbicide solution dripping to cause crop injury. This device should provide at least 10–20% better control than conventional RWAs.

Figure 16.4. A recirculating rope-wick applicator mounted on the front of a tractor. Low air pressure is applied to the front PVC pipe, while the lower PVC pipe (partially obscured by the ropes) has a vacuum to increase transport of herbicide solution. This method keeps ropes saturated, but eliminates dripping of herbicide solution

Roller applicator

The roller applicator was first described by Wyse and Habstritt (1977). The roller is usually constructed of a 20–25 cm aluminium cylinder covered with an absorbent pad of nylon carpet (Koehler *et al.*, 1980). The roller applicator can be either front of rear mounted on tractors, but has most often been rear mounted. Glyphosate solution is applied to the carpet, which rotates to reduce drippage. The herbicide is wiped onto weeds that grow taller than the crop.

In popular articles, the roller applicator is described as the Quacker Whacker, carpet applicator, carpet roller or Minnesota roller. Roller applicators have been used primarily for weed control in turf grasses and soya bean by farmers in the central USA and in Canada. Their use in other parts of the USA or throughout the world has been more limited than use of the RWA. The devices generally have been sold in the USA at $2000–2500 US.

The carpet-covered aluminium cylinder of the roller applicator is usually 3–9 m long. The roller revolves counterclockwise to the direction in which the tractor is travelling. Rotation of the cylinders is accomplished by a hydraulic motor, usually operating at 20–50 r.p.m. Herbicide solution is applied to the carpet by plastic or steel tubing with small holes (usually less than 1 mm) drilled at close intervals (2.5–5 cm) and mounted above the roller. In early models, maintaining proper moisture levels on the carpet for adequate weed control without excessive wetness and dripping of the herbicide was difficult. This problem led to the use of an electronic moisture sensor to maintain an optimum moisture level (Schepers and Burnside, 1979). This increased the effectiveness of the roller applicator.

These applicators have been used to apply glyphosate in soya bean and grain sorghum (Schneider *et al.*, 1982), horticultural crops (Hertz and Duncan, 1980), blueberry (*Vaccinium angustifolium*) (Yarborough and Ismail, 1982), and for woody plant control (Gaultney *et al.*, 1981). In the USA, one application of 10–20% glyphosate solution in a roller applicator will provide 90–100% control of *S. bicolor* if the carpet saturation level is 50% or more. Control will be greatly reduced with lower levels of carpet saturation. Control of more tolerant weeds such as *A. syriaca* may be only 50–80%. There has been no research reported on the amount of glyphosate deposited by roller devices except from the UK Weed Research Organization (WRO), but glyphosate applied with the WRO roller was in a sodium alginate–calcium citrate 'gel'. This practice is not used in roller applicators in the USA, so direct comparisons on glyphosate deposition are not possible. Even so, Lutman, Oswald and Byast (1982) found that the WRO roller deposited more glyphosate on plants than the RWA.

The roller applicator in the USA is normally operated at speeds of 3–6 km h^{-1}. Like the RWA, the optimum speed for the roller applicator is dependent on the level of weed infestation, wind velocity, and air temperature and relative humidity at time of treatment.

Most weeds can be controlled with glyphosate applied in the roller applicator when the carpet is kept wet with a 1:10 glyphosate : water solution. Maintaining an optimum moisture level (50–75%) in the carpet is usually more critical than any specific concentration of herbicide (5–20%).

Roller applicators have been marketed only by about three manufacturers in the USA and we estimate that only a few hundred of these devices have been purchased by farmers. We assume that farmers have used RWAs more extensively than roller applicators because the latter devices are usually more expensive and more complicated to operate since they involve use of pressurized spray systems, motors and moisture sensors. Thus, use of roller applicators offered no overall advantage over use of the RWA in general row-crop use (Furrer, 1979).

Carpet applicators

The Stoneville recirculating carpet applicator was first described by Chandler (1981) and, like the RWA, was developed for post-emergence applications to weeds taller than the crop. The application principle of the carpet applicator is similar to the wipe-on devices described earlier.

The basic components of the carpet applicator are a 2–4 m length of 20 cm aluminium tubing, a pad of nylon carpet, a section of flat expanded metal, and standard cone spray nozzles (*Figure 16.5*). A longitudinal section of the tubing is removed and replaced by a hinged section of expanded metal which supports the carpet. The spray nozzles are mounted 25 cm apart inside the tubing. These nozzles spray herbicide solution onto the back of the carpet pad that covers the opening in the tube. The spray solution moves to the front of the carpet through the carpet fibres by capillary action. Excess spray solution flows from the carpet into a shallow reservoir, is filtered, and returned to the supply tank. The carpet applicator units are mounted horizontally in front of a tractor at a right-angle to the direction of travel and are maintained above the crop.

Chandler (1981) reported excellent (90–100%) control of *S. halepense* with

Figure 16.5. Front view of a Stoneville recirculating carpet applicator mounted on the front of a tractor. Two panels of carpet are raised to expose spray nozzles that spray glyphosate solution onto the back of the carpet. The direction of travel is from right to left

glyphosate : water ratios of 1 : 2, 1 : 4 and 1 : 6. Glyphosate : water ratios of 1 : 8 and 1 : 10 provided only 65% and 55% control, respectively. *Sorghum halepense* control did not vary with speeds of application between 4.5 and 6.9 km h^{-1}. Control of most weeds with glyphosate applied in this device may be more consistent than with the RWA because the wiping surface is much larger. We do not know of research to determine the amount of glyphosate deposited with the carpet applicator.

The carpet applicator was reported to overcome several disadvantages of other devices used to selectively apply glyphosate in row crops including: (a) splattering of the spray solution onto the crop; (b) accumulation of plant debris and soil particles in spray filters, as in recirculating sprayers; (c) the limited volume range of liquid delivered through ropes of RWAs; and (d) adverse effects from low humidity, high temperatures and brisk winds which rapidly dry ropes (Roach and Chandler, 1982).

Chandler (1981) reported that caution was needed in selecting the carpet for the applicator. He stressed (a) the importance of ensuring that the glue used in the carpet is not soluble in water solutions of formulated glyphosate, and (b) the importance of soaking the carpet for a minium of 24 h in a detergent–water solution to remove the sizing and other chemicals from the fibres of the backing that may interfere with herbicide–solution transport.

Apparently only one manufacturer has sold carpet applicators in the USA and only a few hundred are in commercial use. Use of the device will probably not expand rapidly because of its cost ($3000–5000 US) and its general lack of simplicity as compared to the RWA.

The Stoneville shielded wiper is another device using a carpet to apply glyphosate selectively in established row crops. Developed by Chandler (1979; 1980), it consists of a 'shag' carpet attached face-down to cover a 20 × 30 cm opening at the bottom of a fibreglass hood. The glyphosate solution is sprayed downward onto the back of the carpet by a nozzle mounted inside the top front of the hood. This device is mounted on a standard row crop cultivator and is positioned about 2–4 cm above the soil. Used in pairs, each unit is positioned about 4–6 cm from the crop drill. The hood prevents the herbicide from contacting the crop plants; herbicide spray remains in the carpet until weeds are contacted by the carpet. These wipers have been built only on an experimental basis and are not known to be commercially available.

Other wipe-on devices

Wet apron applicators have been used to a limited extent in the midwestern USA to control selectively weeds that grow taller than soya bean. These devices use conventional spray systems to wet a fixed canvas shield which wipes glyphosate onto weeds. Some devices recover and recirculate excess spray solution. Apparently these devices apply less herbicide than devices discussed earlier (Furrer, 1979).

Furrer (1979) reported that apron devices applying 1 : 10 solutions of glyphosate : water provided less control of several weed species, had more equipment problems, and had a lower level of grower acceptance than other wipe-on devices used to apply glyphosate. The apron devices have usually been rear mounted, but this makes optimum height adjustment difficult. The cost of these devices has been about $1300–2000 US for units that are about 4 m wide. The land area treated with wet apron applicators in the USA has been far less than with other wipe-on devices.

A continuous-belt herbicide wiper was reported by Welker and Darlington (1980). This device was developed to apply glyphosate and other herbicides to weeds that grow taller than cranberry (*Vaccinium macrocarpon*) plants. The applicator, about 2 m wide, utilizes an endless belt with a sponge attached to the entire length of the belt to transport herbicide solution from a reservoir to weeds that grow above the crop. A variable pressure wheel squeezes the excess liquid out of the sponge and returns it to the reservoir. Herbicide solution is wiped onto weeds as the belt moves in a horizontal plane perpendicular to the forward motion of the wiper. Forward speeds of about 3.2 km h^{-1} were found to be satisfactory when applying solutions that contained glyphosate in water (6 g l^{-1}). Weed control (90–100%) obtained with glyphosate applied in the wiper was generally equivalent to the level of control obtained when glyphosate was sprayed at 1–2 kg ha^{-1} (Welker and Darlington, 1980). Crop injury with the device was negligible. Apparently commercial adaptation of this device has been limited.

A recently developed device manufactured in the USA utilizes a fabric-covered PVC pipe. In appearance, it looks like a simple substitution of fabric for rope, but the differences are more complex. A PVC tube 5.76 cm in diameter by 2.5–4.5 m in length has perforations along the bottom. This is covered with felt, plastic sheeting and an outer fabric which contacts weeds. A separate 56.8 l reservoir supplies the wiper by means of an electrically-powered solenoid valve. An exceptionally high flow rate allows high travel speed, but requires constant observation and control of the valve by the operator to prevent excessive crop injury. We do not know of published reports on the level of control expected with this device.

Figure 16.6. A hand-operated rope-wick applicator being used to apply glyphosate to *Sorghum halepense* in soya bean (*Glycine max*)

Roguing gloves have been effective in applying glyphosate for weed control (Laws, 1974; Ryan, Cormican and Collier, 1978). Glyphosate solution is transported to the glove through tubing from a reservoir held by the individual who wears the glove. A pad on the surface of the glove is wetted by the solution (usually about 100 g glyphosate per litre of water) and weeds are wetted as the hand operating the device squeezes the glove over the weed. These devices provide effective (95–100%) control, although their use has been limited to small land areas as compared to the tractor-mounted devices discussed previously.

Many different types of hand-operated rope-wick and sponge applicators have been sold throughout the world for applying glyphosate (Frank, 1982) (*Figure 16.6*). These are usually lightweight, 0.1–0.3 m long, and are constructed from PVC pipe which serves as a solution reservoir and wick mount. They are used to apply glyphosate solutions (usually 10–33%, v/v) around homes, gardens and in field and horticultural crops.

Recirculating sprayers

Glyphosate was first applied in the recirculating sprayers (RCS) for weed control in row crops in the early 1970s (McWhorter, 1977). The recirculating sprayer concept of herbicide application originated in the mid-1960s (McWhorter, 1970), but there was very little farmer usage of the device until glyphosate became commercially available.

The recirculating sprayer is used to apply herbicide only to weeds that grow taller than the crop (McWhorter, 1970). Herbicide solutions are usually applied through solid-stream nozzles, above and at right-angles to the rows, so that a trap collects herbicide spray not deposited on weeds (*Figure 16.7*). Trapped solution is returned to the original spray tank by gravity flow on small sprayers, although pumps or venturi-suction systems are used to transfer spray solution back to the original tank on larger recirculating sprayers. The first recirculating sprayers that were marketed in the mid-1970s were of the box type, as shown in *Figure 16.7*. Soon afterwards broadcast-type recirculating sprayers were also marketed (*Figure 16.8*). By 1979 about 5000 RCSs had been sold to farmers by about 17 manufacturers (Wills and McWhorter, 1981). Three of these manufacturers marketed the broadcast RCS, while the others marketed different variations of the box-type RCS.

Farmer usage of recirculating sprayers in the USA reached a maximum in 1978, but usage declined thereafter because of the popular appeal of RWAs. Recirculating sprayers cost $2500–4000 US per sprayer. They were often heavy and cumbersome. Farmers often had difficulty in properly mounting sprayers on tractors, properly calibrating the equipment, and in providing proper maintenance of the equipment over a long period of use. Improper adjustment of the equipment and excess spray pressure often resulted in excessive drift and splatter of the herbicide onto the crop causing crop injury. Crop injury can be minimized with RCSs (McWhorter and Williford, 1980), but they have been largely replaced by other methods of application in most countries.

Glyphosate concentrations in RCSs are usually at 1.1–1.2 kg of active herbicide in water that is sprayed at $100–200 \ l \ ha^{-1}$. Recirculating sprayers are normally expected to recover 70–90% of the herbicide solution sprayed through the nozzles (McWhorter, 1970) so that only 10–30% of the herbicide actually sprayed was deposited in the field. The amount actually used was proportional to the weed population which intercepted the sprays. Spray pressure should be maintained

Figure 16.7. A box-type recirculating sprayer applying glyphosate to *Sorghum halepense* growing taller than soya bean (*Glycine max*). Herbicide spray not deposited on weeds is collected
in the spray-traps and returned (via a suction device) to the
spray tank for re-use

below 100 kPa in RCSs to minimize dripping and splattering herbicide onto the
crop.

Recirculating sprayers can effectively operate at higher speeds than rope-wick,
roller or carpet applicators, and they provide a higher level of weed control with
fewer trips through the field than with wipe-on applicators, particularly in dense
weed infestations. There are no reports to show the amount of glyphosate applied
to individual weeds with the RCS. In most comparative trials the level of control of
S. halepense and *S. bicolor* with the RCS is 10–20% higher than with wipe-on
devices, especially with high levels of weed infestation. Even so, the maintenance
problems, lower crop safety and initial high cost of the equipment precludes any
expanded use of this equipment in the USA.

Shielded sprayers

The Stoneville shielded sprayer was first reported by Jordan and Reames (1976).
This device was designed to shield row crops from glyphosate sprayed onto weeds
growing below the crop canopy. Standard flat-fan spray nozzles were positioned
downward and rearward at approximately 45° to spray glyphosate solution onto a
25 cm band on each side of the crop drill. Metal or fibreglass hoods were mounted
to enclose the spray pattern and allow coverage only of the weeds. Jordan reported

Figure 16.8. A broadcast-type recirculating sprayer mounted on the front of a tractor that is moving from right to left. Herbicide spray that is not deposited on weeds is collected in the trap, drains to the PVC pipe at the bottom, and is pumped back to the spray tank for re-use

excellent (95–100%) control of perennial weeds without injury to cotton using glyphosate at 2.2–4.0 kg ha^{-1}. Only one manufacturer of this particular design is known to have produced units for sale. Commercial usage was unacceptable due to inadequate guidance of the shields and crop injury on rough ground.

Previous to Jordan's research a shielded sprayer was fashioned in California using a vertical baffle adjacent to cotton rows, with one wide-angle spray nozzle mounted over each row middle. Cotton was protected from injury and perennial weed control was excellent with glyphosate at 4–8 kg ha^{-1}. Limited commercial and private farmer production of this design is occurring in California.

Four manufacturers in the southeastern USA are producing shielded sprayers designed to protect row crops from herbicide solutions sprayed to the area between the rows. Nozzle tips include wide-angle, flat-fan spray, single outlet and double outlet spray types. Shields are constructed of sheet metal or rigid plastic measuring approximately 0.5–0.7 × 0.5–0.7 m. Placement is vertical, or nearly so, on either side of the row. Adjustment allows the protected but untreated drill area to range from 10 to 20 cm.

A shielded recirculating RWA has been evaluated. It utilized a high-capacity diamond-braided polyester rope around a hollow plastic tube perforated at 7.5 cm intervals to allow herbicide solution to wet the rope. The tube was pressurized with herbicide on one end and vacuum aspirated on the other so that all unused solution was recovered. The device was designed to apply glyphosate selectively to low-growing weeds on either side of cotton and soya beans.

A hooded sprayer, with plastic hoods mounted on either side of the crop drill, has been evaluated. The hood is open on the bottom, encloses one nozzle per hood, and allows spray application to bands 25 cm on each side of each row. Adjustment allowed protection of the crop and an untreated drill area of as little as 10 cm.

Additional shielded and non-shielded devices designed to selectively apply glyphosate solutions to low-growing weeds between crop rows have been evaluated. Selectivity has often been achieved in two-row prototypes, but has not been practical or effective in commercial units.

Hand-held spray equipment

Glyphosate is extensively used to obtain selective weed control by careful placement of sprays with hand-held knapsack sprayers, high-volume spray equipment utilizing handguns, and other hand-operated nozzle arrangements. Applications of this type are on a spray-to-wet basis with sprays carefully directed only onto weeds. Spray solutions that contain formulated glyphosate at $10–20 \text{ g l}^{-1}$ control most species when uniform and complete coverage is obtained. It is important that coarse spray droplets be applied to avoid drift onto crop plants in close proximity to the weeds. Hand-spray applications are commonplace through the world to control isolated weeds in crops and also in non-crop situations.

Non-selective application methods

Glyphosate is applied to millions of hectares annually using the selective methods discussed earlier, but even more extensive use is made of glyphosate using non-selective methods of application. Conventional application technologies are used to apply glyphosate in a wide range of sites. There are many restrictions, often specific to particular areas, that regulate glyphosate usage with respect to the interval between application and harvest, tank mixtures with other pesticides, and the size of buffer zones around non-target areas.

Conventional ground-broadcast applications

Most ground-broadcast applications of glyphosate are with conventional boom sprayers to areas 1–2 m or several metres wide. Conventional applications of glyphosate are usually in water at $100–400 \text{ l ha}^{-1}$. Foaming of the spray solution during and after preparation may be troublesome and this can be minimized by (a) placing the filling hose below the surface of spray solution, (b) terminating the bypass (and other return) lines of the sprayer at the bottom of the tank, or (c) using an anti-foam or defoaming agent. Normally mechanical agitators should be avoided in preparing glyphosate solutions because of the foaming problem.

Most annual grass and broadleaf weeds are controlled by glyphosate at $0.8–1.0$ kg ha^{-1} when weeds are no more than about 15 cm tall. The normal minimal rate of the herbicide that will provide adequate control when weeds are taller than 15 cm is about 1.7 kg ha^{-1}. Many perennial weeds are controlled by glyphosate at $2.5–4.5$ kg ha^{-1}. Control is usually best when applications are to actively growing plants. Repeat applications may be necessary to control some perennials.

Mistblowers and aerial application

Glyphosate is highly efficacious when applied by helicopter or by fixed-wing aircraft (Barring, 1979; Chappell *et al.*, 1979; Lund-Høie, 1980; Moore, Yortt and Atkinson, 1980; see also Chapter 21). The advantage of aerial spraying is offset to some extent by the potential hazards of damage from drift. There are many ways in which drift can be minimized, but the inherent hazard of drift damage to desirable species has resulted in many restrictions on this type of application by the manufacturer and local, state and national governmental agencies. Applications made in this way in forest areas are discussed by Lund-Høie in Chapter 21.

Glyphosate is highly toxic to the same spectrum of plant species when applied in mistblowers, as when applications are with conventional ground equipment or by air. Mistblowers produce finely atomized droplets, so the use of these devices for weed control is limited by a serious drift hazard.

Mistblowers are usually small power-driven machines that apply highly concentrated herbicides in a fine atomized form at low spray volumes. The air stream from the turbine blower is the principal transport of the herbicide. Mistblowers may be hand-operated or mounted on tractors. These sprayers do not have conventional spraybooms or nozzles, and thus are useful in applying herbicides in thickly wooded areas and in other types of dense plant growth. They are frequently used in areas that are inaccessible to conventional power equipment. A small 2 h.p. knapsack-type mistblower may be hand operated and used to treat vegetation up to 10 m tall, while larger mistblowers (up to 12 h.p.) would more typically be tractor-mounted for treating larger vegetation.

Controlled droplet applicators

Controlled droplet applicator (CDA) units are designed to regulate the size of the discharged spray droplets to improve herbicide efficiency and to provide better control of herbicide drift. This spray concept is not new (Bals, 1975; 1978), but application of glyphosate in CDA equipment has received impetus during the last few years because of the availability of new market sources of this equipment. Two basic types of devices are available—a small hand-held unit (*Figure 16.9*) and larger tractor-mounted devices (McGarvey, 1980).

The reported advantages of CDA equipment are that a narrow range of droplets is produced with more uniform sizes than with hydraulic spray nozzles, resulting in: (a) production of fewer 'fines' which can cause herbicide loss through the vapour activity and particle drift; (b) use of a lower carrier volume, reducing the risk of foliar run-off and reducing the amount of water pumped, hauled and sprayed; and (c) the reduced drift and run-off losses which may allow a lower rate of herbicide per unit area (Doll and Drost, 1980). More than 500 000 CDA applicators were reported to have been sold worldwide by 1980 (McGarvey, 1980).

Hand-held CDA units have a capacity of about 1.8 l of spray solution, an amount that would usually provide coverage of up to 0.25 ha. In the USA, this device has been used primarily to apply glyphosate at a rate of about $0.6 \, l \, ha^{-1}$ of formulated product. The hand-held device is used primarily for weed control on ditchbanks, fencerows, around irrigation equipment, in vineyards and in orchards. The tractor-mounted device was first used by farmers in the USA in 1980. These are usually mounted on a sprayboom that is 6–9 m long. A typical application might be to apply glyphosate in water at $10–15 \, l \, ha^{-1}$, with a tractor speed of about 19

Figure 16.9. A hand-operated control droplet applicator used to apply glyphosate. Slightly larger applicators of this type are mounted 1–2 m apart on tractor booms for broadcast application to larger areas (photograph by courtesy of the Micron Corporation)

km h^{-1}. The tractor-mounted electric- or hydraulically-driven CDA units apply the herbicide liquid that is fed through two openings in the top of the unit and this flows into the base of the rotating disk. The flow rate is controlled by orifice size and pressure, but droplet size is controlled by speed of rotation of the disk. The disk is driven by an electric or hydraulic motor and can be operated over a range of 0–6000 r.p.m., depending on the power combination selected. A disk speed of 2500–3500 r.p.m. is considered optimum for applying herbicides post-emergence in water at about 9–27 l ha^{-1}. A more uniform spray pattern has been reported when units are mounted about 1 m apart on the boom than with wider mountings. Under conditions of variable wind gusts, streaking between swaths has been troublesome at both 1 and 2 m spacings. It was also reported that tilting the units downward (in the direction of travel) at 15–45° may aid in better penetration of the crop canopy by the herbicide drops (Bode and Butler, 1981).

A large number of reports show that the final toxicity obtained with glyphosate is increased 10–20% with CDA equipment, as compared to higher volume applications using hydraulic spray nozzles. Greatest increases in control (20% +) have been reported when glyphosate was applied at less than 1 kg ha^{-1}. While not all research has reported increased effectiveness of glyphosate when applied in CDA equipment (Harris, 1977; Drost and Doll, 1979; Utulu and Akobundu, 1978; Erickson and Duke, 1981), it does appear that the application of glyphosate in a single concentrated droplet provides more activity than when applications are made in more dilute droplets in greater numbers (Ambach and Ashford, 1982; see also

Chapter 7). These researchers felt that the increase in control was caused primarily by the increased surfactant content in the more concentrated droplets, and their research showed that the decreased toxicity in the more dilute droplets could be restored with increased surfactant content.

Even though glyphosate applications in CDA equipment do not always increase control, as compared to conventional applications, it appears that expanded use of this method of application will continue as improved equipment enters the marketplace. Greatly expanded use of this application technology would be made in applying glyphosate in no tillage and eco-fallow situations in the USA and in many areas where the use of larger volumes of diluent presents a handicap.

Injection and frill applications

The control of undesirable tree species is important in silviculture to maintain or improve forest productivity. The application of herbicides by injection into the cambium or in frills cut through the bark is often an important and integral part of timber stand improvement. Glyphosate applied in this manner is effective for the control of certain *Liquidambar* spp., *Populus* spp., *Quercus* spp., *Plantanus* spp., and other species (see also Chapter 21). In combination with other herbicides, glyphosate treatments are effective for the control of many other species (Wickham and Holt, 1976; Mann, 1979; Campbell, 1980; Maass, 1981).

Several types of commercial tree injectors are available with narrow (usually about 12–20 mm) cutting blades. The blades are driven into the trunk of the tree by hand, usually about 0.2–0.4 m above the ground, and the herbicide is injected as the cut is made or immediately after the cut. Using this method, glyphosate is usually applied undiluted with 1 ml of herbicide solution applied for each 5–6 cm of trunk diameter breast high (DBH). Applications are spaced uniformly around the circumference of the trunk.

Frill applications are made after frills are cut about 10–15 mm deep into the tree trunk in a continuous and overlapping manner. Herbicide is applied into the frill immediately after cutting. As with injection, glyphosate is normally applied undiluted with about 1 ml of herbicide applied for each 5–6 cm of trunk DBH. The best control is usually obtained with both injector and frill applications when trees are in active growth after full leaf expansion.

Conclusions

Glyphosate is a very broad-spectrum herbicide. It is relativity non-selective to different plant species, but selectivity can be achieved by mechanical placement of the herbicide on weeds while minimizing contact with desirable species. Glyphosate is also effective when applied with all known established conventional techniques. A large number of innovative application techniques have evolved to apply glyphosate selectively for control of dozens of different weed species in many different cropping situations. The capability of glyphosate to absorb and translocate within a few days of application, and the broad-spectrum control that it provides, makes it one of the most versatile herbicides available.

References

AMBACH, R.M. and ASHFORD, R. (1982). Effects of variations in drop makeup on the phytotoxicity of glyphosate, *Weed Science*, **30**(3), 221–224.

BALS, E.J. (1975). Development of a herbicide handsprayer, *PANS*, **21**, 345–349.

BALS, E.J. (1978). The reasons for CDA (controlled droplet application), *Proceedings of the 1978 British Crop Protection Conference—Weeds*, **2**, 659–666.

BARRING, U. (1979). Results of country-wide trials in forestry—trials into aerial application of glyphosate and triclopyr amine, *Weeds and Weed Control, 20th Swedish Weed Conference*, Uppsala, 1979, 1. Reports, pp. 82–93.

BODE, L.E. and BUTLER, B.J. (1981). Spray characteristics of rotary atomizers, *Pesticide Formulations and Application Systems Symposium*, Kansas City, Missouri, 19 October, 1981, sponsored by ASTM Committee E-35 on Pesticides.

CAMPBELL, T.E. (1980). A comparison of five tree-injected herbicides, *Proceedings of the Southern Weed Science Society*, **33**, 127–131.

CHANDLER, J.M. (1979). Stoneville wiper—a post directed applicator for weed control, *Proceedings of the Southern Weed Science Society*, **32**, 379.

CHANDLER, J.M. (1980). Recent equipment and chemicals for bermudagrass, Abstract, *Weed Science Society of America*, **14**(29).

CHANDLER, J.M. (1981). The ultimate Stoneville applicator for postemergence weed control, *Proceedings of the Southern Weed Science Society*, **34**, 294.

CHAPPELL, W.E., COARTNEY, J.S., HIPKINS, P.L. and LINK, M.L. (1979). Aerial applications of glyphosate for the control of brush in rights-of-way, *Proceedings of the Southern Weed Science Society*, **32**, 242–244.

CORLEY, A.M. and SALLEY, S.C. (1973). *U.S. Patent No. 2, 123, 988*, granted 11 Oct., 1937, United States Patent Office, Washington, D.C.

DALE, J.E. (1978). The rope wick applicator—a new method of applying glyphosate, *Proceedings of the Southern Weed Science Society*, **31**, 332.

DALE, J.E. (1979). Application equipment for roundup—the rope wick applicator, *Proceedings of the Beltwide Cotton Production Research Conferences – 3rd Cotton Weed Science Research Conference*, p. 138.

DALE, J.E. (1980). *U.S. Patent No. 4219964*, dated 2 Sept., 1980, United States Patent Office, Washington, D.C.

DALE, J.E. (1982). Regulation of rope-wick applicators by a solenoid valve, *Proceedings of the Southern Weed Science Society*, **35**, 409.

DERTING, CLAUDE W. (1981). Correlation of rope wick design and components with glyphosate performance, *Proceedings of the Southern Weed Science Society*, **34**, 305–310.

DOLL, J.D. and DROST, D.C. (1980). The controlled droplet applicator for postemergence herbicides, *Proceedings of the Fertilizer, Agricultural Lime and Pesticide Management Conference*, Madison, Wisconsin, **19**, 13–19.

DROST, D.C. and DOLL, J.D. (1979). Using a controlled droplet applicator for postemergence herbicide applications, *Proceedings of the North Central Weed Control Conference*, **34**, 60–63.

ERICKSON, C.G. and DUKE, W.B. (1981). Recent innovations in herbicide application equipment, *Proceedings of the Northeastern Weed Science Society*, **35**, 343–344.

FRANK, J.R. (1982). Weed control applicators for small farms and home gardens, *Proceedings of the Northeastern Weed Science Society*, **36**, 187.

FURRER, J.D. (1979). Comparison of specialized equipment for controlling weed escapes in soybeans, *Proceedings of the North Central Weed Control Conference*, **34**, 63–65.

GALTNEY, L., GIBSON, H.G., HOLT, H. and KRUTZ, G.W. (1981). Will wiping type herbicide applicator work for woody plant control, paper No. 81–1506, *Winter Meeting of the American Society of Agricultural Engineers*, Chicago, Illinois.

GOODE, W.W. (1982). *U.S. Patent No. 1,507,595*, granted 5 Nov., 1923, United States Patent Office, Washington, D.C.

HARRIS, P.B. (1977). Mixed results with CDA spraying, *Arable Farming*, no. 4, pp. 11, 62 and 65.

HAY, C.R. (1929). *U.S. Patent No. 1,764,952*, granted 30 Aug., 1929, United States Patent Office, Washington, D.C.

HERTZ, L.B. and DUNCAN, D.N. (1980). Weed control in established strawberries with glyphosate applied using rope and roller applicator, *Proceedings of the North Central Weed Control Conference*, **35**, 91.

JORDAN, T.N. and REAMES, J. (1976). Controlling bermudagrass in cotton with a hooded sprayer, Mississippi Agricultural and Forestry Experiment Station, *Report No. 1272*, December 1976, 2pp.

KOEHLER, C.B., CRAMER, G.L., IRONS, S.M., SCHEPERS, J.S. and BURNSIDE, O.C. (1980). Roller herbicide applicator, *Farm, Ranch and Home Quarterly*, **27**(1), 12–14.

LAWS, G.W. (1974). A chemical roguing technique with the herbicide glove, *Proceedings of the Southern Weed Science Society*, **27**, 153–154.

LUND-HØIE, K. (1980). The impact of helicopter application of glyphosate on the management of Norwegian forest plantations, *Proceedings of the Conference on Weed Control in Forestry*, Nottingham, 1980, pp. 73–82.

LUTMAN, P.J.W. (1979). The selective application of glyphosate to volunteer potatoes in sugar beet, *Proceedings of the European Weed Research Society Symposium, The Influence of Different Factors on the Development and Control of Weeds*, pp. 375–382.

LUTMAN, P.J.W., OSWALD, A.K. and BYAST, T.H. (1982). The chemical estimation and biological activity of glyphosate deposited on four plant species by one rope wick and two roller applicators, *Proceedings of the 1982 British Crop Protection Conference*, pp. 1001–1009.

MAASS, D. (1981). The use of tree injection in timber stand improvement in Maine, *Proceedings of the Northeastern Weed Science Society*, **35**, 194–198.

MAHANAY, A.J. (1909). *U.S. Patent No. 1,764,952*, granted 16 Jan., 1909, United States Patent Office, Washington, D.C.

MANN, W.F., JR. (1979). Glyphosate is highly effective for tree injection, *USDA Forest Research Service Research Paper No. SO–150*.

MCGARVEY, F.X. (1980). C.D.A. herbicide application, *Weeds Today*, **11**(2), 8–9.

MCWHORTER, C.G. (1970). A recirculating spray system for postemergence weed control in row crops, *Weed Science*, **18**, 285–287.

MCWHORTER, C.G. (1977). Weed control in soybeans with glyphosate applied in the recirculating sprayer, *Weed Science*, **25**, 135–141.

MCWHORTER, C.G. and WILLIFORD, J.R. (1980). Factors affecting the toxicity of glyphosate applied in the recirculating sprayer to johnsongrass (*Sorghum halepense*) and soybeans (*Glycine max*), *Weed Science*, **28**, 59–63.

MOORE, R.W., YORTT, M.L. and ATKINSON, C.G. (1980). Rush and Australian sedge control with glyphosate, *Proceedings of the 33rd New Zealand Weed and Pest Control Conference*, pp. 63–66.

REVELLE, W.F. (1982). The development and manufacture of wick rope for herbicide application, *Proceedings of the Southern Weed Science Society*, **35**, 399–408.

ROACH, J.O. and CHANDLER, J.M. (1982). The Carpet-Bagger: the commercial adaptation of the Ultimate Stoneville Applicator, *Proceedings of the Southern Weed Science Society*, **35**, 411.

RYAN, E.W., CORMICAN, T. and COLLIER, F. (1978). Chemical roguing of bulb crops, *Proceedings of the 1978 British Crop Protection Conference—Weeds*, (1979), **3**, 923–927.

SCHEPERS, J.S. and BURNSIDE, O.C. (1979). Electronic moisture sensor for maintaining herbicide solution on a roller applicator, *Weed Science*, **27**, 559–561.

SCHNEIDER, G.L., KOEHLER, C.B., SCHEPERS, J.S. and BURNSIDE, O.C. (1982). Roller applicator for shattercane (*Sorghum bicolor*) in row crops, *Weed Science*, **30**(3), 301–306.

SEGARS, E.H. and LAMAR, S.C. (1940). *U.S. Patent No. 2,311,782*, granted 23 Feb., 1940, United States Patent Office, Washington, D.C.

UTULU, S.N. and AKOBUNDU, I.O. (1978). An evaluation of a CDA herbicide sprayer in a tropical environment, *Proceeding of a Conference at the International Institute of Tropical Agriculture, Weeds and their Control in the Humid and Subhumid Tropics, 1978*, 1980, 379–386.

WELKER, W.V., JR. and DARLINGTON, T. (1980). A continuous-belt herbicide wiper, *Weed Science*, **28**, 705–708.

WICKHAM, S.H. and HOLT, H.A. (1976). Preliminary tree injection results, *Proceedings of the North Central Weed Control Conference*, **31**, 128, 128A, 129.

WILLS, G.D. and MCWHORTER, C.G. (1981). Developments in post-emergence herbicide applicators, *Outlook on Agriculture*, **10**(7), 337–341.

WU, C.H. and DERTING, C.W. (1981). Operational variables and glyphosate performance through ropewick applicators, *Proceedings of the Southern Weed Science Society*, **34**, 301–304.

WYSE, D.L. and HABSTRITT, C. (1977). A roller herbicide applicator, *Proceedings of the North Central Weed Control Conference*, **32**, 144–145.

YARBOROUGH, D.E. and ISMAIL, A.A. (1982). Selective application of herbicides for aspen control in lowbush blueberries, *Proceedings of the Northeastern Weed Science Society*, **36**, 193–198.

Part VI

Determination of Glyphosate Residues

Chapter 17

Analytical techniques of glyphosate residue analysis

P.C. Bardalaye, W.B. Wheeler and H.A. Moye
University of Florida, USA.

Introduction

Glyphosate, *N*-(phosphonomethyl)glycine, and its major metabolite possess unusual, distinctive and, to the analytical chemist, disconcerting physicochemical properties which distinguish it from most other pesticides when they are being dealt with at the residue level. These properties are closely related to the exceptionally polar nature and resulting high water solubility of both compounds. In addition, the presence of three polar functional groups on glyphosate (phosphonic acid, carboxylic acid and secondary amine) greatly complicate the problem when chemical reagents are selected which are intended to increase the volatility of the herbicide by derivatization, for the purpose of gas chromatographic analysis. Somewhat less difficulty is observed for the major metabolite, aminomethyl-phosphonic acid (AMPA), which possesses only two polar functional groups (phosphonic acid and primary amine).

Various approaches have been taken in derivatizing these two multifunctional compounds. All have been hampered by the fact that both compounds are insoluble in solvents other than water, although AMPA is slightly soluble in other polar solvents, such as ethanol and dioxane. Consequently, conventional acylation and esterification reactions, which typically are performed in anhydride–acid mixtures and ethyl ether, respectively, are slowed, or in some cases completely inhibited, due simply to lack of solubility. Further slowing of these derivatizations in residue samples is due to the fact that substrate co-extractives form a film on the bottom of the reaction vessel restricting reagent–reactant contact.

Probably the most widely used residue procedure is that reported in the *Pesticide Analytical Manual* of the U.S. Food and Drug Administration (*PAM*, FDA) as developed by the chemical's manufacturer, Monsanto, and henceforth called the 'Monsanto procedure'. After extraction and clean-up by ion exchange chromatography on both anion and cation exchange columns, the residue samples are first derivatized by acylating the amino nitrogen with equivolume amounts of trifluoroacetic acid and trifluoroacetic anhydride. These treatments also solubilize the crop co-extractives. However, the second step in the derivatization involves methylation of both the carboxylic and phosphonic acid portions of glyphosate, as well as the phosphonic acid portion of AMPA. The methylations are performed by reaction with either diazomethane or *O*-methyl-*N,N*-dicyclohexyl pseudourea in ether and tetrahydrofuran, respectively. Neither solvent solubilizes the dried residue during the methylation, however.

Efforts in this laboratory to fully solubilize glyphosate for derivatization using conventional solvents have been unsuccessful at the time of writing. Highest solubility has been observed for pyridine (Moye, 1982, unpublished).

Additional efforts in this laboratory to eliminate one of the derivatization steps in order to shorten the procedure for gas chromatographic analysis have only been partially successful. Methylation of glyphosate and AMPA using diazomethane produce multiple peaks which were shown by gas chromatography/mass spectrometry to result from incomplete permethylation. Other methylating reagents were examined, such as N,N-dimethylformamide, dimethyl acetal, dimethylsulphate, methanolic HCl, borontrifluoride-methanol, and borontrichloride-methanol. These reagents produced little or no yield of volatile derivative at residue levels (Moye, 1982, unpublished).

Clearly, these two chemicals are prime candidates for high-performance liquid chromatographic separation employing mobile phases of high polarity, such as water. However, the functionalities of the two compounds are such that they possess very weak molar absorptivities, even at 200 nm; and the lack of conjugated systems prevents them from fluorescing. Consequently, in order to utilize high-performance liquid chromatography for the residues of these compounds, some sort of pre- or post-column derivatization would be in order.

This chapter will discuss those analytical procedures which have been found to be directly applicable to the measurement of glyphosate and aminomethylphosphonic acid residues. From the information given, the readers should be able to understand and select a procedure which would best suit their needs, with consideration being given to substrate type, instrument requirements and level of expertise available.

Table 17.1 lists the various methods, namely, gas–liquid chromatography (GLC) with flame photometric detector (FPD) or electron capture detector (ECD), gas chromatography/mass spectrometry (GC/MS) with flame ionization detector (FID), high-performance liquid chromatography (HPLC), thin-layer chromatography (TLC), etc., currently known for the analysis of glyphosate and its major metabolite, AMPA.

TABLE 17.1   **Methods for analysis of glyphosate and AMPA**

Method	Derivatization	Detection	Applications	Reference
GLC	Methyl-N-trifluoroacetyl ester	FPD	Almost all known food crops, animal tissues, soil, water, etc.	Monsanto (*PAM*, 1977)
GLC	2-Chloroethyl-N-heptafluoro-butyryl ester	ECD	Blueberries (*Vaccinium angustifolium*)	Guinivan, Thompson and Wheeler (1982a)
GC/MS	n-Butyl N-trifluoroacetyl ester	FID	Standards only	Rueppel, Suba and Marvel (1976)
HPLC	No derivatization, intact compounds	Ultraviolet, refractive index	Glyphosate in formulation and technical samples	Burns and Tomkins (1979)

TABLE 17.1 continued

Method	Derivatization	Detection	Applications	Reference
HPLC	Derivatization for fluorogenic labelling	Fluorescence	Cantaloupes (*Cucumis melo*), cranberries (*Vaccinium macrocarpon*), cucumbers (*Cucumis sativus*), blueberries (*Vaccinium angustifolium*), peppers, pumpkins (*Cucurbita maxima*) and squashes (*Cucurbita pepo*)	Moye and Scherer (1977); Moye and St. John (1980); Moye, Miles and Scherer (1983)
HPLC	Derivatization for fluorogenic labelling	Fluorescence	Straw	Roseboom and Berkhoff (1982)
HPLC	Derivatization for fluorogenic labelling	Fluorescence	Water	Cochrane *et al.* (1982)
TLC	Conversion of glyphosate to *N*-nitroso derivative	Ultraviolet degradation followed by fluorogenic labelling	Glyphosate in *Cirsium arvense* roots	Young, Khan and Marriage (1977)
TLC	No derivatization	Spraying with amine specific reagent	Water and soil	Pavoni (1978)
TLC	No derivatization	0.5% ninhydrin in butanol	Bindweeds	Sprankle *et al.* (1978)
TLC	No derivatization	Ninhydrin, copper-nitrate and Rhodamine B	Soils, beans (*Phaseolus* spp.) and peas (*Pisum sativum*)	Ragab (1978); Kader and Ragab (1977)
Colori-metric			Water	Glass (1981)
Amino acid analyser			Standards	Ekstrom and Johansson (1975)
Molecular emission cavity analysis			Water	Ragab, Stiles and Yeo (1979)
Polaro-graphic	Derivatization to nitroso compound		Glyphosate only in water	Brønstad and Friestad (1976)
Polaro-graphic	Derivatization to nitroso compound		Glyphosate only in blueberries (*Vaccinium angustifolium*), cowberries (*Vaccinium vitis-idaea*), raspberries (*Rubus idaeus*), barley (*Hordeum vulgare*), oats (*Avena sativa*), wheat (*Triticum aestivum*), potatoes (*Solanum tuberosum*), soils and water	Friestad and Brønstad (1982)

Gas–liquid chromatography methods

Method I

This is Monsanto's method (*PAM*, 1977) and involves the following steps:

SAMPLE PREPARATION

Pre-extraction with organic solvents
Pre-extraction involved blending the samples (sample sizes were 25–50 g) with one or more of the following solvent systems: *n*-butanol saturated with water; methanol : chloroform (2:1) and methanol : chloroform (1:2). The pre-extracts were discarded.

Extraction with deionized water
The pre-extracted samples were extracted with deionized water using a blender and then filtered or centrifuged to remove any particulate matter. The filtered extract was diluted.

SAMPLE CLEAN-UP

Chromatography on strong anion exchange resin A-101D
A 2.2 × 30 cm column was plugged with glass wool and packed with A101D resin. The column was equilibrated with 1 mol l^{-1} ammonium bicarbonate and then rinsed free of ammonium bicarbonate, using deionized water.
The diluted sample extract was transferred to the column and allowed to flow through at 600–800 ml h^{-1}, followed by a distilled water wash which was discarded. The parent molecule and metabolite were eluted from the column with 0.5 mol l^{-1} ammonium bicarbonate.

Charcoal treatment
Charcoal clean-up was necessary with most samples except water. The fraction collected during anion exchange chromatography was mechanically shaken with charcoal (Darco G–60) and quantitatively filtered, and concentrated using a rotary evaporator.

Chromatography on cation exchange resin AG 50W-X8
A 1.2 × 20 cm column plugged with glass wool and packed with AG 50W-X8 (hydrogen form) resin to a length of 14.5 cm was washed and equilibrated with deionized water.
The sample from the previous step was applied to the column and eluted with deionized water. The fractions to be collected needed to be determined from a column calibrated with standards. The parent compound eluted first followed by the metabolite.
The fractions collected were taken up separately with addition of 1 mol l^{-1} ammonium bicarbonate and evaporated to dryness prior to derivatization.

ANALYSIS: DERIVATIZATION

Derivatization included two steps: *N*-trifluoroacetylation and esterification (methyl ester) of the *N*-trifluoroacetylated compound. The final product amenable to GLC analysis was *N*-trifluoroacetyl trimethyl ester of glyphosate derived from the parent herbicide, and *N*-trifluoroacetyl dimethyl ester of AMPA derived from the metabolite.

Monsanto (*PAM*, 1977) described two methods for derivatization. While both methods used trifluoroacetic acid and trifluoroacetic anhydride for *N*-trifluoroacetylation, one method used *O*-methyl-*N*,*N*'-dicyclohexyl pseudourea and the other diazomethane for esterification to the methyl ester.

Method 1
(Caution: THF is highly inflammable and should be handled with care!)

Derivatization of glyphosate. Moisture was removed from the glyphosate-containing fraction after cationic exchange chromatography by a gentle stream of nitrogen. To the contents were added trifluoroacetic acid, and then trifluoroacetic anhydride; the container was capped and heated and swirled at intervals. After 10 min the mixture was allowed to cool, then evaporated to dryness under a gentle stream of nitrogen. This was followed by addition of 4% methanol in tetrahydrofuran (THF) containing anhydrous phosphoric acid, followed by shaking and then addition of *O*-methyl-*N*,*N*'-dicyclohexyl pseudourea (prepared according to *PAM*, 1977) in THF. There must be an excess of pseudourea to ensure complete derivatization. The tube containing the mixture was tightly stoppered and heated at 80°C for 16–18 h. At the end of the incubation period the contents were cooled to room temperature and adjusted to a desired volume with 4% methanol in THF.

Clean-up of derivatized glyphosate. Additional clean-up of the derivatized glyphosate was necessary in certain samples where interferences showed up in GLC analysis. In such cases, the derivatized glyphosate fraction was taken up with 4% methanol in THF, applied to a Florisil column (75 mm o.d. × 6 cm), topped with anhydrous sodium sulphate and prewashed with THF and then methylene chloride–THF (3:1), and eluted with 4% methanol in THF, and then analysed by GLC.

Derivatization of AMPA. Trifluoroacetic acid was added to the evaporated and dried metabolite fraction collected after cationic exchange chromatography; after standing 5 min, with occasional swirling, trifluoroacetic anhydride was added and the container was capped and heated at 50°C for 30 min. The contents were cooled to room temperature and evaporated to dryness under a gentle stream of nitrogen. To the contents were added 4% methanol in THF containing anhydrous phosphoric acid followed by *O*-methyl-*N*,*N*'-dicyclohexyl pseudourea in THF; the container was tightly stoppered and then heated at 80°C for 16–18 h. At the end of this period the contents were cooled, and the volume adjusted with 4% methanol in THF.

Clean-up of derivatized AMPA. Clean-up of the derivatized metabolite fraction, if necessary to reduce GLC interferences, was achieved by alumina column chromatography (adsorption-type, neutral, Brockman activity I, 80–200 mesh). The column was topped with anhydrous sodium sulphate and pre-washed with 4% methanol in THF. The derivatized metabolite fraction was taken up, applied to the column and eluted with this solvent. GLC analysis proceeded next.

Method 2
(Caution: Diazomethane is very toxic! A fume hood should be used.)

Derivatization of glyphosate.   To the glyphosate-containing fraction (evaporated and dried) was added trifluoroacetic acid, which was allowed to stand 5 min with occasional swirling; trifluoroacetic anhydride was then added, the container was tightly stoppered and heated at 50°C for 10 min. The contents were then evaporated to dryness using a gentle stream of nitrogen, redissolved in methanol, and allowed to stand 5 min; diazomethane–ether solution was then added and the mixture was allowed to stand 30 min at room temperature with intermittent swirling. At the end of the reaction, the excess reagents were removed by gently warming in fume hoods, the solution was concentrated and quantitatively transferred to a centrifuge tube with methanol rinses and 5% sodium sulphate was added. It was then partitioned with methylene chloride.

Clean-up of the derivatized glyphosate.   To achieve additional clean-up to reduce GLC interferences, the derivatized glyphosate was applied to a Florisil column (75 mm o.d. × 6 cm) topped with anhydrous sodium sulphate and pre-washed with methanol and then methylene chloride : acetone (3 : 1). The derivative was eluted with methylene chloride : acetone (3 : 1).

Derivatization of the metabolite.   Trifluoroacetic acid was added to the evaporated and dried AMPA fraction obtained by cationic exchange chromatography, allowed to stand 5 min with occasional swirling, then trifluoroacetic anhydride was added, the container was capped and allowed to stand 30 min at room temperature. The contents were evaporated to dryness using a gentle stream of nitrogen, after which a small volume of benzene was added and then diazomethane–ether solution. The mixture was allowed to stand 30 min at room temperature with intermittent swirling. At the end of the period the excess reagents were removed by gently warming in a fume hood. The volume was adjusted to a desired volume with benzene.

The derivatized metabolite was reported not to need any further clean-up.

ANALYSIS: GLC PARAMETERS

Monsanto (*PAM*, 1977) used a gas chromatograph for glyphosate analysis with a phosphorus–specific flame photometric detector using the following operating conditions: 1.83 m × 6 mm o.d. glass U-shaped column packed with 10% DC-200 on 80–100 mesh chromosorb W (HP) or 3.8% OV-17 on 80–100 mesh Gas-chrom Q; temperatures (°C)—column 185 (for DC-200) or 150 (for OV-17), flash heater 230, detector 185; gas flows (ml min^{-1})—nitrogen 100, air 40, hydrogen 200, oxygen 20. The same operating conditions were used for AMPA, except the column temperatures which were 155°C (for DC-200) and 120°C (for OV-17). Retention time of glyphosate or its metabolite was ca. 2 min; 30 ng of either compound gave approximately a 50% full-scale deflection.

One other column was successfully used: a 1.83 m × 4 mm i.d. glass column packed with 1% Reoplex 400 on 100/120 mesh Gas Chrom Q operated at 130°C, with a nitrogen carrier gas flow of 150 ml min^{-1}; FPD gas flows were hydrogen 140 ml min^{-1}, air 50 ml min^{-1} and oxygen 10 ml min^{-1}. Injection port and detector temperatures were maintained at 210°C. Retention time of the glyphosate was approximately 7 min and that of the metabolite was approximately 4 min; 25 ng of glyphosate gave 50% full-scale deflection at an attenuation of 2^3, whereas AMPA was twice as sensitive (Thompson *et al*, 1980). *Figure 17.1* shows representative chromatograms for standards and fortified crop.

The Monsanto method determined residues of glyphosate and AMPA in barley (*Hordeum vulgare*), grasses, forage, maize (*Zea mays*), oats (*Avena sativa*), rice (*Oryza sativa*), soil, sorghum (*Sorghum bicolor*), water, wheat (*Triticum aestivum*), soya bean (*Glycine max*), forage and hay. Sensitivity was 0.05 µg g^{-1} (50 g sample), 0.10 µg g^{-1} (25 g sample) and 2.5 ng g^{-1} (1 kg water sample). The EPA (USA) obtained 55–70% recovery of glyphosate in soya bean samples fortified at 0.1 and 0.2 µg g^{-1} levels, and 45–60% recovery of the metabolite in the same crop fortified at the 0.1 µg g^{-1} level.

Method II

This GLC method (Guinivan, Thompson and Wheeler, 1982a), described clean-up of blueberry (*Vaccinium angustifolium*) extracts by gel permeation and ion exchange chromatography and GLC analysis of glyphosate and AMPA as their 2-chloroethyl-*N*-heptafluorobutyryl derivatives.

SAMPLE PREPARATION AND CLEAN-UP

Representative 25 g blueberry samples were homogenized and sonicated twice in water using a Polytron apparatus; the mixture was then centrifuged. The supernates were combined and NaOH was added until the pigments turned brown. The mixture was concentrated to ca. 50 ml and extracted with ethyl acetate portions which were discarded. Concentration of the aqueous mixture was accomplished by rotary evaporation and the pH was adjusted to 2.1 with HCl. The sample was filtered and applied to a Bio-Gel P-2 column (2.6 × 100 cm), maintained at a constant flow of 3 ml min^{-1} by use of a peristaltic pump. Calibration of the column was accomplished using ^{14}C-glyphosate and ^{14}C-AMPA. The elution was effected with water adjusted to pH 2.1 with HCl. The first 290 ml were discarded and the next 100 ml were collected. The eluates were concentrated by rotary evaporation and applied to a AG50W-X8 cation exchange column (2.2 × 6.5 cm) equilibrated in pH 2.1 water. A volume of 21 ml eluate was discarded, after which the eluant pH was changed to deionized water, adjusted to pH 7.0 with diluted NaOH, and the next 150 ml were collected. The volume was concentrated by rotary evaporation, followed by evaporation to dryness under nitrogen. The dried samples were stored under vacuum in a desiccator containing phosphorus pentoxide.

DERIVATIZATION

To the dried samples was added BCl$_3$-2-chloroethanol; the tubes were then sealed and heated for 45 min at 110°C, and excess reagent was removed by evaporation in a boiling water bath under nitrogen. Heptafluorobutyric anhydride was added to each tube, which was sealed and heated at 100°C for 45 min. Water was then added to each tube, followed by 5% aqueous ammonia. The aqueous phase was extracted with hexane and the hexane extracts were dried with anhydrous sodium sulphate, concentrated and analysed by GLC.

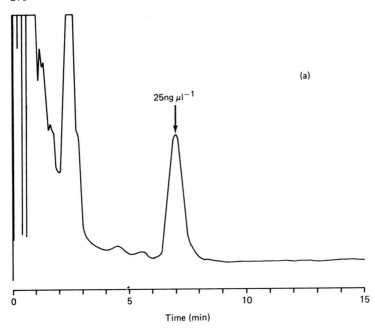

(a)

25ng μl^{-1}

Time (min)

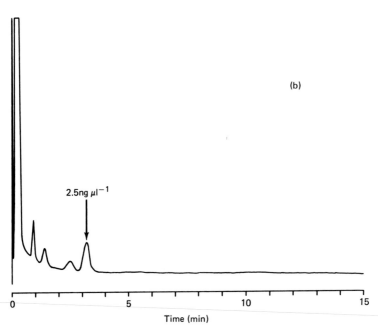

(b)

2.5ng μl^{-1}

Time (min)

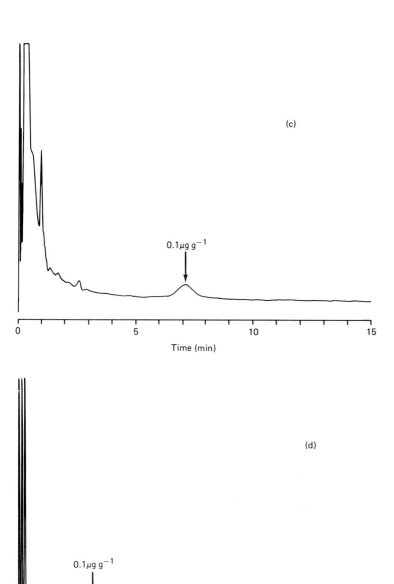

(c)

0.1µg g^{-1}

Time (min)

(d)

0.1µg g^{-1}

Time (min)

Figure 17.1. (a) Chromatogram of glyphosate standard; (b) chromatogram of AMPA standard; (c) chromatogram of avocado (*Persea americana*) control sample fortified with 0.1 µg g^{-1} glyphosate; (d) chromatogram of avocado control sample fortified with 0.1 µg g^{-1} AMPA (from Thompson *et al.*, 1980; reproduced with permission)

ANALYSIS

A gas chromatograph equipped with a ^{63}Ni electron capture detector was used under the following operating conditions:

A 1.83 m × 4 mm i.d. glass column packed with 10% DC-200 on 100–120 mesh Gas-chrom Q was employed; temperatures (°C): detector 300; injection port 250; column temperature held at 130 for 15 min then programmed sequentially at 30 per minute to 210, then held for 7 min, and then to 220 and held for 13 min. Carrier gas was argon–methane (95+5) at a flow rate of 60 ml min^{-1}.

Retention times were 20.19 min for the derivatized AMPA and 33.27 min for the derivatized glyphosate; 5 ng of either compound gave approximately 90% full-scale deflection at attenuation 2^{14}. The instrument was the Hewlett Packard Model 5840A gas chromatograph. Sensitivity of the method was 0.01 µg g^{-1} (15 g sample) for glyphosate and 0.05 µg g^{-1} (±5 g sample) for AMPA. Recoveries for fortified 15 g blueberry samples were 94% (1 µg g^{-1}), 61% (0.5 µg g^{-1}), 66 ± 1% (0.05 µg g^{-1}), and 52 ± 9% (0.01 µg g^{-1}) for glyphosate and 108% (1 µg g^{-1}), 108% (0.5 µg g^{-1}) and 102 ± 0.5% (0.05 µg g^{-1}) for AMPA. Some interferences were encountered with AMPA. *Figure 17.2* shows representative chromatograms for standard, fortified crop and a control crop.

MASS SPECTRAL CONFIRMATION

Mass spectral studies involving electron impact and chemical ionization (isobutane and methane) confirmed that the phosphonic acid and carboxylic acid groups were fully esterified by the BCl_3:2-chloroethanol and that the amino nitrogens were acylated by the heptafluorobutyric anhydride giving *N*-heptafluorobutyryl tri-2-chloroethyl ester of glyphosate and *N*-heptafluorobutyryl di-2-chloroethyl ester of AMPA, respectively (Guinivan, Thompson and Wheeler, 1982b).

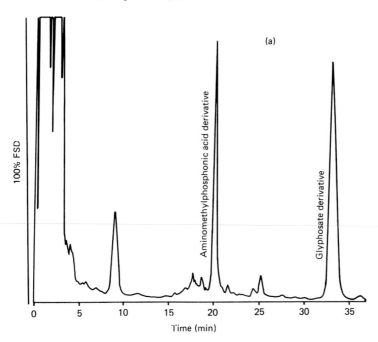

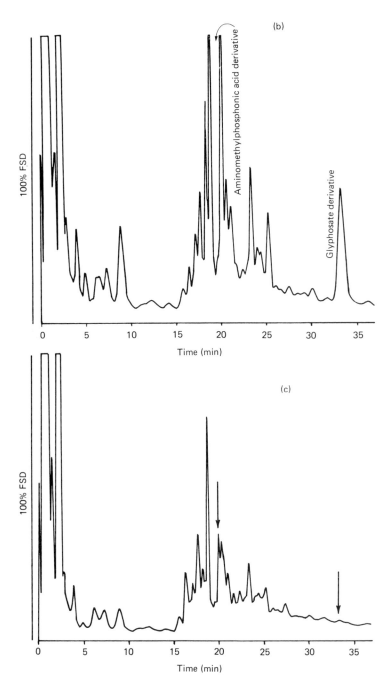

Figure 17.2. Chromatograms of (a) derivatized standard (5 ng) in both glyphosate and AMPA; (b) 0.5 μg g⁻¹ fortified blueberry (*Vaccinium angustifolium*) sample (containing both glyphosate and AMPA); (c) control blueberries (from Guinivan, Thompson and Wheeler, 1982(a); reproduced with permission

Gas–liquid chromatography/mass spectroscopy method

n-Butyl *N*-trifluoroacetyl esters of glyphosate and its metabolite were also reported in efforts designed to find stable derivatives which would permit ready characterization by both gas chromatography and gas chromatography/mass spectrometry (Rueppel, Suba and Marvel, 1976). While its application to residue analysis was not reported, this technique has immense potentialities in analytical method development.

High-performance liquid chromatography methods

Method I

Monsanto developed an HPLC method (Burns and Tomkins, 1979) for the direct determination of glyphosate in formulation and technical samples. The following conditions were reported: a 25 cm × 4.6 mm i.d. column of Partisil SAX; injection with 15 μl loop; detector—Schoeffel 770–195 nm at 0.1 AUFS and a mobile phase of 96% 0.005 mol l^{-1} KH$_2$PO$_4$ and 4% methanol adjusted to pH 2.1 with 85% H$_3$PO$_4$. Ambient temperature was used and the flow rate was 2.3 ml min^{-1} at 8 MPa.

   Retention time under these conditions was 3.7 min. The retention time increased nearly linearly with pH from 1.95 to 4.00. At pH = 4, the retention time was almost six times the retention time at pH = 1.95 when H$_3$PO$_4$ was used to adjust the pH. The retention time also varied linearly with ionic strength from 0.001 to 0.05 mol l^{-1} KH$_2$PO$_4$ at pH = 1.95 adjusted with H$_3$PO$_4$. It was suggested that various mobile phase compositions could be utilized for the determination of glyphosate in various matrices. The response of u.v. (195 nm) and refractive index detectors was nearly linear from 50 μg ml^{-1} to 5 mg ml^{-1}. The detection limits by u.v. adsorption (195 nm) and by refractive index were 5 μg and 2.5 μg, respectively, per injection.

Method II

This method (Moye and Scherer, 1977; Moye and St. John, 1980) had as the basis the fluorogenic labelling of amines. Glyphosate was readily cleaved by the calcium hypochlorite to produce a primary amine. The fluorogenic reagents used were *O*-phthalicdicarboxaldehyde-mercaptoethanol   (OPA-MERC)   reagent   and 9-fluorenylmethyl chloroformate (FMOCCL).

CROP EXTRACTION

A sample of chopped crop was blended with 100 ml chloroform and 200 ml water and then centrifuged at 10 000 r.p.m. for 20 min. The aqueous portion of the supernatant was concentrated by rotary evaporation and the pH was adjusted to 1.0 with concentrated HCl.

SAMPLE CLEAN-UP

This was achieved by cation exchange chromatography on a 100–200 mesh 50W-X8 using 0.1 N HCl as eluting solvent. Glyphosate eluted first, followed by AMPA.

The fractions were separately collected and concentrated using rotary evaporation.

HPLC analysis was performed with pre-column labelling (FMOCCL) or post-column labelling (OPA-MERC).

ANALYSIS

Pre-column labelling

Either the glyphosate or AMPA fraction was placed in a Teflon-capped tube and pH was brought to 11 using K_2CO_3, then water and FMOCCL in acetone were added. The tube was capped and allowed to incubate at 23°C for 20 min. The reaction mixture was then washed three times with ethyl ether, diluted with water and a suitable aliquot was injected onto the HPLC. Comparisons were made to standards which were similarly derivatized.

The following parameters were used for HPLC analysis by pre-column labelling: a 30 cm × 4 mm μ carbohydrate or μ NH$_2$ column with 20 μl injection by sample valve. The detector was an Aminco-Bowman spectrophotofluorometer, model 4-8202, equipped with a model B16-63019 flow through cell. A Corning CS # 0–54 cut-off filter (290 nm) was placed before the photomultiplier tube to reduce the scattered light from the excitation monochromator. Excitation was at 270 nm and emission at 315 nm; a 150 w Xenon arc lamp was used as a source. The slit program was set at 3,3,3,3,3,5.

The mobile phase was pH 4 phosphate buffer (0.1 mol l^{-1}) containing 25% acetonitrile by volume for μ carbohydrate column. The same mobile phase for μ NH$_2$ column (glyphosate analysis). For AMPA analysis on μ NH$_2$ column, the buffer concentration was changed from 0.1 to 0.025 mol l^{-1}.

Retention time on the μ carbohydrate column was 6 min for AMPA and 18 min for glyphosate. On the μ NH$_2$ column, the retention was 7 min. Using pre-column derivatization for residue analysis in cantaloupes, a recovery of 100% was obtained for glyphosate at a fortification level of 0.1 μg g^{-1}. However, the phosphate concentration of the mobile phase had to be changed for analysis of AMPA and several interferences then appeared.

Post-column labelling

Glyphosate and AMPA fractions were adjusted to pH 3–8 with KOH. For post-column labelling a 25 cm × 4 mm column of 13.5 μ Aminex A-27 (Biorad Laboratories) was used. The detector was an American Instrument Co. Fluoromonitor equipped with OPA filters (360 and 455 nm), or a Gilson Spectra/glo fluorometer similarly equipped, or an equivalent. The instrumental arrangement also included two Milton Roy Model 196-0066-001 reagent pumps. Calcium hypochlorite was pumped and mixed with the HPLC column eluant via model CJ3031 Kel-F 'T's (Laboratory Data Control) and 1.6 mm o.d. × 0.5 mm i.d. Teflon tubing. A 10.6 m delay coil of similar tubing (1.9 ml volume) was used to provide a delay time of about 1 min 40 sec before entering another Kel-F 'T' into which the OPA-MERC reagent was pumped; a 0.6 m length of tubing carried the mixture to the fluorometer.

OPA-MERC reagent was prepared by dissolving 1 g OPA in 10 ml dioxane and diluting to 1 l with pH 10, 0.125 mol l^{-1} borate buffer to which 1 ml of MERC was added.

Calcium hypochlorite was prepared by dissolving HTH (Olin Co.) and NaCl in 0.1 mol l^{-1} KH_2PO_4 and adjusting to pH 9.0 with KOH.

Mobile phase was 0.1 mol l^{-1} H_3PO_4 at 1.0 ml min^{-1}. The columns were thermostatted at 62°C.

Using post-column derivatization for residue analysis of cantaloupes (*Cucumis melo*), cranberries (*Vaccinium macrocarpon*), Jalapeno peppers, pumpkin (*Cucurbita maxima*) and cucumber (*Cucumis sativus*), recoveries ranged from 70 to 90% for glyphosate and from 61 to 82% for AMPA at 0.1 µg g^{-1} fortification levels.

Improvement with modifications

Based upon the approach cited above, Moye, Miles and Scherer (1983) described a procedure with improvements in sample size, sample throughput, chromatographic efficiency, etc. The same instrumental conditions were used except that an HA-X10 anion exchange column (Hamilton) was used for the AMPA analyses.

Crop, chloroform and water were placed in a polyethylene centrifuge bottle, blended with a Polytron homogenizer and centrifuged. The supernatant was quantitatively removed and concentrated by rotary evaporation and then the pH was adjusted to 2 with con. HCl.

The sample was placed on a column (19 × 30 cm) packed with 50 g of Dowex 50W-X8, 100–200 mesh that had been previously equilibrated with 0.01 mol l^{-1} HCl. The column was eluted with 0.01 mol l^{-1} HCl. The first 60 ml was discarded; the second 60 ml contained all the glyphosate. Exactly 60 ml more were discarded, and the last 100 ml fraction contained all of the AMPA. The pH of each fraction was adjusted to 3.8 with 1.0 mol l^{-1} KOH, the volume was made to 5 ml and the samples were filtered through glass fibre filter paper.

Mobile phase for the Aminex column was 0.09 ml l^{-1} H_3PO_4–0.01 ml l^{-1} H_2SO_4 (glyphosate analysis); the HA-X10 column (AMPA analysis) was eluted with 0.02 mol l^{-1} KH_2PO_4 buffer at pH 5.0.

The cleavage reagent for glyphosate analysis was prepared by dissolving HTH (Olin Co.) in deionized water and diluting an appropriate volume with phosphate buffer. The OPA-MERC fluorogenic reagent was made by dissolving H_3BO_3 and KOH in deionized water and adding MERC and *o*-phthalaldehyde.

Calcium hypochlorite was pumped at 0.2 ml min^{-1} and the OPA/MERC at 0.4 ml min^{-1} for glyphosate analysis. For analysis of AMPA the hypochlorite pump was turned off and the OPA-MERC pump left at 0.4 ml min^{-1}.

A limit of detection of 0.5 ng (S/N = 3) was reported for both glyphosate and AMPA. Analytical curves were linear from 5 ng to 100 ng for both glyphosate and AMPA. At 0.05 µg g^{-1} level, recovery from cranberries was 87% for glyphosate and 76% for AMPA. At 0.1 µg g^{-1} level, recoveries from cantaloupes, cranberries, cucumbers, blueberries (*Vaccinium angustifolium*), Jalapeno peppers, pumpkins and summer squashes (*Cucurbita pepo*) ranged from 86% to 100% for glyphosate and from 61% to 85% for AMPA. At 1 µg g^{-1}, recoveries from cantaloupes, cucumbers and pumpkins ranged from 88% to 107% for glyphosate and from 88% to 89% for AMPA. Representative chromatograms for standard and fortified cranberries are shown in *Figures 17.3* and *17.4*.

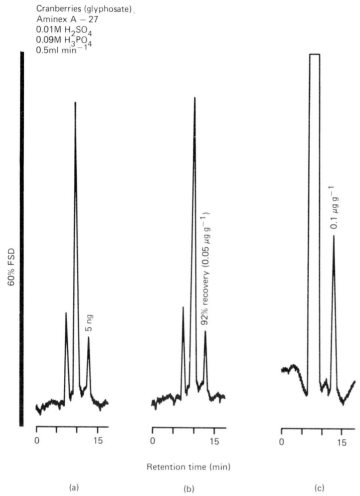

Figure 17.3. Chromatograms of (a) 5 ng glyphosate standard; (b) 0.05 $\mu g\ g^{-1}$ fortified (glyphosate) cranberries (*Vaccinium macrocarpon*); (c) 0.1 $\mu g\ g^{-1}$ (glyphosate) found in field-treated cranberries

Method III

This method (Roseboom and Berkhoff, 1982) was based on the derivatization of glyphosate and AMPA with 9-fluorenylmethyl chloroformate (FMOCCL) and then determination by ion-exchange HPLC with fluorescence detector.

CROP EXTRACTION

The extraction procedure described was the same as that used previously (*PAM*, 1977). A 15 g sample was used.

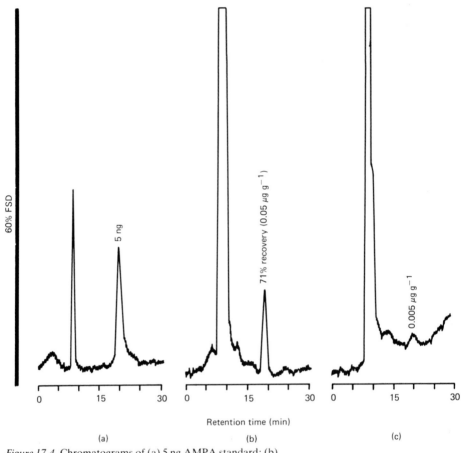

Figure 17.4. Chromatograms of (a) 5 ng AMPA standard; (b) 0.05 μg g⁻¹ fortified (AMPA) cranberries (*Vaccinium macrocarpon*); (c) 0.005 μg g⁻¹ (AMPA) found in field-treated cranberries

SAMPLE CLEAN-UP

Clean-up was achieved on a cation-exchange resin, Bio-Rad AG 50W-X8, with water as eluting solvent. The eluates were collected in two fractions, one containing glyphosate and the other AMPA.

ANALYSIS

The fractions collected were evaporated to dryness in the presence of NH_4HCO_3, residues redissolved in a 0.025 mol l^{-1} borax solution and FMOCCL dissolved in acetone to a concentration of 0.1 mol l^{-1} was added. After standing for 20 min at room temperature, the solutions were extracted with diethyl ether, the organic phases were discarded and the aliquots of aqueous phases were subjected to HPLC analysis.

The HPLC system consisted of a Varian 8500 solvent delivery system, Valco loop injector and Waters 420 fluorescence detector. A 25 cm × 4.6 mm i.d. column, packed with Hypersil APS, a spherical silica gel with aminopropyl groups, was used. The mobile phase used was methanol/water/phosphate buffer at pH 5 for glyphosate and pH 8 for AMPA. The fluorescence detector was equipped with a mercury lamp, the excitation wavelength was 254 nm and the emission wavelength was 313 nm.

The response was linear from 1 to 2000 ng for both glyphosate and AMPA. The limits of detection were 0.3 ng. The method was successfully applied to straw samples. Minimum detectable quantities were 0.1 μg g^{-1} of straw, and recoveries from fortified samples were 70–80% at levels of 0.5–10.0 μg g^{-1}.

Method IV

This method (Cochrane et al., 1982) was based on the derivatization of glyphosate with 7-chloro-4-nitrobenzo-2-oxa-1,3-diazole to give a fluorescent compound. The excitation wavelength maximum was 468 nm and emission wavelength was 540 nm.

Thin-layer chromatography methods

Method I

This method (Young, Khan and Marriage, 1977) was based on the conversion of glyphosate to the N-nitroso derivative with sodium nitrite, TLC separation on silica gel, degradation of N-nitrosoglyphosate to aminomethylphosphonic acid with ultraviolet light, and fluorophore formation from this primary amine with fluorescamine. (Caution: Nitroso derivatives and nitrites may be carcinogens!)

EXTRACTION AND CLEAN-UP

The samples were blended, extracted with water in a boiling water bath, filtered and then evaporated to dryness. The dried extracts were dissolved in 0.12 N HCl and centrifuged. The supernatant was removed and washed with methylene chloride, which was then treated with sodium nitrite (10 mg of sodium nitrite per ml of 0.12 N HCl to give pH 3.0), stirred in the dark for 1 h, and washed again with several portions of methylene chloride, which were discarded. (Caution: Carcinogen!). The aqueous layer was taken for analysis.

Clean-up was achieved by Florisil column chromatography. The nitrosated extract was taken to dryness, dissolved in 10% water in acetonitrile and chromatrographed on a small column (Florisil in a disposable Pasteur pipette and pre-washed with 10% water in acetonitrile). The column was eluted successively with 90, 80, 50 and 0% acetonitrile in water; the eluates were concentrated prior to TLC analysis.

ANALYSIS

Aliquots containing 20, 40 and 60 ng of nitrosated glyphosate (prepared from standard glyphosate) and an aliquot of the sample were spotted on silica gel plates without fluorescent indicator and developed in a solvent system of 95% ethanol : benzene : water (4:1:1). Plates were dried, u.v.-irradiated, sprayed with fluorescamine reagent, and viewed under u.v. light. Then an aliquot of the sample, estimated to contain approximately 40 ng of nitrosated glyphosate, was spotted alongside 30, 35, 40, 45 and 50 ng of standard and analysed as above.

A linear calibration curve was obtained from N-nitrosoglyphosate for 0–80 ng. Quantitative determination was done either by spectrometric measurement of the fluorescent intensity or by comparing easily distinguishable spots differing by ±5 ng at the 50 ng level. Observed precision was ±9% for both methods of quantification.

The limit of detection for glyphosate was 10 ng. The detection limit in *Cirsium arvense* roots was 5 µg g^{-1}, determined in 2 mg sample sizes. Recoveries from fortified samples ranged from 75% at 5 µg g^{-1} to 90% at 100 µg g^{-1}.

Addition of 10 mg NaNO$_2$ ml^{-1} of 0.12 N HCl, giving pH 3.0, was considered to be optimum for nitrosation of secondary amines.

Method II

A method (Pavoni, 1978) was reported to separate glyphosate and AMPA from water or soil extractions by column chromatography on Dowex 1-X8 using 0.2 mol l^{-1} NH$_4$HCO$_3$ as eluting solvent. Eluants were then applied to silica gel 60 F$_{254}$ TLC plates which were developed in 6:2:2 BuOH:HOAC:H$_2$O. R_F values were 0.18 and 0.4 for glyphosate and AMPA, respectively. The detection limit was 0.05 µg g^{-1} in soil and 0.01 µg g^{-1} in water.

Method III

In this method (Sprankle *et al.*, 1978), technical grade glyphosate (98.5%) and reagent grade AMPA were spotted on 500 µm cellulose, silica gel G and silica gel H plates and developed using ethanol:water:15 N NH$_4$OH:trichloroacetic acid: 17 N acetic acid (55:35:2.5:3.5 g:2, v/v/v/w/v with v in ml). ^{14}C-glyphosate standard and glyphosate were separated from possible metabolites in treated *Convolvulus arvensis*. Visualization was achieved by spraying with 0.5% ninhydrin in butanol and heating in an oven to 100°C for 5 min to develop colour. The cellulose-coated TLC plates provided better separation than silica gel G and H plates.

The report did not mention about quantitative determination or residues.

Method IV

This method (Ragab, 1978) used microcrystalline cellulose plates or precoated NM-Polygram cellulose 300 sheets to separate glyphosate and AMPA in a methanol–water solvent system with the addition of a small amount of 0.5 mol l^{-1} NaCl. Compounds were visualized by spraying with ninhydrin reagent, 0.3% in 95% ethanol (w/v), followed by heating in the oven at 100°C, then overspraying with copper nitrate, 1% in 95% ethanol (w/v), and Rhodamine B, 0.2% in 95% ethanol (w/v). The lowest amount detected was approximately 100 and 50 ng of glyphosate and AMPA, respectively. The method was applied to fortified distilled water samples.

A similar TLC method was used for cleaned-up extracts of a sandy loam soil, and also extracts of beans (*Phaseolus vulgaris*) and peas (*Pisum sativum*) (Kader and Ragab, 1977).

Colorimetric method

In this method (Glass, 1981), the organic phosphate in glyphosate was oxidized with hydrogen peroxide to the orthophosphate which was then measured colorimetrically as the phosphomolybdate heteropoly blue complex at 830 nm. Application of the method was reported for water samples only.

Fifty ml aliquots of water samples were fortified with 1–20 ug g^{-1} of glyphosate, the pH was adjusted to ca. 5.0 with 0.1 mol l^{-1} NaOH or 0.1 mol l^{-1} HCl. To each sample, 1.0 ml of 30% H_2O_2 was added. (Caution: H_2O_2 is a very strong oxidant!). The H_2O_2 treated water samples were boiled gently to dryness on an electric hot plate and cooled, followed by dissolution of the residue in 20–30 ml 0.25 mol l^{-1} HCl. After about 40 min the resulting orthophosphate was converted to its phosphomolybdate heteropoly blue complex, formed by adding 2 ml aliquots of a molybdenum(V)–molybdenum(VI) reagent and the absorbance at 830 nm was measured. The orthophosphate content was then determined from a standard curve. The Mo(V)–Mo(VI) reagent was prepared as follows: 35 g ammonium molybdate tetrahydrate was dissolved in 400 ml 6 mol l^{-1} HCl. Then, 3 g metallic zinc were added at ice-cold temperature. Upon dissolution of zinc, 200 ml concentrated HCl and 400 ml concentrated H_2SO_4 were slowly added, followed by dilution to 1 l with deionized water.

A standard curve was obtained by adding 2 ml aliquots of Mo(V)–Mo(VI) reagent to 0.5–5.0 ml aliquots of 50 µg ml^{-1} potassium dibasic phosphate solution which were diluted to 22 ml with distilled water, allowed to stand in a 100°C water bath for 20 min and the absorbance of the blue complex was measured at 830 nm against water as blank. A plot of concentration against absorbance gave a straight line.

The glyphosate residue of the samples was calculated by multiplying the amount of orthophosphate phosphorus by 5.46, a factor derived on the assumption that all of the organic phosphorus in glyphosate were converted to the orthophosphate.

In case of interference from inorganic ions such has arsenate, silicate and nitrate, a reduction step using 0.3–0.5 g granulated zinc and 1 ml concentrated HCl needed to be included after the peroxide digestion step, prior to the addition of reagents for blue complex formation.

The method permitted the detection of a minimum of 50 ug glyphosate. Recoveries of the herbicide in distilled water, river water and run-off water fortified at 1–20 µg g^{-1} level ranged from 91% to 108%.

Amino acid analyser—colorimetric method

This method (Ekstrom and Johansson, 1975) reported the quantitative determination of glyphosate in standard solutions only using an amino acid analyser. Residue analyses from plant or animal matrices, soil, etc., were not reported.

A standard glyphosate solution (360 g l^{-1}) was diluted with citrate buffer pH 2.2

to obtain concentrations of 0.2–1.0 μmol ml^{-1}. The buffer solutions and ninhydrin reagent were prepared by the standard methods.

A 69 cm × 4 mm glass column packed to a height of 55 cm with Beckman spherical cation exchange resin type M82 was used. The eluting solvent was citrate buffer at pH 3.28.

The absorbance of the ninhydrin–glyphosate complex was measured at 570 nm. Elution time for glyphosate was 20 min and the elution volume was 23 ml.

The minimum detectable amount of glyphosate was 1 nmol. However, the smallest amount which could be quantified in a reproducible way was 20 nmol or 3.4 μg glyphosate.

It was also reported (Brønstad and Friestad, 1976) that glyphosate and AMPA could be separated on a chromabead C3 column (Technicon).

Other methods

Molecular emission cavity analysis

The application of this method (Ragab, Stiles and Yeo, 1979) was limited to the analysis of water samples.

Four μl of water fortified with known amounts of glyphosate were injected into a stainless steel molecular emission cavity and heated in a fuel-rich, nitrogen-cooled air–hydrogen flame. The intensity of the HPO emission at 528 nm was then compared with that obtained from standard solution of the chemical in distilled water. For water samples containing less than 10 μg g^{-1} hardness, addition of ammoniacal EDTA greatly improved the recovery. The detection limit of both glyphosate and AMPA in distilled water was 500 μg g^{-1}.

Polarographic method

In this method (Brønstad and Friestad, 1976), glyphosate in acidic aqueous solution was converted to its nitroso-derivative which was amenable to differential pulse polarographic analysis on a dropping mercury electrode. The method was applied to residue analysis in natural water samples. Since AMPA was not amenable to nitrosation, it could not be analysed by this method.

SAMPLE CLEAN-UP

A 1 l water sample was allowed to percolate through resin (300 mm × 20 mm i.d. glass column packed with 15 ml Dowex 1-X8 resin, 50–100 mesh), chloride form at a flow rate of 500–600 ml h^{-1}; this was followed by 200 ml deionized water. The percolates were discarded. The column was eluted with 0.1 mol l^{-1} HCl under the same conditions as above.

DERIVATIZATION

H$_2$SO$_4$ (1:1), 25% KBr solution and 0.2 mol l^{-1} NaNO$_2$ were added to the eluate fraction collected. The contents were swirled and allowed to stand for 15 min, followed by addition of 1 mol l^{-1} ammonium sulphamate solution to destroy excess nitrite.

ANALYSIS

The solution containing the nitroso-derivative was put in the electrolytic cell and deactivated by bubbling high-purity nitrogen through the cell. Polarographic analysis was performed under a nitrogen atmosphere, using the differential pulse mode and pulse heights of 50 mV and a scan rate of 10 mV s^{-1}.

The working electrode was a dropping mercury type, the auxiliary electrode a platinum wire type and the reference electrode a saturated calomel type isolated from the bulk of the solution by a salt-bridge tube.

Glyphosate nitrosoamine gave a single, well-defined, differential pulse wave with a peak potential at -0.78 V.

Oxygen and nitrite must be completely removed in order to obviate interferences. The electrochemistry of glyphosate nitrosoamine was susceptible to pH variations. Lower limit of detection was 35 µg glyphosate per litre of water. Relative standard variation ranged from 22.8% at the lower detection limit to 2.3% at 210 µg l^{-1}.

IMPROVEMENTS WITH MODIFICATIONS

Based upon the approach cited above, Friestad and Brønstad (1982) described a procedure with improvements in clean-up, derivatization, etc.

The herbicide was extracted with water (crops) or with diluted KOH (soils) solution. The pH of the extract was adjusted to > 10. Clean-up and concentration was achieved by anion exchange column chromatography on a strong basic resin in OH$^-$ form. The column was washed with diluted KOH solution followed by elution of glyphosate into a relatively small volume of 1 mol l^{-1} HCl. After treatment with charcoal, glyphosate in the eluate was converted to nitrosoderivative by adding a sodium nitrite solution. The reaction was stopped after 15 min by adding ammonium sulphamate. Differential pulse polarograms of both underivatized and derivatized solutions were recorded, and the differences between the current values of the peak potential (-0.78 V) was used as the basis for quantitation. The instrument used was Princeton Applied Research Model PAR 174 A. Repetitive scannings were from -0.5 to -0.9 V. The potential vs. Ag/AgCl was taken. The parameters for the differential pulse mode were: scan rate 2 mV/sec; amplitude 100 mV; drop time 2 sec.

The method was successfully applied to the residue analysis of glyphosate in blueberries, cowberries (*Vaccinium vitis idaea*), raspberries (*Rubus idaeus*), barley, oat, wheat and potato (*Solanum tuberosum*) at fortification levels of 2 µg g^{-1}. Residue analyses were also extended to soils at fortification levels of 1–4 µg g^{-1}, and to water fortified at 0.025–0.05 µg g^{-1}. Consistent recoveries of 70% or better were reported in all cases. The lower limit of detection was 0.5 µg g^{-1}.

Conclusions

This review surveys the various methods currently known for residue analysis of glyphosate and its major metabolite. While the application of glyphosate to crop lands or to forests has resulted in no detectable pollution to the ecosystem, the analysis of its residues is far from facile. The pure chemical or a clean sample lacking interferences poses few problems in analysis. The herbicide needs to be extracted from various matrices with water, and it defies extraction or any subsequent clean-up with organic solvents. Consequently, the difficulty lies essentially in clean-up. While many of the methods surveyed in this review are claimed to respond well to their respective mission-oriented needs, they have been tested on a limited number of crops or other matrices, and hence their application to other substrates requires more development. On the other hand, Monsanto's method may involve long and complicated steps, and yet it is the only method known to date to have been tested and applied to most common vegetable and animal matrices, soil, water, etc. It must be emphasized that the growing and continuing interests in the use of glyphosate justifies further refinements and developments of residue analytical methods for this chemical.

Note added in proof

A single step derivatization procedure for glyphosate and AMPA was recently reported (Moye and Deyrup, 1983), which allowed for their analysis by gas–liquid chromatography with flame photometric detection. Derivatization was achieved by using *N*-methyl-*N-t*-butyldimethylsilyl trifluoroacetamide, which introduced the dimethyl-*t*-butylsilyl group at active hydrogens.

A high-performance liquid chromatographic method using fluorescence detection and an amine phase column was described (Glass, 1983) for the determination of glyphosate in soil and water samples after derivatization of the herbicide with 9-fluorenylmethyl chloroformate. Lower limits of detection were 0.01 $\mu g\ g^{-1}$ in fortified water, 5 $\mu g\ g^{-1}$ in sandy loam soil and 50 $\mu g\ g^{-1}$ in clay loam soil.

References

BRØNSTAD, J.O. and FRIESTAD, H.O. (1976). Method for determination of glyphosate residues in natural waters based on polarography of the *N*-nitroso derivative, *Analyst*, **101**, 820–824.

BURNS, A.J. and TOMKINS, D.F. (1979). The determination of *N*-(phosphonomethyl)glycine in formulation and technical samples by high pressure liquid chromatography, *Journal of Chromatographic Sciences*, **17**, 333–335.

COCHRANE, W.P., COHEN, H., GREENHALGH, R. and LANOUETTE, M. (1982). The determination of glyphosate in water by high pressure liquid chromatography after fluorigenic labelling by 7-chloro-4-nitrobenzo-2-oxa-1,3-diazole, *Abstracts of the 5th International Congress of Pesticide Chemistry (IUPAC)*, **VII**, C-11.

EKSTROM, G. and JOHANSSON, (1975). Determination of glyphosate (*N*-phosphonomethyl glycine) using an amino acid analyzer, *Bulletin of Environmental Contamination and Toxicology*, **14**, 295–296.

FRIESTAD, H.O. and BRØNSTAD, J.O. (1982). Improved polarographic method for determination of glyphosate herbicide in crop, soil, and water samples, *Abstracts of the 5th International Congress of Pesticide Chemistry (IUPAC)*, **VII**, C-12.

GLASS, R.L. (1981). Colorimetric determination of glyphosate in water after oxidation to orthophosphate, *Analytical Chemistry*, **53**, 921–923.

GLASS, R.L. (1983). *Journal of Agricultural and Food Chemistry*, **31**, 280–282.

GUINIVAN, R.A., THOMPSON, N.P. and WHEELER, W.B. (1982a). Derivatization and cleanup improvements in determination of residues of glyphosate and aminomethylphosphonic acid in blueberries, *Journal of the Association of Official Analytical Chemists*, **65**(1), 35–39.

GUINIVAN, R.A., THOMPSON, N.P. and WHEELER, W.B. (1982b). The verification of the structures of *N*-hepta fluorobutyryl derivatives of glyphosate and aminomethyl phosphonic acid by chemical ionization and electron impact mass spectrometries, *Journal of Agricultural and Food Chemistry*, **5**, 977–982.

KADER, M.H.M.A. and RAGAB, M.T.H. (1977). *Annual Report*, Research Station, Kentville, Nova Scotia, pp. 159–162.

MOYE, H.A. and DEYRUP, C.L. (1983). *97th Annual International Meeting of the Association of Official Analytical Chemists*, Washington D.C., USA.

MOYE, H.A., MILES, C.J. and SCHERER, S.J. (1983). A simplified HPLC residue procedure for the determination of glyphosate herbicide and aminomethylphosphonic acid in fruits and vegetables employing post-column fluorogenic labelling, *Journal of Agricultural and Food Chemistry*, **31**, 61–72.

MOYE, H.A. and SCHERER, S.J. (1977). Dynamic fluorogenic labelling of pesticides for high performance liquid chromatography: detection of *N*-methylcarbamates with *O*-phthalaldehyde, *Analytical Letters*, **10**, 1049–1073.

MOYE, H.A. and ST. JOHN, P.A. (1980). A critical comparison of pre-column and post-column fluorogenic labelling for the HPLC analysis of pesticide residues, in *ACS Symposium Series No. 136*, chap. 6 (Eds. J. Harvey and G. Zweig), Washington, D.C.; American Chemical Society.

PAVONI, G. (1978). Ricerca di glifosate e del sno metabolita principale, l'acido aminometilfosfonico, per TLC (Investigation of glyphosate and its principal metabolite, aminomethylphosphonic acid, by TLC), *Bolletino dei chimici dell'Unione Italiana dei Laboratori Provinciali*, **9**, 157–161; also in *Chemical Abstracts*, **90**, 1748/V.

PESTICIDE ANALYTICAL MANUAL (1977). Monsanto Chemical Co., Vol. 2. Food and Drug Administration, Washington, D.C., Pest. Reg. Sec. 180.364.

RAGAB, M.T.H. (1978). Thin-layer chromatographic detection of glyphosate herbicide (*N*-phosphonomethyl glycine) and its aminomethyl phosphonic acid metabolite, *Chemosphere*, **7**, 143–153.

RAGAB, M.T.H., STILES, D.A. and YEO, J. (1979). The rapid analysis of glyphosate and its major metabolite in water by molecular emission cavity analysis, *Abstracts of the 1979 Meeting of the Weed Science Society of America*, p. 123.

ROSEBOOM, H. and BERKHOFF, C.J. (1982). Determination of the herbicide glyphosate and its major metabolite aminomethylphosphonic acid by high performance liquid chromatography after fluorescence labelling, *Analytica Chimica Acta*, **135**, 373–377.

RUEPPEL, M.L., SUBA, L.A. and MARVEL, J.T. (1976). Derivatization of aminoalkylphosphonic acids for characterization by gas chromatography mass spectrometry, *Biomedical Mass Spectrometry*, **3**, 28–31.

SPRANKLE, P., SANDBERG, C.L., MEGGITT, W.F. and PENNER, D. (1978). Separation of glyphosate and possible metabolites by thin-layer chromatography, *Weed Science*, **26**, 673–674.

THOMPSON, N.P., LYNCH, A.A., BARDALAYE, P.C. and PHILLIPS, R.L. (1980). Glyphosate residues on avocado, *Proceedings of the Florida State Horticultural Society*, **93**, 159–160.

YOUNG, J.C., KHAN, S.U. and MARRIAGE, P.B. (1977). Fluorescence detection and determination of glyphosate via its *N*-nitroso derivative by thin-layer chromatography, *Journal of Agricultural and Food Chemistry*, **25**, 918–922.

Chapter 18

Bioassays for glyphosate

W.G. Richardson
Weed Research Organization, Oxford, UK

Introduction

The term 'bioassay' describes the measurement of response of biological material to a chemical. The purpose may be qualitative, to detect the presence of available chemical, or quantitative, to measure the amount of chemical to which the organism is exposed. Untreated control and standards are needed for a proper qualitative bioassay. The quantitative assay has more complex requirements for standards (Horowitz, 1976b). Only a few such quantitative bioassays exist for glyphosate (e.g. Anon., 1978; Bowmer, 1982a; 1982b), although several qualitative bioassays have been described.

The majority of herbicide bioassays have been developed for soil-acting chemicals, usually to detect and/or estimate residues in soils (Santelmann, 1977). Techniques for the bioassay of foliage-applied herbicides were reviewed by Horowitz (1976a), although most of the herbicides mentioned possessed soil activity and this feature was often employed in the resulting bioassay. Since its introduction in 1971, glyphosate has been generally considered as foliage-acting, being rapidly inactivated in the soil (Sprankle, Meggitt and Penner, 1975a; 1975b), at least at the usual recommended rates. It is not surprising, therefore, that few bioassays have been reported. Although numerous plant physiological processes have been shown to be inhibited, e.g. photosynthesis, transpiration and protein synthesis (Pillai, Davis and Truelove, 1978; Shaner, 1978; Kitchen, Witt and Rieck, 1981), few of these have been utilized for bioassay. The reason for this could be partly that this herbicide is still relatively new, certainly as compared with 2,4-D, but also that use of physiological responses often involves sophisticated equipment and is thus much more expensive than other methods of estimation. The problem of attaining relatively pure extracts of glyphosate from plants or soil prior to chemical or biological assay has been paramount. Several workers (e.g. Rajkomar and Ashford, 1979; Stahlman and Phillips, 1979) have shown reduction in biological effectiveness of glyphosate in the presence of relatively inert materials, and these are prevalent in most situations where glyphosate is used.

Glyphosate bioassays can be conveniently subdivided according to the type of biological material used (plants, microorganisms, etc.) or the parameter of measurement (height, length, weight of plant shoots and/or roots, etc.), or the medium in which the biological material is grown (soil, solution, etc.). In the following discussion, subdivision is primarily on the basis of medium of exposure and secondarily by plant material used. Some consideration will also be given to known effects of glyphosate on biological material which could possibly be developed into bioassays.

The name glyphosate in this chapter refers, in most instances to the commercial formulation Roundup. This is the isopropylamine salt of glyphosate to which, non-herbicidal (n.h.) constituents have been added. Where authors have used the isopropylamine salt alone this will be stated clearly.

Bioassays using glyphosate dispersed in solid media

Shoot bioassays

Sprankle and his co-workers studied the rapid inactivation of glyphosate in soil (Sprankle, Meggitt and Penner, 1975a) and also its adsorption, mobility and microbial degradation (Sprankle, Meggitt and Penner, 1975b). With a pot bioassay technique, they used wheat (*Triticum aestivum*) to detect glyphosate in different soil types after testing this and six other crop species—barley (*Hordeum vulgare*), oat (*Avena sativa*), cucumber (*Cucumis sativus*), maize (*Zea mays*), flax (*Linum usitatissimum*) and soya bean (*Glycine max*)—in sand culture. Several rates of glyphosate were incorporated into the sand above the seeds and pots were sub-irrigated daily. Hoagland's No. 1 nutrient solution, modified with iron chelate, was supplied to the pots at seeding and again 8 and 13 days after planting. The results obtained must be reviewed with caution regarding the availability of glyphosate, in view of later work in which it was shown to be inactivated by Fe^{2+}, Fe^{3+} and other metal salts, which would naturally be present in the nutrient solution (Hensley, Beuerman and Carpenter, 1978).

Sixteen days after sowing, percentage of germination, shoot fresh and dry weights and shoot height were recorded. Plants were raised in the glasshouse at 25°C and 8 klux. Wheat was selected as the most uniform bioassay plant, even though maize, soya bean and flax were more sensitive to glyphosate. The height, shoot fresh and dry weights were reduced 44, 45 and 48% by 0.56 kg ha^{-1}, thus giving an ED_{50} value (the effective dose which reduces weight by 50%) slightly greater than 0.56 kg ha^{-1}. Using this species and replacing the sand by appropriate soil samples provided demonstration of the rapid inactivation of glyphosate in organic and mineral soils and that this was due to adsorption, rather than rapid microbial degradation. Also, pH influenced inactivation in a sandy loam with more glyphosate being bound to the soil at a lower pH. Added phosphate decreased inactivation, the herbicide being reversibly adsorbed to clay and organic matter through the phosphoric acid moiety. These authors also conducted a radioassay to show that soil-applied, ^{14}C-methyl-labelled glyphosate was not readily absorbed by maize and soya bean, but that glyphosate itself was readily absorbed from nutrient solution, when the plants were grown in vermiculite.

Torstensson and Aamisepp (1977) employed bioassays with wheat to study detoxification of glyphosate in two different autoclaved and non-autoclaved soils. In their method, 10 g of air-dried soil was placed in culture tubes. The soil was brought to field capacity and the tubes sealed with a plastic cap. Some were left unsterilized and others were sterilized by autoclaving. Glyphosate (0.9 mg) was added in 1 ml of sterile filtered water. This dose was chosen from a response curve made for one of the soils (*Figure 18.1*) as the concentration giving an initial inhibition of 80–90%. Persistent phytotoxicity in the soil tubes after different incubation periods was determined by placing three germinated wheat seeds (radicle length 1–2 mm) in each tube and measuring plant height after 4 days at 20–22°C. They concluded that the initial rapid inactivation of glyphosate is by adsorption, but that further disappearance of activity depended mainly on microbial degradation.

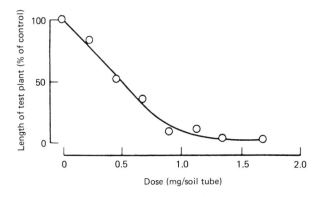

Figure 18.1. Wheat (*Triticum aestivum*) shoot bioassay dose–response curves for glyphosate (from Torstensson and Aamisepp, 1977, by courtesy of Blackwell Scientific Publications Ltd)

Glyphosate at recommended rates is generally regarded as non-phytotoxic through the soil (Sprankle, Meggitt and Penner, 1975a). However, Salazar and Appleby (1982) have shown that bentgrass (*Agrostis tenuis* 'Highland') was affected by 3.4 kg a.i. ha^{-1} of glyphosate when applied directly to the soil surface prior to emergence. Growth of seedlings was significantly reduced in two of the soils they used, even when glyphosate was applied up to 5 days before plant emergence. Their bioassays were conducted in small pots (10 × 10 × 10 cm) in a glasshouse at temperatures between 18 and 24°C without supplementary lighting. Pots were partially filled with screened sandy loam soil which served as a base. A 3.5 cm layer of the glyphosate-treated soil was placed on the base soil. A 0.25 ml volume of bentgrass seeds were sown evenly in two rows in each pot, approximately 1.3 cm deep. The pots were sub-irrigated throughout the experiment and the plants were harvested 5 or 6 weeks after treatment, when dry weights of shoots were measured. In some of their experiments, additional rates of glyphosate were used, but unfortunately ED$_{50}$ values or dose responses were not given. They also showed a reduction of growth of lucerne (*Medicago sativa*) and red clover (*Trifolium pratense*) up to 24 h after glyphosate application, although in these experiments seeds were placed directly onto the soil surface.

The bentgrass bioassay involved only very small quantities of soil and presumably this method could be improved to give a more accurate and relatively cheap bioassay. Although sufficiently sensitive, the variable germination of this species could be a problem, with a relatively high seed rate having to be used. Brewster and Appleby (1972) examined pre-emergence soil activity of glyphosate, but could find no effects on germination, or injury symptoms, on wheat sown 1.2 cm deep in sandy loam soil with doses as high as 34 and 67 kg a.i. ha^{-1}, the herbicide being incorporated into the soil. In later experiments, however, when applied to moist soil 0, 1, 2 or 4 days after wheat had been sown and with irrigation of the pots either by flood or sub-irrigation immediately after application, injury symptoms occurred with rates as low as 1.7 kg a.i. ha^{-1}, especially from the application nearest to emergence. Dose–response curves were not constructed in this work.

Root bioassays

Hensley, Beuerman and Carpenter (1978) studied inactivation of glyphosate by various soils and metal salts by means of root bioassays using modifications of the techniques described by Parker (1964; 1966a) (*Figure 18.2*). One part of various

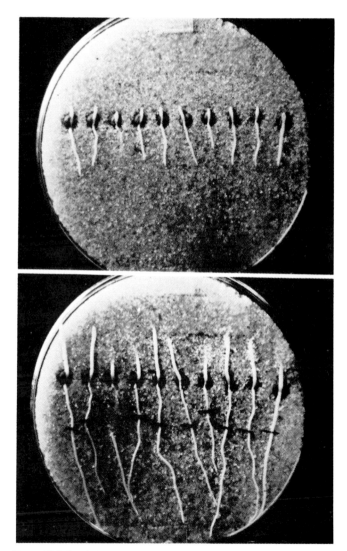

Figure 18.2. Petri-dish/sorghum (*Sorghum vulgare*) bioassay technique of Parker (1966a), adapted by Hensley, Beuerman and Carpenter (1978) for glyphosate

concentrations of glyphosate was added to 10 parts by volume of white quartz sand to which the soils (0, 1, 5, 10 and 25% by volume) had been added. The herbicide concentrations used were 0.66, 1.3, 2.7, 5.3, 11.0 and 21.0×10^{-4} mol l^{-1}. The herbicide, soil or adsorbent and sand combinations were thoroughly mixed by hand and placed in square petri-dishes ($100 \times 100 \times 15$ mm). A hybrid variety of grain sorghum (*Sorghum vulgare*, Pers. var. RS 610) was used as the test plant. This was germinated at 26°C 24 h prior to planting. Ten seeds were planted near the top of the dish immediately upon filling. The dishes were sealed, placed in a holder at 15° from vertical and incubated in the dark at 26°C. Each treatment was replicated at least 4 times. After 8 h, marks were made to indicate the extent of initial root length. Forty-eight hours after planting, growth measurements were made from the 8 h marks. Root growth inhibition by the herbicide treatment was expressed as a percentage of the appropriate controls.

Dose–response curves of percentage inhibition of root growth and glyphosate concentration are shown in *Figure 18.3*. Adsorption was strongly influenced by change in soil type, as shown by variation in degree of inhibition.

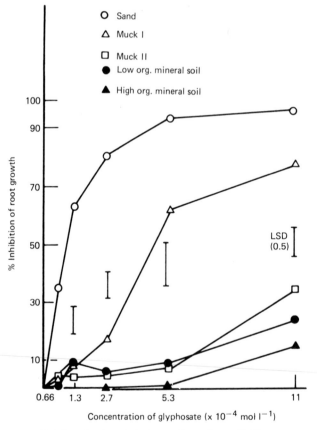

Figure 18.3. Inactivation of glyphosate by various soils (from Hensley, Beuerman and Carpenter, 1978)

Similar root bioassays were carried out to find the effect of different cations on adsorption, using a hybrid variety of grain sorghum (var. NK 180). Hensley, Beuerman and Carpenter (1978) found 50% growth inhibition of roots (ED_{50}) in the quartz sand medium at 2.3×10^{-4} mol l^{-1} concentration. By mixing this concentration with various molar concentrations of each of the metal salts they were able to demonstrate significant reduction of glyphosate activity by $FeCl_3$, $FeCl_2$ and $AlCl_3$ (see also Chapter 4).

Damanakis (1976) adopted this method for studies of glyphosate degradation rate in unsterilized soil. Plotting the percentage of growth inhibition on log-probability graph paper against glyphosate concentration, the ED_{50} value for sorghum was found to be 370 p.p.m. w/w. Degradation was rapid, a dose of 500 p.p.m. becoming biologically inactive in 1 week.

Table 18.1 shows several glyphosate bioassays in solid media.

TABLE 18.1   Summary of glyphosate bioassays in solid media

Species	Substrate	Measurement	ED_{50} value/range	Reference
Wheat (*Triticum aestivum*)	Sand	Height/shoot fresh and dry weight	≈ 0.56 kg ha^{-1}	Sprankle, Meggitt and Penner (1975a; 1975b)
Wheat (*T. aestivum*)	Soil	Plant height	50 μg g^{-1}	Torstensson and Aamisep (1977)
Grain sorghum (*Sorghum vulgare* Pers. cv. RS 610)	Sand	Root growth	$\approx 1.0 \times 10^{-4}$ mol l^{-1}	Hensley, Beuerman and Carpenter (1978)
Grain sorghum (*S. vulgare* Pers. cv. NK 180)	Sand	Root growth	2.3×10^{-4} mol l^{-1}	Hensley, Beuerman and Carpenter (1978)
Grain sorghum (*Sorghum vulgare* Pers.)	Soil	Root length	370 p.p.m. w/w	Damanakis (1976).

Bioassays using glyphosate dispersed in liquid media

Root and other bioassays

Bowmer (1982a; 1982b) developed a bioassay for residue concentrations in irrigation water which had been predicted by tracer and polarography techniques, to confirm that these latter methods gave a reasonable estimate of phytotoxicity. About 15–20 seeds of safflower (*Saffola* 208) or sunflower (*Helianthus annuus*, *Hysun* 30) were placed about 3 cm from the side of a strip of absorbent paper, and every 5 cm along the paper as it was rolled into a loose cartidge. The cartridges were secured loosely and immersed in standard solutions (100 ml) of glyphosate or in samples of drainage water in tall 500 ml beakers, so that the seeds were positioned at the upper side of the rolls. The beakers were covered with watch-glasses and incubated at 25°C for 6–7 days, when root elongation was measured. The concentration required to give a 50% reduction in growth was about 0.4–0.9 g m^{-3} for safflower and about 2.4 g m^{-3} for sunflower. Polarographic and bioassay data showed reasonable correlation. However, the author points out that reduction in glyphosate activity can occur by its reaction with some metal salts and calcium or by chelation with Al^{3+} and Fe^{3+}. Because measurements were made in acidic solution the polarographic technique may not have distinguished this inactivated form from free glyphosate (see also Chapter 4).

At the Research Group of Weed Control in the Institute of Plant Physiology at Shanghai in China, a petri-dish bioassay using flax was developed for glyphosate in solution at concentrations of 0.01 to 10 p.p.m. (Anon., 1978). Wheat, maize and tomato (*Lycopersicon esculentum*) were also screened as possible test species, but flax was chosen because of its sensitivity. Seeds were placed on a nylon mesh frame on water and germinated for 16–18 h at $25 \pm 1°C$. Ten seeds with uniform radicles were chosen (thus overcoming any variable germination) and transferred to 6 cm diameter petri-dishes which contained 8 layers of filter paper. The latter was moistened with 5 ml of the test solutions or distilled water for controls. Petri-dishes were incubated at $25 \pm 1°C$ for time intervals which varied from 0 to 4 days.

Comparisons of root and shoot length were made in the dark and in the light, in the latter a 9-hour daylength period of light at 350 lux being given. At the two lower doses (0.01 and 0.1 p.p.m.), stimulation of growth occurred. At higher rates, roots were found to be more sensitive than shoots, such that root length was preferred as the test parameter. Roots were longer in the dark, with light to some extent inhibiting their growth. After 24 h inhibition was evident, although a two-day period was chosen as optimal for the bioassay. Over longer periods (3 or 4 days), dose–response curves were much flatter, indicating reduced sensitivity. This method was claimed to be simple, efficient and reproducible, the whole process taking only 3 days to complete. However, it is suitable only for concentrations between 0.25 and 5 p.p.m. and so its sensitivity would not be sufficient for all purposes. A straight-line relationship was obtained by plotting the logarithm of concentration against percentage inhibition (Holly and Roberts, 1963).

Hoagland (1977) used a petri-dish bioassay to determine the effects of glyphosate on seed germination and early growth, the seeds being incubated in the dark in solutions of either distilled water or 10^{-3} mol l^{-1} glyphosate. Germination was determined after 24 and 48 h and root plus shoot length after 48 h. The germination of *Rumex crispus* was significantly inhibited. Shoot plus root length was reduced in all species tested, from 79% with sorghum to only 18% with *Sesbania exaltata*. Zemanek and Sterba (1979) investigated the biological effects of 1–1000 mg l^{-1} glyphosate in nutrient solutions and found little effect on germination of white mustard (*Sinapis alba*) and spring barley (*Hordeum vulgare*), but strong suppression of their root growth. Concentrations of 1–32 mg l^{-1} gave substantial inhibition of the growth of cucumber.

Bioassays on rhizomes

The response of 1-node rhizome fragments of *Agropyron repens* has been used in glyphosate bioassays. Coupland and Wyatt (1982) found that unsprouted rhizome nodes were affected more than larger, sprouted ones. They used uniform fragments from clonal stock material, rejecting apices, immature nodes (up to 3 nodes from the apex) and sprouted nodes. All roots and scale leaves were removed to expose the bud. Growth in a sterile (agar) medium or non-sterile (petri-dish/filter paper) medium were compared. Glyphosate at varying concentrations was incorporated throughout the agar medium, while in the petri-dishes, solutions were applied to each end of the rhizomes via small plastic tubes. After 2 or 3 weeks, shoot fresh weight and chlorophyll content were determined. They found root growth too variable to measure. Under non-sterile conditions, shoot fresh weight was reduced by 25–40% at a concentration of 0.1 μg a.i. 40 μl^{-1} per fragment and 63–100% at 1.0 μg a.i. 40 μl^{-1} per fragment.

Hunyadi (1976) also used 1-node rhizome fragments of *A. repens*, enclosing them on filter paper between two long glass plates which were dipped into solutions of glyphosate at concentrations of 1–1000 p.p.m. This apparatus was placed in large glass jars and kept in a darkroom. The rate of shoot and root growth was measured at 3-day intervals over 21 days. However, the method was not very sensitive, inhibition being strong at 100 p.p.m., while at 1 and 10 p.p.m., stimulation of roots and shoots occurred.

Bioassays with *Lemna* species

Damanakis (1976) used *Lemna polyrrhiza* for bioassays of glyphosate in soil extracts to study adsorption, leaching and degradation. He demonstrated that with a concentration of 25 p.p.m. glyphosate in soil extracts, 22 and 42% degradation occurred in 5 and 10 days, respectively. The technique was similar to that which he previously developed for low concentrations of paraquat (Damanakis, 1970) and later developed for determining residues of other herbicides in soils and aqueous solutions (Damanakis, 1972). These bioassays were originated by Funderburk and Lawrence (1963) for paraquat and diquat and by Parker for photosynthetic inhibitors such as ureas and triazines (Parker, 1965) and paraquat (Parker, 1966a; 1966b).

Damanakis (1976) used soil/distilled water extracts contained in shallow 7 cm diameter plastic cups. After allowing to settle for 1 h, 0.3 g of *Lemna* fronds were placed on the surface of the water in each cup. These fronds were taken from a healthy, fast-growing culture, free of algae, which doubled or tripled in fresh weight in a week. In the bioassay to study leaching, instead of weighing the *Lemna*, an estimation of the intensity of chlorosis was attempted, as differences in fresh weight were small, but symptoms (chlorosis) were very clear. An empirical scale of degree of chlorosis from 0 to 4 was set up by selecting 5 cups with different intensities of chlorosis. Each cup from the experiment was compared side by side with the above scale and an estimate of degree of chlorosis made. For greater accuracy, the whole procedure of estimation was repeated twice. In the degradation studies with soil extracts, ED$_{50}$ values of approximately 60 p.p.m. (w/v) were obtained. Thus sensitivity was not very high, but the author preferred these bioassays to chemical methods because they were cheaper and faster and of more relevance, as only biologically active residues of the herbicide were traced and determined.

Hoagland (1978) carried out assays with enzyme extracts of *L. gibba*, although only at one concentration of glyphosate (10^{-3} mol l^{-1}). Various enzyme activities were affected shortly after treatment and in some instances these effects were detected prior to visual damage and before growth effects could be measured. Significant differences in growth were not apparent until 24 h after treatment, but enzyme changes occurred earlier. Growth in fresh weight was inhibited 30% after 72 h, but visual symptoms, such as chlorotic areas in newly developing fronds, occurred in 48 h. The method entailed growing 2 fronds in nutrient solution in culture flasks, kept in continuous light at 25°C. Two weeks' growth was allowed before glyphosate in nutrient solution was added to give a final concentration of 10^{-3} mol l^{-1}. Control flasks were given only an equivalent amount of nutrient solution. Enzyme extracts were prepared 12, 24, 48 and 72 h after treatment. After grinding, the tissue extracts were filtered and centrifuged and the supernatants used to assay 5 enzymes.

In other work on the same species (Hoagland and Paul, 1978) grown in nutrient culture containing glyphosate at 10^{-4} mol l^{-1} concentration, visible damage appeared 48 h after treatment when chlorosis in frond tissue and stunting of roots was recorded. Transmission electron microscope studies of the root tip cells showed progressive damage of chloroplasts, mitochondria and cell walls with increasing exposure from 12 to 24 h. Although this work on *L. gibba* was not intended as a bioassay for glyphosate, the responses recorded might be quantified relative to concentration, to give a relatively quick and simple method of detecting and/or estimating glyphosate.

Table 18.2 summarizes some glyphosate bioassays in liquid media.

TABLE 18.2   **Summary of glyphosate bioassays in liquid media**

Species	Dispersion media	Measurement	ED_{50} value/range	Reference
Safflower	Distilled or drainage water	Root growth	0.4–0.9 g m^{-3}	Bowmer (1982a; 1982b)
Sunflower (*Helianthus annuus*)	Distilled or drainage water	Root growth	2.4 g m^{-3}	Bowmer (1982a; 1982b)
Flax (*Linum usitatissimum*)	Distilled water	Root length	0.25–5 p.p.m.	Anon. (1978)
Sorghum (*Sorghum bicolor*)	Distilled water	Root + shoot length	$>1.0 \times 10^{-3}$ mol l^{-1}	Hoagland (1977)
Maize (*Zea mays*)	Distilled water	Root + shoot length	$\approx 1.0 \times 10^{-3}$ mol l^{-1}	Hoagland (1977)
Barley (*Hordeum vulgare*) and white mustard (*Sinapis alba*)	Nutrient solution	Root growth	1 – 1000 mg l^{-1}	Zemanek and Sterba (1979)
Agropyron repens (nodes)	Distilled water	Shoot fresh weight	0.1–1.0 µg a.i. per 40 µl	Coupland and Wyatt (1982)
Agropyron repens (nodes)	Distilled water	Shoot/root growth	10–100 p.p.m.	Hunyadi (1976)
Lemna polyrrhiza	Soil/distilled water extracts	Degree of chlorosis	60 p.p.m. w/v	Damanakis (1976)
Lemna gibba	Nutrient solution	Growth fresh weight	$>1.0 \times 10^{-3}$ mol l^{-1}	Hoagland and Paul (1978)

Miscellaneous bioassay methods

Although the exact mechanism of action of glyphosate in plants is still not known, various physiological processes, e.g. photosynthesis, have been shown to be affected even though indirectly. Nearly all the previously mentioned assays were possible because photosynthesis was eventually, if not initially, affected, e.g. *Lemna* bioassays. Several methods exist for herbicides which inhibit photosynthesis and although these have been used mainly for ureas and triazines, they could be adapted for glyphosate. Unicellular, photosynthesizing organisms are often employed as the bio-indicating material. Kratky and Warren (1971a; 1971b) used *Chlorella pyrenoidosa*, attempting to improve upon some of the former *Chlorella* bioassay methods (Palmer and Maloney, 1955; Fitzgerald, 1963; Gramlich and

Frans, 1964; Wells and Chappell, 1965; Addison and Bardsley, 1968). Only 18–36 h were required to complete the bioassay.

More recently, Christy, Karlander and Parochetti (1981) studied the effects of glyphosate on the growth rate of *C. sorokiniana* cultured *in vitro* in an inorganic medium containing glyphosate concentrations from 5.91×10^{-6} mol 1^{-1} to 5.91×10^{-4} mol 1^{-1}. A concentration of 1.77×10^{-5} mol 1^{-1} reduced growth rate (estimated by cell counts) by more than 50%. At higher concentrations growth ceased, and at 2.37×10^{-5} mol 1^{-1} cell deterioration resulted.

Richardson, Frans and Talbert (1979) studied the reactions of *Euglena gracilis*, another unicellular green alga, to glyphosate, and observed effects on cell number, chlorophyll content and photosynthesis. Concentrations of 1.2×10^{-3} and 3×10^{-3} mol 1^{-1} glyphosate reduced cell numbers by 12–80% and chlorophyll content by 16–69%, depending on length of exposure. Effects on photosynthesis were assessed by measuring oxygen evolution, which was inhibited by 39–91% at concentrations of 6×10^{-6} and 3×10^{-5} mol 1^{-1}, respectively. In his studies on photosynthetic reactions in *Scenedesmus* spp., another unicellular alga, van Rensen (1974) found that a concentration of 7×10^{-4} mol 1^{-1} inhibited oxygen evolution by 50% after 1 h incubation in light. Truelove, Davis and Jones (1974) and Da Silva, Fadayomi and Warren (1976) used oxygen evolution from cotyledon leaf disks floating on nutrient solution as a bioassay for photosynthetic inhibitors, although glyphosate was not included in their studies (see also Chapters 5 and 6).

Tchan, Roseby and Funnell (1975) developed a rapid bioassay based on oxygen evolution in *Chlorella* spp. The oxygen was estimated by the bioluminescence system of photobacteria. This method gave measurements of diuron, monuron and atrazine in soil and water, within 1 h, at concentrations of 0.02 p.p.m. Whether such a method can be developed for glyphosate depends both upon particular algae and bacteria producing the desired effects and on other factors (see also Chapter 11). Other workers have reported effects of glyphosate on bacteria (Roisch and Lingens, 1974, 1980); microflora (Grossbard and Davies, 1976; Gaziev, 1979; Harris and Grossbard, 1979; Kruglov, Gersh and Shtal'berg 1980; Lönsjö *et al.*, 1980); fungi and actinomycetes (Bogdanovic, 1975), phytoplankton (Setiadarma *et al.*, 1976); and aquatic fauna (Folmar, 1977). In some of these studies, the magnitude of effect was related to glyphosate concentrations suggesting that, depending on sensitivity and other factors, bioassays might be developed.

The use of callus or cell tissue cultures have been suggested as a method of screening new chemicals which inhibit plant growth, and such a system could form a bioassay. Lee (1980) has shown that glyphosate inhibits soya bean and tobacco (*Nicotiana tabacum*) callus cultures. Killmer (1980) and Gresshoff (1979) showed that glyphosate inhibited the growth of cultured carrot (*Daucus carota*) cells. Such methods lend themselves to studies of plant metabolites and other chemicals on inhibition due to herbicides.

Summary and conclusions

To prepare this chapter it was necessary to examine most of the literature published on glyphosate since its introduction in 1972. About 60 references, having relevance to glyphosate bioassays, have been cited and reviewed. Surprisingly few of these are of major importance. However, the sorghum, flax and *Lemna*/root bioassays have potential and advantages over chemical assays in rapidity, sensitivity and reproducibility. Reasons for this situation have been discussed, e.g. glyphosate is foliar and not soil-acting so is not a hazard to a subsequent crop, as would be the case with many soil-acting herbicides. In addition, its low mammalian toxicity reduces the need to check its presence in the biosphere, as was the case with paraquat. There is, however, still a niche for glyphosate bioassays, if only as an alternative to chemical assay which has proved to be time consuming and tedious (see Chapter 17). Its high and non-selective activity on most plant species, including crops, suggests there will always be the environmental hazard of spray drift. Quantification of activity in such situations would be valuable (see Appendix I).

In future bioassay work, more attention should be given to more accurate methods of deposition of glyphosate on the receiving plant surface. Most of the bioassays, in solid or liquid media, have depended upon application early in the plant life-cycle and usually on root rather than shoot uptake, e.g. *Lemna* bioassays. This does not match the normal mechanism of action, so sensitivity has been low. Application later in the plant life-cycle presents other problems for bioassay, i.e. a longer duration, uniformity of material, accurate deposition, etc. A compromise between these extremes may be achieved with callus tissue cultures, which offer a useful and possibly quicker alternative to whole plant bioassays. It is hoped that some, if not all, of the work reviewed here may act as a stimulus for future development of bioassays with this unique herbicide.

References

ADDISON, D.A. and BARDSLEY, C.E. (1968). *Chlorella vulgaris* assay of the activity of soil herbicides, *Weed Science*, **16**, 427–429.

ANON. (1978). A bioassay for glyphosate, *Acta Botanica Sinica*, **20**(3), 276–278.

BOGDANOVIC, V.V. (1975). Herbicide effects on soil microorganisms, *Mikrobiologija*, Yugoslavia, **12**(2), 121–125.

BOWMER, K.H. (1982a). Residues of glyphosate in irrigation water, *Australian Journal of Marine and Freshwater Research*, **33**.

BOWMER, K.H. (1982b). Residues of glyphosate in irrigation water, *Pesticide Science*, **13**(6), 623–638.

BREWSTER, B.D. and APPLEBY, A.P. (1972). Pre-emergence soil activity of *N*-phosphonomethylglycine, *Western Society of Weed Science, Research Progress Report*, p. 90.

CHRISTY, S.L., KARLANDER, E.P. and PAROCHETTI, J.V. (1981). Effects of glyphosate on the growth rate of *Chlorella*, *Weed Science*, **29**, 5–7.

COUPLAND, D. and WYATT, D.F. (1982). A technique using rhizome nodes of *Agropyron repens* to assess herbicidal activity. Some results using glyphosate and fluazifop-butyl, *Proceedings of the 1982 British Crop Protection Conference—Weeds*, pp. 181–185.

DAMANAKIS, M. (1970). A bioassay for the determination of low concentrations of paraquat, *Weed Research*, **10**, 77–80.

DAMANAKIS, M. (1972). A bioassay on *Lemna polyrrhiza* L. for determination of herbicide residues in soils and aqueous solutions. *Annales de L'Institut Phytopathologique, Benaki*, **10**(3), 248–255.

DAMANAKIS, M. (1976). Behaviour of glyphosate in the soil (adsorption, leaching, degradation), *Annales de L'Institut Phytopathologique, Benaki*, **11**(3), 153–167.

DA SILVA, J.F., FADAYOMI, R.O. and WARREN, G.F. (1976). Cotyledon disc bioassay for certain herbicides, *Weed Science*, **24**, 250–252.

FITZGERALD, G.P. (1963). Bioassay for algicidal chemicals in swimming pools, *Water and Sewage Works*, **109**, 361–363.

FOLMAR, L.C. (1977). The toxicity of glyphosate to aquatic fauna, *Abstracts of the Weed Science Society of America Meeting*, pp. 63–64.

FUNDERBURK, H.H. JR. and LAWRENCE, J.M. (1963). A sensitive method for the determination of low concentrations of diquat and paraquat, *Nature, Lond.*, **199**, 1011–1012.

GAZIEV, M.T. (1979). The influence of herbicides on soil microflora in vineyards, *Khimiya v Sel'skom Khozyaïstve*, **27**(5), 61–63.

GRAMLICH, J.V. and FRANS, R.E. (1964). Kinetics of *Chlorella* inhibition by herbicides, *Weeds*, **12**, 184–189.

GRESSHOFF, P.M. (1979). Growth inhibition of glyphosate and reversal of its action by phenylalanine and tyrosine, *Australian Journal of Plant Physiology*, **6**(2), 177–185.

GROSSBARD, E. and DAVIES, H.A. (1976). Specific microbial responses to herbicides, *Weed Research*, **16**, 163–16⁰.

HARRIS, D. and GROSSBARD, E. (1979). Effects of the herbicides Gramoxone and Roundup on *Septoria nodorum*, *Transactions of the British Mycological Society*, **73**(1), 27–34.

HENSLEY, D.L., BEUERMAN, D.S.N. and CARPENTER, P.L. (1978). The inactivation of glyphosate by various soils and metal salts, *Weed Research*, **18**, 287–291.

HOAGLAND, R.E. (1977). Effects of (N-(phosphonomethyl)glycine) on seed germination and early growth, *Plant Physiology*, **59** (6 supplement), 78.

HOAGLAND, R.E. (1978). The effects of N-(phosphonomethyl)glycine on selected enzymes in *Lemna gibba* L, *Proceedings of the 31st Annual Meeting of the Southern Weed Science Society*, p. 285.

HOAGLAND, R.E. and PAUL, R. (1978). Ultrastructural effects of glyphosate on *Lemna gibba* L, *Abstracts of the 1978 Weed Science Society of America Meeting*, p. 78.

HOLLY, K. and ROBERTS, H.A. (1963). Persistence of phytotoxic residues of triazine herbicides in soil, *Weed Research*, **3**, 1–10.

HOROWITZ, M. (1976a). Bioassay techniques for foliar-applied herbicides, *Residue Reviews*, **61**, 113–123.

HOROWITZ, M. (1976b). Application of bioassay techniques to herbicide investigations, *Weed Research*, **16**, 209–215.

HUNYADI, K. (1976). The effect of various herbicides on the early development of one-node *Agropyron repens* (L) Beauv. rhizome fragments, *Kulonlenyomat a Novenyvedelmi Kutato Intezet Evkonyve*, **14**, 141–150.

KILLMER, J.L. (1980). Growth of cultured carrot cells as affected by glyphosate, asulam and various plant metabolites, *Dissertation Abstracts International*, **B41**(6), 2014.

KITCHEN, L.M., WITT, W.W. and RIECK, C.E. (1981). Inhibition of chlorophyll accumulation by glyphosate, *Weed Science*, **29**, 513–516.

KRATKY, B.A. and WARREN, G.F. (1971a). The use of three simple rapid bioassays on 42 herbicides, *Weed Research*, **11**, 257–262.

KRATKY, B.A. and WARREN, G.F. (1971b). A rapid bioassay for photosynthetic and respiratory inhibitors, *Weed Science*, **19**, 658–661.

KRUGLOV, YU. V., GERSH, N.B. and SHTAL'BERG, M.V. (1980). The influence of glyphosate on the soil microflora, *Khimiya v Sel'skom Khosyaïstre*, **18**(10), 42–44.

LEE, T.T. (1980). Characteristics of glyphosate inhibition in soybean and tobacco callus cultures, *Weed Research*, **20**, 365–369.

LÖNSJÖ, H., STARK, J., TORTENSSON, L. and WESSEN, B. (1980). Glyphosate: decomposition and effects on biological processes in soil, *21st Swedish Weed Conference, Uppsala*, **1**, 140–146.

PALMER, C.M. and MALONEY, T.E. (1955). Preliminiary screening for potential algicides, *Ohio Journal of Science*, **55**, 1–8.

PARKER, C. (1964). Methods for the rapid bioassay of herbicides, *Proceedings of the British Weed Control Conference*, **7**, 899–902.

PARKER, C. (1965). A rapid bioassay method for the detection of herbicides which inhibit photosynthesis, *Weed Research*, **5**, 181–184.

PARKER, C. (1966a). The importance of shoot-entry in the action of herbicides applied to the soil, *Weeds*, **14**, 117–121.

PARKER, C. (1966b). Influence of water hardness on the phytotoxicity of paraquat, *Nature, Lond.*, **212**, 1465–1466.

PILLAI, P., DAVIS, D.E. and TRUELOVE, B. (1978). Herbicidal effects on RNA, DNA and protein synthesis, *Proceedings of the 31st Annual Meeting of the Southern Weed Science Society*, p. 278.

RAJKOMAR, I. and ASHFORD, R. (1979). Effect of water quality on phytotoxicity of glyphosate, *Abstracts of the Weed Science Society of America*, pp. 33–34.

RENSEN, J.J.S. VAN. (1974). Effects of glyphosate on photosynthetic reactions in *Scenedesmus* and in isolated spinach chloroplasts, *Proceedings of the 3rd International Congress on Photosynthesis*, pp. 683–687.

RICHARDSON, J.T., FRANS, R.E. and TALBERT, R.E. (1979). Reactions of *Euglena gracilis* to fluometuron, MSMA, metribuzin and glyphosate, *Weed Science*, **27**, 619–624.

ROISCH, V. and LINGENS, F. (1974). Effect of the herbicide N-phosphonomethyl-glycine on the biosynthesis of aromatic amino acids, *Angewandte Chemie*, **13**(6), 400.

ROISCH, V. and LINGENS, F. (1980). Mechanism of action of glyphosate. Effect on growth and on the enzymes of aromatic amino acid biosynthesis in *Escherichia coli, Zeitschrift für Physiologische Chemie*, **361**(7), 1049–1058.

SALAZAR, L.C. and APPLEBY, A.P. (1982). Herbicidal activity of glyphosate in soil, *Weed Science*, **30**, 463–466.

SANTELMANN, P.W. (1977). Herbicide bioassay, *Research Methods in Weed Science Society*, pp. 79–87.

SETIADARMA, D., SOERJANI, M., WIDYANTO, L.S. and SOEWARDI, K. (1976). The effect of some herbicides on phytoplankton populations, *Biotrop Newsletter*, No. 15, p. 13.

SHANER, D. (1978). Effects of glyphosate on transpiration, *Weed Science*, **26**, 513–516.

SPRANKLE, P., MEGGITT, W.F. and PENNER, D. (1975a). Rapid inactivation of glyphosate in the soil, *Weed Science*, **23**, 224–228.

SPRANKLE, P., MEGGITT, W.F. and PENNER, D. (1975b). Adsorption, mobility and microbial degradation of glyphosate in the soil, *Weed Science*, **23**, 229–234.

STAHLMAN, P.W. and PHILLIPS, W.M. (1979). Inhibition of glyphosate toxicity, *Weed Science*, **27**, 575–577.

TCHAN, Y.T., ROSEBY, J.E. and FUNNELL, G.R. (1975). A new rapid specific bioassay method for photosynthesis inhibiting herbicides, *Soil Biology and Biochemistry*, **7**, 39–44.

TORSTENSSON, N.T.L. and AAMISEPP, A. (1977). Detoxification of glyphosate in soil, *Weed Research*, **17**, 209–212.

TRUELOVE, B., DAVIS, D.E. and JONES, L.R. (1974). A new method for detecting photosynthesis inhibitors, *Weed Science*, **22**, 15–17.

WELLS, J.S. and CHAPPELL, W.E. (1965). The effects of certain herbicides on the growth of *Chlorella pyrenoidosa* 7-11-05, *Proceedings of the Northeast Weed Control Conference*, **19**, 449–450.

ZEMANEK, J. and STERBA, R. (1979). Investigating the biological effects of the herbicide glyphosate, *Sbornik Vysoke Skoly Zemedelske v Praze-Suchdole, Fak. Agron. A.*, **30**, 109–123.

Efficacy of Glyphosate

Chapter 19

Efficacy of glyphosate in fruit plantations

D. Atkinson,
East Malling Research Station, UK

Introduction

Weed control in fruit crops is essential for optimum fruit production. Weed competition effects vary with weed species, fruit crop and environmental conditions. Recent publications reviewed by Atkinson and White (1980) showed effects on growth varying from 15 to 96%. Effects on crop, because of fruit size and quality implications, were greater on financial returns than on yield alone. Competition from grass weeds, in the normally herbicide-treated strip around mature apple trees, reduced crop weight by 16 and 35% in 1975 and 1976, and financial returns by 25 and 45%. In experiments where growth, following applications of glyphosate or of other herbicides, e.g. dinoseb, paraquat, propyzamid, was compared in raspberries (Freeman, 1980b), and apple or cherry (Rupp and Anderson, 1980a) with unweeded controls, there were increases of up to 50%. Any evaluation of the effect of a herbicide on a crop must be in the context of the substantial effects that weeds can have on fruit crop performance.

Fruit orchards become infested with a very wide range of weeds, but in a crop left in the field for 20 or 30 years without mechanical cultivations, perennial grass and broad-leaved weeds, including woody weeds, are probably more common and cause greater difficulties than in field crops. Glyphosate can be especially effective against this class of weeds. It has thus the potential to become a major chemical in this commodity group. Perennial weeds have many similarities to perennial fruit crops and so information on the crop tolerance of fruit species to glyphosate is essential to its integration into weed control systems for fruit crops.

This review considers the role of glyphosate in the culture of temperate fruit crops (apples, pears, plums, cherries, peaches, raspberries, strawberries, black currants, gooseberries, vines and pecans) in relation to both weed control and crop tolerance.

The name glyphosate in this chapter refers to the isopropylamine salt of N-(phosphonomethyl)glycine used as the commercial formulation Roundup.

Weed control

The need for a new chemical for use on any crop is related to deficiencies in other chemicals available. The effect of four chemicals currently used in fruit plantations on a range of weed species frequently found in fruit crops is shown in *Table 19.1.* Simazine is the most frequently used residual herbicide, but most perennial weeds are resistant to it. Dichlobenil, propyzamide and 2,4-D all fail to control some major problem weeds of orchards, e.g. *Convolvulus arvensis, Calystegia sepium* and *Rubus* spp., etc. In addition, some of the alternative chemicals have other disadvantages, e.g. the cost of dichlobenil, the environmental conditions needed for propyzamide and the volatility of 2,4-D.

Weed control using glyphosate has been widely studied and effects on perennial broad-leaved and graminaceous weeds in fruit crops are summarized in *Table 19.2.* Glyphosate gave either complete or acceptable control of a wide range of grass weeds, e.g. *Agropyron repens, Cynodon dactylon, Paspalum dilatatum* and *Sorghum halepense.* The rates used in weed control experiments varied from approximately 1 to 9 kg ha^{-1}. The optimum time of application for good control varied between weeds. Good control generally required the combination of a leaf area sufficient to intercept the chemical, active growth and, for many perennial weeds, translocation to below ground storage or extension organs. For most weeds, optimal control was obtained in early summer, before growth was limited by summer drought, and in the autumn when translocation to rhizomes, etc., seemed most active. Rom (1975) found that weed control was better under irrigated conditions than when weeds were suffering from moisture stress.

Most grass weeds were at least susceptible to high rates of glyphosate, but some dicotyledon weeds, e.g. *Equisetum arvense,* were resistant to all rates (Kafadarof and Rognon, 1975). Other species, e.g. *Rhus radicans,* varied in their resistance (Putnam, Love and Pagano 1972; 1974). The permanence of the control for some weeds, e.g. *Convolvulus arvensis,* is equivocal. This is complicated by the difficulty in defining an individual of this species and the proportion of the underground organs active, or in active contact, with the above-ground leafy shoots. For a translocated herbicide, like glyphosate, the physiological state of the weed at the time of treatment is crucial. Data on the control of *C. arvensis* and *A. repens* in orchards are discussed as examples of weed control in orchards.

TABLE 19.1   **The effect of four herbicides, commonly used in fruit plantations, on a range of weeds often found in both soft and top fruit plantations* (after Fryer and Makepeace, 1978)**

Weed species	Dichlobenil	Propyzamide	Simazine	2,4-D
Agropyron repens	MS	S	MR	R
Agrostis sp.	MS	S	R	R
Calystegia sepium	MR	R	R	MS
Capsella bursa-pastoris	MS	MS	S	S
Chenopodium album	S	S	S	S
Cirsium sp.	S	R	R	R
Convolvulus arvensis	MR	R	R	MS
Equisetum arvense	MR	R	R	R
Galium aparine	MS	S	MR	MS
Poa annua	S	S	S	R
Polygonum aviculare	MS	S	MR	MR
Rubus sp.	R	R	R	R
Rumex crispus	S	MR	R	MR
Stellaria media	S	S	S	S
Urtica dioica	MS	R	R	MR

*S, susceptible; MS, moderately susceptible, MR, moderately resistant; R, resistant.

TABLE 19.2 The effect of glyphosate on a range of weed species found in orchards

Weed species	Range of rates found to be effective (kg ha^{-1})	Optimum period	Reference
GRASS WEEDS			
Agropyron repens	1–9	May/June, autumn	Baird, Upchurch and Selleck (1972); Putnam, Love and Pagano (1972); Heikes (1973); Baird, Shaulis and Waywell (1974); Miller and Schubert (1974); Putnam, Love and Pagano (1974); Seddon (1974); Kafadarof and Rognon (1975); Jensen (1976; 1977a; 1977b; 1977c); Antonelli and Formigoni (1977); Metz (1978); Mijatovic (1978); Hilen, Bing and Good (1979); Noye (1979); Freeman (1980b)
Allium canadense	1.7	May	Putnam, Love and Pagano (1974)
Bromus catharticus	1.6–2.5		Castro (1976)
B. inermis	1.7	May	Putnam, Love and Pagano (1974)
Cynodon dactylon	1.1–4.8	July/August, (especially if irrigated), late spring	Lange *et al.* (1973); Rom, Arrington and Brown (1973; 1977); Rom and Talbert (1973); Aitken (1974); Arnold (1974; 1975); Kafadarof and Rognon (1975); Rom (1975); Antonelli and Formigoni (1977); Mijatovic (1978); Sonmez and Karasu (1978); Arnold and Aldrich (1979); Scalabrelli (1979)
Cyperus rotundus	up to 9		Baird, Upchurch and Selleck (1972); Lange *et al.* (1973); Arnold and Aldrich (1979)
Dactylis glomerata	1.7–2.2	May/June	Baird, Shaulis and Waywell (1974); Putnam, Love and Pagano (1974)
Festuca arundinacea	up to 9		Baird, Upchurch and Selleck (1972)
F. rubra	1.7	May	Putnam, Love and Pagano (1974)
Paspalum dilatatum	0.7–5.4		Arenstein (1973); Aitken (1974); Scalabrelli (1979)
Phleum pratense	1.7	May	Putnam, Love and Pagano (1974)
Phragmites communis	1.8–3.0	Autumn	Kafadarof and Rognon (1975); van Himme, Stryckers and Bulcke (1977)
Poa pratensis	up to 9		Baird, Upchurch and Selleck (1972)
Sorghum halepense	1–9	late June/July	Baird, Upchurch and Selleck (1972); Arenstein (1973); Heikes (1973); Lange *et al.* (1973); Rom and Talbert (1973) Rom, Arrington and Brown, (1973; 1977)
BROAD-LEAVED WEEDS			
Artemisia vulgaris	2.9–3.8		Antonelli and Formigoni (1977)
Asclepias syriaca	2.2	May/June	Baird, Shaulis and Waywell (1974)
Calystegia sepium	0.7–4.5	May/July	Baird, Shaulis and Waywell (1974); Kafadarof and Rognon (1975); Scalabrelli (1979)
Campsis radicans	1–3	July	Rom, Arrington and Brown (1973)
Chloris gayana	1.8–5.4		Arenstein (1973)
Cirsium sp.	2.2–3.5	Pre-flowering stage	Heikes (1973); Antonelli and Formigoni (1977); Metz (1978); Sonmez and Karasu (1978)

TABLE 19.2   continued

Weed species	Range of rates found to be effective (kg ha^{-1})	Optimum period	Reference
Convolvulus arvensis	3.0–4.3 (0.7 ineffective)	May–September, weed flowering time	Heikes (1973); Lange *et al.* (1973); Baird, Shaulis and Waywell (1974); Seddon (1974); Kafadarof and Rognon (1975); Wurgler and Neury (1975); Metz (1978); Mijatovic (1978); Scalabrelli (1979)
Equisetum arvense	resistant 3–6		Kafadarof and Rognon (1975)
Gnaphalium obtusifolium	2.3–4.5		Arnold (1974)
Heracleum sphondylium	2.5		Bailey and Davison (1974)
Hypericum perforatum	0.5 almost complete kill		Bailey and Davison (1974)
H. pulchrum			Banwell (1972)
Imperata cylindrica	3.9–4.8		Golan (1976)
Malva rotundifolia	3.6		Kafadarof and Rognon (1975)
Oenothera laciniata	2.3–4.5		Arnold (1974)
Oxalis sp.	3.8–4.8		Antonelli and Formigoni (1977)
Parthenocissus quinquefolia	4.4		Baird, Shaulis and Waywell (1974)
Polygonum amphibium	1–2		Bailey and Davison (1974)
P. aviculare	1.6–2.5		Castro (1976)
Potentilla reptans	3.6		Kafadarof and Rognon (1975)
Rhus radicans	2.2–4.5 (also not controlled 4.4)		Putnam, Love and Pagano (1972; 1974)
Rubus flagellaris	2.2–4.5 (also not controlled 4.4)		Putnam, Love and Pagano (1972; 1974)
Rubus sp.	1.7–4.5	Autumn	Kafadarof and Rognon (1975); Arnold and Aldrich (1979); Frank and King (1979)
Rumex hastatulus	2.3–4.5		Arnold (1974)
Rumex sp.	2.4–3.4		Antonelli and Formigoni (1977); Scalabrelli (1979)
Solanum sp.	2		Jensen (1977b)
Solidago sp.	2		Jensen (1977b)
Sonchus asper	1.6–2.5		Castro (1976)
Taraxacum officinale	2.2 (not controlled 1.5)		Baird, Shaulis and Waywell (1974); Jensen (1976)
Urtica dioica	4.0		Bailey and Davison (1974)
WEED GROUPS			
Annual weeds	0.8–4.4	June, Autumn	Langer (1973); Putnam, Love and Pagano (1974); Jensen (1977c); Rom and Frear (1979); Rupp and Anderson (1980b)
Winter weeds	0.7–1.8		Kafadarof and Rognon (1975)

Convolvulus control

Convolvulus arvensis has an extensive underground reservoir of shoot and root tissue, some situated deep in the soil profile (> 1 m). In late spring to early summer, small above-ground rosettes of leaves are produced. These climb up supporting tissue such as fruit plants, grow in size and flower in June/July. The above-ground portion dies back in the autumn. Rates of glyphosate reported as giving control vary, but range up to 3.6 kg ha^{-1} (Kafadarof and Rognon, 1975).

Seddon (1974) reported rates under 2.2 kg ha^{-1} as ineffective. Kafadarof and Rognon (1975) found some regrowth at 2.7, but not at 3.6 kg ha^{-1}. Most published results suggest the flowering period as optimum for control (Baird, Shaulis and Waywell 1974; Kafadarof and Rognon, 1975; Mijatovic, 1978; Scalabrelli, 1979), while plant size does not seem to be critical. Kafadarof and Rognon (1975) obtained control both when shoots were 10–15 cm long and when they were 30–60 cm long.

Agropyron control

Agropyron repens can be a major perennial weed problem in a range of crops and appears to have received more attention in the orchard situation than any other weed (18 cited papers, *Table 19.2*). Optimum rates for control vary between 1.5 and 2 kg ha^{-1} (Jensen, 1977a; 1977b). Both autumn (Freeman, 1980a; 1980b) and spring (Jensen, 1977c) have been suggested as the best time for control, which even under apparently similar conditions can vary between years. Jensen (1977a) found 2 kg ha^{-1} ineffective in one year, but (Jensen, 1977b) effective in the subsequent year.

Annual weed control

Glyphosate is especially effective against perennial weeds because it is translocated efficiently, but it can also be very effective against annual weeds. Here, unless sprays are repeated or glyphosate is included, as part of an integrated weed control programme with a residual herbicide, substantial re-invasion may occur (see also Chapter 23). Jensen (1977b) and Putnam, Love and Pagano (1974) both found substantial re-invasion of annual weeds following control with glyphosate alone. This can also occur following the control of perennial grasses (Baird, Upchurch and Selleck, 1972). Here, within a short time of achieving grass control with glyphosate, annual weeds gave an 80% surface vegetation cover.

Seed germination is a problem in assessing the control of perennial weeds like *Urtica dioica*, *Rumex obtusifolius* and *Hypericum pulchrum* (Bailey and Davison, 1974). Data on the regrowth of a range of weed types, following glyphosate application in May and in July 1978, in an apple orchard, is shown in *Table 19.3* (Scalabrelli, 1979). Control of annual weeds, monocots and dicots, by May applications was good. No regrowth had occurred by the beginning of September (*Table 19.3*). Applications in July gave good control, but by early September weeds reappeared resulting in substantial ground cover by mid–late October. Control of perennial weeds was better with the July application.

TABLE 19.3   The effect of an application of glyphosate at 2.9 kg ha^{-1} on either 24 May or 10 July, 1978, on the control (%) of a range of weeds (after Scalabrelli, 1979)

Weed	Spray date 24 May		Spray date 10 July		
	Weeks after treatment				
	7	15	4	8	14
Convolvulus arvensis	86	66	100	98	98
Cynodon dactylon	—	—	100	100	100
Annual dicot	100	100	100	79	19
Annual monocot	100	100	100	71	0

Antagonisms

For good weed control, glyphosate should be used in combination with other chemicals. Where glyphosate has been applied in combination with residual herbicides, there has often been antagonism (see Chapters 15 and 23). Baird, Upchurch and Selleck (1972) found that it was better to apply terbacil 1 h after a glyphosate spray rather than tank mixing the two. Seddon (1974) found that tank mixing glyphosate with residual herbicides reduced weed control; diuron was less antagonistic than simazine. Jensen (1976; 1977b) also found antagonism with terbacil.

Relative efficacy

Several studies have compared the efficacy of glyphosate with that of other herbicides; performance has varied between weeds and with the relative rates of the different chemicals used. In the orchard situation, the choice of a chemical or mixture or sequence of chemicals will depend upon the weed spectrum to be controlled. Although glyphosate is reported as being less effective on some weeds than some other chemicals—for example, Bailey and Davison (1974) found both mecoprop and 2,4,5-T more effective on *U. dioica* than glyphosate—its main advantages are the range of weeds controlled and the thoroughness of the control. Chemicals which can be applied as complex mixtures can give as good control, but may have other disadvantages. Scalabrelli (1978) found that although the control of *Cirsium arvense, Rumex* spp., *Cynodon dactylon* and annual monocots and dicots were equally good by glyphosate and a mixture of 2,4-D (3.4 kg ha^{-1}) and dalapon (21.3 kg ha^{-1}), control of *Convolvulus arvensis* was better by the 2,4-D + dalapon mixture. Control of a range of weeds was better by glyphosate than with a mixture of bromoxynil (1.6 kg ha^{-1}) + dalapon (10.5 kg ha^{-1}) + simazine (2.9 kg ha^{-1}). The time of application of chemicals can also influence relative efficacy. In late autumn, glyphosate at 2.2 kg ha^{-1} gave better control of *A. repens* than propyzamide at 1.7–3.4 kg ha^{-1}. In the spring, the opposite was true. More effective weed control by glyphosate, than by other foliar-acting materials, has also been claimed. Frank and King (1979) found in strawberries (*Fragaria* spp.) that glyphosate gave more permanent weed control than did paraquat. Saric and Lucic (1978) found the control of a range of 86 weed species was better with glyphosate than by mixtures of simazine and aminotriazole, aminotriazole + diuron + MCPA, terbumeton + terbuthylazine or dichlobenil.

The time of application for optimum weed control of major orchard weeds occurs during the period when fruit trees or plants are in leaf and so potentially sensitive to glyphosate applications. Crop tolerance is of major importance to fruit crops.

Crop tolerance

There are four major potential routes of entry for a herbicide into a fruit plant: through the trunk or other woody tissue, through the leaves or other green tissue, through the root system as a result of chemical in the soil or via sucker shoots which are growing directly from the root system. The effects of glyphosate on fruit species are summarized in *Table 19.4*. A wide range of fruit and temperate plantation crops have been tested for their sensitivity to glyphosate. In general, applications to the

TABLE 19.4 The effect of glyphosate on tree damage in a number of fruit species

Species		Glyphosate applied to		
	Soil	Suckers	Bark/trunk	Foliage
Apple	——	Putnam (1976a; 1976b); Atkinson (1977); Atkinson et al. (1978a; 1978b; Naber (1977); Ahrens (1978); van Staalduine (1979); Atkinson, Crisp and Hyrycz (1980); Stinchcombe and Stott (1980) *to sucker only*	Curtis (1974); Lord, Murphy and Greene (1975) (*if cut*)	**Damage** Clay (1972); Arenstein (1973); Rom, Arrington and Brown (1973; 1977); Putnam, Love and Pagano (1974); Rom, Brown and Markham (1974); Rom, Brown and Arrington (1976); Seddon (1974); Stott et al. (1974; 1975); Kafadarof and Rognon (1975); Lord, Murphy and Greene (1975); Rom (1975); Putnam (1976b); Antonelli and Formigoni (1977); Naber (1977); Davison (1978); Smith and Treaster (1978); Stinchcombe and Stott (1978b); Crisp and Atkinson (1982)
	Heikes (1973); Mullins, Swingle and Coffey (1973); Baird, Shaulis and Waywell (1974); Hertz (1976); Antonelli and Formigoni (1977); Smith and Treaster (1978); Stinchcombe and Stott (1978a); Rom and Frear (1979); Scalabrelli (1979); Rocha et al. (1980a)	——	Clay (1972); Rom, Arrington and Brown (1973); Bailey and Davison (1974); Putnam, Love and Pagano (1974); Kafadarof and Rognon (1975); Lord, Murphy and Greene (1975); Rom (1975); Rom, Arrington and Brown (1977); Putnam (1976a); Davison (1978); Arnold and Aldrich (1979)	**No damage** Seddon (1974); Stott et al. (1975)
Black currant	——	——	——	**Damage** Rath and O'Callaghan (1974); Rath (1977); Stott et al. (1974) **No damage**
	——	——	Rath and O'Callaghan (1974)	Clay (1972); Rath and O'Callaghan (1974); Stott et al. (1974; 1975)

Table 19.4   continued

Species	Glyphosate applied to			
	Soil	Suckers	Bark/trunk	Foliage
Cherry	——	Atkinson (1977); Atkinson *et al.* (1978a; 1978b) *to sucker only*	Lagerstedt (1979) (*if cut*)	**Damage** Putnam (1976a); Rom and Talbert (1973)
	Putnam, Love and Pagano (1972)	Putnam (1976a)	Putnam, Love and Pagano (1974); Putnam (1976a; 1976b)	**No damage** ——
Filbert	——	——	Lagerstedt (1979) (*if cut*)	**Damage** ——
Gooseberry	——	——	——	**Damage** Clay (1972); Rath and O'Callaghan (1974); Stott *et al.* (1974); Rath (1977)
	——	——	——	**No damage** Rath and O'Callaghan (1974); Stott *et al.* (1974)
Nectarine	Rocha *et al.* (1980c)	——	——	**No damage** ——
Olive	Antonelli and Formigoni (1977)	——	——	**No damage** ——
Orange	——	——	——	**Damage** de Oliveira (1976); Toth and Morrison (1977)
Peach	——	Putnam (1976a; 1976b; Rom and Frear (1979) *to sucker only*	——	**Damage** Rom and Talbert (1973); Rom, Arrington and Brown (1973); Rom, Brown and Arrington (1976); Daniell (1974; 1979); Putnam (1976a); Toth and Morrison (1977); Marriage and Khan (1978a); Weller and Skroch (1980)
	Putnam, Love and Pagano (1972); Arnold (1975); Golan (1976); Antonelli and Formigoni (1977); Daniell (1977); Scalabrelli (1978); Andelic (1979); Arnold and Aldrich (1979)	Putnam (1976a); Rom and Frear (1979)	Rom, Arrington and Brown (1973); Putnam (1976a); Rom and Frear (1979)	**No damage** Daniell (1974)
Pear	——	Putnam (1976a; 1976b); Atkinson (1977); Atkinson *et al.* (1977; 1978a; 1978b); Naber		**Damage** Seddon (1974); de Oliveira (1976); Putnam (1976a; 1976b); Antonelli and Formigoni

TABLE 19.4 continued

Species	Soil	Suckers	Bark/trunk	Foliage
		Glyphosate applied to		
Pear continued	——	(1977); Atkinson, Crisp and Hyrycz (1980) *to sucker only*		(1977); Naber (1977); Stinchcombe and Stott (1980)
	Bailey and Davison (1974); Antonelli and Formigoni (1977); Rocha *et al.* (1980b)	——	Seddon (1974); Putnam (1976a; 1976b); Naber (1977)	**No damage** ——
Pecan	Arnold (1975); Golan (1976); Arnold and Aldrich (1979)	——	——	**No damage** ——
Plum	——	Atkinson (1977); Atkinson *et al.* (1978a; 1978b) Atkinson, Crisp and Hyrycz (1980) *to sucker only*	——	**Damage** Stinchcombe and Stott (1980); Crisp and Atkinson (1982)
	Putnam, Love and Pagano (1972); Rocha *et al.* (1980d); Crisp and Atkinson (1982)	——	Putnam, Love and Pagano (1974); Saric and Lucic (1978)	**No damage** ——
Raspberry	——	Wurgler and Neury (1975); Lawson and Wiseman (1976); Freeman (1980b)	——	**Damage** Clay (1972); Lawson and Wiseman (1974b); Rath and O'Callaghan (1974); Rath (1977); Freeman (1980a)
	——	——	Rath and O'Callaghan (1974); Freeman (1980a)	**No damage** ——
Strawberry	——	——	——	**Damage** Anon. (1977)
	Miller and Schubert (1974); Frank and King (1977; 1979)	——	——	**No damage** ——
Viburnum	Hilen, Bing and Good (1979)	——	——	**Damage** ——
Vine	——	——	——	**Damage** Baird, Shaulis and Waywell (1974); Daniell (1974); Wurgler and Neury (1975); de Oliveira (1976); Antonelli and Formigoni (1977)
	Baird, Shaulis and Waywell (1974); Antonelli and Formigoni (1977)	——	Wurgler and Neury (1975); Antonelli and Formigoni (1977)	**No damage** Daniell (1974)

soil have been safe to most crops. Applications to bark, unless physically damaged, and to suckers (although suckers are usually killed) have usually been safe. Applications to foliage have usually caused damage. There are major differences between groups of species.

Apple

Most work has been done with apple (*Malus* spp.), where most studies have shown foliar applications to be harmful. The immediate effect of an accidental drift or deliberate applications to the foliage is chlorosis, followed by necrosis of the sprayed leaf tissue and the death of affected buds or shoots (Clay, 1972; Curtis, 1974; Rom, Brown and Markham, 1974). This resembles damage caused by other contact herbicides, e.g. paraquat (see *Table 19.6*). With glyphosate, the additional danger is that material applied to a small part of the tree will be translocated throughout the tree. This and the initial damage caused will be influenced by cultivar, the physiology of the tree at the time of application (time of year) and the amount of chemical applied (see also Appendix I).

Rates of glyphosate applied in apple have varied from approximately 1 to 9 kg ha^{-1}. Detailed experiments have often involved the application of small quantities to individual shoots. Clay (1972) found that application of a 0.28–0.56% solution (approximately equivalent to a field application of 1.4–2.8 kg ha^{-1} in 500 l ha^{-1}) caused dormancy and leaf chlorosis in spring. Higher rates, 1.12–2.24% ($\approx$ 5.7–11.4 kg ha^{-1}) were more damaging and reduced both leaf expansion and shoot growth. Spraying a single shoot with 0.1% ($\approx$0.5 kg ha^{-1}) in summer caused the dehiscence of apical leaves and the dormancy of apices on sprayed shoots. Similarly, Curtis (1974) found that sprays of 0.06–0.2 g l^{-1} ($\approx$30–100 g ha^{-1}) caused a temporary suppression in the growth of actively growing shoots, 0.2–0.6 g l^{-1} caused the cessation of terminal growth, and 2–6 g l^{-1} ($\approx$1–3 kg ha^{-1}) caused the death of apical stem tissue and the buds. Shoots sprayed with a concentration of 0.2 g l^{-1} or above showed temporary suppression or cessation of the growth of buds near the tip, while sprays to the basal 20 cm of 40–60 cm long growing shoots caused injury or the death of the shoot at concentrations of 0.6 g l^{-1} and above. At 2–6 g l^{-1}, the shoot death progressed to the base over a period of weeks. Curtis (1974) also found that recent pruning cuts could allow the entry of glyphosate applied between bud burst and petal fall. Concentrations of 0.4–1.2 g l^{-1} applied to cuts up to 2 m from the branch tip damaged spur and terminal shoots (see also Appendix I).

The timing of applications can influence both the severity and type of damage caused. Stott *et al.* (1975) found that an application of 2.5 kg ha^{-1} in December produced chlorotic symptoms in 15% of shoots of both Cox and Egremont Russet. Damage from January and March applications was less severe. Stinchcombe and Stott (1978b) applied glyphosate at a rate equivalent to 2.4 or 4.8 kg ha^{-1} in 450 l, to the distal 20 cm of a shoot in April. They found the treated shoot was killed. The junction between dead and living tissue was at the interface between one- and two-year wood. The rest of the tree was undamaged in both the year of spraying and the subsequent year. Where similar sprays were given in October, there was extensive damage to the whole tree. Kafadarof and Rognon (1975) found that early season simulated drift only caused damage close to the contact points, while Smith and Treaster (1978) found only limited translocation from simulated drift sprays to parts of the tree.

With most herbicides, maximum damage occurs in the year of application. With glyphosate, the most severe damage can occur in the year following application (Stott *et al.*, 1974; Stinchcombe and Stott, 1978a; 1978b; 1980); the additional hazard is translocation. Putnam (1976a) applied ^{14}C-labelled glyphosate to the leaves of 4-year Mac Spur/MM.106 apple trees and found it moved readily from treated leaves on lower branches to other leaves, buds and developing fruit on the same branch, but not to other branches. Rom *et al.* (1974; 1976; 1977) also reported evidence for the translocation of glyphosate applied to shoots, although the extent of movement was variable.

Many studies have investigated the possibility of glyphosate uptake through either bark or soil. Rom, Arrington and Brown (1973), Bailey and Davison (1974) and Stinchcombe and Stott (1978b) all found that applications to the trunk, made at various times in the year, were safe. This was usually so even if the trunk was wounded (Rom, 1975) or for newly planted trees (Heikes, 1973; Putnam, 1976b). Rates of up to 9 kg ha^{-1} applied for 4 years caused no damage (Kafadarof and Rognon, 1975).

Glyphosate has been tested on a number of cultivars. Lord, Murphy and Greene (1975) found that although small amounts of glyphosate, at standard rates, were toxic to either the leaves or wood of current year's shoots, larger amounts were safe when applied to 1-year or older wood, with the exception of dormant MM.111 rootstocks where it caused damage or death. Stinchcombe and Stott (1978b) reported that when the distal 20 cm of a branch of *Malus* cv Hillieri was sprayed in October, there was extensive damage. The number of flowers produced was not affected, but the flowers on sprayed trees were small and misshapen with twisted anthers. For trees on MM.111, 100% of blossoms were damaged, while for trees on seedling and MM.106, comparable values were 79 and 15%. For *Malus × Purpurea* cv Aldenhamensis there were no differences between rootstocks.

Prunus species

Prunus species—peach, plum and cherry—have also been extensively investigated and generally seem more sensitive to glyphosate than apple. Putnam (1976b) found that applications of glyphosate at 13.3 g l^{-1} to varying lengths of newly planted Shasta/Halford peach (*Prunus persica*) stems caused the death of 2–3 of 6 treated trees. Toth and Morrison (1977) found glyphosate applied, at 2.4 kg ha^{-1}, as simulated spray drift to 1.5-year peach (*Prunus persica*) trees caused sprayed trees to shed all leaves within 7 days and death after about 4 weeks. Daniell (1974) investigated effects of rates from 1.1 to 4.4 kg ha^{-1} on trees of varying ages. All rates damaged 1-year trees, but only 4 kg damaged 2-year trees, while 5-year trees were unaffected by spraying the stem.

Disease problems, e.g. plum pox, sometimes require the complete destruction of trees post-grubbing. The possibility of using glyphosate injections to kill completely both aerial parts and roots of cherry (*Prunus* sp.) was investigated by Lagerstedt (1979). Injections killed the tree and after 1 year there had been no resprouting of trees cut off at ground level.

When applied to green stems or leaves of peach, glyphosate caused a necrotic area in the cambium which, under certain conditions, extended into the root system and caused mortality (Daniell, 1979). Part of the applied glyphosate moved within the tree, while the remainder appeared bound. Most rapid movement occurred as a result of August or September applications. Less movement occurred from May applications. Removing treated tissue within 4 h of application, but not after several weeks, reduced damage. Weller and Skroch (1980) studied the effect of leaf dips on peach trees at monthly intervals from May to October. Trees were examined the year after treatment. May applications caused damage restricted to 6 mm diameter shoots near to the point of treatment. If treatments were applied in or after August, all limbs < 25 mm were killed. Tree vigour was reduced by 99% by August and later dips, but by only 50% by earlier applications.

As in apple, different cultivars and species differed in their response to glyphosate. Rom and Talbert (1973) found that peach stocks were more sensitive than cherry stocks. Marriage and Khan (1978a; 1978b) investigated the response of peach rootstocks to glyphosate. Two branches of 10-week seedlings were sprayed with 1–18 mg per plant. 'Blood', 'Bailey' and 'Kalamazoo' were more sensitive than 'Siberian' and 'Rutgers Red Leaf'. Low doses of glyphosate produced necrotic areas on the stems of susceptible varieties soon after treatment. Especially with 'Blood', this later resulted in death. 'Siberian' could tolerate twice and 'Rutgers Red Leaf' three times the standard rate which other varieties could just receive without a measurable growth reduction. Other tree fruits usually responded to glyphosate similarly to either apple or *Prunus* species. In pear (*Pyrus communis*), Seddon (1974) found phytotoxicity due to leaf contact 1 year after a treatment applied in summer, although both dormant and early season applications caused no toxicity. In vine (*Vitis* sp.), Baird, Shaulis and Waywell (1974) found no damage as a result of applications to the trunk. Daniell (1974) reported injury to 1-year but not to 2-year or older plants as a result of stem sprays (see also Chapter 23).

Ribes species

Ribes species—black currants and gooseberries—have been extensively evaluated for their susceptibility to glyphosate at different times during the year (Stott *et al.*, 1974; 1975). Glyphosate at 2.5 kg ha^{-1} was applied in October, December, January or March to black currants (*Ribes nigrum*) or gooseberries (*Ribes uva-crispa*). Applications overall in October generally caused severe shoot injury in spring and a large reduction in crop at harvest. Severe damage also resulted from overall applications in March. Sprays directed at the base of the plant only, in these months, also caused some damage, but no December or January applications resulted in significant shoot injury or crop loss. Damaged bushes produced normal shoot growth by midsummer. Similarly, Rath and O'Callaghan (1974) and Rath (1977) investigated the effect of both overall and directed sprays on growth and subsequent cropping. They found results similar to those reported above, in that black currant bushes damaged by March 1975 sprays cropped as well as control bushes in 1976.

Raspberry

Rath and O'Callaghan (1974) found that directed sprays to the base of raspberry (*Rubus idaeus*) canes caused damage in October but not in January. Affected plants showed no adverse effects in the second season following treatment (Rath, 1977). Freeman (1980a; 1980b) reported that applications of glyphosate in spring, after the new sucker shoots had emerged, resulted in retardation or complete kill of canes. Glyphosate translocated to the current year's fruiting can caused interveinal chlorosis and necrosis and, as a result of reduced sucker growth in the year of application, reduced numbers of fruiting canes and crop in the subsequent year. Up to 55% of suckers were deformed the following year. In addition, glyphosate tended to reduce the soluble solid content of the fruit. Ingelog (1977) also reported changes in fruit composition in raspberries, while Wurgler and Neury (1975) reported translocation of applied glyphosate from suckers to other shoots. Results similar to those of Freeman have been reported for basal applications pre-bud burst (Lawson and Wiseman, 1974a; 1976).

Strawberry

Strawberries are probably the fruit crop most similar to broad-leaved field crops. Glyphosate has been used both pre- and post-planting. Application to weeds pre-planting can be effective (Davison, 1978), and may need to be applied only to part of the field. If strawberries are planted into a former grass sward within 1 week of spraying, severe damage can be caused (Rath and O'Callaghan, 1974). Where the grass is removed pre-planting, damage is reduced. Similar results have been obtained (Anon., 1977). Treatments applied post-planting have sometimes caused damage (Rath and O'Callaghan, 1974; Metz, 1978), but not in other trials (Miller and Schubert, 1974; Frank and King, 1979). The variation may be partly related to translocation to parent plants from runners in the inter-row areas.

Root suckers

Root suckers are present on most fruit crops. Although a part of the crop plant, which can come into contact with herbicides, they also form an unusual weed control problem and so are dealt with separately.

Root suckers occur on older fruit trees and are unavoidably sprayed during normal weed control operations. They provide a potential means of entry to the mature tree. The effect of spraying suckers with glyphosate has been extensively studied with respect to both crop tolerance and sucker control (Atkinson, 1977; Atkinson, Petts and Hyrycz, 1978a; Atkinson et al., 1978b; Atkinson, Crisp and Hyrycz, 1980; van Staalduine, 1979).

Atkinson et al. (1978b) compared the effect of glyphosate at 2.5 kg ha^{-1} applied to the suckers of apple, cherry, pear and plum trees at several sites in the UK and Ireland in winter, April and June. None of the sprays caused any damage to the parent trees, although control was best with the full-leaf (June) spray, and for cherry and plum. The pattern of sucker regrowth was similar to that after spraying a single scion shoot on a tree (Putnam, 1976a). Even when glyphosate was applied to the sucker base, movement within the sucker was strongly acropetal. Spraying the same species, at 7.5 kg ha^{-1}, in May, June or July (Atkinson, Petts and Hyrycz, 1978a) caused no damage to parent trees, but gave 35–96% control of mature (not initiated in the current year) and 67–100% control of young (current year) suckers (*Table 19.5* and *Figure 19.1a, b*). The susceptibility of suckers to glyphosate varied during the year and between species.

Prunus suckers were relatively more susceptible than either those of apple or pear in June, but less so in July. Mature suckers of most species were generally poorly controlled, except with apple; young suckers were usually well controlled. Even with cherry, where control of the number of suckers was least good (*Table 19.5*), sucker control, in terms of the total sucker growth reduction, was effective and commercially acceptable in the year after spraying (*Figure 19.1*). The effect on

TABLE 19.5   The effect of glyphosate on the number of suckers dead (%) at the end of the year of treatment (from Atkinson, Petts and Hyrycz, 1978a)

| Month of spraying | Species | | | |
	Apple	Cherry	Pear	Plum
1976 Mature suckers				
May	2	15	14	7
June	9	35	37	60
July	96	19	51	30
1977 Current year suckers				
July	95	67	100	82

sucker regrowth in the year following the spraying of young suckers varied between species, but was best with apple and pear. Sprays of glyphosate in the late autumn were less effective than those in summer (Atkinson, Crisp and Hyrycz, 1980). With pear trees, autumn sprays resulted in re-translocation, back into the parent tree, which was apparent as damage in the year after spraying.

Stinchcombe and Stott (1980), in similar experiments, found no adverse effects from late season sucker sprays on apple. Rom, Arrington and Brown (1977) also found translocated damage as a result of spraying suckers or low branches, and van Staalduine (1979) observed serious damage to Belle de Boskoop apple trees as a result of September sprays to the suckers. Safe application of the glyphosate to suckers and often effective sucker control has also been reported by Meador (1975), Putnam (1976a; 1976b), Wertheim, van Staalduine and Groeneveld (1977), Ahrens (1978) and van Staalduine (1979).

Putnam (1976a) investigated the fate of ^{14}C-glyphosate applied to either apple or pear suckers. All the applied activity remained in the treated sucker. Analysing reasons for the safety of sprays to suckers, Atkinson et al. (1978b) and Atkinson, Crisp and Hyrycz (1980) suggested that, regardless of the site of application, maximum damage was always at the shoot tip which presumably immobilized much of the transported chemical in dead tissue. However, the damage resulting from autumn sprays on pear and the good control of sucker regrowth suggests that some basipetal transport must have occurred, and van Staalduine (1979) found some damage to the root system of apple trees where young suckers were sprayed in June.

The presence of suckers is also a problem in raspberries. Lawson and Wiseman (1974a) obtained good sucker control with glyphosate and, under conditions where disking was being used to sever root connections, no translocation back into parent plants. In contrast, Freeman (1980a; 1980b) found some movement to parent plants of glyphosate applied to the suckers which resulted in damage.

Methods of application

Most studies on the use of glyphosate in fruit crops have employed conventional high-volume sprays, of approximately 500 l ha^{-1}. A few studies have investigated methods which could reduce the possibility of drift (see also Chapter 16). Selleck et al. (1980) investigated the possibility of controlling tall weeds with wiper and wick applicators. They found this an effective means of control in strawberry, provided

Figure 19.1(a). Sucker growth in June 1978 on unsprayed
11-year cherry (*Prunus* sp.) tree (Merton Glory/F12/1)

Figure 19.1(b). Sucker growth in June 1978 on 11-year cherry
(*Prunus* sp.) tree treated similarly to that in *Figure 19.1(a)*,
but sprayed with glyphosate in July 1977

the wiper did not contact the crop. This method would also be useful in top fruit, where there is spatial separation of low branches and weeds. Alternatives to the use of conventional sprays which have been tested for glyphosate applications are hooded sprayers (Daniell, 1980) and the micron herbi (Rom and Frear, 1979). In most orchards, applications of glyphosate for weed control are, as for most other chemicals, likely to be as high-volume sprays for some time to come (see also Chapter 16).

Integration into orchard systems

To be successful in a commodity, any chemical—and its method and timing of application—must be fully integrated into the growing system. The major advantages of glyphosate are the range of weed species against which it is effective and the efficiency and permanence of the control usually achieved. Its main disadvantages are that it is difficult to tank mix with the residual herbicides which are needed to give season long control of the normally occurring range of annual and perennial weeds found in the orchard, and, because of its potential for translocation, the danger of substantial crop damage or death as a result of accidentally applied sprays or drift (see also Appendix I).

In the traditional orchard tree (e.g. *Figure 19.1b*) both lower branches and fruit were well clear of the ground, so that the application of glyphosate or other herbicides to weeds did not give much risk of direct contact with tree leaves because of a physical separation of crop and weed. In addition, high-volume sprays reduced the possibility of drift. Intensive fruit-growing systems result in trees where both foliage and fruit are either in contact with or close to the soil surface for part or much of the year. Here the risk of accidental contact between chemical and crop plants is high. True crop tolerance to herbicides is of importance for this type of growing system. For perennial grass control a number of chemicals will give good weed control and are well tolerated by the tree in situations where glyphosate is damaging (*Table 19.6*). If glyphosate is to be used in this type of orchard, it will need to be applied by a modified wiper system or at a time when tree tolerance is high. This logic is reflected in the current approval for glyphosate use in fruit in the UK. Newly planted plum trees seem especially sensitive to glyphosate sprays (*Figure 19.2a,b*), even when it is in contact only with a single lower branch. This emphasizes the need for perennial weed control to be carried out pre-planting

TABLE 19.6   The effect of either spraying a 30 cm length of shoot or application to the soil in May 1981 on the damage visible in May 1982 to newly planted trees of Victoria/Pixy* (from Crisp and Atkinson, 1982)

Chemical	Soil application	Shoot application	
		Damage found on	
	whole tree	whole tree	treated shoot
Glyphosate	0	3	5
Fluazifop-butyl	0	0	0
Paraquat	0	1	4
Sethoxydim	0	0	0
Simazine	0	0	0

*0 = no damage; 5 = dead.

Figure 19.2(a). The effect of glyphosate sprayed on a single 30 cm length of shoot on newly planted plum trees, Victoria/Pixy, in the year after spraying. The growth of non-glyphosate trees can be seen in the background for comparison

Figure 19.2(b). Detailed picture of glyphosate-sprayed shoot (foreground) and other shoots in the year following treatment. Surviving shoots show typical glyphosate-damage symptoms

wherever possible and perhaps for trees to be grown so as to facilitate glyphosate application, i.e. with low branches removed, where there is a need for perennial weed control in young orchards. Comparisons of the timing of sprays, optimum for weed control, i.e. at weed flowering time and when weeds are in active growth, with those which result in maximum crop damage, i.e. during maximum vegetative shoot growth, show substantial overlap. To allow glyphosate use, means of effecting physical separation are needed.

Any analysis of the need for herbicide application must involve an evaluation of losses due to crop damage and benefits due to weed control. This is especially true for soft fruit crops such as strawberry. Here, if an increasing perennial weed problems exists, it may be necessary to sacrifice some plants in order to get good weed control. The value of established top fruit trees makes this a less attractive option. Pre-planting perennial weed control is important for all fruit crops, but if killed vegetation remains, strawberry plants in contact with dead vegetation can be adversely affected. The use of glyphosate pre-harvest in cereals (see Chapter 27) will lead to the production of straw which may remain contaminated with glyphosate for prolonged periods (see Chapter 11) and potentially could damage strawberries if used for 'strawing down' strawberry fields. A large range of continually changing factors will influence the exact way any herbicide is used in a particular crop.

Conclusions

Glyphosate is a herbicide which is effective in controlling many of the problem perennial weeds in fruit orchards. Although other chemicals may give better control of some individual weeds, no other chemical gives such good control of such a wide range of weeds. Unfortunately the periodicity of active growth (and so optimal control) in most perennial weeds coincides with active fruit tree growth and herbicide sensitivity, resulting in potential for serious damage by the chemical. Many studies have shown that applications of glyphosate are safe for most species unless the chemical actually comes into contact with leaves, especially on actively growing shoots. In addition, fruit species vary in their susceptibility to glyphosate, with *Prunus* species (especially peach) and some *Ribes* and *Rubus* species being particularly susceptible to sprays contacting young bark. Safe periods will depend upon driftless methods of application, tree-training or plant-growing methods which give physical separation of chemical and crop and the use of carefully timed 'windows' when weeds are sensitive (e.g. early spring) and crops still resistant. Pre-planting weed control may delay the advent of perennial weed problems in fruit plantings and thus the need for glyphosate use, until the trees are more mature, which should restrict any damage to a smaller proportion of the tree (Daniell, 1974).

In pome and stone fruit, root suckers can be a potential hazard when spraying weeds. Results suggest that suckers rarely move glyphosate to the parent tree and that glyphosate can give good sucker control. Growing systems are continually being changed to take account of changing cultural practices, and so some fruit growing systems may need modifications to their geometry if glyphosate is to be used regularly. A study of the economics of the use of a number of herbicides suggested that, even in the young orchard, glyphosate gave the best value in terms of tree growth per unit chemical cost (Rupp and Anderson, 1980b). It is this which is likely to determine its continued application as one of a small number of herbicides used regularly and consistently in fruit plantations.

References

AHRENS, J.F. (1978). Glyphosate for weed control in apple orchards, *Proceedings of the Northeastern Weed Science Society*, **32**, 189.

AITKEN, J.B. (1974). Influence of glyphosate on grasses in peaches and pecans, *Proceedings of the 27th Annual Meeting of the Southern Weed Science Society*, pp. 170–175.

ANDELIC, R. (1979). Studies on the possibility of using total herbicides before planting perennial crops, *Zastita Bilja*, **30**, 97–103.

ANON. (1977). Annual reports of the German plant protection service, *Jahresberichte der Deutschen Pflanzenschutzdienstes, 1976*, **23**, 131.

ANTONELLI, C. and FORMIGONI, A. (1977). Control of perennial weeds with glyphosate in tree fruits, *Stato Attuale della Lotta alle Maleibe Delle Colture Arboree, Ortofloricole e Cerealicole*, Bologna, pp. 139–143.

ARENSTEIN, Z. (1973). Glyphosate: a new contact weed killer in orchards, *Phytoparasitica*, **1**, 72.

ARNOLD, C.E. (1974). Weed control for low chilling peaches, *Proceedings of the Tropical Region, American Society for Horticultural Science*, **18**, 140–145.

ARNOLD, C.E. (1975). Evaluation of promising herbicides for peaches and pecans, *Hortscience*, **10**, 339.

ARNOLD, C.E. and ALDRICH, J.H. (1979). Weed control in immature pecan (*Carya illinoensis*) and peach (*Prunus persica*) plantings, *Weed Science*, **27**, 638–641.

ATKINSON, D. (1977). The effect of the herbicide glyphosate on fruit trees with suckers, *Report of East Malling Research Station for 1976*, pp. 189–190.

ATKINSON, D., CRISP, C.M. and HYRYCZ, K.J. (1980). The effects of late season applications of glyphosate and fosamine to fruit trees with root suckers, *Proceedings of the 1980 British Crop Protection Conference—Weeds*, pp. 311–314.

ATKINSON, D., PETTS, S.C. and HYRYCZ, K.J. (1978a). Further studies on the use of glyphosate on fruit trees with root suckers, *Proceedings of the 1978 British Crop Protection Conference—Weeds*, pp. 191–196.

ATKINSON, D., STOTT, K.G., O'KENNEDY, N.D., ABERNETHY, W. and ALLEN, J.G. (1978b). The use of glyphosate in fruit trees: effects on the suckers and on the trees, *Weed Research* **18**, 19–23.

ATKINSON, D. and WHITE, G.C. (1980). The effect of weeds and weed control on temperate fruit orchards and their environment, in *Pests, Pathogens and Vegetation*, pp. 415–428 (Ed. J.M. Thresh), London, Pitman.

BAILEY, J.A. and DAVISON, J.G. (1974). The response to glyphosate of *Cirsium arvense, Heracleum sphondylium, Hypericum perforatum, Polygonum amphibium, Rumex obtusifolius* and *Urtica dioica* in orchards, *Proceedings of the 12th British Weed Control Conference*, pp. 655–662.

BAIRD, D.D., SHAULIS, N.J. and WAYWELL, C.G. (1974). Glyphosate for herbaceous perennial weed control in northeastern apple orchards and vineyards, *Proceedings of the Northeastern Weed Science Society*, **28**, 205–212.

BAIRD, D.D., UPCHURCH, R.P. and SELLECK, G.W. (1972). Phosphonomethyl glycine, a new broad spectrum post-emergence herbicide, *Proceedings of the 24th Annual California Weed Conference*, pp. 94–98.

BANWELL, M.G. (1972). The role of herbicides in modern fruit management, *Proceedings of the 11th British Weed Control Conference*, pp. 1002–1011.

CASTRO, H.R. (1976). Chemical weed control in orchards, *Trabajos y Resumenes III Congreso Asociacion Latinoamericana de Matezas Alam*, **3**, 146–155.

CLAY, D.V. (1972). Response of various fruit crops to glyphosate, *Proceedings of the 11th British Weed Control Conference*, pp. 451–457.

CRISP, C.M. and ATKINSON, D. (1982). The tolerance of newly planted plum and apple trees to a number of graminocides, *Proceedings of the 1982 British Crop Protection Conference—Weeds*, pp. 249–254.

CURTIS, O.F. (1974). Apple response to local application of glyphosate on foliage or pruning wounds. *Proceedings of the Northeastern Weed Science Society*, **28**, 219.

DANIELL, J.W. (1974). Tolerance of Muscadine vines, pecans, peaches and christmas trees to glyphosate, *Proceedings of the 27th Annual Meeting of the Southern Weed Science Society*, p. 176.

DANIELL, J.W. (1977). Weed control in non bearing peaches, *Proceedings of the 30th Annual Meeting of the Southern Weed Science Society*, p. 180.

DANIELL, J.W. (1979). Movement of glyphosate in peach trees, *Proceedings of the 32nd Annual Meeting of the Southern Weed Science Society*, p. 161.

DANIELL, J.W. (1980). Use of modified equipment to apply glyphosate (Roundup) for weed control in tree crops, *Proceedings of the 33rd Annual Meeting of the Southern Weed Science Society*, p. 89.

DAVISON, J. (1978). Pre-planting action—key to strawberry weed control, *Grower*, **90**, 177–179.

FRANK, J.R. and KING, J.A. (1977). Evaluation of glyphosate and paraquat on strawberries, *Proceedings of the Northeastern Weed Science Society 1977*, **31**, 271.

FRANK, J.R. and KING, J.A. (1978). Directed sprays of glyphosate and paraquat for strawberry culture, *Abstract of the 1978 Meeting of the Weed Science Society of America*, pp. 5–6.

FRANK, J.R. and KING, J.A. (1979). Glyphosate and paraquat for inter-row weeding of strawberries (*Fragaria × ananassa*), *Weed Science*, **27**, 385–388.

FREEMAN, J.A. (1980a). Quack grass control in raspberries, *Acta Horticulturae*, **112**, 85–94.

FREEMAN, J.A. (1980b). Evaluation of herbicides for quack grass control in raspberries, *Research Review Agriculture Canada*, pp. 5–6.

FRYER, J.D. and MAKEPEACE, R.J. (1978). *Weed Control Handbook*, Vol. 2, Oxford; Blackwell.

GOLAN, Y. (1976). Control of *Imperata cylindrica* in young pecan and peach orchards, *Phytoparasitica*, **4**, 153.

HEIKES, P.E. (1973). Evaluation of (MON 2139) herbicide for control of several perennial noxious weeds, *Proceedings of the Western Society of Weed Science*, **26**, 35–36.

HERTZ, L.B. (1976). Effect of weed control and rootstock on growth and yield of McIntosh apples, *Proceedings of the North Central Weed Control Conference*, **31**, 107–108.

HILEN, A.G., BING, A. and GOOD, G.L. (1979). Glyphosate injury as the result of pre-plant treatment, *Proceedings of the Northeastern Weed Science Society*, **33**, 245–250.

HIMME, M. VAN, STRYCKERS, J. and BULCKE, R. (1977). Band treatments over the rows under apple and pear trees, *Rijksunlversiteit*, Gent, Belgium, pp. 102–105.

INGELOG, T. (1977). Taste and flavour changes in berries after herbicide spraying, *Var Foda*, **29**, 223–238.

JENSEN, K.I.N. (1976). Quack grass control in apple orchards, *Annual Report, 1976, Research Station, Kentville*, Nova Scotia, pp. 12–16.

JENSEN, K.I.N. (1977a). Quack grass control in apple orchards with fall applied pronamide and glyphosate, *Annual Report, 1977, Research Station, Kentville*, Nova Scotia, pp. 46–47.

JENSEN, K.I.N. (1977b). Weed control in apple orchards, *Annual Report, 1977, Research Station, Kentville*, Nova Scotia, pp. 47–48.

JENSEN, K.I.N. (1977c). Weed control in orchards with spring and summer treatments, *Annual Report, 1977, Research Station, Kentville*, Nova Scotia, pp. 48–50.

KAFADAROF, G. and ROGNON, J. (1975). The use of glyphosate to control weeds in orchards, *Compte Rendu de la 8e Conference du Columa*, pp. 189–198.

LAGERSTEDT, H.B. (1979). Tree kill trials with glyphosate and other herbicides, *Proceedings of the Western Society of Weed Science*, **32**, 100–101.

LANGE, A., KEMPEN, H., MCHENRY, W. and LEONARD, O. (1973). Roundup—a new perennial weed killer, *California Agriculture*, **27**, 6–7.

LANGER, C.A. (1973). The use of metribuzin and glyphosate in high density orchard weed control, *Proceedings of the Northeastern Weed Science Society*, **27**, 262.

LAWSON, H.M. and WISEMAN, J.S. (1974a). The control of raspberry suckers in uncultivated plantations, *Proceedings of the 12th British Weed Control Conference*, pp. 315–322.

LAWSON, H.M. and WISEMAN, J.S. (1974b). Herbicide evaluation, *Report of the Scottish Horticultural Research Institute for 1973*, pp. 24–25.

LAWSON, H.M. and WISEMAN, J.S. (1976). Experiments on the limitation of cane growth in raspberry rows, *Proceedings of the 1976 British Crop Protection Conference—Weeds*, **1**, 281–288.

LORD, W.J., MURPHY, M.L. and GREENE, D.W. (1975). Glyphosate phytotoxicity to clonal apple rootstocks and McIntosh apple trees, *Proceedings of the Northeastern Weed Science Society*, pp. 319–323.

MARRIAGE, P.B. and KHAN, S.U. (1978a). Differential varietal tolerance of peach (*Prunus persica*) seedlings to glyphosate, *Weed Science*, **26**, 374–378.

MARRIAGE, P.B. and KHAN, S.U. (1978b). Differential tolerance of peach seedlings to glyphosate, *Abstract 1977 Meeting of the Weed Science Society of America*, pp. 4–5.

MEADOR, D.B. (1975). Control of suckers on apple trees, *Transactions of the Illinois State Horticultural Society for 1974*, **108**, 114–115.

METZ, K. (1978). Research experience in strawberry growing, *Obstbau*, **3**, 46–47.

MIJATOVIC, K. (1978). Long term control of *Cynodon dactylon* (Pers), *Convolvulus arvensis*, and *Agropyron repens* (L) Beauv. in apple orchards with Roundup, *Proceedings of the Roundup Seminar*, Madrid, pp. 41–46.

MILLER, C.J. and SCHUBERT, O.E. (1974). Evaluation of glyphosate, metribuzin and pronamide for quack grass control prior to setting strawberries, *Proceedings of the West Virginia Academy of Sciences*, **46**, 61–69.

MULLINS, C.A., SWINGLE, H.D. and COFFEY, D.L. (1973). Growth and yield response of apple trees to certain herbicides, *Proceedings of the 26th Annual Meeting of the Southern Weed Science Society*, pp. 225–229.

NABER, H. (1977). Herbicide injury, *Gewasbescherming*, **8**, 1–7.

NOYE, G. (1979). Weed control in apple orchards, *Tidsskrift for Planteavl*, **82**, 587–598.

OLIVEIRA, M.M. DE (1976). A contribution to the study of the effects of glyphosate (Roundup) on pear trees, vines and orange trees, *Proceedings II Simposio Nacional de Herbologia Oeiras*, **2**, 183–193.

PUTNAM, A.R. (1976a). Fate of glyphosate in deciduous fruit trees, *Weed Science*, **24**, 425–430.

PUTNAM, A.R. (1976b). Toxicity and fate of glyphosate in deciduous fruit trees, *Proceedings of the North Central Weed Control Conference, 1975*, **30**, 186.

PUTNAM, A.R., LOVE, A.P. and PAGANO, G. (1972). Control of annual and perennial weeds in orchards with glyphosate, *Proceedings of the North Central Weed Control Conference*, **27**, 68–69.

PUTNAM, A.R., LOVE, A.P. and PAGANO, G. (1974). Response of deciduous fruit trees and several orchard weeds to glyphosate, *Abstracts, Meeting of the Weed Science Society of America*, pp. 114–117.

RATH, N. (1977). Chemical weed control, *Horticulture Research Report 1976*, An Foras Taluntus, pp. 77–80.

RATH, N. and O'CALLAGHAN, T.F. (1974). Trials on the use of glyphosate in soft fruit crops, *Proceedings of the 12th British Weed Control Conference*, pp. 613–619.

ROCHA, M.A.L., SANTOS, H.R., PELISSARI, A., ANTONANZAS, E.L., KELLER, H.A. and ELFES, H. (1980a). Efficacy of glyphosate for weed control in commercial apple orchards, *Resumos XIII Congresso Brasileiro de Herbicidas e Ervas Daninhas, Bahia*, pp. 84–85.

ROCHA, M.A.L., SANTOS, H.R., PELISSARI, A., ANTONANZAS, E.L., KELLER, H.A. and ELFES, H. (1980b). Efficacy of glyphosate for weed control in commercial pear orchards, *Resumos XIII Congresso Brasileiro de Herbicidas e Ervas Daninhas, Bahia*, p. 85.

ROCHA, M.A.L., SANTOS, H.R., PELISSARI, A., ANTONANZAS, E.L., KELLER, H.A. and ELFES, H. (1980c). Efficacy of glyphosate for weed control in commercial nectarine orchards, *Resumos XIII Congresso Brasileiro de Herbicidas e Ervas Daninhas, Bahia*, p. 86.

ROCHA, M.A.L., SANTOS, H.R., PELISSARI, A., ANTONANZAS, E.L., KELLER, H.A. and ELFES, H. (1980d). Efficacy of glyphosate for weed control in commercial plum orchards, *Resumos XIII Congresso Brasileiro de Herbicidas e Ervas Daninhas, Bahia*, pp. 86–87.

ROM, R.C. (1975). Field evaluation of herbicides in tree fruits 1974, *Mimeograph Agricultural Experiment Station, University of Arkansas*, **233**, 22pp.

ROM, R.C., ARRINGTON, G. and BROWN, S. (1973). Field evaluation of herbicides in tree fruits, *Mimeograph Agricultural Experiment Station, University of Arkansas*, **225**, 29pp.

ROM, R.C., ARRINGTON, E.H. and BROWN, S.A. (1977). Glyphosate use in non-bearing apple orchards, *Arkansas Farm Research*, **26**, 13.

ROM, R.C., BROWN, S.A. and ARRINGTON, E.H. (1976). Some glyphosate effects on apple and peach trees, *Proceedings of the 29th Annual Meeting of the Southern Weed Science Society*, p. 190.

ROM, R.C., BROWN, S.A. and MARKHAM, J.D. (1974). Glyphosate toxicity to apple trees, *Hortscience*, **9**, 594–595.

ROM, R.C. and FREAR, C. (1979). Field evaluation of herbicides in tree fruits, 1978, *Mimeograph Agricultural Experiment Station, University of Arkansas*, **270**, 17pp.

ROM, R.C. and TALBERT, R.E. (1973). Field evaluation of herbicides in fruit and nut crops, *Mimeograph Agricultural Experiment Station, University of Arkansas*, **212**, 30pp.

RUPP, L.A. and ANDERSON, J.L. (1980a). Effect of herbicides on growth of non-bearing apple and tart cherry trees, *Hortscience*, **15**, 391.

RUPP, L.A. and ANDERSON, J.L. (1980b). Annual weed control in young orchards with glyphosate, dinoseb and paraquat, *Proceedings of the Western Society of Weed Science*, **33**, 59–67.

SARIC, T. and LUCIC, P. (1978). The results of six year experiments with herbicides in plum orchards, *Fragmenta Herbologica Jugoslavica*, **6**, 106–115.

SCALABRELLI, G. (1978). Chemical weed control on a peach high density planting: preliminary observations, *Mededelingen Fakulteit Landbouwwetenschappen Rijksuniv Gent*, **43**, 1161–1166.

SCALABRELLI, G. (1979). Two years' results of a chemical weed control on apple high density planting, *Mededelingen Fakulteit Landbouwwetenschappen Rijksuniv Gent*, **44**, 717–724.

SEDDON, J.C. (1974). Field performance of the isopropylamine salt of glyphosate for the control of *Agropyron repens* and other weeds in top fruit orchards, *Proceedings of the 12th British Weed Control Conference*, pp. 595–602.

SELLECK, G.W., CORELL, T., BING, A. and LYNN, L.B. (1980). Treatment of tall weeds in horticultural crops with glyphosate using wiper and wick applicators, *Proceedings of the Northeastern Weed Science Society*, **34**, 412–414.

SMITH, E.M. and TREASTER, S.A. (1978). Phytotoxicity of glyphosate on landscape plants, *Research Circular, Ohio Agricultural Research and Development Centre*, **236**, 53–54.

SONMEZ, S. and KARASU, H.H. (1978). Weed control in orchards using simtal, diutral and Roundup, *Plant Protection Research Annual Report*, Zirai Mucadele Araskirma Yilligi, pp. 169–170.

STAALDUINE, D. VAN. (1979). Sucker control in orchards, *Mededelingen Fakulteit Landbouwwetenschappen Rijksuniv*, Gent, **44**, 675–686.

STINCHCOMBE, G.R. and STOTT, K.G. (1978a). Glyphosate toxicity to *Malus* pollinators, *Report of the Long Ashton Research Station for 1977*, p. 23.

STINCHCOMBE, G.R. and STOTT, K.G. (1978b). Tolerance of *Malus* cv Hillieri and *Malus* × *purpurea* cv Aldenhamensis pollinators to glyphosate applied in April or October, *Proceedings of the 1978 British Crop Protection Conference—Weeds*, pp. 201–208.

STINCHCOMBE, G.R. and STOTT, K.G. (1980). The effect of autumn applications of glyphosate on fruit tree sucker control and on parent tree damage, *Proceedings of the 1980 British Crop Protection Conference—Weeds*, pp. 303–309.

STOTT, K.G., HARPER, C.W., CLAY, D.V., RATH, N., UPRICHARD, S.D. and ABERNETHY, W. (1974). The response of blackcurrants, gooseberries and apples to overall or directed applications of glyphosate made between October and March, *Proceedings of the 12th British Weed Control Conference*, pp. 603–611.

STOTT, K.G., HARPER, C.W., JEFFERIES, C.J. and BELCHER, A. (1975). Glyphosate, *Report of the Long Ashton Research Station for 1974*, pp. 30–31.

TOTH, J. and MORRISON, G. (1977). Glyphosate drift damages fruit trees, *Agricultural Gazette of New South Wales*, **88**, 44–45.

WELLER, S.C. and SKROCH, W.A. (1980). Glyphosate applications to peach leaves at various times and rates and their effects on subsequent tree growth, *Proceedings of the 33rd Annual Meeting of the Southern Weed Science Society*, p. 88.

WERTHEIM, S.J., STAALDUINE, D. VAN and GROENEVELD, R.M.W. (1977). Research on the control of root suckers, *Fruitteelt*, **67**, 184–185.

WURGLER, W. and NEURY, G. (1975). Transport of glyphosate in vines, raspberry plants and bindweed with some morphological effects, *Compte Rendu de la 8e Conference du Columa*, pp. 841–851.

YOUNG, R.S. (1979). Bramble control in apple orchards with glyphosate, *Proceedings of the Northeastern Weed Science Society*, **33**, 143–144.

Chapter 20

Clearance of glyphosate for use on minor crops in the USA

M.E. Burt, G.M. Markle and R.H. Kupelian
Rutgers University, New Brunswick, New Jersey, USA

Introduction

The Interregional Research Project No. 4 (IR-4 Project), which is described in this chapter, is a national programme for the clearance of pesticides for use on minor or speciality crops and is a cooperative research effort of the State Agricultural Experiment Stations, the US Department of Agriculture (USDA), the US Environmental Protection Agency (EPA), the Food and Drug Administration (FDA), and pesticide manufacturers or registrants. The programme was initiated in 1963, expanded to include pesticide clearances for ornamental uses in 1977 and is, at the present time, being expanded to provide a means of clearance for veterinary drugs for use on both minor and major animal species and biorational pest control agents; for example, viruses, bacteria and other unicellular organisms and naturally occurring chemicals.

Organization of the IR-4 Project

The personnel involved in the IR-4 Project are located in every state. The IR-4 Project is coordinated on a national basis from IR-4 Headquarters located at the New Jersey Agricultural Experiment Station, Rutgers University. A Regional Co-ordinator organizes research activities in each of the four USDA regions and the offices of the Northcentral, Northeastern, Southern and Western Regional Coordinators are located at Michigan State University, Cornell University in New York, the University of Florida and the University of California at Davis, respectively. There are 54 IR-4 State Liaison Representatives, one for each of the states and US Territories, including the District of Columbia, Guam, Puerto Rico and the Virgin Islands. The IR-4 Liaison Representatives are scientists appointed by the Directors of their respective State Agricultural Experiment Stations to define pest control technology needs of farmers, growers and home owners in their states, with respect to the production of food, fibre, feed, ornamental plants, nursery stock and forestry plantings. The IR-4 Regional Co-ordinators and State Liaison Representatives network is joined by four USDA–Agricultural Research Service (USDA–ARS) scientists per region and a member of the USDA–ARS National Program Staff coordinates the organization of the USDA research programme.

The recognized definition of minor pesticide uses are those uses that have a market potential that is not sufficient to justify economically the pesticide manufacturer or registrant devoting time and financial resources to the development of data needed to support tolerance establishments and product registrations. When a minor use pesticide clearance request is received from grower or pesticide user groups, by way of the State Liaison Representative and the Regional Co-ordinator, IR-4 Headquarters reviews the use and safety of the pesticide. After a favourable review, IR-4 Headquarters contacts the pesticide manufacturer or registrant in order to confirm that the companies are willing to register the new use if the IR-4 Project conducts the field research and chemical residue analyses needed to obtain the necessary pesticide tolerance.

Once the manufacturer agrees to register the new use, the IR-4 Project develops a specific research outline for the necessary field studies and plans for residue analyses. The Regional Co-ordinator or the USDA–ARS counterpart coordinates completion of the field research projects and the residue samples from these projects are analysed for pesticide residues by one of the four Regional IR-4 Laboratories or one of the associated USDA laboratories. The IR-4 Regional Laboratories are located in the same universities as the Regional Co-ordinators and the USDA laboratories, that are involved in the analyses of IR-4 residue samples, are located in Beltsville, Maryland; Tifton, Georgia; and Yakima, Washington. In addition to the Regional Laboratories, several other state agricultural experiment station laboratories are designated as 'satellites' and, as such, are also involved in pesticide residue analyses of samples from IR-4 field research projects.

Standardized reports of the completed field studies and pesticide residue determinations are forwarded to IR-4 Headquarters. These data are organized, reviewed, analysed and written into pesticide tolerance petitions. After a thorough review of the petition and accompanying field research and residue data by the manufacturer or registrant, the petition is reviewed by the EPA. The EPA will establish the proposed tolerance for residues of the pesticide in or on the particular crop after reviewing the residue data obtained by the IR-4 Project and other data, such as toxicology data, provided by the manufacturer or registrant in support of tolerances and registrations. Once EPA establishes a tolerance for pesticide residues, the use of the pesticide in question can be registered.

The clearance of glyphosate

A specific example of the involvement of the IR-4 Project in the clearance of pesticides for use on minor crops can be demonstrated by reviewing the research projects with the herbicide glyphosate, N-(phosphonomethyl)glycine, as the isopropylamine salt, in the commercial formulation Roundup.

Completed projects

CRANBERRIES

The first glyphosate tolerance established by the EPA, based upon a petition written by the IR-4 Project, was for the clearance of its use for weed control in cranberries (*Vaccinium macrocarpon*). Several years of research work demonstrated that wiper applications of glyphosate directly on the weeds infesting cranberry bogs was the most practical application method for this crop (Welker and Darlington, 1980). Requests for this clearance from the cranberry-growing regions were received by IR-4 and field research was initiated in Massachusetts, New Jersey, Washington and Wisconsin by State Agricultural Experiment Station and USDA personnel. Weeds in the cranberry bogs were wiped with 6, 10, 20 or 25% solutions of Roundup in either July or September. Glyphosate applications did not cause any crop injury or decrease in yield.

Samples of mature cranberries from these research projects were collected in September and analysed for residues of glyphosate and its metabolite, aminomethylphosphonic acid, at the University of Massachusetts and the IR-4 Regional Laboratory at the University of Florida. The analytical method followed was provided by Monsanto Agricultural Products Company. It should be noted that the EPA regulates the parent compound, glyphosate, and its metabolite, aminomethylphosphonic acid, and all glyphosate tolerances are expressed as combined residues of glyphosate and aminomethylphosphonic acid. For this reason, all samples from glyphosate research projects are analysed for both glyphosate and aminomethylphosphonic acid (see also Chapter 17). The limit of detection for both compounds ranges from 0.01 to 0.05 p.p.m.

Results of the cranberry field and residue studies were used as the basis for writing a tolerance petition. After favourable reviews of the petition by the manufacturer and EPA, a 0.2 p.p.m. tolerance for the combined residues of glyphosate and aminomethylphosphonic acid was established in May 1981 (Johnson and Stubbs, 1981a). The clearance of glyphosate for use in cranberry production is valuable in that it has been estimated, with the use of wiper application methods, that the increase in production is worth $2400 per hectare (W.V. Welker, personal communication; see also Chapter 16). Based upon the cranberry acreage in the major growing regions (Anon., 1980), the use of glyphosate translates into approximately $23 million additional profit to the cranberry growers and financial savings for the consumer.

PAPAYA AND GUAVA

Directed spray applications of glyphosate were demonstrated to be efficacious and useful in controlling several weed species, for example, *Eleusine indica, Portulaca oleracea, Paspalum* spp. and *Erechtites heiracifolia,* which commonly infest Hawaiian papaya (*Carica papaya*) plantations (Nishimoto and Hibbard, 1979). Based on the herbicide's proven effectiveness, requests for the clearance of glyphosate for use in controlling weeds on papaya and guava (*Psidium guajava*) plantation floors were received from Hawaii.

Field studies to obtain fruit samples for residue analyses were initiated with both crops at the University of Hawaii. Glyphosate was applied as a directed spray to papaya plantation floors at the rates of 0.12 kg a.i. ha^{-1}, 2.4 kg a.i. ha^{-1} and 8 kg a.i. ha^{-1}. Plantations in two different locations were involved in the papaya study. In one plantation, glyphosate was applied on 16 February, 23 June and 19 October; in the other, glyphosate was applied on 3 May, 8 August and 16 December. Fruit were sampled for residue analyses at 1 and 14 days after the last glyphosate applications.

The application rates investigated in the guava studies were 2.4 kg a.i. ha^{-1} and 9.6 kg a.i. ha^{-1}. Plantations in two locations were also involved in the guava study. The first plantation received glyphosate applications on 4 January, 18 May and 29

August; the second plantation received glyphosate applications on 25 August, 1977, 27 January and 31 August. Fruit were sampled for residue analyses 1 and 14 days after the last glyphosate application. It must be emphasized that, in order to prevent plant injury, glyphosate must be applied as a directed spray to plantation floors and contact with leaves, fruit and immature bark must be avoided.

The fruit samples from the papaya and guava studies were analysed for residues of glyphosate and aminomethylphosphonic acid at the University of Hawaii and the final reports for the field and residues studies were used as a basis for writing a tolerance petition. After favourable review by the manufacturer and EPA, a 0.2 p.p.m. tolerance for combined residues of glyphosate and aminomethylphosphonic acid in or on papaya and guava was established in September 1981 (Johnson and Stubbs, 1981b). Glyphosate is now registered for use in papaya and guava production.

MANGO

Requests were received from Florida and Puerto Rico for the use of glyphosate in mango (*Mangifera indica*) plantations. The tolerance petition was submitted, without mango residue data, to the EPA with the resulting 0.2 p.p.m. tolerance for combined residues of glyphosate and aminomethylphosphonic acid being established in November 1981 (Johnson and Stubbs, 1981c). Since the tolerance petitions for papaya and guava were being reviewed by the EPA and glyphosate tolerances were established for several other tree crops (Anon., 1981), it was decided that the available residue data were adequate to extrapolate from the established and pending tree crop tolerances to include mangos.

The completed glyphosate research projects described above resulted in the establishment of 0.2 p.p.m. tolerance levels. Although this particular tolerance level was fixed, it must be emphasized that residues of glyphosate and aminomethylphosphonic acid were not detected in any of the crop samples analysed. Residue data are available from many of the glyphosate research projects in progress. These are described below. As with the completed research projects, residues of glyphosate and aminomethylphosphonic acid have not been detected in samples from glyphosate-treated crops.

Projects in progress

The IR-4 Project has many other glyphosate research projects in various stages. The characteristics and potential for pesticide residues in the crops involved in these projects and the ones mentioned before have been reviewed previously (Magness, Markle and Compton, 1971). After the analysis of available residue samples the project on the cucurbit commodity group, which includes cantaloupe (*Cucumis melo*), cucumber (*Cucumis sativus*), pumpkin (*Cucurbita pepo*), squash (*Cucurbita pepo, C. moschata* Duch.) and watermelon (*Citrullus lanatus*), will be complete. Several other glyphosate projects will be completed in 1982; for example, acerola cherry (*Malpighia glabra*); small fruit, which includes blackberries (*Rubus* spp.), blueberries (*Vaccinium corymbosum*), raspberries (*Rubus* spp.) and strawberries (*Fragaria* × *ananassa*); pineapple (*Ananas comosus*); and taniers (*Xanthosoma* spp.).

Future projects

Additionally, 1982 field research projects are scheduled for onions (*Allium cepa*), parsnips (*Pastinaca sativa*), rhubarb (*Rheum* spp.) and yams (*Dioscorea* spp.). The purpose of the projects with onions, parsnips, rhubarb and yams is to obtain crop safety data; residue analyses will not be required, since tolerances for other commodities within the respective commodity groups have been established.

Conclusions

The IR-4 Project has been very successful in obtaining clearances for the safe use of pesticides on minor crops. The continued cooperation IR-4 receives from the State Agricultural Experiment Stations, USDA, EPA, the pesticide industry, farmers and growers and pesticide user groups assures that the needs for crop protection chemicals, such as glyphosate, in minor crops will continue to be met.

Acknowledgements

This chapter has been published as New Jersey Agricultural Experiment Station Publication No. F-27200-1-82, and was supported by state, U.S. Hatch Act, and other U.S. Department of Agriculture funds.
The authors thank Monsanto Agricultural Products Company for their support of glyphosate research projects and critical review of this manuscript.

References

ANON. (1980). *United States Department of Agriculture Agricultural Statistics*. Washington, D.C.; US Government Printing Office.

ANON. (1981). *Code of Federal Regulations Title 40: Protection of the Environment*, Section 180.364. Washington, D.C.; US Government Printing Office.

JOHNSON, E.L. and STUBBS, D. (1981a). Glyphosate; tolerances and exemptions from tolerances for pesticide chemicals in or on raw agricultural commodities, *Federal Register*, **46**, 27936–27937.

JOHNSON, E.L. and STUBBS, D. (1981b). Glyphosate; establishment of tolerances, *Federal Register*, **46**, 47223–47224.

JOHNSON, E.L. and STUBBS, D. (1981c). Glyphosate; tolerances and exemptions from tolerances for pesticide chemicals in or on raw agricultural commodities, *Federal Register*, **46**, 54546–54547.

MAGNESS, J.R., MARKLE, G.M. and COMPTON, C.C. (1971). *Food and Feed Crops of the United States; A Descriptive List Classified According to Potentials for Pesticide Residues*. New Brunswick; New Jersey Agricultural Experiment Station.

NISHIMOTO, R.K. and HIBBARD, K.L. (1979). Glyphosate for weed control in *Carica papaya*, *Proceedings of the 7th Asian Pacific Weed Science Society Conference*, **7**, 71–73.

WELKER, W.V. and DARLINGTON, T. (1980). A continuous-belt herbicide wiper, *Weed Science*, **28**, 705–708.

Chapter 21

Efficacy of glyphosate in forest plantations

K. Lund-Høie
Norwegian Plant Protection Institute, Norway

Introduction

All over the world there is an increasing need for wood for use as building material
and as fibres for the paper industry; for these purposes, conifers represent the most
attractive material.

A common silvicultural practice is to regenerate a conifer stand by planting on an
exposed area as soon as possible after the previous harvest. The main objective is to
get the conifers established as soon as possible. If the growth of the plants is stunted
by for example unwanted vegetation, time and therefore potential production is
lost. Consequently, intensive vegetation management is a very important part of
this silvicultural system.

Of the different alternatives for vegetation management, progressively more
attention has been focused on chemical methods because, compared with
non-chemical methods, herbicides are more efficient, economic and require less
labour.

The phenoxyacetic acids, 2,4-D and 2,4,5-T, served this purpose for more than
30 years, until 2,4,5-T was banned in several countries in the early 1970s. At this
time, glyphosate appeared as an alternative. Biological experiments carried out
since 1971, in both Europe and the USA, suggested glyphosate as a herbicide with
great potential in forestry and with herbicidal activity on both monocots and dicots.
An advantage with glyphosate is its selectivity in several coniferous species.

This chapter reviews current knowledge and the potential for glyphosate use in
forest plantations.

The name glyphosate in this chapter refers to the isopropylamine salt of
N-(phosphonomethyl)glycine used as the commercial formulation Roundup.

The behaviour of glyphosate in forest species

Absorption

In monocots, e.g. *Agropyron repens*, the uptake of glyphosate occurs relatively
rapidly (Sprankle, Meggitt and Penner, 1975). In the woody species, which
predominate in forest plantations, absorption is generally slow. Lund-Høie (1979a)

328

found an absorption period of almost 2 weeks for ash (*Fraxinus excelsior*) and, for Norway spruce (*Picea abies*), about one-half of this (Lund-Høie, 1976). The amount of glyphosate absorbed by woody species (Lund-Høie, 1976; 1979a) seems independent of the thickness of the leaf cuticle. Leaves of ash, for example, which have a thick cuticle, absorbed more glyphosate than those of birch (*Betula verrucosa*) with a thin cuticle (Lund-Høie, 1979a). Compared to deciduous species, Norway spruce absorbs limited quantities of glyphosate. Consequently, restricted needle penetration is probably an important basis for the high tolerance to glyphosate shown by most conifers (Lund-Høie, 1980).

Translocation

Systemic, foliage-applied herbicides are translocated with assimilates according to the 'source' to 'sink' principle (Ashton and Crafts, 1982). This also applies to glyphosate. In woody species including conifers, however, the distribution pattern of glyphosate differs from the above in one important way. Along the path of translocation in the sieve tubes, part of the translocated herbicide will accumulate in either stem or root tissue with meristematic activity. Some glyphosate will also move from the phloem to the xylem and move upwards with the transpiration stream accumulating mainly in the youngest aerial shoots in transpiring leaves or needles. From these leaves or needles, glyphosate will be retranslocated with time, accumulating in the meristems of the youngest shoots (Lund-Høie, 1976; 1979a; 1983a). A consequence of this distribution pattern is that, in conifers, the toxic symptoms due to glyphosate applications always show first in the top shoots (see also Appendix I).

Metabolism

Residual effects of glyphosate in woody species are relatively restricted. As reported by Lund-Høie, (1976; 1979a), the breakdown of glyphosate with the evolution of carbon dioxide, derived from the carbon in the methyl group of the glyphosate molecule, has been recorded in several woody species, including Norway spruce. This is probably the main reason why glyphosate damage in conifers is usually restricted to top shoots, produced in the year of application.

Application techniques

The use of glyphosate in forest situations can conflict with the interests of the general public. In modern silvicultural systems increasing weight has to be given to forestry both as an ecosystem where wildlife is important and as a source of public recreation. Methods of glyphosate use must be adapted so as to balance all the different interests within the forest system.

Glyphosate can be used either non-selectively for preplanting site preparation or selectively to reduce the impact of competing ground vegetation or brushwood species which can adversely affect the coniferous species.

To control brushwood, the most economic and widely used method of glyphosate application is via the foliage. For larger trees, glyphosate can be injected into the stem or applied to a cut stump surface. This will prevent the regrowth of suckers from the cut stumps or the roots (*Figure 21.1*).

Figure 21.1. Suckers from a stump of birch (*Betula verrucosa*).
The sprouting can be effectively prevented by cut surface
treatment with glyphosate

Foliage application

The effect of a foliage application is dependent both on the rate of glyphosate per
unit area and on parameters such as temperature, precipitation and light. An
understanding of all these factors is necessary to maximize the effect of foliage
application.

Influence of environmental factors

Temperature and light have a large effect on both efficiency and the selective
properties of glyphosate (Lund-Høie, 1979a; 1983a; 1983b).

Because of the slow uptake of glyphosate in woody species, the tolerance of
Norway spruce appears highly dependent on temperature, both at the time of
application and during the 3–4 days after application. High temperatures seem to
increase the phytotoxic effect of glyphosate, especially during periods of rapid
shoot elongation. An experiment with ^{14}C-glyphosate revealed that the tolerance
of Scots pine (*Pinus sylvestris*) to glyphosate was decreased by a reduced light
intensity before and at the time of application (Lund-Høie, 1983a).

In wet periods, the 'wash-off' of glyphosate from the leaves will reduce the
efficiency of the compound; because of relatively slow uptake, woody species are
more vulnerable in this respect than grasses or herbaceous species. The type of
spraying equipment used will also influence the precipitation 'resistance'. Mist
blowers, which deposit compound on both sides of the leaves, require a shorter
period of fine weather following application than do boom sprayers.

Spray equipment

In the control of perennial weeds, including woody species, roots represent the main target. However, in woody species glyphosate will be translocated in both the phloem and xylem. The quantity translocated in the xylem will depend on the application rate and the distance from the receptor area, the foliage where the spray was deposited, to the strongest sink (in most cases the roots). The longer this distance, the more glyphosate will be concentrated in the youngest aerial shoots, while the toxic effect on the roots will be diminished. Effective control of brushwood will therefore be dependent not only on its height, but also on the application technique (Lund-Høie, 1980). For example, when spraying with an aircraft like a helicopter, most of the spray liquid will be deposited on the upper half of the crown, with only a small volume able to penetrate to the lower part of the crown.

Ground-based equipment results in the opposite effect, with most of the spray liquid deposited on the lower regions of the crown. This gives a shorter path to the roots and consequently greater effectiveness. To compensate for the unfavourable distribution of the spray liquid throughout dense crowns, when using aircraft, about a 50% higher rate of glyphosate is required than when using ground equipment (Lund-Høie, 1980).

Aircraft application

According to Gratkowski (1974), helicopters are the most expensive type of aircraft to operate. They have, however, proved far more useful and adaptable than fixed-wing aircraft for spraying forest plantations (*Figure 21.2*). This seems to be a common experience in many countries (Bärring, 1979a; Etholén, 1981; Nordby, 1982). To ensure maximum deposition of glyphosate on the target areas, technical factors such as boom height, nozzle type and position, liquid pressure, operating speed and flight height have to be monitored. Climatic factors, e.g. wind velocity and temperature, are also key factors, as are the distance that the droplets must fall and their size (Stewart and Gratkowski, 1976; Akesson and Yates, 1979; Nordby, 1982).

Stricter regulations with respect to application and better training of the applicators mean that drift is no longer considered to be a serious problem. In an experiment conducted in Norway, using helicopters, it was found that with a wind velocity of 5 m s^{-1}, less than 1% of the spray volume drifted beyond 100 m from a swath when applied 4 m above soil level. At a wind velocity of about 2 m s^{-1}, the corresponding drift was about 0.1% (Nordby and Lund-Høie, 1976). In Norway, the addition of a thickening agent to the spray liquid is not considered necessary.

Aircraft equipment

Several types of helicopter have been used to make the applications. In Norway, for example, a Bell 206 has been used with great success since 1979. The loading capacity of this helicopter is 350–400 l, and the spray equipment used is of the Simplex 2700 type with a spray boom of 12.5 m equipped with Tee Jet fan nozzles No. 6508. These are directed backwards at an angle of 45°. This helicopter operates at a speed of about 64 km h^{-1} and a flying height of about 5 m above the brushwood

Figure 21.2. Control of brushwood from helicopter

canopy. At a spraying pressure of about 2 bars, the spray volume is about 60 l ha^{-1}. At the above spraying height the boom produces a swath of about 15 m (Lund-Høie, 1980). When using aircraft, the efficiency of glyphosate seems highly dependent on air speed; Bärring (1979b) considers the lowest possible speed to be best (see also Chapter 16).

Ground equipment

In forestry, low-volume applicators, with a spray volume of 90–200 l ha^{-1}, such as portable-knapsack mist blowers and tractor-mounted mist blowers are commonly used (Brown, 1975) (*Figure 21.3*). Both of the above mist blowers produce droplets mostly in the 100–200 μm range, which gives a good coverage of the foliage. A high initial droplet velocity even enables penetration of dense foliage.

Portable-knapsack mist blowers can blow the spray up to about 5 m in a horizontal direction and up to 2–3 m vertically (Brown, 1975). The capacity of this equipment is about 1–2 ha per 8-hour day. In Norway, knapsack mist blowers have been used for more than 30 years, but are now progressively being replaced by tractor-mounted mist blowers. Those used in Norway (Hardi NK-600 Combi, manufactured by Hartvig Jensen & Co. A/S, Denmark) have a spray volume of about 200 l ha^{-1} and allow the operator to achieve relatively uniform coverage of foliage over a distance of about 20 m. Ultra low-volume sprayers, with a spray volume of 2–10 l ha^{-1}, have been tested in the UK with encouraging results (Rogers, 1975).

Figure 21.3. Control of mixed vegetation from tractor-mounted mist blower

Rates of application

The dosage of glyphosate needed to control either the worst weeds, or brushwood, will vary with the spray equipment used, the training of the spraying operators, the density and height of the vegetation and the climatic conditions prevailing. Consequently, the rate required varies, depending on the conditions at particular locations.

Table 21.1 shows the rates used in Norway for low-volume applications under varying temperature conditions (Lund-Høie, 1982). The dosages concern release applications. The reason for reducing dosages under high temperatures before 10

TABLE 21.1   Dosages of glyphosate (kg a.i. ha⁻¹) for different types of spraying equipment

Temperature conditions	*Knapsack mist blower*		*Tractor-mounted mist blower*		*Helicopter*	
			*Before/after 10 August**			
	Before	After	Before	After	Before	After
Normal (10–25°C at appl. and the first 24 h after appl.)	0.75	0.85	0.65	0.75	1.15	1.15
Temp. at appl. lower than 10–12°C and expected temp. the first 24 h after appl. below 15°C	+10%	+10%	+10%	+10%	+10%	+10%
Temp. at appl. higher than 24–25°C and expected hot weather the first 24 h after appl.	−10%		−10%		−10%	

*Northern Hemisphere date.

August (Northern Hemisphere) is to ensure sufficient tolerance to glyphosate by the conifers Norway spruce and Scots pine. For site preparation, the normal dosages plus 10% is recommended. The spray volumes for each of the types of equipment mentioned in *Table 21.1* has to be adjusted according to the height of the brushwood; from medium values of 120, 230 and 260 l ha^{-1} for knapsack mist blowers, tractor-mounted mist blowers and helicopters, respectively, up to a volume 50% above the medium level, for brushwood of about 5 m height.

The dosages given in *Table 21.1* for helicopter application are approximately those used in other countries (Lanz, 1977; Newton, 1977; Bärring, 1979b).

SUSCEPTIBILITY OF WOODY/WEED SPECIES

Table 21.2 contains data derived from a number of different countries (Lund-Høie, 1975; Rubow, 1976; 1978; Lanz, 1977; McCavish, 1977; Newton, 1977; Bärring, 1978; Minko, 1978). The sensitivity of the species listed in *Table 21.2* assumes optimum conditions and times of applications.

TABLE 21.2   Susceptibility of some important forest species and weeds to glyphosate at 1–1.5 kg a.i. ha^{-1}

Species	Susceptible	Moderately susceptible	Tolerant
Brushwood	*Betula* spp. *Corylus avellana* *Fagus silvatica* *Populus tremula* *Prunus padus* *Prunus serotina* *Sambucus* spp. *Sorbus aucuparia*	*Acer platanoides* *Alnus* spp. *Calluna vulgaris* *Fraxinus excelsior* *Quercus* spp. *Salix* spp.	*Ulmus glabra*
Broad-leaf weeds	*Chamaenerion angustifolium* *Filipendula ulmaria* *Rubus idaeus*	*Aconitum septentrionale* *Cirsium arvense* *Vaccinium myrtillus*	*Anemone hepatica* *Anemone nemorosa* *Equisetum* spp. *Rubus fruticosus* *Urtica dioica* *Vaccinium vitis-idaea*
Grasses	*Agropyron repens* *Agrostis gigantea* *Agrostis stolonifera* *Agrostis tenuis* *Arrhenatherum elatius* *Calamagrostis* spp. *Dactylis glomerata* *Deschampsia flexuosa* *Holcus lanatus* *Holcus mollis* *Juncus* spp. *Molinia caerulea*	*Carex* spp. *Deschampsia caespitosa* *Phragmites communis*	*Alopecurus pratensis* *Festuca pratensis* *Festuca rubra*
Ferns	*Athyrium* spp. *Dryopteris* spp. *Matteuccia struthiopteris* *Pteridium aquilinum*		*Polypodium vulgare*
Conifers	*Larix* spp. *Picea pungens* *Pinus montana* *Pinus strobus*	*Abies procera* *Pinus contorta* *Pinus radiata* *Tsuga* spp.	*Abies nordmanniana* *Picea abies* *Picea sitchensis* *Pinus sylvestris* *Pseudotsuga* spp.

Glyphosate is effective against a broad spectrum of problem forest weeds. The tolerance of desirable species, e.g. *Vaccinium* spp., and *Anemone* spp., is important from an environmental point of view. The tolerance to glyphosate of the most commercially important conifers—Norway spruce, Sitka spruce (*Picea sitchensis*), Scots pine and fir (*Pseudotsuga* spp.)—is adequate for standard application.

Time of application

For the purpose of site preparation, glyphosate can be applied at any time in the period from when the leaves are fully developed until autumn colours can be seen in foliage (Lund-Høie, 1975; Bärring, 1979b). Probably as a result of better root growth, which causes glyphosate to be more readily translocated to the roots, brushwood is better controlled by autumn application than by application in early summer. Flowering species seem less susceptible to glyphosate at flowering than either before or after this stage (Lund-Høie, 1975). The tolerance of conifers is generally higher during the period when top shoot growth has stopped and new shoots are matured, rather than when shoots are actively elongating.

To ensure safe application, glyphosate should not be applied before the coniferous plants have reached their safe growth stage. In the period between the end of shoot growth and the stage when the new shoots have matured, normal dosages have to be adjusted according to the temperature. In southern Norway, between 58° and 62° latitude and below about 300 m above sea level, selective applications from knapsack mist blowers are recommended from the middle of July. Applications from tractor-mounted mist blowers and helicopters, independent of latitude, are not recommended before 1 August. Bärring (1979a) suggests 1 August as an acceptable starting date for helicopter applications in northern Sweden. In southern Sweden helicopter applications should be restricted until after 10 August.

Effect on the growth of the conifers

Plants sensitive to glyphosate are completely killed so that, as a result, the soil is supplied with huge quantities of organic matter. The breakdown of this organic matter releases nitrogen and other macro- and micro-elements which are necessary for growth. A consequence is a tremendous increase in the amount of available amonium nitrogen in the soil, especially in the second year after glyphosate application (Lund-Høie, 1979b; 1980). Some of the nitrogen is probably washed out of the soil. Analyses suggest, however, that this is less than expected, probably because of the low pH in most forest soils and the fact that glyphosate applications generally cause lowering of pH. Nitrification will thus be limited and so restrict the loss of nitrogen. Lund-Høie (1979b; 1980) found raised nitrogen concentration in spruce needles after a glyphosate application. This increase in nitrogen is the basis for increased growth. Field experiments have demonstrated increases, of 20–30% after 2 years and up to 50% after 5 years, of the top shoot growth (see Chapter 11).

Ecological consequences

Pollution of water sources and wild berries, as a consequence of glyphosate applications, does not seem to be a serious problem (Lund-Høie, 1979b; Siltanen *et al.*, 1981). The direct spraying of a lake, from a helicopter, with glyphosate at 0.75

kg a.i. ha^{-1} did not result in glyphosate residues, in the surface water immediately after the application, of more than 0.7 mg kg^{-1} (Lund-Høie, 1979b). No traces of glyphosate were detected 1 h after application.

Glyphosate residues in wild berries, of *Vaccinium* spp. and raspberry (*Rubus idaeus*), picked in areas sprayed with 1–1.5 kg ha^{-1} glyphosate, were less than 1 mg kg^{-1}, even in berries picked immediately after an application. However, the quality of the berries seems to be lowered (Ingelög *et al.*, 1977).

Tree injection/hatching

Glyphosate is also an effective herbicide when injected into trees (*Figure 21.4*). This method, however, is less important than foliage applications, but has been discussed by Newton (1977), Bärring (1978) and Lund-Høie (1982).

A programme based on 1 ml of 18% glyphosate in water per injection and an injection frequency of 1 for each 5 cm of the stem diameter, has given excellent results on most deciduous trees, especially in the late summer. Injections in spring or early summer, except for the period with heavy sap flow, can also give acceptable results.

Stump treatment

Glyphosate, at a concentration of 8–10% in water, applied to the stump surface after the cutting of brushwood, will eliminate or reduce the sprouting of most deciduous trees (Bärring, 1978; Christensen, 1981; 1982; Etholén, 1981; Kiærbølling, 1981; Lund-Høie, 1982). Both experimental and practical use have shown that the inhibiting effect of glyphosate is more pronounced on stump-sprouting species, like ash (*Fraxinus excelsior*), or birch (*Betula* spp.), than on root sprouting species like aspen (*Populus* spp.).

Figure 21.4. Stem injection/hatching

With stem injections, stump treatments can be used throughout the year, except during periods of heavy sap flow. In an attempt to rationalize the cutting/chemical operation, several models of motorized saws equipped to do the chemical treatment, together with the cutting, have been tested (Christensen, 1981; Kiærbølling, 1981). However, a number of problems remain to be solved before such combined equipment can be generally accepted.

Conclusions

Experimental and practical use since 1971 have shown glyphosate to be a very useful tool in weed/brushwood management in forest situations for both site preparation and to release the conifers from the adverse effect of brushwood competition.

To optimize the efficacy of glyphosate, knowledge about the physiological properties of the compound, its behaviour in plants regarding uptake and translocation, and how these processes are affected by environmental factors, is essential.

Professional applicators are vital and continuous training is a key factor in this respect. Increased general public concern about the use of pesticides, including that of glyphosate in forestry, makes regulations with respect to application essential. Such regulations should not only protect the environment from misapplication, but also force the applicators to maintain high technical and professional standards.

References

AKESSON, N.B. and YATES, W.E. (1979). Improving the efficiency of aircraft application, *Proceedings of the Symposium, IX International Congress of Plant Protection*, pp. 199–204.
ASHTON, F.M. and CRAFTS, A.S. (1982). *Mode of Action of Herbicides*. New York; Wiley.
BÄRRING, U. (1978). Results of trials in forestry, *19th Swedish Weed Conference*, pp. J1–J10.
BÄRRING, U. (1979a). Experiences with glyphosate in aircraft experiments (in Swedish), *Sveriges Skogsvårdsförbunds Tidsskrift*, **2**, 44–53.
BÄRRING, U. (1979b). Results of trials in forestry. Trials into aerial application of glyphosate and trichlopyr amine, *20th Swedish Weed Conference*, pp. 82–93.
BÄRRING, U. (1980). Results of trials in forestry, *21st Swedish Weed Conference*, pp. 58–66.
BÄRRING, U. (1981). Results of trials in forestry, *22nd Swedish Weed Conference*, pp. 79–80.
BIGGIN, P. (1980). Weed control in conifer transplant lines, *Proceedings of Weed Control in Forestry Conference*, pp. 175–181.
BROWN, R.M. (1975). Chemical control of weeds in the forest, *Forestry Commission Booklet*, no. 40.
CHAPPEL, W.E., COARTNEY, J.S., HIPKINS, P.L. and LIRNK, M.L. (1979). Aerial applications of glyphosate for the control of brush in rights-of-way, *Proceedings of the Southern Weed Science Society*, **32**, 242–244.
CHRISTENSEN, P. (1981). Testing of motorized saw for cutting equipped with Enso-spraying attachment (in Danish), Pyntegröntprosjektet. Institut for Ukrudtsbekæmpelse, Flakkebjerg, 4200 Slagelse, Denmark.
CHRISTENSEN, P. (1982). Biological effect on selected brushwood species after cutting with motorised saw equipped with Enso-spraying attachment (in Danish), Pyntegröntprosjektet. Institut for Ukrudtsbekæmpelse, Flakkebjerg, 4200 Slagelse, Denmark.
ETHOLÉN, K. (1981). Chemical control of vegetation in forestry in Finland, *22nd Swedish Weed Conference*, pp. 89–95.
GRATKOWSKI, H. (1974). Herbicidal drift control, *USDA Forest Science*, Technical Report, PNW-14.
HUSS, VON J. (1978). Testing of new herbicides for pre-planting site preparation (in German), *Der Forst-und Holzwirt*, **10**, 215–218.
INGELÖG, T., ERNE, K., PAULSSON, A.-M., JONASSON, H. and HOLMGREN, A. (1977). Taste and flavour changes in woodland berries after herbicide spraying (in Swedish), *Vår Föda* (6), 223–237.

KIÆRBØLLING, L. (1981). Test results regarding experiments with motorized cutting equipment with a spraying attachment of model Enso. Biological part (in Danish), Skovteknisk Institut Amalievej 20, 1875 Copenhagen, Denmark.

LAMB, D. (1975). Weed control in tropical forest plantations using glyphosate, *Pans*, **21**(2), 177–181.

LANZ, W. (1977). Experimental experiences with glyphosate in forest science (in German), *Proceedings of the EWRS Symposium on Methods of Weed Control and Their Integration*, pp. 15–23.

LANZ, W. (1978). New prospects in the management of hardwood forest (in German), *Der Forst-und Holzwirt*, **7**, 146–150.

LUND-HØIE, K. (1975). *N*-phosphonomethylglycine (glyphosate), an alternative to commercial pre- and postemergence herbicides for the control of unwanted plant species in forest plantations in Norway, *Scientific Reports of the Agricultural University of Norway*, **54**(6).

LUND-HØIE, K. (1976). The correlation between the tolerance of Norway spruce (*Picea abies*) to glyphosate (*N*-phosphonomethylglycine) and the uptake, distribution and metabolism of the herbicide in the spruce plants, *Scientific Reports of the Agricultural University of Norway*, **55**(21).

LUND-HØIE, K. (1979a). The physiological fate of glyphosate-^{14}C in *Betula verrucosa* and *Fraxinus excelsior*. The effect of ammonium sulphate and the environment on the herbicide, *Scientific Reports of the Agricultural University of Norway*, **58**(30).

LUND-HØIE, K. (1979b). Ecological consequences of forest applications with herbicides (in Norwegian), *Aktuelt fra Landruksdepartementets opplysningstjeneste*, (1), 14–29.

LUND-HØIE, K. (1980). The impact of helicopter application of glyphosate on the management of Norwegian forest plantations, *Proceedings of Weed Control in Forestry Conference*, pp. 73–81.

LUND-HØIE, K. (1982). Application methods and rating programme by using glyphosate (in Norwegian), *Norsk Skogbruk*, (9), 36–38.

LUND-HØIE, K. (1983a). The influence of different light conditions on the distribution pattern of glyphosate (*N*-(phosphonomethyl)glycine) in Scots pine (*Pinus sylvestris* L.), *Scientific Reports of the Agricultural University of Norway*, **62**(27), 1–11.

LUND-HØIE, K. (1983b). The influence of temperature on the phytotoxic effect of glyphosate on Norway spruce (*Picea abies* L.), *Crop Protection*, **2**(4), 409–416.

MCCAVISH, W.J. (1977). Forest weed control of grass using glyphosate at low volume in lowland Britain, *Information Note no. 27*, issued by The Forestry Commission Research and Development Division.

MINKO, G. (1978). Glyphosate for the control of competing vegetation in *Pinus radiata* plantations at Myrtleford, *Proceedings of the 1st Conference of the Council of the Australian Weed Science Society*, pp. 304–316.

NEWTON, M. (1977). Silvicultural applications of glyphosate, School of Forestry, Oregon State University.

NORDBY, A. (1982). Methods and spraying equipment for chemical control of brushwoods in forest plantations (in Norwegian), *Norsk Skogbruk*, (9), 10–13.

NORDBY, A. and LUND-HØIE, K. (1976). Foliage application in forest regeneration areas—herbicidal drift by helicopter application (in Norwegian), *Norsk Skogbruk*, (6/7), 6–7.

ROEDIGER, K.-J. (1978). Experiences with Roundup. Five years old experiments with pre- and postplanting applications in Norway Spruce (in German), *Der Forst-und Holzwirt*, (7), 151–155.

ROGERS, E.V. (1975). Ultra low volume herbicide spraying, *Foresty Commission Leaflet 62*.

RUBOW, T. (1976). The use of glyphosate in forestry (in Danish), *Statens planteavlsforsök Melding nr. 1306, 78. årgang*.

RUBOW, T. (1978). Experiences regarding the tolerance of conifers to herbicides (in Danish), *Ugeskrift for agronomer, hortonomer, forstkandidater og licentiater*, (10), 203–210.

RUBOW, T. (1981). Chemical control of bracken (*Pteridium aguilinum*) (in Danish), *Statens planteavlsforsök Melding nr. 1639, 83, årgang*.

SILTANEN, H., ROSENBERG, C., RAATIKAINEN, M. and RAATIKAINEN, T. (1981). Triclopyr, glyphosate and phenoxyherbicide residues in cowberries, bilberries and lichen, *Bull. Environmental Contamination and Toxicology*, **27**, 731–737.

SPRANKLE, P., MEGGITT, W.F. and PENNER, D. (1975). Absorption, action and translocation of glyphosate, *Weed Science*, **23**(3), 235–240.

STEWART, R.E. and GRATKOWSKI, H. (1976). Aerial application equipment for herbicidal drift reduction, *USDA Forest Science, General Technical Report PNW-54*.

SUTTON, R.F. (1978). Glyphosate herbicide: an assessment of forestry potential, *The Forestry Chronicle*, February, pp. 24–28.

YATES, W., AKESSON, N.B. and BAYER, D.E. (1978). Drift of glyphosate sprays applied with aerial and ground equipment, *Weed Science*, **26**(6), 597–604.

Chapter 22

Efficacy of glyphosate in nursery stock and amenity horticulture

D.W. Robinson
Agricultural Institute, Kinsealy Research Centre, Dublin, Eire

Introduction

Glyphosate is a particularly useful herbicide for nurserymen and amenity land managers. Although first marketed in the UK in 1974, glyphosate had become by 1977 the most frequently applied translocated herbicide in plant nurseries in England (Greaves, Sly and Cutler, 1979). It was accepted relatively quickly by nurserymen because of its wide weed spectrum, its toxicity to many problem perennial weeds and its high degree of selectivity when used as a carefully directed spray.

The total amount of herbicides used in ornamentals is low compared with that used in larger acreage crops such as cereals and sugar beet. As labour costs rise, however, it becomes more feasible to use repeated applications of expensive herbicides and to follow the use of soil-acting herbicides with spot applications of other chemicals. Hence, in nursery stock the total amount of herbicide used per acre can be high.

Hardy ornamentals can be grown under field conditions or they may be produced in containers to facilitate sale throughout the year. Although glyphosate is used in both types of production, its main value is in field-grown crops. Perennial weeds are more prevalent in this situation, especially weeds such as *Agropyron repens* and *Cirsium arvense* which are very susceptible to glyphosate. Perennial weeds have an opportunity to become established in field-grown stocks because the plants are sometimes left in the same position for several years. In addition, the small size of many nurseries, the intensive nature of production methods used and the rapid turnover, often hinder fallowing operations and the eradication of perennial weeds before planting the next crop. Perennial weeds are seldom a problem in container-grown plants because of the use of weed-free substrates.

Glyphosate will damage most plants if foliage is wetted by the spray (Smith and Treaster, 1978). Selectivity in most cases depends on the ability of the operative to wet the weeds while avoiding crop foliage. This can be done more easily in field-grown crops than in small, closely planted, container-grown plants.

Adoption of chemical means of weed control for woody ornamentals has been less rapid than in other sectors of agriculture. Initial reluctance on the part of nuserymen and landscape contractors is due to several factors. The range of plants grown by nurserymen is usually very extensive. One of the largest tree nurseries in

Britain grows over 3500 cultivars of 1500 species (Jones, 1980) and many species are grown to a limited extent on individual nurseries. Although the value of woody ornamentals is high, possibly £160 000–£250 000 per hectare at wholesale levels, there has been a shortage, in some areas, of labour competent to use herbicides effectively.

Weeds harm woody ornamentals in several ways and many factors must be included in assessing the value of weed control. As with other crops, weeds compete for light, moisture and nutrients. Slow crop growth due to weed competition can result in poor quality plants. Fretz (1973) reported growth losses ranging from 47 to 75% depending on weed species and weed densities. Reduction in plant size of crops that are in a nursery for one year may result in lower prices being achieved and, with longer term crops, an extra year's growth may be necessary to produce a saleable plant (Davison, 1971). Moreover, the need to remove, by hand, perennial weeds such as *A. repens* or *Convolvulus* spp. from crop roots can delay the lifting of field-grown plants. In addition, inadequate control of weeds can create a poor image, especially where the public is allowed access to nurseries to inspect growing crops.

In many countries weed control is considered to be the biggest problem in the production of woody ornamentals. In field-grown nursery stock in the UK the cost of hand work was estimated at £250 per hectare in 1972; this could be reduced to £60 by the use of herbicides (Cox, 1973). In container nurseries in Florida, the cost of hand weeding was over $9000 per hectare in 1975; herbicides could reduce this cost to $1500 (Weatherspoon, 1977).

Soil-acting herbicides, with their residual activity, can control germinating weeds for long periods. They are essential in any herbicide programme in nursery stock (Corell, 1979) and woody ornamentals (Robinson, 1980). Because of the high levels of nutrients and organic matter in nursery soils and the use of frequent irrigation, the effect of soil-acting herbicides on nurseries is sometimes less satisfactory than in agricultural situations. Carpenter (1978) attributes the increase in the population of perennial weeds in nurseries to the repeated use of soil-acting herbicides. It is therefore necessary to supplement the use of these herbicides by sequential treatment with translocated and contact herbicides. For this purpose, glyphosate is increasing rapidly in popularity (Corell, 1979).

The name glyphosate in this chapter refers to the isopropylamine salt of *N*-(phosphonomethyl)glycine used as the commercial formulation Roundup.

Weed control in nurseries and amenity areas

Glyphosate is effective against many annual grasses and broad-leaved weeds in nurseries (Fretz, 1974), but its main value as a herbicide is for the control of perennials (*Figure 22.1*). The perennating organs of these weeds often become closely intertwined with the roots of trees and shrubs. In this situation the ability of glyphosate to translocate over long distances and to kill weeds that cannot be controlled by manual or mechanical means is particularly useful.

Glyphosate was the only herbicide out of nine treatments to give control of *Cynodon dactylon* (Hathaway and Whitcomb, 1975). This is one of the worst weeds in nurseries in Oklahoma and is also a serious problem in established ground-cover plantings (Rice, 1982). There are many references to good control of *A. repens* (Ahrens, 1974a), a major perennial weed in nursery stock in Long Island (Corell,

Figure 22.1. Control of perennial weeds with directed spray of glyphosate (1.5 kg ha^{-1}) without damage to *Robinia pseuda-cacia*

1979) and many other areas. A dose of 0.8–1.7 kg ha^{-1}, applied in autumn or spring, practically eliminated this weed and 0.6 kg ha^{-1} in August followed by 0.8 kg ha^{-1} in June gave 97% control (Ahrens, 1975). Good control of *A. repens* under rose bushes (Anon., 1976a) and in landscape plantings (Bing, 1977) has also been reported.

Excellent control of *Cirsium arvense* has been achieved in junipers with autumn treatment (Dunwell, Boe and Lee, 1978) and there is evidence of effective (Carpenter, 1978) and rapid translocation in roots (Dunwell, Boe and Lee, 1978). Other perennial weeds in nursery stock against which glyphosate has proved effective are *Sorghum halepense* (Goodale *et al.*, 1975), *Rhus radicans* (Bing, 1977) and *Cyperus rotundus* (Grubben, 1974). Glyphosate at 0.6–1.1 kg ha^{-1} was more effective than asulam at 3.4–4.5 kg ha^{-1} against *Taraxacum officinale* and *Cerastium vulgatum* (Ahrens, 1974b).

Some common weeds in nurseries are not controlled by a single application of a low dose of glyphosate. *Convolvulus arvensis* required repeated application at 1.1–2.2 kg ha^{-1} (Bing, 1976) or 2.2–3.4 kg ha^{-1} for control (Bing, 1977). Two applications of glyphosate at 4.5 kg ha^{-1} gave 99% control of *C. arvensis* at the end of the first season (Carpenter and Hensley, 1974). In contrast, the closely related *Calystegia sepium* proved difficult to control, even by repeated applications of glyphosate at 2.2–3.4 kg ha^{-1} (Bing, 1977), although Kline and Selleck (1978) reported satisfactory control for a period of 12 months with doses of 3.4 and 4.5 kg ha^{-1}. In some situations the effect of glyphosate on *C. arvensis* can be enhanced by appropriate hand work before spraying–integrated weed management that can be justified in high-value crops. Bing (1975) obtained nearly perfect control of *C. arvensis* with glyphosate applied at 1.7 kg ha^{-1} directly on vines untangled from their support plants.

Artemisia vulgaris has proved to be very susceptible to glyphosate (Bing, 1976; Bing, 1977) and may be controlled at different periods of the year. July, August and September treatments resulted in complete control (Gouin, 1977b) and spring, summer and autumn treatments were also effective, without serious visible injury to ground-cover plants (Bing and Selleck, 1978).

In contrast to *A. vulgaris*, the time of application of glyphosate is important with some weeds. Better control of *Rubus* spp. on Christmas tree farms was achieved by spraying with glyphosate in July than in mid-June and best results were obtained with treatments in August and September. *Rubus*, in partial shade, was just as susceptible to glyphosate as plants in full sun (Gouin, 1977b). September applications applied to control *Rubus* spp. in Christmas tree plantations also killed other woody weeds, including *Robinia pseudacacia*, *Populus grandidentata*, *Spiraea tomentosa* and *Acer rubrum*. Rum cherry (*Prunus serotina*) and blueberry (*Vaccinium myrtilloides*) appeared to be tolerant of doses of 0.77–2.27 kg ha^{-1} (Gouin, 1979).

Variable results have been recorded with *Oxalis* spp. Only partial control was obtained in France (Bain *et al.*, 1974) and better results were achieved with black plastic left in position for 1 year. Repeated applications were more effective and gave satisfactory control under glass, but the herbicide proved toxic to glasshouse ornamentals (Anon., 1976b).

The wide weed spectrum of glyphosate makes it useful for the spot treatment of weeds that have survived overall application with a soil-acting herbicide. A high standard of weed control is required in nurseries usually throughout the season. One post-emergence herbicide, such as glyphosate, that will affect all weeds, obviates the need for more frequent applications of different herbicides and for mixtures of more specific herbicides. Spot treatment with glyphosate can be applied most conveniently in standard trees where crop foliage can be avoided easily. In this situation glyphosate has proved effective in standard *Sorbus* spp. for the control of *Convolvulus* spp. and in transplanted oak (*Quercus palustris*) for the control of *Cardaria draba* (Wallis, 1978). Spot treatment was also effective for the control of *Rumex acetosella* in nursery containers.

Because of the absence of residual activity and the generally poor competitive effect of widely spaced, field-grown nursery stock, glyphosate treatments need to be repeated or to be used in conjunction with soil-acting herbicides. Many reports emphasize the rapid recolonization of land with weeds after a single application. While glyphosate at 1.1–4.5 kg ha^{-1} severely reduced weed populations especially of grasses, treated areas were quickly invaded by other broad-leaved weeds such as *Portulaca oleracea* and *Veronica peregrina* (Haramaki and Kuhns, 1979). Two to three applications of glyphosate in nursery stock liners were needed to control weeds throughout the growing season (Frank and King, 1978), but were more effective than paraquat (Frank and King, 1979a). The superiority of glyphosate over paraquat as a post-emergence treatment was confirmed in later trials (Frank, 1980). *Artemisia vulgaris* was controlled by a November treatment but recovered by May and needed retreatment (Ahrens, 1976; Bing and Selleck, 1978; see also

TABLE 22.1 Control of *Artemisia vulgaris* with repeated applications of glyphosate (from Ahrens, 1976)

Treatment	Rates (kg a.e. ha^{-1})			Date of assessment*			
	30 Nov.	2 May	17 July	2 May	19 June	17 July	24 Sept.
None	—	—	—	0	0	0	0
Glyphosate	0.5	0	0.5	5.7	0.7	0	4.0
	0.5	0.5	0.5	5.7	7.3	4.5	7.0
	1.1	0	1.1	7.2	0.7	0	7.5
	1.1	1.1	1.1	7.2	7.3	4	8.5

*0= no control; 10 = 100% control.

Table 22.1). Applications of glyphosate in spring, summer or autumn, although effective, all required a follow-up treatment for satisfactory weed control (Bing and Selleck, 1978).

Because of its effect on established weeds, but lack of residual activity, glyphosate has been tested in sequences and in combinations with soil-acting herbicides, even though tank mixes with these herbicides may reduce glyphosate activity (Baird *et al.*, 1971). Haramaki (1977) obtained long-term, effective weed control in narrow leaf evergreens with glyphosate at 2.2 kg ha^{-1} in mixtures with simazine, diuron or hexazinone. Frank and King (1979b) reported that alachlor plus simazine combined with glyphosate reduced weed cover by 85–90% after 10 days, decreasing to 25–30% after 80 days in newly planted and established nurseries of yew (*Taxus* spp.), holly (*Ilex* spp.), juniper (*Juniperus* sp.) and Kurume azalea (*Rhododendron* sp.). Glyphosate has also been used successfully following treatment with oxyfluorfen, prodiamine and oryzalin (Frank, 1980). Glyphosate at 0.4 and 0.8 kg ha^{-1} + simazine + oryzalin gave better control of established winter annual weeds than simazine + oryzalin alone (Ahrens, 1981). As discussed in Chapter 15, mixtures can often be used advantageously, in spite of the antagonistic effect of soil-acting herbicides.

Nursery stocks

Because of its foliar action and rapid breakdown in the soil, glyphosate is valuable to the nurseryman as pre-planting and post-planting treatments.

Pre-planting treatments

The short residual life of glyphosate in the soil is both an advantage and a disadvantage. It is a disadvantage, as follow-up treatments with glyphosate or some other herbicide are necessary to extend the period of weed control. On the other hand, lack of persistence enables glyphosate to be used effectively as a pre-planting treatment either to kill weeds or to enable nursery stock to be planted into established turf. An important benefit in both cases is the avoidance of soil tillage which would bring up dormant but viable weed seeds from lower soil depths into the germinating zone.

In normal circumstances there would be a delay of 7–14 days between spraying with glyphosate and planting nursery stock to allow translocation from treated vegetation to underground storage organs. To study the likelihood of glyphosate uptake by newly planted stock, Smith and Treaster (1978) planted a range of deciduous and evergreen species into soil that had been treated only 3 h previously with a high dose of 9 kg ha^{-1}. Despite this excessive dose and the absence of any delay in planting there was no evidence of root uptake by the nursery stock. Bing (1979) also recorded no adverse effect on 13 species of nursery liner, planted 5–6 days after spraying with doses of 2.2–17.9 kg ha^{-1}.

Frank and King (1978), using doses of 4.5, 9.0 and 13.4 kg ha^{-1}, also showed that glyphosate was satisfactory prior to planting 16 species of bare-root, lining-out stock into a field of established, actively growing turf.

Although pre-planting treatments have given satisfactory results in practice, root uptake and damage can occur in some circumstances. Hilen, Bing and Good (1979) conducted laboratory and field experiments to induce glyphosate injury so that they could characterize its specific nature. Dormant 1-year rooted cuttings of a range of plants grown in aerated, full-strength Hoagland's solution to which doses, equivalent to 1.1, 2.2, 4.5 and 9.0 kg ha^{-1} of the isopropylamine salt of glyphosate, were added, resulted in pronounced necrosis in shoot cortical cells, although conducting tissue remained substantially intact and viable. Approximately 90% of all buds failed to break and all plants died after 4 weeks. Plants were also damaged if the herbicide was placed in close proximity to their roots. Plants transplanted into a mixture of soil plus chopped rhizomes and above-ground parts of A. repens that had been treated with glyphosate were injured to various degrees. There was evidence that Viburnum plicatum var. tomentosum, Ligustrum amurense, Forsythia × intermedia and Taxus cuspidata were more tolerant to glyphosate in the growing medium than Prunus mahaleb and Prunus domestica, with Malus sp. and Ligustrum × ibolium intermediate (Table 22.2). Further evidence of glyphosate uptake by roots was obtained from experiments where the herbicide was sprayed on A. repens at 0–9.0 kg ha^{-1} and at excessive doses of 16.8 and 33.7 kg ha^{-1}. The grass was incorporated as soon as the spray had dried and rooted cuttings were planted directly into the prepared beds. Damage did not occur on all species; actively growing Viburnum plicatum was sensitive to both normal and excessive doses, but Forsythia was uninjured even by excessive amounts.

Salazar and Appleby (1982), working with seeds of common bent (Agrostis tenuis), lucerne (Medicago sativa) and red clover (Trifolium pratense), also showed that glyphosate could be soil active under particular conditions and recommended

TABLE 22.2 **The survival of test plants grown in a medium compost of glyphosate-treated** *Agropyron repens* **clippings incorporated into clay loam soil (from Hilen, Bing and Good, 1979; reproduced with permission)**

Rate of glyphosate (kg a.i. ha^{-1})	Plant survival after four weeks*											
	Privet (Ligustrum × ibolium)			Apple (Malus sp.)			Wild plum (Prunus domestica)			Cherry laurel (Prunus mahaleb)		
	Days between application and tillage											
	0	1	3	0	1	3	0	1	3	0	1	3
0	0	1	0	0	1	1	1	0	1	2	1	0
2.2	0	0	1	0	0	1	2	3	0	0	3	1
4.5	0	0	0	1	0	0	3	0	3	3	1	1
9.0	0	0	0	0	0	0	3	3	3	3	2	3

*Date represent number of plants dead after 4 weeks out of a total of 3 plants per treatment.

that maximum opportunity should be afforded for adsorption to occur before planting desirable crops. Although the risk of damage to germinating seeds is likely to be greater than to newly planted shrubs and trees, the fact that root uptake can occur in some circumstances suggests that more investigations are required about differences in plant susceptibility to glyphosate and the conditions under which herbicide uptake from soil can occur.

Post-planting treatments

Glyphosate has proved to be a fairly safe herbicide in nurseries provided it is used judiciously as a carefully directed spray. Leaf wetting of ornamentals may cause serious injury. Burt and Neel (1975) showed that foliage sprays of glyphosate at 1.1 and 2.2 kg ha^{-1} were usually sub-lethal, but even the lower dose caused too much damage. There are several reports of damage to nursery stock from overall sprays, but absence of injury when the same doses were used as directed treatments. *Lonicera japonica* var. *purpurea* was 40–50% defoliated by glyphosate, applied overall at 1.1, 2.2 and 3.4 kg ha^{-1} in August, but treatment around other plants was well tolerated (Whitcomb *et al.*, 1976). Under the same conditions overall sprays killed a few terminal shoots of *Juniperus chinensis* cv. 'Pfitzeriana', but no damage occurred following the use of directed sprays. Similarly glyphosate, applied as a directed spray, was not toxic to 3-year-old *Cornus* spp., but killed plants when applied to the foliage (Funk, Smith and Davis, 1980).

The results indicate that pre-planting and directed applications are generally safe in nursery stock, but more variable results have been obtained where glyphosate was applied as an overall spray. The degree of damage resulting from foliar-applied sprays varied with the species, time of application, dose and amount of foliage wetted.

EFFECT OF SPECIES

Ahrens (1974b) demonstrated that woody ornamentals differed widely in their tolerance to leaf wetting with glyphosate. Conifers generally showed more tolerance than broad-leaved evergreens or deciduous plants when treated during the summer or autumn (Gouin, 1977a; Smith and Treaster, 1978). Bing (1975) reported that established liners of holly (*Ilex crenata*), juniper (*Juniperus chinensis* var. *procumbens*), white pine (*Pinus strobus*) and Norway spruce (*Picea abies*) were not affected by an overall spray at 1.1–3.4 kg ha^{-1} in July, but *Ligustrum ovalifolium*, *Liquidambar styraciflua*, maple (*Acer palmatum*), rose (*Rosa multiflora*) and apple (*Malus sieboldii*) were seriously damaged. Hathaway *et al.* (1975) treated various portions of the foliage of several ornamentals with glyphosate in July. Honeysuckle (*Lonicera japonica*) was injured, but *Yucca filimentosa*, *Ilex vomitoria*, *Juniperus chinensis* cv. 'Pfitzeriana' and *Euonymus fortunei* were unaffected by the spray.

Whitcomb (1977) reported that ornamental plants and fruit trees in the family *Rosaceae* were particularly susceptible to glyphosate even at low rates. This was confirmed by Bing (1975) and by Shaw (1981), who recorded severe injury on roses even when the spray was applied carefully (see also Chapter 19).

Good results with glyphosate on conifers have been obtained during the dormant period, e.g. *Juniperus* spp., *Tsuga canadensis* (Ahrens, 1978a) and *Thuja occidentalis nigra* (Ahrens, 1979), but many conifers also showed a good degree of tolerance to glyphosate applied during the autumn, e.g. *Juniperus chinensis* cv. 'Pfitzeriana', *J. chinensis* cv. 'Hetzii', *J. chinensis* var. *procumbens* and *J. sabina* var. *tamariscifolia* (Dunwell, Boe and Lee, 1978). *Picea abies, Picea pungens* 'Glauca', *Pinus nigra, P. silvestris, P. thunbergii, Taxus × media* 'Brownii' also showed no damage when sprayed in August with glyphosate at 3.4 kg ha^{-1} (Smith and Treaster, 1978). Dunwell, Boe and Lee (1977) reported no damage to *Juniperus chinensis, J. chinensis* var. *procumbens* and *J. sabina* when sprayed in September with doses of 2.2, 3.5 and 4.4 kg ha^{-1}.

Although conifers show more tolerance than deciduous plants, occasionally damage has been reported following spray wetting during the growing season. Glyphosate at 0.4 and 0.8 kg ha^{-1} plus surfactant applied in June and July damaged actively growing *Thuja occidentalis* cv. 'Nigra,' but similar doses + simazine + oryzalin caused no injury when applied in April to dormant plants (Ahrens, 1981). A dose of 2.2 kg ha^{-1} caused a slight leaf-burn on *Pinus palustris* (Self and Pounders, 1975).

Where conifers are damaged during the growing season, the injury is often temporary. Bing (1977) reported that glyphosate at 2.2–3.4 kg ha^{-1} killed the tips of branches of *Juniperus* and *Taxus* spp., but that the damage was soon masked by new growth. *Tsuga canadensis* scorched easily, but grew new branches and foliage. Bing and Selleck (1978) also reported rapid recovery of *T. canadensis* after initial scorching (see also Chapter 21).

Some differences between species and genera of conifers in susceptibility to glyphosate have been recorded. There was some evidence that *Juniperus horizontalis* cv. 'Wiltonii' is more susceptible than *J. sabina* (Haramaki and Kuhns, 1979). Glyphosate applied at 0.6–1.1 kg ha^{-1} in autumn caused slight growth suppression in *Taxus cuspidata*, but *Pinus* spp., *Picea* spp. and *Pseudotsuga menziesii* were uninjured (Ahrens, 1974b). *Thuja occidentalis* was damaged by glyphosate at 3.4 kg ha^{-1} in August but, in this experiment also, *Pinus* and *Picea* spp. were uninjured (Smith and Treaster, 1978).

In addition to conifers, many other species show some tolerance of glyphosate at certain times. Application at 3.4 kg ha^{-1} applied to the foliage in August caused no injury to the evergreen *Euonymous alatus* and to the deciduous trees *Gingko biloba* and *Tilia euchlora* (Smith and Treaster, 1978). *Cotoneaster horizontalis* tolerated glyphosate at 1.2 and 2.4 kg ha^{-1} in July, but not in September (Gouin, 1977a). Newly planted or established *Euonymus fortunii* cv. 'Colorata' showed no significant phytotoxic symptoms or decreased top growth following treatment with glyphosate at 2.2, 4.5 and 6.7 kg ha^{-1} (Schubert and Alemazkoor, 1977). Box (*Buxus sempervirens*), holly (*Ilex glabra*) and pyracanth (*Pyracantha coccinea lalandii*) also showed some tolerance of spray wetting with glyphosate (Haramaki, Kuhns and Grenoble, 1980).

TIME OF APPLICATION

With at least one apple cultivar and with some *Malus* pollinators there is evidence of a greater risk of translocation and severe damage from spray wetting of foliage in the autumn than at other times of the year (Stinchcombe and Stott, 1980). Atkinson, Petts and Hyrycz (1978) suggest that the absence of translocation, when glyphosate is sprayed on root suckers during the period February to July, could be due to the chemical, which seemed to move acropetally, becoming immobilized in the dead sucker-shoot tip. There is some evidence of basipetal movement from autumn applications at a time when shoots are non-dormant but non-growing

(Atkinson, Crisp and Hyrycz, 1981). Although the response of ornamentals to glyphosate has not been studied as extensively as that of fruit crops, autumn and early winter sprays appear to be more phytotoxic to ornamentals than applications at other times of the year. For example cotoneaster (*Cotoneaster horizontalis*) did not show any visible toxic symptoms when treated in July, but exhibited moderate to severe marginal chlorosis when sprayed in September (Gouin, 1977a). Glyphosate applied at 3.4 kg ha^{-1} to branches of plants, belonging to 45 species and cultivars in August injured approximately 75% of the plants, but translocation of the herbicide was not extensive and damage was largely confined to the sprayed plant part (Smith and Treaster, 1978). Some plants can be susceptible to glyphosate during the winter period. Dormant *Spiraea* with a few attached leaves was injured by glyphosate (Ahrens, 1978a). However, many deciduous plants can be sprayed successfully at this period, provided all leaves have fallen. Glyphosate at 0.3–1.1 kg ha^{-1} had no adverse effect on deciduous azaleas during the dormant season, but damaged evergreen azaleas and *Kalmia latifolia* (Ahrens, 1978a).

EFFECT OF DOSE AND AMOUNT OF FOLIAGE WETTED

The phytotoxicity of glyphosate on nursery stock may also depend on the dose used. The ground-cover ivy (*Hedera helix*) tolerated overall sprays of 0.6–1.7 kg ha^{-1} (Bing, 1977), but was damaged by a dose of 3.4 kg ha^{-1} (Smith and Treaster, 1978).

The degree of plant injury will be influenced by the amount of plant foliage wetted by the spray. A sensitive plant may be killed if all its foliage is sprayed, but show only slight damage if only a proportion of its foliage is wetted (Hathaway *et al.*, 1975).

Experiments by Ahrens (1977) suggest that glyphosate may be applied to the uninjured, mature bark of ornamentals without damage. Treatment with 3.4–6.7 kg ha^{-1} caused no injury, but killed most basal sprouts when applied to the lower trunk of newly planted 1-year-old whips of Norway maple (*Acer platanoides*), *Gleditsia triacanthos* f. inermis, *Platanus orientalis*, rowan (*Sorbus aucuparia*), oak (*Quercus palustris*) and small-leaved lime (*Tilia cordata*). Glyphosate applied at 2.2–9.0 kg ha^{-1} to wet thoroughly 50–200 mm diameter trunks of *Platanus acerifolia* trees also caused no injury to bark or foliage (Bing and Corell, 1979). However, glyphosate can damage plants by entering through wounds in the bark (see Appendix I). Pruning before treatment with glyphosate at 1.1–1.7 kg ha^{-1} was associated with injury in pine (*Pinus strobus*), yew (*Taxus cuspidata*) and juniper (*Juniperus horizontalis*) (Ahrens, 1974b).

ROOT UPTAKE

As discussed in the section on Pre-planting Treatments, there is little evidence of damage to plants by glyphosate absorbed through the roots where normal herbicidal doses are used. Nevertheless there are situations where damage may occur to established plants as a result of root uptake (Coupland and Lutman, 1982). Apart from the risk of root transfer (from treated weeds to crop plants) there is also a risk of direct root uptake where plant roots are growing in a 'non-soil' substrate. Doses of 1.3–2.6 kg ha^{-1} damaged many species of ornamentals which had been allowed to root into sand beds on which containerized plants were standing (Anon., 1974). Shaw (1981) also reported a case of suspected damage to roses as a result of root uptake.

EFFECT OF VAPOUR

There is a trend in Britain and Ireland for an increasing amount of nursery stock to be produced under glass or plastic (J.C. Kelly, personal communication). The question arises of possible damage from the vapour activity of herbicides applied to protected crops. Ahrens (1978b) showed that glyphosate caused no damage and would appear to be a likely candidate for glasshouse use.

Woody ornamentals in amenity areas

As leisure time increases, the need for recreational areas becomes greater (Broadbent, 1980). Rising energy costs are also contributing to an increase in importance of local parks and home gardens as recreational areas. Data collected for the Nationwide Outdoor Recreation Plan, from 2500 householders in the USA, indicated that people would be satisfied wth less energy-expensive activities if they were available locally (Munson, 1980). Munson suggested that the change from frequent travel to using facilities close to home could alter the long-range plans and needs for parks in the community.

Herbicides can greatly reduce the labour required for maintaining amenity areas (Ahrens, 1979), just as they reduce the labour required for weeding nurseries (Weatherspoon, 1977). Although less research has been conducted on the use of herbicides for amenity areas than for the nursery industry, the scope for 'spin-off' is considerable and information on the use of glyphosate on nursery stock is directly applicable in amenity situations where woody ornamentals are used.

In the present period of high labour costs, the potential of herbicides as a cheap and effective means of controlling weeds in amenity horticulture is very great. Climatic and soil conditions in Britain and Ireland facilitate the development of attractive, colourful landscape areas with comparatively little attention to manuring, irrigation and pest and disease control. However, control of weeds is essential and this operation requires a large proportion of manpower time (Wright, 1978).

Some of the problems retarding the use of herbicides in amenity areas are the small size and irregular shape of most of the plantings, and the mixture of woody ornamentals that they are likely to contain, either as a patchwork or in horizontal layers of vegetation. Consequently, weed control treatments are more difficult to apply than in the nursery where the plants are grown in straight rows and possibly in herbicide-compatible groupings.

Because of the high cost of alternative methods of weed control, it is often feasible in amenity areas to apply glyphosate by means of wiper applicators (see also Chapter 16), wicks or herbicide gloves. Although the use of these measures is time consuming, compared with spraying, it overcomes many of the problems that often limit the use of glyphosate in amenity plantings and avoids the risk of severe injury as a result of spray drift.

Systems of weed control in landscape plantings

With very few exceptions the landscape manager will aim for season-long weed control. In this objective he will have much in common with the nurseryman. The solution will be the same in both cases—usually a programme based on soil-acting herbicides or mixtures of herbicides followed by directed application of appropriate translocated or contact herbicides to control surviving weeds (Corell, 1979; Robinson, 1980). Glyphosate and paraquat are the most commonly used herbicides in each of these classes (Greaves, Sly and Cutler, 1979).

Problems of inadequate weed control in nurseries can be passed on to amenity areas. Perennial weeds can be inadvertently transplanted to the landscape site on the roots of field-grown nursery stock. Carpenter (1978) showed that physical barriers against perennial weed growth were not totally successful, but a directed spray of glyphosate at 2.2 kg ha^{-1} reduced the problem of perennial weeds and lowered weeding costs by a factor of eight. Bing (1977) also reported good control of a number of perennial weeds including *Artemisia vulgaris, Polygonum cuspidatum* and *A. repens*.

In addition to the herbicidal benefits of glyphosate, Ahrens (1974b) considered that, as damage to conifers is likely to be slight, the temporary growth suppression that may occur is an added advantage in landscape plantings.

The development of effective post-emergence grass killers, selective on broad-leaved plants, e.g. alloxydim sodium and fluazifop butyl, will encourage the use of glyphosate on grassed-down areas to facilitate the direct planting of shrubs into killed swards. In this way the need for soil cultivation before planting can be eliminated (Robinson, 1975) and well-structured soil can be retained at the surface where it is most useful. The availability of effective grass suppressors that can be used if necessary as overall post-emergence sprays should now enable landscape contractors to plant direct into killed grass areas with greater confidence.

Ground-cover plants

Low-growing ground-cover plants are increasing in popularity in many countries. In the years immediately after planting, these plants can suffer severely from weed competition. In later years, well-established, mature ground-cover plantings can largely prevent seed germination and will suppress weed growth. Hand weeding of newly planted ground cover is expensive; two hand weedings of untreated plantings required an estimated total of 20 man min m^{-2} in the first 2 years after planting at a cost of \$1.02 m^{-2} (Ahrens, 1979). Because hand weeding is so expensive and mechanical cultivation is impractical, chemical means of controlling weeds are especially valuable in ground-cover plantings. Where weeds cannot be controlled and severe infestation occurs, expensive renovation of plantings will be required (Rice, 1982). In these circumstances the demand for effective selective herbicides is increasing, and glyphosate has been tested on a number of popular ground-cover species.

Good control of weeds without damage to *Pachysandra terminalis* was recorded by a number of workers (Bing, 1977; Bing and Selleck, 1978; Smith and Treaster, 1978). In a tolerance trial on 8 species of ground cover with doses of glyphosate from 1.2 to 4.4 kg ha^{-1}, *Rosemarinus officinalis* showed extreme tolerance with little injury evident even at the 4.4 kg ha^{-1} dose (*Table 22.3*). *Gazania ringens*, Rose of Sharon (*Hypericum calycinum*) and *Drosanthemum hispidum* tolerated doses up to 2.2 kg ha^{-1}. *Baccharis pilularis*, strawberry (*Fragaria chiloensis*), *Osteospermum fruticosum* and *Myoporum parvifolium* were most sensitive (Rice, 1982). Glyphosate was well tolerated by ivy (*Hedera canariensis*) at 2.2 or 4.5 kg ha^{-1}, while *Carpobrotus edulis* showed some tolerance of doses up to 2.2 kg ha^{-1} (Humphrey, 1976).

TABLE 22.3   Effect of glyphosate applied 15 November on 8 ground cover species (from Rice, 1982)

Rate (kg salt ha^{-1})	Crop injury*							
	Gazania	Baccharis	Hyperi-cum	Drosanthe-mum	Fragaria	Osteosper-mum	Rosmari-nus	Myopo-rum
0.0	0.0	1.0	0.0	0.0	0.0	0.0	0.0	0.0
1.2	1.0	1.3	1.0	0.0	0.7	1.0	0.0	1.0
2.2	1.0	2.7	1.0	0.3	2.0	3.3	0.0	3.0
4.4	1.7	6.3	1.0	8.0	5.7	8.0	0.0	8.7
LSD 5%	0.6	1.1	—	0.6	0.7	1.3	—	2.4

*Assessed 25 February; 0 = no injury, 10 = plant death.

Plant tolerance

The published information on the effect of glyphosate on nursery stock and woody ornamentals shows that some risk is associated with the use of foliage sprays. Although good results have generally been obtained with conifers and some other genera, it is still difficult to predict toxicity effects with certainty as many factors are likely to influence plant tolerance. Apart from wide differences in susceptibility between genera, e.g. *Picea* and *Rosa*, the effect of foliage-applied sprays will be influenced by the physiological status of the plants during and after treatment (Lanini and Radosevich, 1982). As glyphosate translocates in the phloem, photosynthesis is also likely to influence the distribution of the herbicide within the plant and the time of the year may also influence the direction of movement (Atkinson, Petts and Hyrycz, 1978).

In general, shrubs are less likely to be damaged when dormant either because of a heat dormancy period in mid-summer (Whitcomb, 1977) or during the winter. Some deciduous plants are likely to be particularly vulnerable when translocates are moving basipetally in the autumn. Most conifers have a relatively short active growing period and in many cases injury has been absent when this period was avoided. Much more information is required on the relationship between physiological factors and glyphosate activity.

Conclusions and the future

Glyphosate has been widely accepted as a herbicide in nursery stock and amenity horticulture. It controls a broad range of weeds, including many problem perennials, and can be used with a good degree of safety around many woody ornamentals when applied as a carefully directed spray.

Its short residual life in the soil enables it to be used effectively as a pre-planting herbicide, but root uptake can occur in some circumstances, e.g. from sand beds penetrated by the roots of containerized nursery stock.

Foliage sprays have been used successfully on some conifers and a small number of other genera. Tolerance of foliage sprays depends on many factors including species, dose, amount of foliage wetted and on the physiological state of the plants before and after treatment. Damage may occur as a result of absorption of glyphosate through wounds or immature bark, and it is still difficult to predict with certainty the effect of foliar application on many species.

Experience gained with glyphosate in nursery stock can be readily adapted for amenity plantings of woody ornamentals. Here, the problem of weed control is even more difficult because of the small size and irregular shape of most of the plantings and the large number of different ornamental species used. Mechanical methods of control are impossible and hand weeding is tedious and expensive. Depending on the types of plants used and the weeds present, glyphosate may be useful as a directed spot treatment, applied selectively by means of a wiper applicator or, in a few species, as an overall spray (see also Chapter 16).

Fashions in gardens and planted landscapes change with time, reflecting the problems, education, affluence and available technology of each period. At present, landscape designers are becoming increasingly aware that managers are facing very great maintenance problems because of the high cost of labour. Shrinking budgets could force them to take a new approach to landscape design.

Today's increasingly leisured and environmentally aware population has complex landscape and recreational needs. Although the demand for a low input 'natural' environment is increasing, there is a continuing requirement for well-planned gardens and parks. With the large cost-savings possible with glyphosate and other herbicides, a new style of landscape design could develop in which appropriate amenity areas would be planned from the outset to take full advantage of herbicides. Such areas might consist of low- or medium-growing ground-cover plants, with other trees and shrubs as specimen plants used in bold textural masses and large blocks of colour.

Several plant species have been identified that are attractive and have some tolerance of glyphosate applied to the foliage. These include *Juniperus* spp., *Picea* spp., *Pinus* spp., *Pachysandra terminalis* and *Rosemarinus officinalis*. Further tolerant ornamentals are likely to be identified and more information will become available on safe periods for the application of glyphosate on a number of species. Because weed control is such a problem in landscape management, plants with a high tolerance of broad-spectrum herbicides, such as glyphosate and simazine, could become more popular with landscape designers in the future. Plants that tolerate both a soil-acting and leaf-acting herbicide will be especially valuable and their use in designs, specifically because of their herbicide tolerance, could provide a new approach to land maintenance.

References

AHRENS, J.F. (1974a). Preplant herbicides for control of quackgrass in ornamentals, *Proceedings of the Northeastern Weed Science Society*, **28**, 372–378.

AHRENS, J.F. (1974b). Selectivity of glyphosate and asulam in ornamental plantings and Christmas trees, *Proceedings of the Northeastern Weed Science Society*, **28**, 361–368.

AHRENS, J.F. (1975). Further experiments on the control of quackgrass in ornamentals, *Proceedings of the Northeastern Weed Science Society*, **29**, 349–350.

AHRENS, J.F. (1976). Chemical control of *Artemisia vulgaris* in ornamentals, *Proceedings of the Northeastern Weed Science Society*, **30**, 303–307.

AHRENS, J.F. (1977). Post-emergence herbicides on the bark and basal sprouts of shade trees, *Proceedings of the Northeastern Weed Science Society*, **31**, 335–339.

AHRENS, J.F. (1978a). Control of established weeds in container-grown nursery stock, *Proceedings of the Northeastern Weed Science Society*, **32**, 300.

AHRENS, J.F. (1978b). Phytotoxicity of vapours from herbicides on soil in plastic containers, *Abstracts of the 1978 Meeting of the Weed Science Society of America*, p. 34.

AHRENS, J.F. (1979). Herbicides for ground cover plantings, *Proceedings of the Northeastern Weed Science Society*, **33**, 256–259.

AHRENS, J.F. (1981). Chemical control of established weeds in field-grown arborvitae, *Proceedings of the Northeastern Weed Science Society*, **35**, 248.

ANON. (1974). Container-grown nursery stock. Herbicides on sand beds, *Report of the Efford Experimental Horticultural Station 1973*, pp. 163–165.

ANON. (1976a). *Annual Report 1975*, Proefstation voor Boomkwekerij, Boskoop, Netherlands, p. 133.

ANON. (1976b). Research into flowering plant production in the Netherlands in 1975, Proefstation voor de Boomkwekerij, Linnaeuslaan 2a, Aalsmeer, Netherlands, pp. 217–218.

ATKINSON, D., CRISP, C.M. and HYRYCZ, K.J. (1981). The effect of late-season application of glyphosate and fosamine to fruit trees with root suckers, *Proceedings of the 1980 British Crop Protection Conference—Weeds*, **1**, 311–314.

ATKINSON, D., PETTS, S.C. and HYRYCZ, K.J. (1978). Further studies on the use of glyphosate on fruit trees with root suckers, *Proceedings of the 1978 British Crop Protection Conference—Weeds*, **1**, 191–196.

BAIN, C., LABIT, B., MIMAUD, J. and TANGUY, M. (1974). Results of experiments in 1973 carried out by the Crop Protection Service: weed control, *Phytoma*, no. 261, pp. 7–13.

BAIRD, D.D., UPCHURCH, R.P., HOMESLEY, W.B. and FRANZ, J.E. (1971). Introduction of a new broad-spectrum, post-emergence herbicide class with utility for herbaceous perennial weed control, *Proceedings of the North Central Weed Control Conference*, **26**, 64–68.

BING, A. (1975). Further studies on the use of glyphosate on ornamentals, *Proceedings of the Northeastern Weed Science Society*, **29**, 336–339.

BING, A. (1976). Summary of 1975 nursery weed control experiments, *Proceedings of the Northeastern Weed Science Society*, **30**, 296.

BING, A. (1977). Glyphosate to control perennial weeds in landscape plantings, *Proceedings of the Northeastern Weed Science Society*, **31**, 327.

BING, A. (1979). Glyphosate as a preplant treatment for nursery liners and gladiolus, *Proceedings of the Northeastern Weed Science Society*, **33**, 242–244.

BING, A. and CORELL, T. (1979). Application of glyphosate to the stems of sycamore trees, *Proceedings of the Northeastern Weed Science Society*, **33**, 255.

BING, A. and SELLECK, G.W. (1978). The control of mugwort (*Artemisia vulgaris* L) in ornamental plantings, *Abstracts of the 1977 Meeting Weed Science Society of America*, p. 47.

BROADBENT, L. (1980). Foreword, *Proceedings of the Weed Control in Amenity Plantings Conference*, University of Bath, pp. 7–8.

BURT, E.O. and NEEL, P.L. (1975). Weed control for ornamental plants, Annual Research Report 1972, Agricultural Research Centre, 3205, SW 700 Avenue Fort Lauderdale, Florida 33314, USA, p. 230.

CARPENTER, P.L. (1978). A system for the control of perennial weeds on landscape sites, *HortScience*, **13**(3), section 2, p. 348.

CARPENTER, P.L. and HENSLEY, D.L. (1974). The use of glyphosate to control field bindweed (*Convolvulus arvensis*) in nursery plantings, *HortScience*, **9**(3), section 2, pp. 32–33.

CORELL, T. (1979). Nursery weed control on Long Island, *Proceedings of the Northeastern Weed Science Society*, **33**, 240–241.

COUPLAND, D. and LUTMAN, P.J.W. (1982). Investigations into the movement of glyphosate from treated to untreated plants, *Annals of Applied Biology*, **101**, 315–321.

COX, R.J. (1973). Weed control in nursery stock production, *Proceedings of the 11th British Weed Control Conference*, **3**, 1096–1099.

DAVISON, J.D. (1971). Weed science in the service of the intensive producer—fruit and ornamental crops, *Proceedings of the 10th British Weed Control Conference*, **3**, 909–916.

DUNWELL, W.C., BOE, A.A. and LEE, G.A. (1977). Canada thistle control in selected junipers with fall-applied glyphosate, *HortScience*, **12**(4), section 2, p. 398.

DUNWELL, W.C., BOE, A.A. and LEE, G.A. (1978). Canada thistle control in selected junipers with fall-applied glyphosate, *HortScience*, **13**(3), 297–298.

FRANK, J.R. (1980). Nursery weed control with oxyfluorfen, prodiamine, oryzalin, glyphosate and paraquat, *HortScience*, **15**(3), section 2, p. 413.

FRANK, J.R. and KING, J.A. (1978). Glyphosate and paraquat for the establishment of woody nursery stock, *Proceedings of the Northeastern Weed Science Society*, **32**, 284.

FRANK, J.R. and KING, J.A. (1979a). Directed spray applications with glyphosate and paraquat in a woody plant nursery, *Abstracts of the 1979 Meeting of the Weed Science Society of America*, pp. 51–52.

FRANK, J.R. and KING, J.A. (1979b). Herbicide combinations for use in establishing and maintaining woody nursery plants, *Proceedings of the Northeastern Weed Science Society*, **33**, 262–263.

FRETZ, T.A. (1973). Weed competition research studies container production losses, *American Nurseryman*, October 1973, p. 14.

FRETZ, T.A. (1974). Evaluation of herbicide combinations for use in shade tree nurseries, *Research Summary of the Ohio Agricultural Research and Development Centre*, no. 79, pp. 65–70.

FUNK, H., SMITH, L.D. and DAVIS, G.G. (1980). Evaluation of herbicide toxicity of *Ilex*, *Euonymus* and *Cornus*, *Proceedings of the 33rd Annual Meeting of the Southern Weed Science Society*, p. 298.

GOODALE, T., HATHAWAY, R.D., WARD, J.D. and WHITCOMB, C.E. (1975). Controlling common bermudagrass with hand-applied application of Roundup, *Research Report P-724*, Oklahoma State University, Agricultural Experiment Station Nursery Research Field Day, pp. 20–21.

GOUIN, F.R. (1977a). Controlling perennial weeds in established landscape plantings, *Proceedings of the Northeastern Weed Science Society*, **31**, 326.

GOUIN, F.R. (1977b). Controlling rip-shins (brambles) and mugwort with glyphosate, *Proceedings of the Northeastern Weed Science Society*, **31**, 328.

GOUIN, F.R. (1979). Controlling brambles in established Christmas tree plantations with glyphosate, *HortScience*, **14**(2), 189–190.

GREAVES, D.A., SLY, J.M.A. and CUTLER, J.R. (1979). Hardy nursery stock: 1971–1976, *Survey Report 14*, MAFF, DAFS, 127 pp.

GRUBBEN, G.J.H. (1974). Control of *Cyperus rotundus* L. in market garden crops in Dahomey, *Proceedings of the 26th International Symposium in Crop Protection*, part 1, **39**(2), 483–492, Mededelingen, Fakulteit Landbouwwetenschappen, Gent.

HARAMAKI, C. (1977). Control of perennial and annual weeds in established plantings of narrowleaf evergreens, *Proceedings of the Northeastern Weed Science Society*, **31**, 329–334.

HARAMAKI, C. and KUHNS, L. (1979). An evaluation of glyphosate used on shade trees and evergreen liners, *Proceedings of the Northeastern Weed Science Society*, **33**, 251–254.

HARAMAKI, C., KUHNS, L. and GRENOBLE, D. (1980). The use of glyphosate in weed infested nursery beds, *Proceedings of the Northeastern Weed Science Society*, **34**, 315–318.

HATHAWAY, R.D., WARD, J.D., GOODALE, T. and WHITCOMB, C.E. (1975). Effect of Roundup (glyphosate) on woody landscape plants, *Research Report, P-724*, Oklahoma State University, Agricultural Experiment Station Nursery Research Field Day, pp. 17–18.

HATHAWAY, R.D. and WHITCOMB, C.E. (1975). Controlling common bermudagrass in non-production areas, *Research Report P-724*, Oklahoma State University Agricultural Experiment Station Nursery Research Field Day, pp. 18–19.

HILEN, G., BING, A. and GOOD, G.L. (1979). Glyphosate injury as a result of preplant treatments, *Proceedings of the Northeastern Weed Science Society*, **33**, 245–250.

HUMPHREY, W.A. (1976). Weed control in ground covers, *Proceedings of the 28th Annual California Weed Conference*, pp. 115–117.

JONES, A. (1980). Annual weed control in amenity plants—herbicide choice, *Proceedings of the Weed Control in Amenity Plantings Conference*, University of Bath, pp. 58–63.

KLINE, W.L. and SELLECK, G.W. (1978). Factors affecting hedge bindweed control with glyphosate, *Proceedings of the Northeastern Weed Science Society*, **32**, 283.

LANINI, W.T. and RADOSEVICH, S.R. (1982). Herbicide effectiveness in response to season of applications and shrub physiology, *Weed Science*, **30**, 467–475.

MUNSON, K. (1980). More recreation, less energy cost, in *Cutting Energy Costs, The 1980 Yearbook of Agriculture*, US Department of Agriculture, 397 pp.

RICE, R.P. (1982). Tolerance of eight groundcover species to glyphosate, *1982 Research Progress Report of the Western Society of Weed Science*, p. 97.

ROBINSON, D.W. (1975). Herbicides in the landscape and garden, *Journal of the Royal Horticultural Society*, **100**, 554–559 and 600–606; **101**, 35–41.

ROBINSON, D.W. (1980). Present and future role of herbicides in amenity land management, *Proceedings of the Weed Control in Amenity Plantings Conference*, University of Bath, pp. 70–78.

SALAZAR, L.C. and APPLEBY, A.P. (1982). Herbicidal activity of glyphosate in soil, *Weed Science*, **30**, 463–466.

SCHUBERT, O.E. and ALEMAZKOOR, S. (1977). Quackgrass control in purpleleaf winter-creeper with glyphosate, methazole and pronamide, *HortScience*, **12**(4), section 2, p. 399.

SELF, R.L. and POUNDERS, C.T. (1975). Weed control and phytotoxicity studies on container-grown ornamentals, *Proceedings of the Southern Nurserymen's Association Research Conference, 20th Annual Report*, p. 117.

SHAW, A. (1981). Rose production—research shadow, *Gardeners' Chronical and Horticultural Trade's Journal*, 2 July, 1981, pp. 21–22.

SMITH, E.M. and TREASTER, S.A. (1978). Phytotoxicity of glyphosate on landscape plants, *Research Circular of the Ohio Agricultural Research and Development Centre, No. 236. Ornamental Plants—1978. A Summary of Research*, pp. 53–54.

STINCHCOMBE, G.R. and STOTT, K.G. (1980). The effect of autumn application of glyphosate on fruit tree sucker control and on parent tree damage, *Proceedings of the British Crop Protection Conference Weeds*, **1,** 303–309.

WALLIS, L.W. (1978). Nursery stock: control of perennial weeds, *Experiments and Developments in the Eastern Region (1977)*, MAFF, ADAS, Brooklands Avenue, UK, pp. 280–284.

WEATHERSPOON, D.M. (1977). Weed control for ornamental plants, *Annual Research Report of the Institute of Food and Agricultural Sciences*, Florida, 1975, p. 364.

WHITCOMB, C.E. (1977). Using Roundup in the nursery—a summary, *Research Report P-760*, Oklahoma State University Agricultural Experimental Station Nursery Research Field Day, pp. 4–5.

WHITCOMB, C.E., HATHAWAY, R.D., GOODALE, T.W. and WARD, J.D. (1976). Using Roundup (glyphosate) for bermudagrass control in the landscape, *Proceedings of the Southern Nurserymen's Association Research Conference, 21st Annual Report*, p. 136.

WRIGHT, T. (1978). Current trends in maintenance techniques—a short review, *Proceedings of the Course on 'The modern management of important gardens and parks'*, Wye College (London University), Ashford, Kent, pp. 22–30.

Chapter 23

Efficacy of glyphosate in viticulture

J.F. Hebblethwaite and G.R. Schepens
Monsanto, Brussels, Belgium

Introduction

In most countries where vines are grown, there are three distinct periods at which weed control is important. These periods correspond with late winter/early spring, mid-summer and late summer:

Jan.	Feb.	Mar.	Apr.	May	June	July	Aug.	Sept.	Oct.	Nov.
Winter/spring annuals/ biannuals/perennials					Summer annuals/ perennials			Late summer annuals/ perennials		

Vineyards of Central Europe, the Mediterranean area and the USA are infested with a wide range of annual and biannual weeds. Some of the annuals and biannuals are growing in importance. In the Champagne area of France, the biannual *Epilobium tetragonum* has become important following continuous use of the triazine herbicides such as simazine, terbuthylazine and terbumeton (Rouas, 1981). Among other spring annuals, *Senecio vulgaris* and *Sonchus oleraceus* also exhibit some tolerance to triazines.

In some areas of France, in particular Champagne, Bordeaux, Mâcon and Languedoc, certain summer annuals such as *Solanum nigrum* (Rouas, 1981), *Digitaria* sp., *Setaria* sp., *Echinochloa crus-galli* (Agulhon *et al.*, 1981), *Amaranthus* sp. and *Polygonum persicaria* are increasing in importance under traditional chemical weed control based on triazine herbicides.

The most important weeds in vineyards, however, are perennials. In California and the north eastern USA, increasing use of pre-emergence herbicides for control of annuals and some perennials has resulted in the spread of other less sensitive perennials such as *Convolvulus arvensis*, *Cyperus rotundus*, *C. esculentus*, *Cynodon dactylon*, *Sorghum halepense* and *Agropyron repens* (Lange *et al.*, 1973; Rogers *et al.*, 1978).

In Central Europe and the Mediterranean, the use of herbicide programmes for control of annuals and some perennials has resulted in the spread of other perennials, the most important being *C. dactylon*, *Convolvulus arvensis*, *A. repens*,

355

S. halepense, C. rotundus, Aristolochia clematitis, Rubus sp. and *Cirsium arvense.* Introduction of no tillage into vineyards also has a tendency to aggravate perennial weed infestations (Agulhon *et al.*, 1975; Kafadarof and Rognon, 1975; Heinzle *et al.*, 1977; Kafadarof and David, 1977; Stalder, Potter and Barben, 1977; Cantele and Zanin, 1978; Coelho, 1978; Daris, 1978).

This review considers, first, the use of glyphosate for control of perennial weeds in vineyards and, secondly, its role in a programme for control of important annual and perennial weeds in early spring and summer.

The name glyphosate in this chapter refers to the isopropylamine salt of *N*-(phosphonomethyl)glycine used as the commercial formulation Roundup.

Weed control

Perennial weed control

Glyphosate has made a major contribution to perennial weed control in vineyards. Since its activity on *Cynodon dactylon* and *Convolvulus arvensis* was reported in 1975 (Kafadarof and Rognon, 1975) and since its commercial introduction in 1976, it has become the accepted treatment for control of *C. dactylon* in May/June in vineyards in France. Performance on this weed is demonstrated in *Table 23.1* (Kafadarof and Rognon, 1975). From these and other trials, Kafadarof and David (1977) demonstrated that a single application of glyphosate at 4.3 kg ha^{-1} still gave, on average, between 65 and 80% control in the fourth to fifth summer after application. This was comparable to 4–5 successive treatments of aminotriazole in spring at 5 kg ha^{-1} or 3–4 treatments of aminotriazole + dalapon at 5 + 5 kg ha^{-1}. Follow-up spot or blanket treatments of surviving patches enables elimination or near elimination of this weed. Similar results on *C. dactylon* were reported by Heinzle *et al.* (1977), where four successive annual applications of glyphosate at 4.5 kg ha^{-1} reduced ground cover from 65% at the beginning of the experiment in 1972 to 0.5% in 1977. In other treatments, ground cover was reduced from 61% in 1972 to 10.5% in 1977 by treatments in 1972, 1973 and 1975 and from 65% in 1973 to 1.5% in 1977 following treatments in 1973 and 1974 at 4.5 kg ha^{-1}. In France, single sprays of glyphosate at 2.9 kg ha^{-1} did not require re-treatment the following

TABLE 23.1   Mean control (%) of *Cynodon dactylon* **in vineyard trials in France (after Kafadarof and Rognon, 1975)**

No. of sites assessed	Days after treatment	Glyphosate (kg ha^{-1})				Amino-triazole (kg ha^{-1})	Amino-triazole (kg ha^{-1}) + dalapon (kg ha^{-1})
		2.7	3.6	4.5	5.4	5.0	5+5
	1st treatment						
24	92	79	90	94	96	35	73
18	394	80	88	92	93	37	60
5	745	73	81	87	88	16	47
	2nd treatment (1–2 years after the 1st treatment)						
12	79		88	96	97	97	45	68
4	420		93	98	99	99	49	72

year (Agulhon *et al.*, 1975); in Greece, Daris (1978) demonstrated that annual applications of glyphosate in 1972, 1973 and 1974 at 4.8 kg ha^{-1} reduced coverage of *C. dactylon* to negligible levels so re-treatment was unnecessary in 1975 and 1976; and in Portugal, glyphosate at 1.8–4.3 kg ha^{-1} gave 90% control or better 3–7 months after treatment (Coelho, 1978).

Glyphosate also gave excellent control of other perennial grass weeds common in vineyards. In 30 commercial scale trials in New York State vineyards, glyphosate at 1.68 kg ha^{-1} gave an average of better than 95% control of *Agropyron repens* (Rogers *et al.*, 1978). Julliard and Ancel (1973), working in France, demonstrated 98% control of this weed 1 year after the application of glyphosate at 4.5 kg ha^{-1}. Kafadarof and Rognon (1975) reported excellent results at 1.8 kg ha^{-1}.

Studies in Greece by Daris (1978) showed that a single application of glyphosate at 4.8 kg ha^{-1} in 1972 reduced the infestation of *Sorghum halepense* by 90% 1 year after treatment, whereas a second application in 1973 eliminated it. In California, good season-long control of *S. halepense* was obtained with applications 2 months apart in spring and mid-summer (Lange *et al.*, 1973). Kafadarof and Rognon (1975) also reported excellent control of *S. halepense* at 1.8–2.7 kg ha^{-1}. For seedling control, follow-up treatment may be necessary the following year.

Coelho (1978) demonstrated excellent control of *Paspalum paspaloides* at 1.08–4.3 kg ha^{-1}, while Kafadarof and Rognon (1975) reported good control of *P. distichum* at 4.5 kg ha^{-1} although here, due to reinfestations, frequent re-treatments were necessary. Heinzle *et al.* (1977) obtained complete control of *Agrostis stolonifera* at 3.6 kg ha^{-1} and Kafadarof and Rognon (1975) excellent control at 1.8 kg ha^{-1}. In South Africa, glyphosate at 1.44 kg ha^{-1} gave excellent control of *Pennisetum clandestinum* and repeat applications to regrowth eliminated this weed (Hebblethwaite, unpublished).

In three trials on *Cyperus rotundus*, Coelho (1978) reported 70–97% control in assessments made 1–3 months after treatment with glyphosate at 2.88–3.60 kg ha^{-1}. Results on *C. esculentus* were somewhat better, with 2.16–3.60 kg ha^{-1} giving 80–99% control. However, Daris (1978) demonstrated the need for repeated applications of glyphosate for the control of *C. rotundus* as reinfestation was rapid even in the year following 3 consecutive annual applications at 4.8 kg ha^{-1}. In South Africa, Hebblethwaite (unpublished) obtained 95% control of *C. rotundus*, 140 days after treatment, following 2 applications of glyphosate at 2 kg ha^{-1} 50 days apart. The literature suggests that the optimum period for control of most perennial grasses is summer to mid-summer, as they approach or reach the flowering stage (see also Chapter 19).

Convolvulus arvensis has an extensive underground system of rhizomes and shoot tissue. Repeat applications of glyphosate at various intervals are required for effective control. In general, application at bud and bloom stage gives the best results. Efficacy of glyphosate on *C. arvensis* in France is shown in *Table 23.2* (Kafadarof and Rognon, 1975). The results showed excellent performance 1 year after treatment at 3.6–5.4 kg ha^{-1}. Reinfestation on these and other trials, however, was rapid in the third and fourth years after treatment, necessitating annual spot treatments or treatment every 2–4 years, when reinfestation becomes troublesome (Kafadarof and David, 1977). In other trials, re-treatment of this weed was not necessary in the third year after treatment with glyphosate at 4.5 kg ha^{-1} (Agulhon *et al.*, 1975), whereas 2 consecutive annual applications of glyphosate at 4.5 kg ha^{-1} avoided the need for applications in the third and fourth years (Heinzle *et al.*, 1977). Similar results were obtained in Greece by Daris

TABLE 23.2   Mean control (%) of *Convolvulus arvensis* **in vineyard trials in France (after Kafadarof and Rognon, 1975)**

No. of sites assessed	Days after treatment	Glyphosate (kg ha^{-1})				Terbu-thylazine + terbu-meton	Oxadia-zon
		2.7	3.6	4.5	5.4	10.0	2.0
	1st treatment						
29*	87	83	90	93	94	62(a)	41(b)
22†	376	80	88	89	91	56(c)	20(a)
	2nd treatment (1–2 years after the 1st treatment)						
13	74	90	95	96	97	69(d)	—

(a) 19 sites, (b) 26 sites, (c) 12 sites, (d) six sites.
*Nine sites comprising 2 dates of application.
†Six sites comprising 2 dates of application.

(1978). After 1 application at 4.8 kg ha^{-1} in May 1972, *C. arvensis* rapidly regrew, but following a second application in May 1973 the treated area remained relatively free for the following three years. In Switzerland, Stalder, Potter and Barben (1977) demonstrated reduction in ground cover of *C. arvensis* from 27% in 1974 to 1% in 1976, following glyphosate applications of 1.8 kg ha^{-1} in 1974, 1975 and 1976. A split application of glyphosate at 0.9 kg ha^{-1} in May and 0.9 kg ha^{-1} in early July 1976 also reduced the infestation from 22 to 3% in the same year and proved superior to a single application at 1.8 kg ha^{-1}.

In New York State vineyards, glyphosate at 2.24 kg ha^{-1} applied at bud to bloom stage in 1973 resulted in 80% control of *C. sepium* and 90% control of *C. arvensis* at the end of the season. One year after treatment, control had dropped by 10–15% and a second application in June 1974 was required to maintain complete control to October 1974 (Selleck, Zabadal and McCargo, 1975). These results on *C. arvensis* were confirmed in a series of 45 trials in commercial vineyards in 1975 and 1976, where average control varied from 75 to 80% 1 year after treatment. In a trial with 14 sites, *C. sepium* control varied from 45 to 55% (Rogers *et al.*, 1978). In France, Agulhon *et al.* (1975) also found *C. sepium* more difficult to control than *C. arvensis* and Kafadarof and Rognon (1975) reported a dose of 4.5 kg ha^{-1}, with a follow-up spot treatment the following year, necessary to control *C. sepium* (see also Chapter 19).

Glyphosate is also effective on other perennial broad-leaved weeds found in vineyards. Heinzle *et al.* (1977) reported regrowth from *Rubus* sp. following summer treatment at 4.5 kg ha^{-1} in France and Kafadarof and David (1977) and Julliard and Ancel (1973) reported good results with *Rubus* sp. following treatment in the autumn, after vine leaf drop. In New York State, Rogers *et al.* (1978) obtained, on average, 85% control of *Rubus* sp. 1 year after treatment at 3.6 kg ha^{-1}.

The effect of glyphosate on other perennial broad-leafed weeds is summarized in *Table 23.3*.

Kafadarof and David (1977) reported control of the following additional perennial weeds in vineyards: *Pastinaca sativa, Phragmites communis, Carex* sp., *Sedum* sp., *Mentha* sp., *Sambucus* sp., *Inula viscosa, Polygonum amphibium, Allium* sp., *Eryngium campestre, Pteridium aquilinum, Chondrilla juncea, Lactuca*

TABLE 23.3   Performance of glyphosate on other perennial broad-leaved weeds

Weed species	Effective dosage rates (kg ha^{-1})	Optimum treatment time	Reference
Aristolochia clematitis	1.8–2.7	At flowering, April/May	Agulhon et al. (1975); Kafadarof et al. (1975; 1977)
Cirsium arvense	1.8	From 30 to 50 cm to flowering	Kafadarof et al. (1975; 1977)
Artemisia vulgaris	2.7	From 30 to 50 cm to flowering	Agulhon et al. (1975); Kafadarof et al. (1975; 1977)
Hypericum perforatum	3.6	At flowering	Agulhon et al. (1975)
Rumex sp.	1.8		Julliard and Ancel (1973); Kafadarof et al. (1975; 1977)
Cardaria draba	1.8		Julliard and Ancel (1973); Kafadarof et al. (1975; 1977)
Tussilago farfara	1.12–2.7		Kafadarof et al. (1975; 1977); Selleck et al. (1975)
Potentilla reptans	3.6–4.5		Julliard and Ancel (1973); Kafadarof et al. (1975; 1977)
Asclepias syriaca	2.24–4.48		Selleck et al. (1975); Rogers et al. (1978)
Apocynum cannabinum	3.36–5.6		
Parthenocissus quinquefolia	3.36–4.48		

perennis, Medicago sp., Holcus sp., Brachypodium sp., Clematis vitalba, Bryonia dioica, Rosa canina, Plantago sp., Urtica dioica, Ranunculus repens.

Perennial weeds, difficult to control with glyphosate, were Equisetum sp., Hedera helix and Rubia peregrina (Kafadarof and David, 1977). Heinzle et al. (1977) also reported regrowth and unsatisfactory control of Equisetum sp. following application as high as 9 kg ha^{-1} (see also Chapter 19).

Annual weed control

Glyphosate controls, post-emergence, a wide range of annual weeds. At rates between 0.72 and 1 kg ha^{-1} Kafadarof and Rognon (1975) obtained control, in France, of many late winter/early spring annuals and biannuals such as Lolium sp., Stellaria media, Poa sp., Senecio vulgaris, Veronica sp., Sonchus sp., Diplotaxis sp., Crepis sp., Calendula arvensis, Papaver sp., Galium aparine, Lamium sp., Fumaria sp., Hordeum murinum, Avena spp., Matricaria sp. Some species such as Geranium sp., Erodium sp., Euphorbia sp. and, to a lesser extent, Mercurialis annua required higher rates.

Emerged summer annuals such as Setaria sp., Digitaria sp., Echinochloa crusgalli, Amaranthus sp., Chenopodium album, Eleusine indica and Tagetes minuta were also well controlled at 0.72–1 kg ha^{-1}

Programmes

Glyphosate has little or no soil activity, so rapid reinfestation of weeds from seed occurs following treatment (Cantele and Zanin, 1978). To maintain good season-long control, either repeated applications are required or inclusion in a programme with residual herbicides (see also Chapters 19 and 22). Cantele and Zanin (1978) reported excellent results from a summer application of glyphosate, following spring treatment with simazine. In commercial practice, early spring applications of terbuthylazine + terbumeton or aminotriazole + simazine for annual/biannual weed control are often followed by a summer treatment of glyphosate for control of perennials such as *Cynodon dactylon*. In the drier Mediterranean areas, 2–3 applications of glyphosate have often proved sufficient to maintain relatively weed-free conditions throughout the season. An initial application at 0.72–1 kg ha^{-1} is effective on late winter/early spring annuals followed by higher rates in mid-summer for perennial weed control. Late-germinating summer annuals can be controlled by 0.72–1 kg ha^{-1} if foliar contact with the vines can be avoided.

Recently, mixtures of glyphosate and residual herbicides, especially glyphosate + simazine, have been evaluated (see also Chapter 15). Kafadarof, David and Rass (unpublished) found glyphosate at 1 kg ha^{-1} + simazine 3 kg ha^{-1} gave excellent results when applied to late winter/early spring weeds. They also found that the addition of ammonium sulphate often improved the performance of this mixture on certain weeds and in particular on *Lolium* sp. Glyphosate + simazine in late winter/early spring, followed by a summer treatment of glyphosate alone, gave excellent all-round control of annual and perennial weeds and has been widely tested in vineyards throughout the Mediterranean area and Germany F.R. with excellent results. Some summer annual weeds such as *Solanum nigrum*, *Digitaria* sp., *Setaria* sp., *Echinochloa* sp., *Amaranthus* sp. (Rouas, 1981; Agulhon *et al.*, 1981) and *Polygonum persicaria* escape spring treatments of simazine. These species are effectively controlled post-emergence by glyphosate. However, seed germination can still be a problem following this treatment. To find a solution, a number of residual herbicides are being tested in mixture with glyphosate.

Crop tolerance

Glyphosate has little or no soil activity, and damage to vines from root uptake has not been reported. In 8 trials in France in the early 1970s, application of glyphosate at 0.9 and 1.8 g l^{-1} to a 20–40 cm length of the main stem of 1–3-year-old vines did not result in any damage (Kafadarof and Rognon, 1975). In 10 other trials, Kafadarof and Rognon (1975) assessed the effect of glyphosate on vines following the treatment of a single leaf with a concentration of 0.9 g l^{-1}. Applications prior to flowering resulted in desiccation of the treated leaf, and new growth from the tip of the treated shoot showed some characteristically malformed leaves (see also Chapter 19). Partially treated shoots were desiccated, but only in the worst cases did translocation result in the malformation of some leaves on other parts of the vinestock. These minor leaf symptoms tended to disappear 1 year after treatment. Damage from applications after flowering were more severe. At this time, leaf contact must be avoided. After flowering, the portion of a branch treated becomes partially or completely desiccated with translocation damage more evident and persistent. This translocation damage is characterized by malformed leaves and shortened internodes and is visible the following spring/summer.

These findings were largely confirmed by Wurgler and Neury (1977), who showed that treatment of 1 leaf at the base of 4 shoots with a glyphosate concentration of 4 g l^{-1} resulted in leaf malformations at the shoot extremities. These malformations, together with shoot inhibitions, were more severe from end-June onwards. Leaf symptoms decrease in the second and third years after treatment. They also showed translocation from a treated shoot to other shoots from the same branch ('horn') arising from the main stem. Leaf malformations on these other shoots were more severe from late June/early July treatment than early June. Little material was translocated from a shoot through the older wood of the branch ('horn') to other branches and shoots on the main stem, but it tends to increase from late June onwards. Wurgler and Neury (1977) showed that applications of glyphosate to the lower leaf surface resulted in more translocated leaf symptoms than application to the upper leaf surface.

Symptoms of leaf malformation were described by Shaulis, Crowe and Rogers (1978) in trials where various parts of the vine plant were treated. These symptoms are described in *Table 23.4*. Further direct and translocated leaf symptom effects on the roots of young potted vines are described by Lee and Cahoon (1981). Growth, as measured by pruning weight, was reduced by glyphosate sprayed in a vineyard in Samaria in Israel at 3.6 kg ha^{-1} (Gur, Gil and Bravdo, 1979). Drift on to lower leaves was the suspected cause. This was accompanied by a lowering of the reducing sugar content in the canes.

In general, the risk of damage to the vines is small from treatments applied in May/June, when most perennial weeds, including *Convolvulus arvensis*, are at the

TABLE 23.4   The symptoms* of injury by glyphosate translocated in grapevines (after Shaulis, Crowe and Rogers, 1978)

Tissue	Symptom
Leaf:	
surface†	Rugosity, with inverveinal tissue depressed
petiolar sinus lobes†	Widened to as much as 240°. Terminal lobe remains prominent; lateral lobes are irregular to absent
size	Stunted
margin	Irregular, frequently appearing torn
symmetry	Reduced
colour	Interveinally chlorotic, as yellow green
location of affected leaves	
—from current season's application	Apical to the point of application and usually persisting to the shoot apex
—from previous season's application	Primarily on leaves on non-lateral shoots with malformation increasing towards apex. On lateral shoots, malformation is less pronounced and then more severe on basal leaves
Bud rest breaking	Very infrequent in weed control efforts
Shoot	
maturity	Reduced to few or no internodes with periderm
size	Stunting, over a wide range of severity
lateral shoot development	In extreme cases there is a profusion of stunted lateral shoots

*These symptoms were encountered with applications of glyphosate intended to cause injury.
†These are more characteristic of glyphosate injury.

correct stage for application in the Mediterranean area. At this time, contact with the upper leaf surface of low hanging vine shoots will, at worst, result in limited shoot desiccation and some leaf malformation, generally of a temporary nature. In other areas, safe application may be earlier, namely May to mid-June. If applications are made after this time, leaf contact must be avoided and, in low vineyards, shields must be used.

Effect on wine

The possible effects of glyphosate on wine production (Kafadarof, unpublished) were studied at 6 locations in France using the following assessments:

(1) *Must analysis:* total acidity; tartaric acid; malic acid; pH; density; sugars; alcohol content.
(2) *Fermentation tests.*
(3) *Wine analysis:* density; ebullioscope alcoholic degree; pH; dry extract; total acidity; volatile acids; corrected volatile acidity; fixed acidity; free sulphur; total sulphur; sugars; iron; air behaviour; intensity—DO 420 + DO 520; colour—DO 420/DO 520.

Anthocyans, tannin, total polyphenols and permanganate index were determined on some samples. There were no significant analytical differences between treated and untreated musts. Complete wine analysis did not show any significant differences between treated and untreated for the various factors. Differences in fermentation were negligible in all cases, although there was a tendency for better sugar fermentation with the glyphosate-treated vines from one of the locations. Wine tasting repeated several times by Cetex oenologists and by tasting commissions did not reveal any unfavourable effects on taste, smell or visual qualities between treated and untreated samples.

Methods of application

Work throughout Europe and the USA has demonstrated that glyphosate works better in lower volumes of water. When using hydraulic nozzles, volumes of 100–400 l ha^{-1} are optimal. In the Mediterranean area, and particularly in Spain, hand-held CDA equipment has been successfully used to apply glyphosate, in early spring prior to bud burst in vines, using 10–40 l ha^{-1} of spray volume.

To avoid contact with shoots and leaves in low-trellised and bush vines, a wide range of low-boom and shielded equipment has been developed (Bruge, 1976). Hand-held wiping equipment using a 33% glyphosate solution has also given good control of spot infestations of perennial weeds (see also Chapter 16).

Conclusions

No other herbicide has given the degree of control in vineyards of the range of weeds which is achieved with glyphosate. This herbicide is particularly effective for the control of perennial weeds and has become the most widely accepted treatment for control of the two major vineyard species, *Cynodon dactylon* and *Convolvulus arvensis*, in the Mediterranean area, Central Europe and the USA. Glyphosate also controls, post-emergence, a broad range of annual weed species in vineyards and has, therefore, been effectively used in programmes for control of winter/early spring annuals, summer perennials and summer annuals. It is often used in summer for control of perennial weeds following spring treatments with residual herbicides. In the drier Mediterranean areas, 2–3 applications of glyphosate alone have been sufficient to give season-long control of weeds in vineyards. More recently, glyphosate has been tested in mixture with residual herbicides, and glyphosate + simazine has been used commercially in Mediterranean and Central European vineyards as an early spring application for control of late winter/early spring weeds. This treatment, followed by a summer application of glyphosate for perennial weed control, gives excellent all-round weed control.

Glyphosate can be used with safety in vineyards if carefully applied. The risk of vine damage is small from treatments applied prior to flowering in mid- to late June, when most perennial weeds are at the correct stage for application. At this time, some contact with the upper leaf surface of low-hanging vine shoots will, at worst, result in limited shoot desiccation and some leaf malformation, generally of a temporary nature. If applications are made after flowering (July/August), leaf contact must be avoided as serious damage can result.

Glyphosate had no adverse effects on the fermentation process, in wine production, or on taste, smell or visual qualities.

References

AGULHON, R., DUMARTIN, O., GAGNE, R., HEINZLE, Y., MEYER, E. and MOIROUD, A. (1975). Latest trial results for perennial weed control in vineyards, *Proceedings of the 8th Columa Conference*, Paris, **3**, 858–868.

AGULHON, R., DUMARTIN, P., HEINZLE, Y. and ROZIER, J.P. (1981). Trials for contest of several weeds resistant to herbicides currently used in vineyards, *Proceedings of the 1st Columa Conference*, Versailles, pp. 625–634.

BRUGE, G. (1976). Importance of equipment for glyphosate application in viticulture, *Phytoma—Crop Protection*, April, pp. 14–20.

CANTELE, A. and ZANIN, G. (1978). Three years of experiments with chemicals for weed control in Veneto vineyards, *Review of Agronomy*, **13**(3), 396–409.

COELHO, A.D. (1978). The use of Roundup in Portuguese vineyards, *Proceedings of the Roundup Seminar*, Madrid, pp. 73–101.

DARIS, B.T. (1978). Results on control of perennial weeds in Greek vineyards, Presentation at the 58th General Assembly, Athens, *O.I.V. Bulletin*, no. 574, pp. 552–559.

GUR, A., GIL, Y. and BRAVDO, B. (1979). The efficacy of several herbicides in the vineyard and their toxicity to grapevines, *Weed Research*, **19**, 109–116.

HEINZLE, Y., AGULHON, R., DUMARTIN, P. and ROZIER, J.P. (1977). Trials for control of several perennial weeds currently infesting vineyards, *Proceedings of the 9th Columa Conference*, Paris, **3**, 770–779.

JULLIARD, B. and ANCEL, J. (1973). New opportunities for perennial weed control in vineyards, *Proceedings of the 7th Columa Conference*, Paris, **3**, 787–797.

KAFADAROF, G. and DAVID, H. (1977). Report on 6 years experimentation and on 2 years of use of glyphosate in vineyards, *Proceedings of the 9th Columa Conference*, Paris, **3**, 735–747.

KAFADAROF, G. and ROGNON, J. (1975). The use of glyphosate for weed control in vineyards, *Proceedings of the 8th Columa Conference*, Paris, **3**, 831–840.

LANGE, A.H., ELMORE, C.L., FISHER, B.B., SWANSON, F.H. and DONALDSON, D.R. (1973). Glyphosate for perennial weed control in trees and vines. A progress report, Agricultural Extension, University of California, May 1973, pp. 1–20.

LEE, D.K. and CAHOON, G.A. (1981). Research note. Glyphosate (Roundup) toxicity to Niagara grapevines, *American Journal of Enology and Viticulture*, **32**(3), 247–250.

ROGERS, R.A., ZABADAL, T.J., CROWE, D.E. and JORDAN, T.D. (1978). The relation of the phytotoxicity of glyphosate to its injury-free use in vineyards. Part II: Injury-free use in New York vineyards, *Proceedings of the Northeastern Weed Science Society*, **32**, 254–259.

ROUAS, G. (1981). Trial for control of *Epilobium tetragonum* and *Solanum nigrum* in Champagne area, *Proceedings of the 11th Columa Conference*, Versailles, pp. 635–641.

SELLECK, G.W., ZABADAL, T. and MCCARGO, S.M. (1975). Glyphosate for weed control in vineyards, *Proceedings of the Northeastern Weed Science Society*, **29**, 237–238.

SHAULIS, N.J., CROWE, D.E. and ROGERS, R A. (1978). The relation of the phytotoxicity of glyphosate to its injury-free use in vineyards. Part I: Glyphosate studies as a basis for injury-free use, *Proceedings of the Northeastern Weed Science Society*, **32**, 246–253.

STALDER, L., POTTER, C.A. and BARBEN, E. (1977). New experiences with integrated measures for the control of *Convolvulus arvensis* and *Convolvulus sepium* in vineyards, *Proceedings of the EWRS Symposium Methods of Weed Control and Their Integration*, Mainz, pp. 221–228.

WURGLER, W. and NEURY, G. (1977). The vine vegetation 2 and 3 years after glyphosate absorption, *Proceedings of the 9th Columa Conference*, Paris, **3**, 748–753.

Chapter 24

Efficacy of glyphosate in the control of aquatic weeds

P.R.F. Barrett
Weed Research Organization, Oxford, UK

Introduction

In prehistoric times, water weeds probably interfered with man's early attempts at fishing and boating. With the advent of agriculture, land drainage and irrigation became necessary and man dug channels to move water. These channels provided ideal growing conditions for aquatic plants, which colonized them and reduced the efficiency of the channels by impeding flow. Some form of weed control became necessary and for centuries the weeds were cut by hand and removed from the channels. This process was not entirely wasteful because some of the emergent weeds such as *Phragmites australis* and *Schoenoplectus lacustris* could be used for thatching and making baskets and matting. In recent times, however, these crafts have almost died out and it has been suggested (Robson, 1976) that man's activities, such as the use of agricultural fertilizer and the disposal of sewage effluent, are stimulating the growth of weeds and making the problem worse.

Changing agricultural practices and increasing labour costs are forcing farmers and engineers to seek new, and more efficient, forms of weed control. Machines have been developed which can operate on the banks or in the water to cut the weeds and, more recently, herbicides have been shown to provide an effective alternative.

The name glyphosate in this chapter refers to the isopropylamine salt of *N*-(phosphonomethyl)glycine used as the commercial formulation Roundup.

Methods of weed control

The type of weed and the situation in which it is growing are the factors which most influence the choice of weed-control technique. Aquatic weeds are normally described as being emergent, floating or submerged, and the algae as filamentous or unicellular, depending on their growth form. Individual species may occur in more than one group, for example *Sagittaria sagittifolia* produces submerged, floating and emergent leaves at different times during the growing season. The other factor influencing the choice of weed control is the situation in which weeds are growing. The weeds may be present in a narrow channel, partly obstructed by trees and crossed by numerous bridges, or they might cover many hundreds of hectares in a large lake.

The two most common methods of controlling aquatic weeds are mechanical and chemical. Other methods which are attracting increasing interest are biological control, such as the use of herbivorous fish (Opuszynski, 1972) and environmental control by, for example, planting trees to shade the water surface (Dawson, 1978).

All of these techniques have limitations and none of them is sufficiently versatile to cope with all types of weeds and all the situations in which they can grow. Individual machines or herbicides must be regarded as management tools to be selected or rejected on the basis of the individual weed problem.

Glyphosate in relation to other herbicides used in the aquatic environment

Robson (1978) estimated that about 25 herbicides were in use throughout the world for aquatic weed control. In most countries, some form of government control exists to regulate the use of these herbicides. Depending on the problems and requirements of individual countries, different herbicides may be permitted or rejected. For example, acrolein, which is highly toxic to fish, is considered to be a useful herbicide in irrigation systems, where no fishing interest exists, because it is fast acting against submerged weeds but does not harm irrigated crops.

Herbicides are normally used in one of two ways. They are either sprayed directly onto the exposed foliage at or above the water surface or they are added to the water and absorbed by submerged foliage or through the roots. Some herbicides such as diquat and 2,4-D amine can be used in either way, but against different weeds. Diquat is effective against *Lemna* spp. when sprayed onto the fronds at 1.0 kg a.i. ha^{-1}, but it can also be used against submerged weeds when added to the water at a concentration of 1.0 mg a.i. l^{-1}. If a water body of 1 m depth and 1 ha in area is considered, then the dose required to control the floating weed (1 kg ha^{-1}) is only 10% of the dose required to control submerged weeds. Similar values apply to other herbicides, and it can be seen that emergent or floating weeds, onto which a foliar spray can be directed, may be more cheaply controlled with herbicides than submerged weeds.

Glyphosate is one of the herbicides applied against emergent and floating species. Unlike diquat or 2,4-D amine, it appears to be totally ineffective against submerged species. Glyphosate is a herbicide which is well translocated in a basipetal direction in emergent and floating weeds. However, Comes and Yang (1981) showed that both the absorption and translocation of glyphosate was poor in the submerged weeds which they tested. They suggested that diminished basipetal translocation of herbicides and nutrients may be attributable to the reduced vascular systems in most submerged plants compared with terrestrial species.

It is not easy to compare glyphosate with other herbicides used in the aquatic environment because properties which are desirable in one situation may be disadvantageous in another. Factors such as cost, selectivity, speed of action, time of application and persistence can all influence the choice of herbicide. Dalapon, for examples is a cheap and effective herbicide for the control of *Phragmites australis,* but is less effective against *Glyceria maxima.* Both these species are susceptible to glyphosate which would, therefore, be preferable in situations where both species were present. Glyphosate is generally more effective against broad-leaved species, particularly perennials, than 2,4-D amine. Other herbicides which have been used for the control of various emergent and floating species include aminotriazole, ammonium sulphamate, asulam, dicamba, fenoprop and paraquat. Most, if not all, of the weeds which are susceptible to one or more of these herbicides are also susceptible to glyphosate. It is, therefore, a broad spectrum herbicide particularly useful for general control of mixed populations of emergent and floating weed species (*Figure 24.1*)

Figure 24.1. Glyceria maxima, growing in a water meadow, was sprayed with glyphosate at 2 kg ha^{-1}. The photograph shows a treated plot 1 year after application

Emergent and bankside weeds

There are many emergent and bankside weeds which cause problems, particularly in the smaller water courses (see also Chapter 28). The stems impede flow during the summer months and in the autumn both stems and leaves collapse into the water causing further blockage. Many species produce rhizomes which grow out from the sides of the channel and produce large numbers of adventitious roots which trap silt and effectively reduce the channel size. In large water bodies, emergent weeds can cause problems by colonizing the margins and, in extreme cases, forming floating islands, as has happened in Lake Chad (Okafor, 1982) and other large tropical lakes.

Glyphosate has been used in many countries as an effective means of controlling these weeds. *Table 24.1* lists some of the species known to be susceptible to glyphosate and the countries in which trials have been reported.

The spray volumes reported in these trials show considerable variation, ranging from 3000 1 ha^{-1} (Evans, 1978) down to a few litres per hectare applied by

TABLE 24.1 Published references to emergent and bankside weeds susceptible to glyphosate

Species	Dose (kg ha^{-1})	Country	Reference
Agrostis stolonifera	1.8	UK	Seddon (1981)
Alisma spp.	1.8	Sweden	Evans (1978)
	1.8	UK	Seddon (1981)
Alternanthera philoxeroides	3.3	USA	Evans (1978)
Arundo donax	2.2–4.4	USA	Schrader and Alpers (1977)
Aster spinosus	2.2–4.4	USA	Schrader and Alpers (1977)
Carex spp.	1.8	USA, Sweden, Belgium, Germany	Evans (1978)
Catabrosa aquatica	1.8	UK	Seddon (1981)
Cynodon dactylon	4.4	USA	Schrader and Alpers (1977)
Eleocharis spp.	1.5	USA	Lembi (1978)
	2.0	USA	Evans (1978)
Equisetum arvense	4.0–8.0	USA	Coupland and Peabody (1981)
Glyceria maxima	2.0	UK	Barrett (1976)
	1.4	Belgium	Evans (1978)
	1.0	Australia	Smith (1979)
	1.8	UK	Seddon (1981)
	2.3	UK	Eaton *et al.* (1981)
Helianthus ciliaris	2.2–4.4	USA	Schrader and Alpers (1977)
Juncus effusus	1.5	USA	Lembi (1978)
	1.8	Sweden	Evans (1978)
Nasturtium officinale	1.4	UK	Evans (1978)
	1.8	UK	Seddon (1981)
Panicum purpurascens	3.3	USA	Orsenigo (1975)
P. repens	2.5–3.0	USA	Evans (1978)
Paspalum distichum	1.1–2.2	USA	Schrader and Alpers (1977)
	1.2	Japan	Shibayama and Miyahara (1977)
		Australia	Bowmer (1979)
Pennisetum purpureum	3.3	USA	Orsenigo (1975)
	3.3	USA	Evans (1978)
Phalaris arundinacea	1.8	UK, Germany, Sweden, USA	Evans (1978)
	1.5	USA	Lembi (1978)
	1.8	UK	Seddon (1981)
P. canariensis	1.1–4.4	USA	Schumacher and Kern (1976)
Phragmites australis	5.4–10.8	Portugal	Fernandez *et al.* (1978)
	1.8	UK	Seddon (1981)
Salix spp.	2.0	USA	Evans (1978)
	1.5	USA	Lembi (1978)
Scirpus atrovirens	1.5	USA	Lembi (1978)
S. lacustris	2.7	Sweden	Evans (1978)
S. maritimus	1.0	UK	Hanley (1981)
Sorghum halepense	1.1–4.4	USA	Schumacher and Kern (1976)
	2.2	USA	Schrader and Alpers (1977)
Sparganium erectum	2.3	UK	Eaton *et al.* (1981)
Typha spp.	1.1–4.4	USA	Schumacher and Kern (1976)
	5.4–7.2	Portugal	Fernandez *et al.* (1978)
	2.7–3.0	Belgium, Spain, UK, USA	Evans (1978)
	1.5	USA	Lambi (1978)

rope-wick applicators in which the herbicide was diluted by 50% to 180 g a.i. l^{-1} (Evans, 1982) (see also Chapter 16). The important factor is that the herbicide should not be sprayed to the point of run-off and this will vary from species to species, depending on morphology and cuticular structure. Volume rates of 200–600 l ha^{-1} are recommended by the manufacturers for emergent weed control. There is no reason to suppose that lower volume rates applied by controlled drop application techniques would not be as effective as they are on terrestrial weeds, as was shown by Turner and Loader (1978).

In practice, difficulties can arise when attempts are made to apply glyphosate to emergent weeds. The weeds can grow in inaccessible places where neither boat-mounted nor land-mounted spraying equipment can reach adequately, and they can grow to considerable heights making hand-operated spray equipment difficult to use. In these situations, long lances and long-throw jets are sometimes used, but these can result in poorer distribution and, therefore, a lower level of control. Nevertheless, when correctly applied, the efficacy of glyphosate is well proven on a broad spectrum of aquatic weeds (see *Table 24.1*).

Timing of treatments

The timing of the treatment is important, so that the plants are sprayed during their most susceptible growth stages. Many authors reported poor levels of control from treatments applied too early or too late in the season. Early treatments may be ineffective because of inadequate leaf area for herbicide absorption and because late developing shoots are screened by their more advanced neighbours. Furthermore, poor control might be expected from early application because translocation into the rhizome system is inadequate during the early stages of growth when new stems and leaves are being formed. Late applications can also produce poor results, and this may be due to the onset of senescence before the glyphosate has been fully translocated into the rhizome system. Partial failure has also occurred when the weeds have been cut or damaged before or shortly after glyphosate has been applied.

Evans (1978) suggested that the optimum time for treatment of most aquatic species is likely to be around the time of flowering or just after. The disadvantage of delaying treatment until the flowering stage is reached is that the weeds are then fully grown and are causing major impedence to flow. Cave (1981) stated that, in some instances, the risk of leaving weeds in drainage ditches could be unacceptable and that the engineers were sometimes forced to cut the weed at an earlier stage. Another disadvantage is that, several weeks after spraying, it is necessary to cut and remove the dead weed to prevent it collapsing into the channel. Evans (1978) reported that trials in Germany had shown that early season treatment of *P. australis* could produce commercially acceptable levels of control and dispense with the need for a post-treatment cutting operation. However, a spot treatment of surviving plants was necessary in the following season.

Floating weeds

This group of weeds can be subdivided into the free-floating weeds such as *Lemna* spp. and *Salvinia* spp. and the rooted species including *Nuphar* spp. and *Nymphaea* spp. (*Figure 24.2*). The free-floating and rooted species known to be susceptible to glyphosate are listed in *Table 24.2*.

Figure 24.2. The effect of glyphosate sprayed at 2 kg ha⁻¹ onto a mixed population of *Nuphar lutea* and *Nymphaea alba*. The swath was 4 m wide and the photograph, taken 2 years after treatment, shows almost no regrowth into the treated area

TABLE 24.2   Published references to floating weeds susceptible to glyphosate

Species	Dose (kg ha⁻¹)	Country	Reference
Eichhornia crassipes	2.0	Netherlands	Pieterse and Van Rijn (1974)
	2.0 (+ 2,4-D)	Indonesia	Widyanto *et al.* (1977)
	5.4	Portugal	Fernandez *et al.* (1978)
	1.18–1.44	South Africa	Evans (1978)
	3.36	USA	Evans (1978)
Lemna spp.	1.44	UK	Evans (1978)
	1.44	UK	Seddon (1981)
Nelumbo lutea	1.5	USA	Lembi (1978)
Nuphar advena	2.24	USA	Blackburn (1974)
	1.5	USA	Lembi (1978)
N. lutea	1.5	UK	Barrett (1974a)
	2.0	UK	Barrett (1974b)
Nymphaea alba	2.0	UK	Barrett (1978)
N. odorata	2.2	USA	Welker and Riemer (1978)
Pistia stratiotes	2.0	Netherlands	Pieterse and Van Rijn (1974)
	3.0	Philippines	Bua-ngam and Mercado (1977)
Polygonum amphibium	1.5	USA	Lembi (1978)
Salvinia spp.	2.0	Netherlands	Pieterse and Van Rijn (1974)

Timing of treatments

Timing of application is as important with floating-leaved species as with emergent weeds. Treatments applied before full leaf emergence on the surface will be less effective, as will late treatments onto senescent leaves.

Floating-leaved plants can often be more difficult to treat effectively than emergent species partly because at least some of the leaves on each plant must be exposed with a dry upper surface above water level. It is usually necessary to mount the sprayer in a boat. Apart from the difficulty of moving the boat through dense weed beds, the passage of the boat can submerge the leaves, washing off any herbicide on them or reducing the efficacy of any treatment until the leaves had dried again. Free-floating species can also drift, so that they can be missed by successive spray swaths. In many instances, two or more subsequent spraying operations may be needed after the initial treatment to obtain good control. Aerial application of glyphosate can overcome some of these problems, but in some countries this is not permitted because of the danger of drift onto nearby susceptible crops.

Recolonization by floating weeds

In general, the free-floating weeds can reproduce more rapidly than the rooted weeds, particularly by budding off daughter plants. Widyanto and Soerjani (1978) suggested that *Eichhornia crassipes* could double the number of floating leaves every 7–10 days under good conditions. It has proved almost impossible, in practice, to obtain 100% control of this plant, when it is growing in dense infestations, with a single application of herbicide because of the screening effect of one plant by another. The surviving plants can recolonize the area very rapidly unless re-treated at regular intervals. Widyanto and Soerjani (1978) calculated that it was necessary to kill at least 50% of the surviving population each week in order to prevent the population from increasing.

Rooted species, although slower growing than most floating plants, can recolonize rapidly, particularly if they produce large numbers of viable seeds. Welker and Riemer (1978) found that a single application of glyphosate to *Nymphaea odorata* was unsatisfactory because the treated area was recolonized by seedlings within 2 years. They found that a second application to control the seedlings was necessary and this controlled the weed for at least 3 years.

Resistant species

Two species of floating weed which appear to be resistant to glyphosate are *Potamogeton natans* and *Nymphoides peltata*. M.C. Fowler (personal communication) reported that, when glyphosate was sprayed onto the floating leaves of *P. natans*, some scorch was observed, but the plant rapidly replaced the damaged leaves and recovered. S. Hanley (personal communication) reported similar observations on *N. peltata*.

Total and localized weed control

In many drainage and irrigation systems it is necessary to maintain the bed and banks of the channel completely free of weeds to maximize the water-carrying capacity. Where the colonizing weeds consist of emergent and floating species, glyphosate is an excellent herbicide for this purpose, because of its wide spectrum of susceptible species. Where floating weeds occur in lakes it is also necessary to attempt total weed control, because of their rapid rate of reproduction and because it is almost impossible to keep localized areas clear of drifting weed.

In many other situations it is only necessary to clear weeds from localized areas where they are causing problems. There are four advantages to restricting the treatment to localized areas. First, it reduces the total amount of herbicide used and, therefore, the cost. Secondly, it reduces the impact on the ecosytem and preserves the habitat of many aquatic invertebrates, fish and birds in areas where the weed can be tolerated. Thirdly, the surviving plants at the margins of the treated area help to shade the water and reduce the growth of submerged weeds and algae. As was shown earlier, these can be more difficult and expensive to control than the emergent or floating species. Fourthly, localized control reduces the visual impact which is important when herbicides are used for amenity purposes.

Glyphosate can be used for localized control because, although it has a broad spectrum, its effects are limited to the area onto which the herbicide spray is directed. Trials in the UK, at the Weed Research Organization, showed no effect of glyphosate on submerged weeds at concentration up to 10 mg a.e. l^{-1} and in field trials (Barrett, 1974a) there was no effect on *Nuphar lutea* outside the treated areas.

Localized control can be useful for opening access areas for boating and fishing and for clearing channels through overgrown streams and ditches to improve the water-carrying capacity.

Selective application

Although the broad spectrum properties of glyphosate are often beneficial, there are certain circumstances where a more selective approach is required. For example, many emergent species colonize the banks of drainage or irrigation channels. Some, such as *P. australis*, may even spread out into the adjoining crops. A herbicide treatment must not damage the crops nor the grasses which are often planted deliberately on the banks of the channels to stabilize them and prevent slippage. Where the canopy of *P. australis* is dense, some selectivity can be achieved with conventional sprays because the short-growing grasses underneath are screened from the spray droplets by the taller weed. Relatively sparse growth of *P. australis* may, however, still need to be controlled without damage to the underlying plants. Recently, Evans (1982) showed that rope-wick applications can give satisfactory control without damage to the underlying plants (see also Chapter 16).

Conclusions

The number of herbicides used in or near water is small and likely to remain so in the foreseeable future. Most countries insist on strict testing to show that a herbicide is safe for the user, and the public in general as well as domestic livestock, fish and other forms of wildlife in the aquatic environment. Tests for aquatic uses are especially stringent since herbicides which carry recommendations for use in aquatic situations may also be applied in potable or irrigation catchments and could contaminate the supplies. Manufacturers are reluctant to develop herbicides for aquatic use because, apart from the need to carry out these tests, the market is small when compared with much larger markets in cereals and other crops.

Glyphosate has been used worldwide for aquatic weed control and has been accepted as safe for that use in most countries. It is evident from the lists of susceptible species in *Tables 24.1* and *24.2* that it is capable of controlling many of the more troublesome emergent and floating weed species. It is likely that further research would greatly increase those lists and add some of the less common weeds. The mode of action of glyphosate makes it ideally suited to aquatic use. It is easily translocated down to the underground structures (Sprankle, Meggitt and Penner (1975) which are common in many aquatic plants and which may, as in the case of *Nuphar* spp., be several metres from the point of entry at the water surface. It is relatively slow acting and there are no reports of deoxygenation of the water which can occur when large masses of weed decompose suddenly. Glyphosate is rapidly degraded in water (Sacher, 1978) and in the UK, for example, no interval is required between the application of glyphosate to water weeds and the use of that water for irrigation.

Many of the weeds listed in *Tables 24.1* and *24.2* are susceptible to other herbicides, but none of the alternatives normally used in water has as wide a spectrum of susceptible species as has glyphosate. Where individual species occupy large areas there may be other, cheaper herbicides which can be equally effective. However, it is more common to find aquatic weeds growing in mixed communities where the suppression of one species may encourage the growth of another. In these situations, glyphosate is better able to control all the weeds than any of the alternative herbicides and can, in the long term, provide a more economic solution to the problem.

References

BARRETT, P.R.F. (1974a). The susceptibility of *Nuphar lutea* L. to some foliage applied herbicides, *Proceedings of the EWRS 4th Symposium on Aquatic Weeds*, pp. 253–258.

BARRETT, P.R.F. (1974b). The effect of spraying large plots of *Nuphar lutea* L. with glyphosate, *Proceedings of the 12th British Weed Control Conference*, **1**, 229–232.

BARRETT, P.R.F. (1976). The effect of dalapon and glyphosate on *Glyceria maxima* (Hartm) Holmberg, *Proceedings of the 1976 British Crop Protection Conference—Weeds*, pp. 79–82.

BARRETT, P.R.F. (1978). The place of glyphosate among aquatic herbicides in Great Britain, *Proceedings of the Roundup Seminar*, Madrid, pp. 24–26.

BLACKBURN, R.D. (1974). Chemical control of ditchbank and aquatic weeds in Florida drainage ditches, *USDA–ARS Annual Report*, Southern Region, Florida Antilles area.

BOWMER, K.H. (1979). Management of aquatic weeds in Australia irrigation systems, *Proceedings of the 7th Asian Pacific Weed Science Society Conference*, pp. 219–222.

BUA-NGAM, T. and MERCADO, B.L. (1977). Response of *Pistia stratiotes* L. to selective and non-selective herbicides in rice, *Philippines Weed Science Bulletin*, **4**, 1–6.

CAVE, T.G. (1981). Current weed control problems in land drainage channels, *Proceedings of the AAB Conference on Aquatic Weeds and Their Control*, pp. 5–14.

COUPLAND, D. and PEABODY, D.V. (1981). Effect of four foliage applied herbicides on field horsetail (*Equisetum arvense*), *Journal of the Weed Science Society of America*, **29**, 113–119.

DAWSON, F.H. (1978). Aquatic plant management in semi-natural streams: the role of marginal vegetation, *Journal of Environmental Management*, **6**, 213–221.

EATON, J.W., MURPHY, K.J. and HYDE, T.M. (1981). Comparative trials of herbicidal and mechanical control of aquatic weeds in canals, *Proceedings of the AAB Conference on Aquatic Weeds and Their Control*, pp. 105–116.

EVANS, D.M. (1978). Aquatic weed control with the isopropylamine salt of *N*-phosphonomethyl glycine, *Proceedings of the EWRS 5th Symposium on Aquatic Weeds*, pp. 171–178.

EVANS, D.M. (1982). Phragmites control with glyphosate through selective equipment, *Proceedings of the EWRS 6th Symposium on Aquatic Weeds*, pp. 209–211.

FERNANDES, J.D., GUERREIRO, A.R., VASCONCELOS, T. and MOREIRA, I. (1978). Essais de lutte coutre les plautes aquatiques Portugal, *Proceedings of the EWRS 5th Symposium on Aquatic Weeds*, pp. 189–194.

HANLEY, S. (1981). The effect of glyphosate on *Scirpus maritimus*, *Proceedings of the AAB Conference on Aquatic Weeds and Their Control*, pp. 199–200.

LEMBI, C.A. (1978). Results of 1978 aquatic herbicide trials in Indiana, *Proceedings of the North Central Weed Control Conference*, **33**, 102–103.

MARQUIS, L.Y., COMES, R.D. and YANG, C.P. (1981). Absorption and translocation of fluridone and glyphosate in submerged vascular plants, *Weed Science*, **29**(2), 229–236.

OKAFOR, L.I. (1982). A preliminary survey of the major aquatic weeds of Lake Chad, Nigeria, *Proceedings of the EWRS 6th Symposium on Aquatic Weeds*, pp. 10–19.

OPUSZYNSKI, K. (1972). The use of phytophagous fish to control aquatic plants, *Aquaculture*, **1**, 61–73.

ORSENIGO, J.R. (1975). Chemical control of ditchbank weeds in peat and sandy soil areas of south Florida, *Annual Research Report*, Institute of Food and Agricultural Science, University of Florida, Gainsville, p. 252.

PIETERSE, A.H. and VAN RIJN, P.J. (1974). A preliminary study on the response of *Eichhornia crassipes*, *Salvinia auriculata* and *Pistia stratiotes* to glyphosate, *International Symposium on Crop Protection*, Gent, **39** (issue 2), 423–427.

ROBSON, T.O. (1976). Aquatic weeds in Great Britain—their occurrence and significance as weeds, *British Crop Protection Council Monograph 16, Aquatic Herbicides*, pp. 1–6.

ROBSON, T.O. (1978). The present status of chemical aquatic weed control, *Proceedings of the EWRS 5th Symposium on Aquatic Weeds*, pp. 17–25.

SACHER, R.M. (1978). Safety of Roundup in the aquatic environment, *Proceedings of the EWRS 5th Symposium on Aquatic Weeds*, pp. 315–322.

SCHUMACHER, R.W. and KERN, A.D. (1976). Vegetation control on aquatic sites with glyphosate, *Proceedings of the North Central Weed Control Conference*, p. 106.

SEDDON, J.C. (1981). The control of aquatic weeds with the isopropylamine salt of *N*-phosphosomethyl glycine, *Proceedings of the AAB Conference on Aquatic Weeds and Their Control*, pp. 141–148.

SHIBAYAMA, H. and MIYAHARA, M. (1977). Seasonal changes in the growth of aquatic weeds and their control, *Proceedings of the 6th Asian Pacific Weed Science Society Conference*, **1**, 258–262.

SHRADER, T. and ALPERS, G. (1977). Perennial weed control on Southwestern irrigation ditches, *Proceedings of the Southern Weed Science Society Conference*, **30**, 336–344.

SMITH, R.S. (1979). Control of *Glyceria maxima*, *Proceedings of the 7th Asian Pacific Weed Science Society Conference*, pp. 249–251.

SPRANKLE, P., MEGGITT, W.F. and PENNER, D. (1975). Absorption, action and translocation of glyphosate, *Weed Science*, **23**(3), 235–240.

TURNER, D.J. and LOADER, M.P.C. (1978). Controlled drop application of glyphosate, difenzoquat and dichlorprop, *Monograph British Crop Protection Council*, **22**, 179–184.

WELKER, W.V. and RIEMBER, D.N. (1978). The effects of multiple applications of glyphosate upon waterlilies, *Proceedings of the North East Weed Science Society Conference*, p. 338.

WIDYANTO, L.S., BURHAN, H.A., SUSILO, H. and NUR, M. (1977). New combinations of herbicides to control water hyacinth (*Eichhornia crassipes* (Mart) Solms.), *Proceedings of the 6th Asian Pacific Weed Science Society Conference*, **1**, 285–293.

WIDYANTO, L.S. and SOERJANI, M. (1978). Water hyacinth management in Indonesia, *Proceedings of the Malaysian Plant Protection Conference*, pp. 342–352.

Chapter 25

Efficacy of glyphosate for weed control in the tropics and sub-tropics

P.J. Terry
Weed Research Organization, Oxford, UK

Introduction

Most of the world's poorest countries are found in the tropics, where illiteracy, poverty, insecurity of land tenure and many other social factors are severe constraints to crop production. A vast potential exists for improving agricultural productivity in these countries, and herbicides have a certain future in the advances that must be made. Glyphosate has proved to be an exceptionally useful herbicide for the tropics, since it controls a wide range of weeds, particularly perennial species, which hitherto have evaded successful control. To date, the owners of estates, where cash crops such as rubber, oil palm, coffee and tea are grown, have derived the greatest benefit from glyphosate. Small-holders in subsistence agriculture usually lack the knowledge, capital and resources to use glyphosate, although they undoubtedly have problems that could be solved by this herbicide. This chapter does not discriminate between simple and advanced levels of farming, but states how glyphosate has been used in tropical situations which are familiar to both rich and poor farmers.

The chapter covers some of the important crops and weeds which occur between the tropics of Capricorn and Cancer. However, much of the published work on these species originates from sub-tropical regions, such as northern and southern Africa, Israel, southern USA, Northern Australia and New Zealand, and it was deemed necessary to review this literature. Crops and weeds of the highland tropics which are more usually associated with temperate and Mediterranean climates are excluded (but see also Chapters 19 and 23), except where relevant to the control of particular tropical weeds.

The first section examines the effect of glyphosate on specific weeds, emphasis being placed on those considered to be among the most serious in the world. This, inevitably, gives greatest attention to perennial grasses, but some perennial sedges and dicots, annual species and parasitic weeds are also reviewed. The second section describes the use of glyphosate in tropical crops, indicating possible management systems and application rates and cautioning against damage by incorrect usage.

The name glyphosate in this chapter refers to the isopropylamine salt of *N*-(phosphonomethyl)glycine used as the commercial formulation Roundup.

Weed control

The term 'weed control' is a common, but ambiguous, expression used to describe the suppression, inhibition or eradication of weed growth. It is often applied to the aerial components of the plant, frequently ignoring the subterranean organs which are so important in the survival, growth and dispersal of perennial weeds. This is unfortunate when describing the performance of glyphosate, whose high activity against perennating organs distinguishes it from most other herbicides. Where possible, examples are only given when this property is recognized as being an intrinsic part of the control achieved against perennial weeds. Citations of 'good control' or 'poor control' are difficult to avoid or quantify and their relevance must be interpreted according to the situation in which they are used. For example, 1 month's control of a perennial sedge in, say, groundnuts could be very acceptable but not in a plantation crop such as coffee.

Perennial grasses

CYNODON DACTYLON

Throughout the tropics and sub-tropics, *C. dactylon* is found as a weed of virtually every crop and is particularly important in plantation crops such as sugar cane (*Saccharum officinarum*), coffee (*Coffea arabica*), citrus and many others (see also Chapters 19 and 23). It is a very variable species, existing in two distinct morphological types, those with only above-ground stolons and those with subterranean rhizomes. Such variation almost certainly affects the susceptibility to glyphosate and may account for some of the variable control obtained. Climatic factors can also be important: laboratory studies have shown that glyphosate is more damaging to *C. dactylon* at 100% r.h. than at 40% and, at the lower r.h., toxicity is greater at 32°C than at 22°C (Jordan, 1977a).

Rao *et al.* (1981) eliminated *C. dactylon* from a tea nursery within 3 weeks of applying 0.8 kg ha^{-1}, but in Florida citrus, doses required for 97–100% control over 12–30 weeks varied from 1.1 to 4.2 kg ha^{-1} (Tucker, Baird and Phillips, 1977). In South Africa, split applications of 2.2 + 1.1 kg ha^{-1} are considered to be slightly superior to a single application of 3.3 kg ha^{-1} (Monsanto Co. recommendations).

Cultivation after application improves control of *C. dactylon* in Israel (Vanunu, Amir and Lifshitz, 1976), although the optimum timing is not clear: in one trial, cultivation 15 days after treatment was better than at 0, 30 or 45 days; in another trial, 3 or 6 days was better than 9 days.

In Zambia, trials were carried out to improve glyphosate activity using various additives and spray volumes (Zambia, 1980). It was concluded that while 1.08 kg ha^{-1} gave markedly better control of *C. dactylon* than 0.54 kg ha^{-1}, the lower dose can be almost as effective when mixed with ammonium sulphate at 5.0 kg ha^{-1} and applied at 20 l ha^{-1} with a CDA sprayer (*Table 25.1*) (see also Chapter 15).

TABLE 25.1   Percentage control of *Cynodon dactylon* **43 days after application at 2 spray volumes (after Zambia, 1980).**

Dose (kg ha^{-1})	Spray volume			
	200 l ha^{-1}		20 l ha^{-1}	
	$-(NH_4)_2 SO_4$	$+(NH_4)_2 SO_4$	$-(NH_4)_2 SO_4$	$+(NH_4)_2 SO_4$
0.54	45	65	70	90
1.08	88	94	88	88

DIGITARIA ABYSSINICA

D. abyssinica is one of the most important weeds in East Africa, occurring in plantations, cereals and many small-holder crops. Field trials in Tanzania have demonstrated good activity with glyphosate: doses of 1.0 and 2.0 kg ha^{-1} as double applications or as single applications followed by paraquat reduced ground cover of foliage by 74–98% and fresh weights of rhizomes were also considerably reduced (Terry, 1974a). Prolific growth of annual weeds occurred after *D. abyssinica* had been controlled.

IMPERATA CYLINDRICA

I. cylindrica is widely distributed in the tropics, where up to six varieties are recognized. Var. *africana* causes problems in West Africa (Ivens, 1976) and *major*, claimed to be the most aggressive variety (Hutchinson and Dalziel, 1972), is distributed from South East Asia to East Africa. Large variations of ecotypes in Iraq (Al-Juboory and Hassawy, 1980) and Indonesia (Naiolo, 1981) have been recognized and undoubtedly occur in other regions. These, together with climatic and edaphic factors, must surely influence the efficacy of glyphosate against this species.

Much of the research on the control of *I. cylindrica* has been carried out in Malaysia, Indonesia and India, particularly in plantations of oil palm (*Elaeis guineensis*) (Wong, 1981), rubber (*Hevea brasiliensis*) (Yeoh and Pushparajah, 1976), tea (*Camellia sinensis*) (Rao *et al.*, 1976; 1981; Srinivasan *et al.*, 1981) and, to a lesser extent, clove (*Eugenia caryophyllus*) (Arif and Putrawan, 1977). *I. cylindrica* is generally considered to be susceptible to glyphosate, although doses reported to give effective control vary between 0.8 kg ha^{-1} (Rao *et al.*, 1981) and 3.08 kg ha^{-1} (Abad, San Juan and Galleg, 1981), with median acceptable doses around 2.2 kg ha^{-1}. The duration of control varies, but over 90% control from single application for periods exceeding 21 weeks are cited (Yeoh and Pushparajah, 1976; Srinivasan *et al*, 1981; Wong, 1981). Of course, the efficacy and duration of control depends upon subsequent management: establishment of vigorous ground covers or intensively cultivated crops is more likely to prevent regrowth than uncropped land. Regrowth is almost inevitable in any cropping system and contingencies for retreatment, either by overall spraying, spot spraying or weed wiping, are standard practices.

An important factor influencing the activity of glyphosate against *I. cylindrica*, and one which is relevant in plantations, is shade. In an extensive series of trials, Wong (1981) noted that in open conditions of 0–30% shade, 4.4 kg ha^{-1} provided over 95% control of leaves and rhizomes 150 days after application, but similar control was obtained with only 2.2 kg ha^{-1} where shade exceeded 30%. Similar responses to shade were observed by Yeoh and Pushparajah (1976) and Arif and Subagio (1976). Wong (1981) showed that where there is little shade, the season of application also influences glyphosate activity; higher doses are required for control in the dry season (monthly average rainfall 300 mm). However, these differences were not apparent under shade (*Figure 25.1*).

Soil moisture is also believed to affect performance, better control of *I. cylindrica* being achieved on sandy soils than on wetter clays (Yeoh and Pushparajah, 1976). This was confirmed under greenhouse conditions, where glyphosate activity was reduced by extreme soil moisture stress (water tension -88 to -96 kPa) (Moosavi-Nia and Dore, 1979), a fact attributed to physiological and

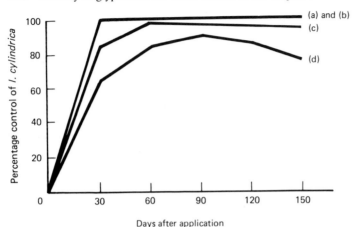

Figure 25.1. Control of *Imperata cylindrica* with glyphosate:
(a) 4.4 kg ha^{-1} in 0–30% shade applied in wet or dry season,
(b) 2.2 kg ha^{-1} in >30% shade applied in wet or dry season,
(c) 2.2 kg ha^{-1} in 0–30% shade applied in dry season, (d) 2.2
kg ha^{-1} in 0–30% shade applied in wet season (after Wong,
1981)

morphological behaviour of the *Imperata* species. Under field conditions, drought was blamed for poor control of *I. cylindrica* in Sri Lanka (Srinivasan *et al.*, 1981), where any stress conditions, including insect damage, recent slashing or dust on the foliage, are thought to reduce the efficacy of glyphosate.

Arif and Sutomo (1982) see shortages of labour and clean water as problems for the large-scale clearance of *Imperata*-infested land and have sought to overcome these by improved methods of application. Knapsack sprayers with high- and low-volume nozzles, CDA equipment, a mist blower, a power sprayer and tractor-mounted high- and low-volume applicators were compared in a series of trials where glyphosate was applied at 1.8 and 2.2 kg ha^{-1} in volume rates of 10–1200 l ha^{-1} (see also Chapter 16). Tractor-mounted and hand-held weed wipers were also tested for applying 0.36 kg ha^{-1} glyphosate in 3 l ha^{-1}. Although each type of equipment had its strengths and weaknesses, glyphosate was shown to be effective over a wide range of volume rates, provided that it was evenly distributed. The 75% control of *Imperata*, 58 days after application of 0.36 kg ha^{-1} with a tractor-mounted rope wick, is inferior to the 98–99% control obtained with CDA and hydraulic nozzles at 2.2 kg ha^{-1} but is, none the less, an encouraging result for this relatively new technique. Indeed, current research in Indonesia with hand-held weed wipers is revealing promising results with this equipment for controlling *I. cylindrica* in small-holder agriculture (Bacon and Terry, unpublished).

Despite the success of glyphosate in controlling *I. cylindrica* there is still scope for work on low-volume application (including aerial spraying), minimum tillage systems and improving the rainfastness, all of which could significantly affect the use of this herbicide.

ORYZA LONGISTAMINATA

This rhizomatous weed of cultivated rice is a problem in West Africa, where it also occurs in waterlogged land and in shallow water at the edge of lakes. It is susceptible to glyphosate at doses of 2.0–5.0 kg ha^{-1} (Diarra, 1978), but the economics of such treatments are uncertain.

OTTOCHLOA NODOSA

O. nodosa is a major weed of oil palm and rubber plantations in Malaysia and Indonesia, where it is often the dominant species in association with *Paspalum conjugatum*. Wong (1977) obtained an average of 99% control from 3 estates, 60 days after treatment with 0.56 kg ha^{-1} glyphosate. Only slight regeneration occurred after 180 days, from encroaching unsprayed areas. At 0.37 kg ha^{-1}, the average control at 30, 60 and 180 days after treatment was 86, 96 and 76%, respectively. Selective control of *O. nodosa* in ground-cover legume (*Pueraria phaseoloides*) is possible with 0.5 kg ha^{-1} glyphosate, the legume recovering from initial phytotoxicity to form an almost pure stand (Hussein and Weng, 1977).

PANICUM SPP.

Control of *P. maximum* is generally good in the tropics with glyphosate doses of 2.2 kg ha^{-1} (Colliot *et al.*, 1978) although results are best when applied as the plant comes into flower. Trials in Florida citrus have produced 95–100% control 12 weeks after applying 1.1–3.3 kg ha^{-1} (Tucker, Baird and Phillips, 1977).

Good control of *P. repens* in tea has been obtained in Sri Lanka. Glyphosate at 2.16 kg ha^{-1} gave 95% control for 38 weeks, while 1.44 and 1.80 kg ha^{-1} gave 82 and 91% control, respectively, over the same period. Slightly poorer control (70–91%) was obtained in a relatively drier year (Srinivasan *et al.*, 1981). Significant improvements in glyphosate activity against *P. repens* were obtained with spray additives of kaolin. For example, glyphosate 0.84 kg ha^{-1} + kaolin 2.5 kg ha^{-1} gave a 98% reduction of shoot numbers 4 months after treatment compared with 55 and 93% reductions by glyphosate without additives at 0.84 and 1.26 kg ha^{-1}, respectively (Sharma and Sundar, 1981). A series of trials in citrus in Florida demonstrated the long-term efficacy of single and multiple applications at various times of year (Tucker, Baird and Phillips, 1977). Results were a little variable between sites: for example, single applications of 3.3 kg ha^{-1} gave 90% control for 7 weeks, 95% for 12 weeks, 68% for 26 weeks, 65% for 30 weeks and 60% for 1 year. Even so, the potential for glyphosate in this situation at doses of 2.2–8.9 kg ha^{-1} was well demonstrated.

PASPALUM SPP.

Shade-tolerant *P. conjugatum* is one of the most serious weeds of plantation crops in the tropics, particularly in the Asian region, but also in West Africa. Rao, Kotoky and Sarmah (1981) obtained 83% control of *P. conjugatum* in tea 6 weeks after treatment with 0.8 kg ha^{-1} glyphosate and up to 93% control for over 12 weeks was possible with split applications of 1.2 kg ha^{-1} at 0 and 7 weeks. Srinivasan *et al.* (1981) claim that glyphosate at 0.25, 0.33 and 0.50 kg ha^{-1} gave 94, 98 and 95% control of *P. conjugatum*, respectively, at 90 days after treatment and an average of 68% control after 180 days.

Hussein and Weng (1977) evaluated glyphosate at 0.25–1.0 kg ha^{-1} against *P. conjugatum* and *Ottochloa nodosa* in a ground-cover legume (*Pueraria phaseoloides*) used in Malaysian rubber and oil palm plantations. Doses of 0.33,

0.5, 0.75 and 1.0 kg ha^{-1} all reduced the presence of grasses from initial covers of 47–65% to less than 10%. The highest dose severely damaged the legume, but injury from the other rates was transient: both grass and legume covers were reduced for up to 30 days after treatment, but thereafter the legume recovered to establish an almost pure stand. The median dose of 0.5 kg ha^{-1} appears to be the optimum, providing practical and economic alternatives to hand weeding.

P. dilatatum, an important weed of several tropical and sub-tropical countries, was well controlled in Israeli citrus for more than 7 weeks with glyphosate at 1.56 kg ha^{-1} in a spray volume of 620 l ha^{-1} and for more than 5 months at doses of 0.72–1.44 kg ha^{-1} in 200–400 l ha^{-1} (Oren and Beeri, 1978). Slashing the *P. dilatatum* before spraying did not appear to reduce glyphosate activity and is recommended 15 days before treatment. Follow-up spot treatments may be necessary for season-long control. Monsanto Company recommendations for South Africa suggest that cutting should facilitate easier application, but caution that dense cuttings must be removed before spraying and that there should be enough regrowth to provide sufficient absorptive leaf area.

P. paspaloides, formerly known as *P. distichum*, is a common weed of annual and perennial crops in warm climates. It is well controlled by glyphosate at 2.0–3.0 kg ha^{-1}, but regrowth from seeds can cause rapid reinfestation, necessitating repeat sprays with glyphosate or other herbicides. *P. paspaloides* has become a problem in transplanted and dry-seeded rice in the Philippines where minimum and zero-tillage are practised. Research at the International Rice Research Institute (IRRI, 1977) has revealed three effective methods of control:

(1) 2.0 kg ha^{-1} glyphosate applied 7 DBT (days before transplanting) followed by ploughing 2 DBT.
(2) 1.5 kg ha^{-1} glyphosate applied 7 DBT, followed by 1.0 kg ha^{-1} paraquat 3 DBT.
(3) 1.0 kg ha^{-1} glyphosate applied 7 DBT, followed by 1.5 kg ha^{-1} paraquat 3 DBT.

Glyphosate alone at 2.0 kg ha^{-1} and at 1.5 kg ha^{-1} followed by 1.0 kg ha^{-1} paraquat gave poor control of *Fimbristylis littoralis*, an annual sedge weed commonly associated with rice (*Oryza sativa*). In dry-seeded rainfed rice, *P. paspaloides* is not adequately controlled by zero-tillage using glyphosate alone at 3.0 kg ha^{-1}, but dependable control is possible with 2.0 kg ha^{-1} in a minimum tillage system (IRRI, 1977).

In plantation crops, glyphosate should not be applied until *P. paspaloides* has developed lush foliar growth with a high leaf–root ratio. Late season doses of 2.88 kg ha^{-1} are recommended for South Africa, with follow-up sprays of 1.44 kg ha^{-1} if necessary (Monsanto Co. recommendations).

Control of *Paspalum* species in fruit crops and vines is discussed by Atkinson (Chapter 19) and Hebblethwaite and Schepens (Chapter 23).

PENNISETUM SPP.

P. purpureum is often cropped in pastures, but when present in coconut (*Cocos nucifera*) plantations it is not easy to eradicate and is more expensive to control than *Imperata* (Abad *et al.*, 1981). Trials in the Philippines compared glyphosate at 1.64–3.28 kg ha^{-1} on *P. purpureum* slashed 1 or 2 weeks before application. No regrowth occurred within 3 months when doses of 2.05 kg ha^{-1} or greater were applied 2 weeks after slashing, but regrowth was present at all doses where the interval was reduced to 1 week. The difference is attributed to the surface area of foliage at spraying (Abad *et al.*, 1981).

P. clandestinum green weight was reduced 60% by 1.5 kg ha^{-1} glyphosate in the high altitude (2600 m) savannahs of Colombia (Romero and Mejia, 1976). Less activity was obtained by 2 applications of 0.75 kg ha^{-1} 2 weeks apart and 0.5 kg ha^{-1} stimulated growth. Shade and low temperatures impaired control. The Monsanto Company claims that *P. clandestinum* is very susceptible to glyphosate, and that application at any time during the active growth period gives excellent control at a dose of 1.8 kg ha^{-1} with follow-up sprays of 1.06 kg ha^{-1} if necessary.

SORGHUM HALEPENSE

S. halepense, mainly a weed of the sub-tropics, is reported to be one of the most difficult species to control. Much of the research on this weed has been carried out in North and South America, where it is a frequent problem in cotton (*Gossypium hirsutum*), soya bean (*Glycine max*), maize (*Zea mays*) and other crops.

Parochetti, Wilson and Burt (1975) obtained 100, 88 and 100% necrosis of rhizomes 7 weeks after application of 1.12, 1.68 and 2.24 kg ha^{-1} glyphosate, respectively. From the results of many workers it seems that rhizomatous *S. halepense* is well controlled by doses of 2 kg ha^{-1} or greater and best results are achieved when applied at or just before flowering. Control of seedling *S. halepense* requires a residual herbicide: Glover *et al.* (1976) obtained excellent control with alachlor, nitralin, trifluralin and vernolate applied to land cultivated 12–14 days after glyphosate was applied to the rhizomatous grass. Baird and Upchurch (1973) found that a delay of 14–21 days between glyphosate application and subsequent tillage was necessary to obtain maximum control of rhizomatous *S. halepense.*

The feasibility of applying glyphosate with a recirculating sprayer has been demonstrated by McWhorter and Williford (1980), where doses of 0.56 and 1.12 kg ha^{-1} provided sufficient control of *S. halepense* to greatly increase soya bean yields. Dale (1979) used rope-wick applicators to selectively control *S. halepense* in soya bean at doses of 0.07 and 0.28 kg ha^{-1} (see also Chapter 16).

Perennial sedges

CYPERUS ESCULENTUS

C. esculentus is a weed of considerable importance throughout the tropics and sub-tropics, where it is found in many crops. It is superficially similar to *C. rotundus,* but beneath the soil surface each plant produces numerous slender stolons on which a daughter shoot or a terminal tuber is formed. Fragmentation of the rhizomes, either naturally or by cultivation, leaves high populations of isolated, often dormant, tubers in the soil which are not reached by translocated herbicides applied to the emerged shoots. This is an important factor where glyphosate is used and may account for some of the variable levels of control achieved. Extensive propagation of *C. esculentus* by seed can occur and this can reduce the duration of control by non-residual herbicides.

From reports of many workers, mostly in North America, the lowest dose of glyphosate required for reliable control of *C. esculentus* is about 2.0 kg ha^{-1}, although as little as 1.0 kg ha^{-1} can be effective, especially when applied with ammonium sulphate (Locascio, 1977; Suwanketnikom and Penner, 1978). Unfortunately, the enhancement of glyphosate activity against many weeds by ammonium salts is not a reliable phenomenon.

The timing of glyphosate application is important in determining the level of control of *C. esculentus*. Better control is generally obtained by applications early in the season (Jordan, Jordan and Guzon, 1980; Canada, 1981; McCue and Sweet, 1981), and this is probably related to stage of growth of the weed. Stoller, Wax and Matthieson (1975) found *C. esculentus* to be more susceptible at the 4–6 leaf stage than at 6–8 leaves. In Chile, Kogan and Gonzalez (1979) obtained greater reductions of tuber numbers and subterranean dry matter from glyphosate applied at the 9–11 leaf stage than when applied at the pre-flower stage (*Table 25.2*).

TABLE 25.2   **Effect of glyphosate on tuber numbers and subterranean dry matter of** *Cyperus esculentus* **100 days after shoot emergence (after Kogan and Gonzalez, 1979)**

Stage of application	Glyphosate concentration (% a.i.)*	Tubers per plant†	Subterranean dry matter per plant† (g)
9–11 leaves	0.18	0.8 a	0.23 a
(21 days after emergence)	0.36	0.1 a	0.10 a
	0.54	0.2 a	0.30 a
Pre-flowering	0.18	24.2 d	4.13 d
(66 days after emergence)	0.36	17.0 bc	2.40 bc
	0.54	19.3 c	4.75 b
Untreated control	—	54.8 e	11.52 e

* Each polybag was sprayed with the same volume of solution.
† Means in a column followed by the same letter are not significantly different at $P = 0.05$ by Duncan's multiple range test.

Stoller, Wax and Matthieson (1975) measured tuber viability of plants treated 4 weeks earlier with 1.1 and 2.2 kg ha^{-1} glyphosate and obtained only 3% and 0% kill, respectively; bentazon, in comparison, at 0.8 and 1.7 kg ha^{-1}, gave 86 and 96% kill. Better control by early applications is not always confirmed: Linscott, Hagin and Tharawanich (1978) report better control of plants 20–25 cm high than with those 10–12 cm in 1 year of field trials and, in glasshouse work, Boldt and Sweet (1974) observed that applications made before *C. esculentus* was 20 cm high were less effective than those made later.

Environmental factors may account for some differences in performance; Tharawanich and Linscott (1975) showed that activity of glyphosate against *C. esculentus* is reduced by increased temperature and length of photoperiods.

There is no doubt that *C. esculentus* can be controlled by glyphosate, but optimum dose rates and timing need to be determined under local conditions.

CYPERUS ROTUNDUS

C. rotundus is reputed to be the worst weed in the world (Holm, 1969) because of its widespread distribution in warm climates, frequency and severity of infestation in many crops and its tolerance of most attempts at control. This situation changed with the availability of glyphosate; effective long-term control became possible and is reported by several workers. Terry (1974b) obtained 88 weeks' control in a Tanzanian coffee estate with a total dose of 4.0 kg ha^{-1} and 95–100% control of foliage was possible with 2.0 kg ha^{-1} (*Figure 25.2*). The optimum dose of glyphosate under normal conditions seems to be about 2.0 kg ha^{-1}, with 4.0 kg ha^{-1} tending to give only marginally better control of foliage than 2.0 kg ha^{-1} (see, for example, Magambo and Terry, 1973; Zandstra and Nishimoto, 1975). Usually 1 kg ha^{-1} is less effective, but with frequent spraying can give good control (Zandstra and Nishimoto, 1975).

Figure 25.2. Application of glyphosate in a coffee (*Coffea arabica*) plantation to control *Cyperus rotundus*. The author is standing on a plot treated with 2 kg ha^{-1}. Two plots beyond had repeated applications. Foreground: *C. rotundus* untreated

The efficacy of a herbicide against *C. rotundus* must be judged not only on its foliar kill, but also on its ability to destroy the extensive system of tubers and basal bulbs. Glyphosate at 1.0, 2.0 and 3.0 kg ha^{-1} gave an approximate 50% reduction in number of tubers at 60 days after application and, of the remaining tubers, 40–68% failed to germinate (Chase and Appleby, 1979a). Magambo and Terry (1973) also observed a marked reduction in sprouting of tubers by glyphosate 21–24 weeks after treatment, and although they appeared viable in a tetrazolium test, their failure to germinate within 60 days indicated that they would eventually die (Doll and Piedrahita, 1977). Zandstra and Nishimoto (1977) studied the effect of glyphosate on *C. rotundus* using benzyl adenine to force the sprouting of viable tubers. Following the application of 4.0 kg ha^{-1} glyphosate to 6-, 12- and 24-week-old plants they obtained 0, 5 and 32% sprouting, respectively, from tubers on intact rhizome/tuber chains compared with 74, 53 and 54% from untreated plants. Separation of tubers from the connecting rhizomes did not increase sprouting in the glyphosate treatments, but up to 77–90% occurred in isolated tubers from untreated plants. The translocation of glyphosate, as manifested by the suppression of tuber sprouting, was confirmed by autoradiography following applications of ^{14}C-glyphosate (Zandstra and Nishimoto, 1977).

Since the activity of glyphosate is dependent upon it reaching the tubers via intact rhizomes, cultivation before or after application influences the level of control. Zandstra and Nishimoto (1975) treated *C. rotundus* plants in the field at 2, 4, 6, 12 and 24 weeks after tilling with glyphosate at 1.0, 2.0 and 4.0 kg ha^{-1}, to determine the optimum period of non-disturbance for good control. Glyphosate applied after 12 weeks of non-disturbance gave almost complete mortality of foliage and more than 75% mortality of tubers, but when applied at 2, 4, 6 and 24 weeks there was insufficient control of tubers and repeat applications were necessary (*Table 25.3*).

The effect of cultivations after applying glyphosate were studied in El Salvador (Chase and Appleby, 1979a). They found that at doses of 1.0, 2.0 and 3.0 kg ha^{-1}, a period of 3 days between application and tillage was sufficient for 90% control.

TABLE 25.3   Effect of glyphosate treatments on shoot density and tuber sprouting of *Cyperus rotundus* **5 months after initial application (after Zandstra and Nishimoto, 1975)**

Glyphosate dose (kg ha^{-1})	Frequency of application (weeks)	Shoot density at initial application* (shoots 0.3 m^{-2})	Shoot density 5 months after initial application* (shoots 0.3 m^{-2})	Tuber sprouting 5 months after initial application* (%)
1.0	2	138.0 ab	7.0 a	78.3 de
2.0	2	140.3 ab	1.3 a	55.0 cd
4.0	2	143.0 ab	1.3 a	41.7 bc
2.0	4	140.7 ab	9.3 a	58.3 cd
4.0	4	179.0 abc	7.7 a	40.0 bc
2.0	6	269.0 cd	10.0 a	53.3 cd
4.0	6	239.3 cd	8.7 a	25.0 ab
2.0	12	278.0 d	0.9 a	10.0 a
4.0	12	190.0 bcd	0.3 a	5.0 a
2.0	24	86.7 a	67.0 b	93.3 e
4.0	24	96.3 a	46.0 b	91.7 e
0 (control)	—	—	—	95.0 e

*Means in a column followed by the same letter are not significantly different at $P = 0.05$ by Duncan's multiple range test.

Intervals of 11–23 days between application and tillage generally gave slightly less control, but when applications were repeated 35 days after the initial tillage and the plots re-tilled, over 90% control of plants was obtained. Untilled treatments gave less control (75%) at 8 months than tilled ones (84–89%), showing the eventual advantage of tillage. CIAT (1975) also confirmed the rapid uptake and translocation of glyphosate in pot experiments. Tuber sprouting 95 days after application of 2 kg ha^{-1} glyphosate was 77, 59, 9, 2, 1 and 0% from pots where leaves had been removed 12, 24, 36, 48, 72 and 120 h after application, respectively.

Environmental factors affect the activity of glyphosate on *C. rotundus*. Chase and Appleby (1979b) found that glyphosate effectiveness was reduced under high moisture stress and low humidity. A treatment of 2 kg ha^{-1} was more effective in reducing regrowth of scapes (flower stems) at 90% than at 50% r.h. and more effective at −0.2 MPa than at −1.1 MPa of plant water potential. Regrowth of treated plants subjected to water potentials of −0.1 to −0.8 MPa was reduced 54–60%, while at −1.1 MPa the growth inhibition was only 34%. A time interval of as little as 8 h between application and clipping of the plants was sufficient to give 47% reduction in regrowth at 90% r.h. compared with a 19% reduction at 50% r.h.

Shade also influences control of foliage and subsequent sprouting of tubers (CIAT, 1975). Whereas 94–96% control of foliage was obtained in 0–63% shade 28 days after application of 1.5 kg ha^{-1} glyphosate, this fell to 91% in 73% shade and 60% control in 92% shade.

A novel approach to controlling *C. rotundus* combines biological and chemical methods. Quimby and Frick (1980) coated larvae of the nutsedge moth (*Bactra verutuna* Zeller) with glyphosate and placed them on *C. rotundus* plants. In one series of tests, larvae without glyphosate caused reductions in plant dry weights of 5–83%, but coated larvae enhanced this activity by 15–75%. This technique may be relevant where it is difficult to apply glyphosate directly on to the plants.

Perennial dicots

LANTANA CAMARA

Glyphosate is usually not recommended for the control of woody shrubs, but good activity against *L. camara* is reported from Florida, where 3.3 kg ha^{-1} gave 98% control 17 weeks after treatment, compared with 90% control from 2,4,5-TP at 2.2 kg ha^{-1} (Tucker, Baird and Phillips 1977).

MERREMIA spp.

Merremia spp. are important creeping and climbing weeds of plantation crops in tropical regions of Southeast Asia, Australia and islands in the Southwest Pacific. One species in particular, *M. peltata*, grows to 30 m and can smother banana (*Musa accuminata*) and forest plantations. Miller (1982) evaluated glyphosate in the Solomon Islands at doses of 0.5–4.0 kg ha^{-1} on a mixed stand of *M. peltata*, *M. pacifica* and *M. bracteata*. The lowest dose suppressed growth for 6–8 weeks without killing the creepers, but effective control was obtained at 1.5 kg ha^{-1}, confirming the efficacy of glyphosate against *Merremia* spp. in Papua New Guinea (Lamb, 1975).

MIKANIA spp.

M. micrantha is often associated with *Imperata cylindrica* in plantation crops of Southeast Asia, but total control of this important creeping weed is obtained with glyphosate at 1.12–2.24 kg ha^{-1} (Wong, 1975a). In glasshouse trials, Parker (1978) obtained good control of *M. micrantha* at 1.0 and 2.0 kg ha^{-1}, but not at 0.5 kg ha^{-1}, and this was improved by the addition of ammonium sulphate. Wong (1975a) and others have mistaken *M. micrantha* for *M. cordata*, a less aggressive species of relatively minor importance as a weed.

OXALIS LATIFOLIA

This cosmopolitan species occurs in temperate and tropical climates, where it is sometimes a serious weed of many crops, including plantations, nurseries and ornamentals. Attempts at control have usually, at best, given only temporary suppression of growth because of the weed's ability to rapidly produce dormant underground bulbs and bulbils. This makes timing of control measures critical for success. The work of Cox and Kerr (1981), in New Zealand, has given some of the most promising results, although it is not clear how far they can be extrapolated to tropical conditions. Oxadiazon at 2.0 kg ha^{-1} and glyphosate at 2.0 kg ha^{-1} were applied as single, multiple or alternate treatments to *O. latifolia* at various times of the year and their effects on populations of the vegetative propagules were measured in the following season. Only a sequence of 4 applications of oxadiazon achieved near complete elimination of propagules, but the most cost-efficient annual control programme was judged to be oxadiazon 2.0 kg ha^{-1} in the early part of the season followed by glyphosate 2.0 kg ha^{-1} 4 months later.

Annual weeds

In general, most tropical annual weeds are susceptible to glyphosate at normal dose rates of 1.0–2.0 kg ha^{-1}, sometimes less, providing they are actively growing and their leaves are contacted by the herbicide. Examples of susceptible species include *Brachiaria distichophylla, Digitaria sanguinalis, Echinochloa crus-galli, Rottboellia exaltata, Amaranthus retroflexus, Cassia obtusifolia, Chenopodium album* and *Euphorbia hirta*. Annual sedges (Cyperaceae) are probably susceptible, but IRRI (1977) did not control *Fimbristylis littoralis* with glyphosate at 2.0 kg ha^{-1}. There are few reports of tolerance to glyphosate, but *Euphorbia heterophylla* is cited as being resistant (Machado Neto and Lusvarghi, 1980). Despite their susceptibility to glyphosate, annual weeds are often a problem on glyphosate-treated land, and it is common to see claims of poor control of these species.

Parasitic weeds

Chemical control of parasitic weeds presents unique problems in selectivity because of the close relationship with the host plants. Success depends upon the tolerance of the host and susceptibility of the parasite, but it has been obtained for two species of *Orobanche* (broomrapes) on three crops.

Kasasian (1973) reported complete control of *O. crenata* when glyphosate at 0.2 kg ha^{-1} was applied 6 weeks after sowing broad beans (*Vicia faba*) in pots. No crop damage occurred, but the margin of safety was low. This activity was confirmed under field conditions in Egypt, where three or four sequential sprays at 3-week intervals gave an 87% reduction in the number of *O. crenata* spikes (Zahran *et al.*, 1980). Kasasian (1973) also obtained promising selective control of *O. aegyptiaca* with glyphosate at 0.05 kg ha^{-1} applied to tobacco (*Nicotiana tabacum*) and tomato (*Lycopersicon esculentum*).

Another serious parasitic weed, *Striga asiatica* (= *S. lutea*), has been directly and indirectly controlled in the USA (Langston and Eplee, 1974). Glyphosate at 0.56 and 1.12 kg ha^{-1} applied to emerged *Striga* plants on maize (*Zea mays*) at various stages of growth gave 92 and 98% control, respectively. Maize tolerance was marginal until the lower 4.5 cm of the stem were no longer green. Indirect control was possible by killing the alternative grass host *Digitaria sanguinalis* at the same dose rates of glyphosate. Late-season applications in maize, soya bean and cotton caused no significant injury to the crops.

Promising selective control of *Cuscuta campestris* and *C. indecora* on lucerne (*Medicago sativa*) is reported from the USA (Dawson and Saghir, 1982). Glyphosate was applied at 0.075–0.6 kg ha^{-1} in 860 l ha^{-1} water to vigorous dodder with shoots 20–60 cm long. All external *C. campestris* was killed, but some abnormal regrowth, mainly of *C. indecora,* arose from surviving remnants of tendrils and embedded haustoria. Lucerne remained green and vigorous after applications of 0.075 kg ha^{-1}, thus making possible effective and inexpensive control of this serious parasite.

Miscellaneous weeds

Ferns (Pteridophytes) are very common in plantations of rubber, oil palm and forests. *Pteridium esculentum* and *Nephrolepis biserrata* are early and noxious colonizers of cleared peat swamp forest in Malaysia and control is recommended before establishment of pineapple (*Ananas comosus*) (Lee and Enoch, 1977). Rao, Kotoky and Sarmah (1981) have noted increased infestations of ferns like *P. aquilinum* and *Nephridium* spp. in tea, and anticipate that they will become serious problems. There seems to be a dearth of published information on the use of glyphosate to control tropical ferns, but the results of trials in India are encouraging: 0.4 and 0.8 kg ha^{-1} gave 70 and 93% control, respectively, of *P. aquilinum* and *Nephridium* spp. 14 weeks after application (Rao, Kotoky and Sarmah, 1981). A Monsanto Company technical leaflet for Southeast Asia also claims control of *Cyclosorus aridus*.

The monocotyledonous family Commelinaceae contains several important perennial weeds, including *Commelina benghalensis*, *C. diffusa*, *C. erecta*, *Murdannia nudiflora* and several others (Wilson, 1981). They are widely distributed in the tropics and sub-tropics, occurring as weeds of numerous crops. They are often difficult to control: fleshy stolons can survive and regrow after mechanical damage from cultivation; dense mats of vegetation are difficult to penetrate and wet with foliar applied herbicides.

An established stand of *C. benghalensis* has been partially controlled by glyphosate in India, where 0.6, 1.2 and 2.4 kg ha^{-1} in 400–500 l ha^{-1} water gave 60, 70 and 80% control, respectively (Rao, Kotoky and Sarmah, 1976). However, up to 2.0 kg ha^{-1} glyphosate gave poor control of *C. diffusa* in the Cameroons (Paviot, 1977). It seems that post-emergence herbicides such as 2,4-D, paraquat and glyphosate are only effective against young *Commelina* plants.

Weed succession

Ungerminated seeds or perennating organs, unemerged seedlings or shoots and young plants shielded from sprays of glyphosate are unharmed by the herbicide and can rapidly take over from those species which are killed. Often, their growth is suppressed by a dominant sward of perennial grasses or sedges, but they quickly become established when glyphosate removes this source of competition. Many authors report this phenomenon, including Terry (1974b) and Chase and Appleby (1979a) after controlling *Cyperus rotundus,* Terry (1974a) after controlling *Digitaria abyssinica* and Basuki, Soedarsan and Ruswandi (1980) after controlling mixed perennial grasses, and it is typified by results obtained after the control of *Imperata cylindrica* in Malaysian rubber small-holdings (*Figure 25.3*).

Succession by cover crop legumes can be a positive advantage, but it is more common for those weeds which necesitate further control measures to take over. These may involve the further use of glyphosate or more economical herbicides, but there is a need for a flexible, integrated system. Soil-acting residual herbicides such as diuron and post-emergence products such as paraquat or 2,4-D are examples of herbicides which can complement the activity of glyphosate. However, the timing of applications of these herbicides can be critical if they are not to antagonize their own, or glyphosate's, activity. Although there are reports to the contrary, it is usually inadvisable to mix and apply any other herbicide with glyphosate (see also Chapter 15).

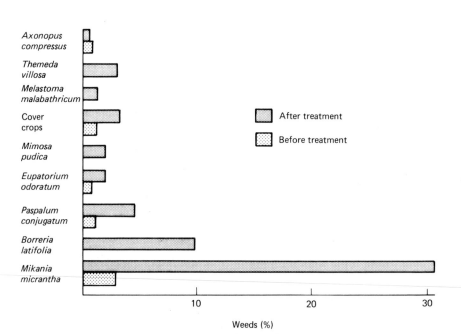

Figure 25.3. Weed succession 335 days after application of glyphosate to *Imperata cylindrica* in Malaysia (from Yeoh, 1980)

Crops

Glyphosate is active against so many tropical weeds that few crops of warm climates can fail to benefit in some way from the use of this herbicide. However, the sensitivity of most crops to glyphosate imposes limitations on the way it is used.

Land preparation

Glyphosate, like paraquat, leaves no soil residues to damage crops present at application or planted later. Hence, it has found wide acceptance as a means of land preparation, enabling minimum- or zero-tillage techniques to be employed, especially where paraquat-resistant perennial weeds are present.

Glyphosate at rates ranging from 0.27 to 3.24 kg ha^{-1} have been applied to weed and pasture species 8 h to 14 days before direct drilling of rice in Australia, with no adverse effect on crop establishment (Fellowes, Tydens and Swain, 1979). It has also been used in the Philippines for controlling *Paspalum paspaloides* prior to transplanting and direct-seeding rice, although in the case of the latter, minimum tillage using application rates of 1.0, 2.0 and 3.0 kg ha^{-1} gave markedly higher yields than where there was no tillage (IRRI, 1977).

In Nigeria, Ndahi (1982) evaluated glyphosate and paraquat at 0.5, 1.0 and 2.0 kg ha^{-1} as substitutes for seedbed preparation by tillage. Against a predominantly grassy weed flora, all treatments, with the exception of 0.5 kg ha^{-1} paraquat, gave acceptable yields of sorghum (*Sorghum bicolor*) and bulrush millet (*Pennisetum typhoides*). Akobundu (1977), also in Nigeria, obtained better broad-spectrum weed control with 1.0 kg ha^{-1} glyphosate than with the same dose of paraquat applied as zero-tillage treatments before planting maize. However, tank mixtures with either atrazine + alachlor or atrazine + metolachlor reduced the efficacy of glyphosate.

Treated weed foliage can sometimes damage subsequent crops: both glyphosate at 2.24 kg ha^{-1} and paraquat at 1.12 kg ha^{-1} as zero-tillage treatments have caused such damage in transplanted tobacco (Chappel and Link, 1977) (see also Chapter 19).

Successful pre-planting control depends to a large extent upon there being adequate weed foliage for uptake of the herbicide, necessitating, perhaps, delayed spraying and, hence, delayed planting. This could be undesirable for agronomic or practical reasons, but can be overcome where pre-irrigation is feasible to encourage weed growth. Where land preparation is delayed by unharvested crops, there is some evidence that pre-harvest applications of glyphosate can be used to control certain weeds, but timing is critical if the seed crop is not to be damaged or reduced. In the USA this is judged to be when grain moisture is below 35% in maize or during senescence in soya bean, where glyphosate at 2.24 kg ha^{-1} is used to control *Sorghum halepense* (English, Jeffery and Connell, 1977). Glyphosate at 2.24 and 4.48 kg ha^{-1} has been applied up to 14 days before lifting groundnuts (*Arachis hypogaea*), without adversely affecting germination of the harvested seed (Mason and Murray, 1979).

'Conservation tillage', whereby minimum- and zero-tillage techniques are integrated with cropping practices and cover crops to conserve soil structure and moisture and to reduce soil erosion, has relevance to both large-scale and peasant agriculture. Glyphosate has an important role to play in the development of such practices. It is also possible to use glyphosate in conjunction with tillage, providing that adequate exposure of the herbicide to the weeds is permitted. This has been discussed in relation to specific weeds and illustrates the value of glyphosate for land preparation prior to the planting of annual and perennial crops.

Perennial crops

Probably the greatest use of glyphosate in the tropics and sub-tropics is for weed control in perennial crops. This is because they can support the cost of herbicides and also because they often have acute weed problems which can be solved with glyphosate. Perennial crops are generally tolerant of directed applications of glyphosate providing leaves and other green tissues do not come into contact with the spray. Summarized uses of glyphosate in some perennial crops are given below, together with information on crop tolerance.

AVOCADO (PERSEA AMERICANA)

Glyphosate at $0.84–4.20$ kg ha^{-1} is recommended in Hawaii, but not more than 8.9 kg ha^{-1} per year is advised. There should be an interval of at least 14 days between application and harvest and treated areas should not be grazed within 8 weeks of treatment (Nishimoto and Yee, undated).

BANANA (MUSA ACCUMINATA)

In the Canary Islands, $1.08–2.52$ kg ha^{-1} of glyphosate have been used safely in trials for the control of *Cyperus rotundus* and *Cynodon dactylon* (Álvarez de la Peña, 1978).

CITRUS (CITRUS spp.)

Glyphosate at $1.7–3.3$ kg ha^{-1} is active against a wide range of weeds in citrus in Florida (Tucker, Baird and Phillips, 1977). It can be safely used as a directed spray, but when glyphosate at 1.7, 3.3 and 6.6 kg ha^{-1} is deliberately applied to citrus trees, various degrees of toxicity occur depending upon age, position sprayed, tissue maturity and dose rate. Symptoms include defoliation, twig die-back, malformed regrowth and callus inhibition around wound areas (Tucker, 1977). Translocation from sprayed limbs is minimal, but it is quite marked in citrus seedlings (see also Appendix I).

CLOVE (EUGENIA CARYOPHYLLUS)

Single and multiple applications of spray solutions containing 0.29% glyphosate have been used in Indonesia to control *Imperata cylindrica* (Arif and Putrawan, 1977). Light phytotoxic symptoms occurred when glyphosate was deliberately applied to leaves of the young crop.

COCOA (THEOBROMA CACAO)

Repeat applications of 1.0 and 2.0 kg ha^{-1} have been used in young Indonesian cocoa plantations (Basuki, Soedarson and Ruswandi, 1980) but, in Brazil, where glyphosate was applied in 17-month-old trees, apical buds of the cocoa plants were killed (Pereira *et al.*, 1980).

COCONUT (COCOS NUCIFERA)

Glyphosate has been applied in 'polybag' coconut nurseries at 1.64 kg ha^{-1} to control *Cyperus rotundus* in the Philippines (Abad, San Juan and Galleg, 1981). Follow-up sprays were recommended for new emerging weeds. No visible phytotoxic effects on the crop were observed, but in the Ivory Coast, where glyphosate at 1.4 kg ha^{-1} gave good weed control outside the tree circle, Coomans and Delorme (1978) recommended avoiding spray contact with the leaves of coconut palms.

COFFEE (COFFEA ARABICA)

Terry (1974b) and Chawdhry (1975) report successful control of perennial weeds in coffee, in East Africa, with glyphosate dose rates of 2.0–6.0 kg ha^{-1} as single or repeat applications (see *Figure 25.2*). Directed sprays caused no crop damage, but Chawdhry (1975) demonstrated that growth of suckers on clean-stumped coffee could be severely retarded by deliberately spraying them with glyphosate. An abnormally high number of suckers were also produced from the sprayed stumps and leaf distortion occurred.

DATE PALM (PHOENIX DACTYLIFERA)

Glyphosate has been used in date palms at a spray concentration of 1.8%. Suckers around the base of the palms were scorched and partially desiccated, but regrowth occurred later (Israel, 1978).

FORESTRY

In Papua New Guinea, glyphosate at 2.0 kg ha^{-1} shows considerable promise as a herbicide in forest plantations with mixed weed populations (Lamb, 1975). Miller (1982) obtained good control of *Merremia* spp. in Solomon Islands forests, but the potential for using glyphosate in tropical forests, other than in nurseries, must be doubtful on economic grounds.

MACADAMIA (MACADAMIA TERNIFOLIA)

Glyphosate at 0.84–4.20 kg ha^{-1} is recommended in Hawaii as a directed spray (Nishimoto and Yee, undated). Repeat applications may be necessary, but not more than 8.9 kg ha^{-1} per year should be applied. Spray contact with trees established for less than 2 years should be avoided. The minimal period between application and harvest should be 21 days.

OIL PALM (ELAEIS GUINEENSIS)

Studies in Malaysia have shown that directed applications of 2.2–4.4 kg ha^{-1} do not adversely affect crop yield or frond production (Wong, 1981). Glyphosate was not readily absorbed by oil palm roots and residues were not detectable in either the mesocarp or kernel palm oil.

PAPAYA (CARICA PAPAYA)

Glyphosate applied to papaya trees less than 1 m tall can cause considerable injury. Although foliar growth can recover, trunk diameters may be reduced for several months after application. Directed sprays of glyphosate to trees more than 1.1 m tall generally do not injure papaya, even at rates as high as 9.0 kg ha^{-1}, provided they have brown bark (Nishimoto and Hibbard, 1979).

PINEAPPLE (ANANAS COMOSUS)

Pineapple is damaged by glyphosate at doses of 1.0 and 2.0 kg ha^{-1} (Gaillard and Haury, 1974), so it must be very carefully directed between rows or applied as a pre-planting treatment.

RUBBER (HEVEA BRASILIENSIS)

Glyphosate is a standard herbicide for use in rubber plantations in Malaysia and Indonesia. Application rates of up to 2.2 kg ha^{-1} are used for perennial weed control, but may be as little as 0.5 kg ha^{-1} when used to control grasses in ground cover legumes (Hussein and Weng, 1977). Young rubber trees are tolerant of glyphosate: no adverse effects on height and girth increments were observed after spraying 4.5 + 4.5 kg ha^{-1} glyphosate at 3-month intervals on brown bark of trees 1.5–1.8 m tall (Wong, 1975b).

SUGAR CANE (SACCHARUM OFFICINARUM)

Glyphosate is extremely toxic to sugar cane foliage, but older plants are less susceptible. Inter-row spraying is very risky, but weeds in young cane can be more safely controlled by using gravity-flow drippers and weed wipers (Hawaii, 1980). Spot-roguing of volunteer cane and kill of diseased stools is possible with 3.6% solutions of glyphosate applied with wipers or low-pressure hand sprayers.

Glyphosate is used quite extensively to kill young ratooning sugar cane before re-establishment using a minimal-tillage system (South Africa, 1978). Field trials have shown small differences in activity between dose rates of 2.2, 2.9 and 3.6 kg ha^{-1} at spray volumes of 24, 50 and 320 l ha^{-1}, but there are considerable differences in the susceptibilities of varieties. NCo 376 and NCo 310 are most effectively killed by glyphosate, but NCo 273 is not satisfactorily controlled (South Africa, 1978).

TEA (CAMELLIA SINENSIS)

Good to excellent control of perennial weeds in tea by glyphosate is widely reported from Africa (Magambo and Kilavuka, 1975) and Asia (Rao, Kotoky and Sarmah, 1981). Typical dose rates are 1.0–2.0 kg ha^{-1} applied as directed sprays. Tea appears to be relatively tolerant of glyphosate and there are reports of no damage from dose rates as high as 1.68 kg ha^{-1} applied directly to the bushes (India, 1978). However, Magambo and Kilavuka (1982) have demonstrated leaf damage and reduced internode growth of young, directly sprayed shoots at doses of 2.0–8.0 kg ha^{-1} and advise that precautions be taken to avoid drift of glyphosate sprays onto tea bushes.

Annual crops

Glyphosate can be used in many tropical and sub-tropical cropping systems, provided it is applied to the weeds with no, or very little, contact with the crop. Examples of its use in selected crops are given below, but there is considerable scope for the utilization of glyphosate in many other crops.

COTTON (GOSSYPIUM spp.)

Glyphosate toxicity varies with cotton genotype, but even the most resistant of 405 genotypes tested for glyphosate tolerance yielded significantly less seed cotton after overall applications than untreated controls (Jordan and Bridge, 1979). Directed sprays can cause severe damage if drift occurs (Ethiopia, 1973), but doses of 3.4 kg ha^{-1} applied to the basal 2.5 cm of 60 cm high cotton plants can cause minimal injury and season-long control of S. halepense (Banks and Santelmann, 1977). Directed applications can be safely made with shielded nozzles which prevent contact of glyphosate with the crop (Jordan, 1977b; Howell and Frans, 1980).

The recirculating sprayer can safely apply glyphosate above cotton to control volunteer Helianthus annuus (Abernathy, Hollingsworth and Keeling, 1977) and S. halepense (Jordan and Bridge, 1976) and the spraying of small weeds beneath the cotton canopy has been explored (Mullins, 1976). A Stoneville wiper has given 68–83% control of C. dactylon in the treated band and 50–73% control in the band between applicators with glyphosate applied at 2.2–3.3 kg ha^{-1} (Chandler, 1981). In Texas, glyphosate at 0.21 kg ha^{-1} applied with a rope-wick applicator gave more than 95% control of Solanum elaeagnifolium (Abernathy and Keeling, 1979).

Pre-sowing applications of glyphosate have been used to control C. dactylon (Kleifeld, 1976) and C. rotundus (Pulver and Castelar, 1974). S. halepense has been controlled in cotton by autumn applications of 2.24 kg ha^{-1} followed, in spring, by DSMA (Overton, Jeffery and Mullins, 1976) or trifluralin (Norton and Merkle, 1976). In cotton grown under minimum-tillage, glyphosate and diuron gave consistent control of weeds (Kerr, Royster and Long, 1976).

GROUNDNUT (ARACHIS HYPOGAEA)

Presowing combinations of cultivation and glyphosate at 1.62 and 3.24 kg ha^{-1} have given good control of Cynodon dactylon in groundnut (Vanunu, Amir and Lifshitz, 1976). Overall sprays of glyphosate are damaging but at 0.5 kg ha^{-1} recovery is possible after 2 weeks (Soejono and Selamat, 1975).

Glyphosate applied in a recirculating sprayer has controlled S. halepense at 0.68–1.02 kg ha^{-1} (Boyles et al., 1978) and Desmodium tortuosum and Cassia obtusifolia at 0.63–3.75% v/v (Hauser and Buchanan, 1978). Groundnuts were not injured appreciably if the spray was at least 10–15 cm above the crop canopy.

Glyphosate applied at 2.24 and 4.48 kg ha^{-1} to groundnut 14 days before digging gave excellent top kill of S. elaeagnifolium and resulted in significantly higher yields, despite moderate crop injury. Treatments carried out up to 7 days before digging were less successful (Mason and Murray, 1979).

MAIZE (ZEA MAYS)

Maize is susceptible to glyphosate and extensive damage can occur after directed sprays (Parochetti, Wilson and Burt, 1975). Injury is transient if doses as low as 0.5

kg ha^{-1} are used (Soejono and Selamat, 1975) and 0.56–1.12 kg ha^{-1} can be safely applied to the lower, non-green, stalk to control *Striga lutea* (Langston and Eplee, 1974). Weed wipers and recirculating sprayers may have some potential for use in maize, but there is little evidence for this in the literature.

Many workers report the use of glyphosate for zero-tillage maize: at 1.12–3.36 kg ha^{-1}, maize yields were increased when grown with a wheat cover crop (Rodrigues, 1979); Akobundu (1977) claims that glyphosate at 1.0 kg ha^{-1} is superior to paraquat at the same dose; 2.0 kg ha^{-1} failed to control weeds adequately for direct drilling in the Philippines (Manuel and Zabate, 1979), but good control of *Cynodon dactylon* was obtained with CDA applications and additives in Zambia (Zambia, 1980).

Pre-harvest treatments of glyphosate can be used to control *S. halepense* and other weeds in maize, but they should not be applied until the grain moisture falls below 30% and the black layer has formed at the base of the kernel, otherwise yields are reduced and progeny seedlings are damaged (Jeffery, English and Connell, 1981).

RICE (ORYZA SATIVA)

Glyphosate at a concentration of 2000 p.p.m. controlled *Scirpus maritimus* when applied 10–15 days before transplanting rice (Ryang, Chun and Moon, 1978) and good control of *Paspalum acuminatum* is possible with rates of 1.1–2.2 kg ha^{-1} applied 2 weeks before water-sowing rice (Baker, 1975). In upland rice, IRRI (1979) found that it was not advantageous to control weeds in a stale seedbed with glyphosate.

Minimum-tillage, but not zero-tillage, is a dependable alternative to conventional tillage in rice, where difficult weeds are not a problem (IRRI, 1976). Glyphosate at 2 kg ha^{-1} applied 7 days before transplanting eliminated *P. paspaloides* but not the annual sedge *Fimbristyllis littoralis*. In dry-sown rice, 2 kg ha^{-1}, combined with minimum-tillage, gave the highest yields (IRRI, 1978). Weed and pasture species have been controlled by 0.36–0.45 kg ha^{-1} glyphosate applied before direct seeding and rates up to 3.24 kg ha^{-1} had no adverse effect on crop establishment and vigour (Fellowes, Tydens and Swain, 1979).

Cumbungi (*Typha* sp.) has been successfully controlled in rice by applying glyphosate with a rope wick (Australia, 1980).

SORGHUM (SORGHUM BICOLOR)

In trials to compare methods of seedbed preparation, yields of sorghum from plots treated with glyphosate at 1.0–2.0 kg ha^{-1} were no different from those prepared by conventional tillage and were better than those treated with paraquat at 0.5–2.0 kg ha^{-1} (Ndahi, 1982).

Good control of volunteer *Z. mays* and *S. bicolor,* with little or no injury to the crop, has been obtained with glyphosate applied with roller applications and rope wicks (Furrer *et al.,* 1980; Schneider *et al.,* 1982). Glyphosate at 0.68–1.02 kg ha^{-1}, applied with a recirculating sprayer, controlled *S. halepense* where the weed was more than 60 cm higher than the crop (Boyles, Mason and Santelmann, 1978).

Glyphosate applied 2 weeks before harvest at 3.36 and 5.6 kg ha^{-1} has given good control of *Brunnichia cirrhosa* and *Campsis radicans* (de Felice and Oliver, 1980).

SOYA BEAN (GLYCINE MAX)

Much of the work to develop glyphosate for use in soya bean has been done in the USA, where large-scale, highly mechanized production systems are used in conjunction with chemical weed control.

Glyphosate applied as overall sprays to soya bean causes severe injury at doses of 0.3 kg ha^{-1} (Stoller, Wax and Matthieson, 1975), but at doses of 0.28–0.56 kg ha^{-1} injury is least to cv. 'Bragg', intermediate in effect on cvs. 'Forrest', 'Pickett' and 'Tracy', and most injurious to cv. 'York' (Connell and Jeffery, 1975). It would be logical, therefore, to select a relatively tolerant cultivar where there is any risk of drift or accidental contact with glyphosate.

Directed inter-row sprays of glyphosate have been tested at 0.14–0.56 kg ha^{-1} applied with two nozzles in soya beans of different heights (Gebhardt, 1974). The results indicate that glyphosate can be used for post-emergent directed application in soya bean, provided that it is applied with coventional 65° nozzles when the soya beans are approximately 15 cm high. Spray-wetting the plant to a height of 10 cm reduces the yield, but not when sprayed to 5 cm.

Recirculating sprayers have been developed which direct a stream of herbicide above the crop to intercept weeds that emerge above the canopy. Various combinations of nozzles, spray pressures, glyphosate doses, surfactants, anti-foam agents and weed-to-crop height differentials have been tried with the recirculating sprayer (McWhorter and Williford, 1980; Carlson and Burnside, 1981; see also Chapter 16). Slight injury to soya bean can occur through spray drift, dripping or splashing but, with the exception of one combination of surfactants and nozzles, no yield reductions occur (McWhorter and Williford, 1980). Soya bean cultivars 'Forrest' and 'Tracy' are more tolerant of glyphosate applied by recirculating sprayer than cultivars 'Hill' or 'Bragg', and this could affect their competitiveness in heavy weed infestations (McWhorter and Williford, 1980). Glyphosate applied at doses of 1.1–2.2 kg ha^{-1}, with the recirculating sprayer, has given 74–98% control of *Sorghum halepense* (McWhorter and Williford, 1980), 0–88% control of *Asclepias syriaca*, 78–97% control of *Sorghum bicolor* and 73–100% control of volunteer *Zea mays* (Carlson and Burnside, 1981).

Weeds growing above the soya bean canopy can also be controlled by roller applicators. After testing a range of operating conditions, Schneider *et al.* (1982) obtained acceptable control of *S. bicolor* in soya beans with 5–20% solutions of glyphosate, 50% carpet saturation and speeds of 3.2–9.6 kg h^{-1}, but control was poor with 2.5% glyphosate at 25% carpet saturation. Eleven to 22% of the soya bean plants were damaged by 2.5–10% glyphosate, but yields were not affected where the *S. bicolor* populations were high.

Rope-wick applicators are safe, effective and economical for applying glyphosate to weeds in soya bean, but Derting (1980) has shown that proper adjustment and operation are essential. Dale (1981) applied only 0.1 kg ha^{-1} glyphosate before sowing and another 0.1 kg ha^{-1} at pod-set to obtain approximately 90% control of *S. halepense* in 2 years of trials, compared with 33 and 70% control obtained with single-spray applications of 2.2 kg ha^{-1} before sowing. Yields averaged over 2 years were not significantly different between rope-wick and conventional spray applications. In comparisons between rope-wick applicators and a recirculating sprayer, there were no differences in the control of *S. halepense* (88–100%) and volunteer *Z. mays* (97–100%), but soya bean yields were reduced by the recirculating sprayer where the thicker leaves and stems of maize spattered glyphosate onto the crop (Dale, 1981) (see also Chapter 16).

Glyphosate has been used in minimal- and zero-tillage soya beans to control a wide range of weeds, including *Cynodon dactylon* (Malezas, 1980), *Cyperus esculentus* (Bullock and Jeffery, 1980), *S. halepense* (Dale, 1981), volunteer *S. bicolor* (Hardcastle, 1976) and many others. It is particularly useful against perennial weeds and, like paraquat, is effective against many emerged annual species. Pyon and Park (1977) obtained better weed control and higher soya bean yields with glyphosate, but Wilson and Hines (1981) obtained good control with paraquat and glyphosate. Where conventional tillage and zero-tillage with glyphosate are compared, the results can vary; for example, Burnside, Wicks and Carlson (1980) found glyphosate at 0.8 kg ha^{-1} and tandem disking were equally effective in producing a weed-free seedbed for soya beans. French (1979) obtained higher soya bean yields with conventional tillage, but Hardcastle (1976) found glyphosate treatment to be better than tillage. The differences are related to the weeds present at application, regrowth and whether or not other herbicides have been used in mixtures or sequences with glyphosate.

Pre-harvest applications of glyphosate have been successfully used to control *S. halepense* and other actively growing perennial weeds. Yields, seed germination and oil content are reduced if glyphosate is applied too soon before the maturity of soya bean, but glyphosate has no adverse effect on the crop if applied 7–12 days before full maturity, or after the onset of senescence when the leaves have turned yellow and started to drop (Azlin and McWhorter, 1981; Jeffery, English and Connell, 1981).

Conclusions

Glyphosate controls many of the most serious weeds of tropical and sub-tropical countries, including perennial grasses and sedges that hitherto have not been successfully controlled by most other methods. It has become a standard product for weed management in rubber, oil palm, coffee, tea and other plantation crops, usually as part of an integrated programme with other herbicides. It is also used effectively in the preparation of seedbeds for annual crops, where minimum- and zero-tillage techniques are implemented.

Application equipment has been developed to ensure placement of glyphosate on the weeds while minimizing harmful contact with the crop and reducing wastage on non-target areas. Wipers, such as rope wicks, are very promising for small-holders in developing countries, where robust, inexpensive and reliable application equipment is needed.

Glyphosate is easily washed off by rain. This lack of rainfastness of glyphosate is a serious constraint to its use in many countries where it is difficult to predict and guarantee rain-free periods after application. It is hoped that this problem will be overcome with improved formulations.

A further constraint shared with many other herbicides in developing countries is the relatively high cost of glyphosate compared with existing methods of weed control. Several additives look promising for reducing the dose rates which, together with economical methods of application, will ensure the more widespread use of glyphosate.

The combination of activity, versatility of application and toxicological safety has been the reason for the success of glyphosate, enabling it to be utilized in so many crops against so many weeds by all levels of farming that are to be found in the tropics and sub-tropics.

References

ABAD, R.G., SAN JUAN, N.C. and GALLEG, V.C. (1981). Studies on the control of noxious weeds (*Cyperus rotundus* L., *Imperata cylindrica* L. and *Pennisetum purpureum* Schum.) of coconut, *Proceedings of the 6th Indonesian Weed Science Society Conference*, Medan, pp. 25–39.

ABERNATHY, J.R., HOLLINGSWORTH, D. and KEELING, J.W. (1977). Control of volunteer sunflower in rotational crops, *Progress Report No. PR-3438*, Texas Agricultural Experiment Station, 3pp.

ABERNATHY, J.R. and KEELING, J.W. (1979). Silverleaf nightshade control in cotton with glyphosate, *Proceedings of the 32nd Annual Meeting of the Southern Weed Science Society*, p. 380.

AKOBUNDU, I.O. (1977). Advances in weed control in conventional and no-tillage maize, *Proceedings of the 7th Conference of the Weed Science Society of Nigeria*, Umudike, pp. 10–18.

AL-JUBOORY, B.A. and HASSAWY, G.S. (1980). Comparative morphological development of cogongrass (*Imperata cylindrica*) in Iraq, *Weed Science*, **28**(3), 324–326.

ÁLVAREZ DE LA PEÑA, F.J. (1978). Herbicides in banana plantations (in Spanish), *Proceedings of the Mediterranean Herbicide Symposium*, Madrid, **2**, 263–270.

ARIF, A. and PUTRAWAN, I.M. (1977). The effects of dalapon–sodium and glyphosate on young clove trees, *Proceedings of the 6th Asian–Pacific Weed Science Society Conference*, Jakarta, pp. 408–413.

ARIF, A. and SUBAGIO, H. (1976). Studies on alang-alang [*Imperata cylindrica* (L.) Beauv.] control with dalapon–sodium in open and shade conditions, *Proceedings of Biotrop Workshop on Alang-alang*, Bogor, pp. 113–133.

ARIF, A. and SUTOMO, T. (1982). Testing of new applicators for Roundup use in Lalang control in Indonesia, *Proceedings of the International Conference on Plant Protection in the Tropics*, Kuala Lumpur, Malaysia.

AUSTRALIA (1980). *Annual Report 1979–80*, Department of Agriculture New South Wales, Government Printer, 108pp.

AZLIN, W.R. and MCWHORTER, C.G. (1981). Preharvest effects of applying glyphosate to soybeans, *Weed Science*, **29**(1), 123–127.

BAIRD, D.D. and UPCHURCH, R.P. (1973). Post-emergence characteristics of a new herbicide, MON-0468, on johnsongrass, *Proceedings of the Southern Weed Science Society Conference*, **25**, 113–116.

BAKER, J.B. (1975). Brookpaspalum test, *66th Annual Progress Report (1974)*, Rice Experiment Station, Crowley, Louisiana, p. 101.

BANKS, P.A. and SANTELMANN, P.W. (1977). Glyphosate as a post-emergence treatment for johnsongrass control in cotton and soybeans, *Agronomy Journal*, **69**(4), 579–582.

BASUKI, SOEDARSAN, A. and RUSWANDI (1980). Weed shifts in a cocoa plantation due to herbicide (in Indonesian with English summary), *Menara Perkebunan*, **48**(5), 133–138.

BOLDT, P.F. and SWEET, R.D. (1974). Glyposate studies on yellow nutsedge, *Proceedings of the Northeastern Weed Science Society*, **28**, 197–204.

BOYLES, M., MASON, J. and SANTELMANN, P.W. (1978). Evaluation of glyphosate for johnsongrass control with a recirculating sprayer in four crops, Abstract, *Proceedings of the 31st Annual Meeting of the Southern Weed Science Society*, p.207.

BULLOCK, F.D. and JEFFERY, L.S. (1980). Weed control in no-tillage soybean–wheat double cropping system, Abstract, *Proceedings of the 33rd Annual Meeting of the Southern Weed Science Society*, p. 43.

BURNSIDE, O.C., WICKS, G.A. and CARLSON, D.R. (1980). Control of weeds in an oat (*Avena sativa*)–soybean (*Glycine max*) ecofarming rotation, *Weed Science*, **28**(1), 46–50.

CANADA (1981) Report. In *Research Branch Report 1980*, Agriculture Canada, Research Station, Harrow, p. 232.

CARLSON, D.R. and BURNSIDE, O.C. (1981). Use of the recirculating sprayer to control tall weed escapes in crops, *Weed Science*, **29**(2), 174–179.

CHANDLER, J.M. (1981). Perennial grass control in cotton, Abstract, *Proceedings of the 34th Annual Meeting of the Southern Weed Science Society Conference*, p. 27.

CHAPPELL, W.E. and LINK, L.A. (1977). Evaluation of herbicides in no-tillage production of barley tobacco (*Nicotiana tabacum*), *Weed Science*, **25**(6), 511–514.

CHASE, R.L. and APPLEBY, A.P. (1979a). Effect of intervals between application and tillage of glyphosate control of *Cyperus rotundus* L, *Weed Research*, **19**(3), 207–211.

CHASE, R.L. and APPLEBY, A.P. (1979b). Effects of humidity and moisture stress on glyphosate control of *Cyperus rotundus* L, *Weed Research*, **19**(4), 241–246.

CHAWDHRY, M.A. (1975). Weed control in Kenya coffee with glyphosate, *PANS*, **21**(1), 58–63.

CIAT (1975). Weed control, *Annual Report 1975*, Centro Internacional de Agricultura Tropical, Cali, Colombia, G28–G33.

COLLIOT, F., DAMOTTE, P., ROGNON, J. and SCHEPENS, G.R. (1978). Possibilities offered by glyphosate for weed control in tropical crops (in French), *3ᵉ Symposium sur le Désherbage des Cultures Tropicales*, Dakar, pp. 557–565.

CONNELL, J.T. and JEFFERY, L.S. (1975). Tolerance of soybean cultivars to glyphosate, dinoseb and a mixture of dinoseb plus naptalam, Abstract, *Proceedings of the 28th Annual Meeting of the Southern Weed Science Society*, p. 59.

COOMANS, P. and DELORME, M. (1978). Chemical weed control in young coconut plantations—first results (in French), *3ᵉ Symposium sur le Désherbage des Cultures Tropicales*, Dakar, tome 2, 364–371.

COX, T.I. and KERR, R.M. (1981). *Oxalis latifolia* control programmes with oxadiazon and glyphosate, *Proceedings of the 8th Asian Pacific Weed Science Society Conference*, Bangalore, pp. 231–234.

DALE, J.E. (1979). A non-mechanical system of herbicide application with a rope wick, *PANS*, **25**(4), 431–436.

DALE, J.E. (1981). Control of Johnsongrass (*Sorghum halepense*) and volunteer corn (*Zea mays*) in soybeans (*Glycine max*), *Weed Science*, **29**(6), 708–711.

DAWSON, J.H. and SAGHIR, A.R. (1982). Low rates of glyphosate control dodder selectively in alfalfa, *Haustorium*, no.8, 2–3.

DERTING, C.W. (1980). Response to the operational factors which influence rope wick effectiveness, Abstract, *Proceedings of the North Central Weed Control Conference*, **35**, 63.

DIARRA, A. (1978). Observations on wild rice and a study of control methods, Mopti, 1977 (in French), *3ᵉ Symposium sur le Désherbage des Cultures Tropicales*, Dakar, tome 1, pp. 228–243.

DOLL, J.D. and PIEDRAHITA, W. (1977). Effect of glyphosate on the sprouting of *Cyperus rotundus* L. tubers (in Spanish), *Revista COMALFI*, **4**(2), 59–69.

ENGLISH, J.R., JEFFERY, L.S. and CONNELL, J.T. (1977). The effects of fall applications of glyphosate on Johnsongrass (*Sorghum halepense* (L.) Pers.), soybeans and corn, *Abstracts of the Weed Science Society of America, 1977 Meeting*, p. 31.

ETHIOPIA (1973). *Progress Report for the Period April 1972 to March 1973*, Institute of Agricultural Research, Melka Werer Research Station, Ethiopia, pp. 155–191.

FELICE, M.S. DE and OLIVER, L.R. (1980). Redvine and trumpetcreeper control in soybeans and grain sorghum, *Arkansas Farm Research*, **29**(3), 5.

FELLOWES, R.W., TYDENS, N.M. and SWAIN, J.M. (1979). Control of weed and pasture species with glyphosate, prior to direct-drilling rice, *Proceedings of the 7th Asian–Pacific Weed Science Society Conference*, Sydney, pp. 281–283.

FRENCH, C.M. (1979). Herbicide use in double cropping soybean tillage systems, *Dissertation Abstracts International, B*, **39**(8), 3629.

FURRER, J.D., LUESCHEN, W.E., MARTIN, A.R. and BURNSIDE, O.C. (1980). The use of glyphosate in rope wicks and roller applicators for controlling shattercane and volunteer corn in grain sorghum, Abstract, *Proceedings of the North Central Weed Control Conference*, **35**, 58–59.

GAILLARD, J.P. and HAURY, A. (1974). Toxicity and inhibitory effect of some herbicides in pineapples. Study of the action of bromacil (in French), *Fruits*, **29**(11), 745–755.

GEBHARDT, M.R. (1981). Cultural and chemical weed control systems in soybeans (*Glycine max*), *Weed Science*, **29**(1), 133–138.

GLOVER, D.K., JEFFERY, L.S., CONNELL, J. and MORGAN, T.H. (1976). Systems of Johnsongrass control in soyabeans, *Down to Earth*, **31**(4), 14–20.

HARDCASTLE, W.S. (1976). Volunteer sorghum control in no-till soybeans, Abstract, *Proceedings of the 29th Annual Meeting of the Southern Weed Science Society*, p. 60.

HAUSER, E.W. and BUCHANAN, G.A. (1978). Progress report: control of broadleaf weeds in peanuts with the recirculating spray technique, Abstract, *Proceedings of the 31st Annual Meeting of the Southern Weed Science Society*, p. 330.

HAWAII (1980). *Annual Report 1979*, Hawaiian Sugar Planters' Association, Experimental Station, Aiea, Hawaii, 80pp.

HOLM, L. (1969). Weed problems in developing countries, *Weed Science*, **17**(1), 113–118.

HOWELL, S. and FRANS, R. (1980). Preliminary studies on control of bermudagrass in cotton, Abstract, *Proceedings of the 33rd Annual Meeting of the Southern Weed Science Society*, p. 29.

HUSSEIN, I. and WENG, W.P. (1977). Use of glyphosate for selective control of *Paspalum conjugatum* and *Ottochloa nodosa* in established legume cover crops, *Proceedings of the 6th Asian–Pacific Weed Science Society Conference*, Jakarta, pp. 403–407.

HUTCHINSON, J. and DALZIEL, J.M. (1972). *Flora of West Tropical Africa*, 2nd edn, vol. III, p. 2. London; Crown Agents.

INDIA (1978). *50th Annual Report 1976*. United Planters' Association of Southern India, Tea Scientific Department, India, pp. 16–19.

IRRI (1977). Zero and minimum tillage, *IRRI Annual Report 1976*, pp. 192–194.

IRRI (1978). *Annual Report for 1976*, International Rice Research Institute, Philippines, pp. 192–194.

IRRI (1979). *Annual Report for 1977*, International Rice Research Institute, Philippines, pp. 450–451.

ISRAEL (1978). Experiments on weed control with glyphosate (Roundup), *Proceedings of the Roundup Seminar*, Madrid (supplementary papers), pp. 25–40.

IVENS, G.W. (1976). *Imperata cylindrica* (L.) Beauv. in West African agriculture, *Proceedings of the Biotrop Workshop on Alang-alang*, Bogor, pp. 149–156.

JEFFERY, L.S., ENGLISH, J.R. and CONNELL, J. (1981). The effects of fall application of glyphosate on corn (*Zea mays*), soybeans (*Glycine max*) and johnsongrass (*Sorghum halepense*), *Weed Science*, **29**(2), 191–195.

JORDAN, L.S., JORDAN, J.L. and GUZON, D.A. (1980). Glyphosate for weed control in subtropical orchards, Abstract, *Proceedings of the North Central Weed Control Conference*, **35**, 91–92.

JORDAN, T.N. (1977a). Effects of temperature and relative humidity on the toxicity of glyphosate to Bermudagrass (*Cynodon dactylon*), *Weed Science*, **25**(5), 448–451.

JORDAN, T.N. (1977b). Hooded sprayer for glyphosate application in cotton, Abstract, *Proceedings of the 30th Annual Meeting of the Southern Weed Science Society*, p. 417.

JORDAN, T.N. and BRIDGE, R.R. (1976). Selectivity of glyphosate to cotton cultivars, johnsongrass and bermudagrass, *Proceedings of the 29th Annual Meeting Southern Weed Science Society*, pp. 53–57.

JORDAN, T.N. and BRIDGE, R.R. (1979). Tolerance of cotton to the herbicide glyphosate, *Agronomy Journal*, **71**(6), 929–931.

KASASIAN, L. (1973). Control of *Orobanche*, *PANS*, **19**(3), 368–371.

KERR, H.D., ROYSTER, C.M. and LONG, S.S. (1976). Chemicals for managing weeds in agronomic crops, *Research Report No. P–735*, Oklahoma Agricultural Experiment Station, Stillwater, USA, pp. 25–28.

KLEIFELD, Y. (1976). Control of *Cynodon dactylon* in cotton, *Phytoparasitica*, **4**(2), 148.

KOGAN, M. and GONZALEZ, M.I. (1979). Yellow and purple nutsedge vegetative propagule production and the effect of MSMA and glyphosate, *Proceedings of the Western Society of Weed Science Annual Meeting*, **32**, 87–92.

LAMB, D. (1975). Weed control in tropical forest plantations using glyphosate, *PANS*, **21**(2), 177–181.

LANGSTON, M.A. and EPLEE, R.E. (1974). The use of glyphosate in witchweed control, *Abstracts of the 1974 Meeting of the Weed Science Society of America*, p. 115.

LEE, S.A. and ENOCH, I.C. (1977). Weed succession in the peat swamp forest cleared for pineapple cultivation, *Proceedings of the 6th Asian–Pacific Weed Science Society Conference*, Jakarta, **II**, 375–380.

LINSCOTT, D.L., HAGIN, R.D. and THARAWANICH, T. (1978). Control of yellow nutsedge (*Cyperus esculentus*) and other weeds before summer planting of alfalfa (*Medicago sativa*), *Weed Science*, **26**(4), 399–402.

LOCASCIO, S.J. (1977). Weed control for commercial vegetable production, *Annual Research Report 1975*, Institute of Food and Agricultural Sciences, Florida, p. 241.

MACHADO NETO, J.G. and LUSVARGHI, H.N. (1980). Effects of various rates of glyphosate on weed communities in crops, *Resumos XIII Congresso Brasiliero de Herbicidas e Ervas Daninhas*, Itabuna, p. 118.

MAGAMBO, M.J.S. and KILAVUKA, C.I. (1975). Preliminary observations on the effect of glyphosate on *Cyperus* weeds in young tea, *Tea in East Africa*, **15**(1), 11–14.

MAGAMBO, M.J.S. and KILAVUKA, C.I. (1982). Effect of glyphosate on shoot growth of tea, *Tropical Pest Management*, **28**(3), 315–316.

MAGAMBO, M.J.S. and TERRY, P.J. (1973). Control of purple nutsedge (*Cyperus rotundus*) with glyphosate, *Proceedings of the 4th Asian–Pacific Weed Science Society Conference*, Rotorua, pp. 191–194.

MALEZAS (1980). Weed control in direct drilling (in Spanish), *Malezas*, **8**(4), 11–15.

MANUEL, J.S. and ZABATE, P.Z. (1979). Weed control in corn (dry season, 1978), *Weed Science Report 1977–78*, University of the Philippines at Los Baños, College of Agricultrure, Department of Agronomy, Laguna, Philippines, pp. 32–38.

MASON, J.F. and MURRAY, D.S. (1979). Effects of glyphosate applied preharvest to Spanish peanuts, *Proceedings of the 32nd Annual Meeting of the Southern Weed Science Society*, p. 67.

MCCUE, A.S. and SWEET, R.D. (1981). Summer and fall controls of yellow nutsedge (*Cyperus esculentus* L.), Abstract, *Proceedings of the Northeastern Weed Science Society*, **35**, 87.

MCWHORTER, C.G. and WILLIFORD, J.R. (1980). Factors affecting the toxicity of glyphosate applied in the recirculating sprayer to johnsongrass (*Sorghum halepense*) and soybeans (*Glycine max*), *Weed Science*, **28**(1), 59–63.

MILLER, F. (1982). Evaluation of glyphosate for use against *Merremia* spp. in the Solomon Islands, *Tropical Pest Management*, **28**(4), 347–354.

MOOSAVI-NIA, H. and DORE, J. (1979). Factors affecting glyphosate activity in *Imperata cylindrica* (L.) Beauv. and *Cyperus rotundus* L. I. Effect of soil moisture, *Weed Research*, **19**(2), 137–143.

MULLINS, J.A. (1976). Recent developments in pesticide application equipment, Abstract, *Proceedings of the 1976 Beltwide Cotton Production Research Conference*, Memphis, Tennessee, p. 174.

NAIOLO, B.N. (1981). Growth variation of some Indonesian alang-alang clones, *Proceedings of the 8th Asian-Pacific Weed Science Society Conference*, Bangalore, pp. 291–294.

NDAHI, W.B. (1982). Evaluation of glyphosate and paraquat as substitutes for seedbed preparation by tillage in a hoe farming system, *Tropical Pest Management*, **28**(1), 10–13.

NIGERIA (1977). Farm systems and intercropping programme, Report to the Board of Governors on the work of the Institute for Agricultural Research, Samaru, Zaria, Nigeria (1975–76), 65pp.

NISHIMOTO, R.K. and HIBBARD, K.L. (1979). Glyphosate for weed control in *Carica papaya*, *Proceedings of the 7th Asian–Pacific Weed Science Society Conference*, Sydney, pp. 71–73.

NISHIMOTO, R.K. and YEE, W.Y.J. (undated). A guide to chemical weed control in tropical and subtropical fruit and nut crops in Hawaii, *Circular 423*, Cooperative Extension Service, College of Tropical Agriculture and Human Resources, University of Hawaii at Manoa.

NORTON, K.R. and MERKLE, M.G. (1976). Fall applied herbicides for controlling johnsongrass, Abstract, *Proceedings of the 29th Annual Meeting of the Southern Weed Science Society*, p. 61.

OREN, Y. and BEERI, M. (1978). Improving and reducing control costs of *Paspalum dilatatum* in citrus with Roundup, *Proceedings of the Roundup Seminar*, Madrid, pp. 19–23.

OVERTON, J.R., JEFFERY, L.S. and MULLINS, J.A. (1976). Control of johnsongrass with Roundup applied in the fall in a crop rotation system, *Tennessee Farm and Home Science*, no. 100, pp. 7–9.

PARKER, C. (1978). Pot experiments with some new herbicides on tropical perennial weeds, *3ᵉ Symposium sur le Désherbage des Cultures Tropicales*, Dakar, tome 1, 288–296.

PAROCHETTI, J.V., WILSON, H.P. and BURT, G.W. (1975). Activity of glyphosate on Johnsongrass, *Weed Science*, **23**(5), 395–400.

PAVIOT, J. (1977). A new herbicide trial in a cacao plantation at the station of Nkoemvone, *Cafe Cacao The*, **21**(1), 41–46.

PEREIRA, R.C., MARCONDES, D.A.S., FONTES, J.L., CHEHATA, A.N. and GERALDO, E.R. (1980). Effect of post-emergence herbicides in cocoa crops (in Portuguese), *Resumos XIII Congresso Brasileiro de Herbicidas e Ervas Daninhas*, Bahia, pp. 30–31.

PULVER, E. and CASTELAR, J. (1974). Control of nutsedge (*Cyperus rotundus* L.) with EPTC and glyphosate (in Spanish), *Asociación Latinoamericana de Malezas 'ALAM' y Sociedad Colombiana de Control de Malezas y Fisiología Vegetal 'COMALFI'. Resúmenes de los Trabajos en el II Congreso ALAM y VI Seminario, COMALFI*, Cali, Colombia, pp. 59–60.

PYON, J.Y. and PARK, H.W. (1977). No-tillage systems for soybeans following barley, *Proceedings of the 6th Asian–Pacific Weed Science Society Conference*, Jakarta, pp. 381–386.

QUIMBY, P.C., JR. and FRICK, K.E. (1980). Control of nutsedge with glyphosate-coated *Bactra*, Abstract, *Proceedings of the 33rd Annual Meeting of the Southern Weed Science Society*, p. 195.

RAMOS, M. (1976). Chemical weed control in soybeans sown with zero-tillage (in Portuguese), *Resumos XI Seminario Brasileiro de Herbicidas e Ervas Daninhas*, Londrina, p. 96.

RAO, V.S., KOTOKY, B. and SARMAH, S.N. (1981). Perennial weed control in tea, *Proceedings of the 8th Asian-Pacific Weed Science Society Conference*, Bangalore, pp. 295–299.

RAO, V.S., RAHMAN, F., SINGH, H.S., DUTTA, A.K., SAIKIA, M.C., SHARMA, S.N. and PHUKAN, B.C. (1976). Effective weed control in tea by glyphosate, *Indian Journal of Weed Science*, **8**(1), 1–14.

RODRIGUES, J.J. DO V. (1979). Exudation of glyphosate from treated vegetation and its implications in increasing yields in no-till corn and soybeans, *Dissertation Abstracts International, B*, **40**(5), 1991.

ROMERO, C.E. and MEJIA, V.E. (1976). The efficiency of glyphosate and dalapon in controlling Kikuyu grass (*Pennisetum clandestinum* Hochs) (in Spanish), *Trabajos y Resúmenes, III Congreso Asociación Latinomericana de Malezas 'ALAM' y VIII Reunión Argentina de Malezas y su Control 'ASAM'*, Mar del Plata, **5**, 69–88.

RYANG, H.S., CHUN, J.C. and MOON, Y.H. (1978). Control of perennial weed *Scirpus maritimus*

L. in reclaimed paddy fields of west seashore. III. Control of *S. maritimus* with herbicides (in Korean), *Journal of the Korean Society of Crop Science*, **23**(1), 74–80.

SCHNEIDER, G.L., KOEHLER, C.B., SCHEPERS, J.S. and BURNSIDE, O.C. (1982). Roller applicator for shattercane (*Sorghum bicolor*) control in row crops, *Weed Science*, **30**(3), 301–306.

SHARMA, V.S. and SUNDAR, K.R. (1981). Kaolin and ammonium sulphate as additives to increase the herbicidal efficacy of glyphosate, *Proceedings of the 8th Asian–Pacific Weed Science Society Conference*, Bangalore, pp. 335–339.

SOEJONO, A.T. and SELAMAT, S.T. (1975). Weed population in a multiple cropping system and the effect of herbicide application, *Proceedings of the 3rd Indonesian Weed Science Society Conference*, Bandung, pp. 212–226.

SOUTH AFRICA (1978). *Annual Report 1977–78*, South African Sugar Association Experiment Station, p. 26.

SRINIVASAN, V., NEGI, N.S., PERERA, C.S. and ARCEO, L.M. (1981). Development of the isopropylamine salt of glyphosate for weed control in tea, *Proceedings of the 8th Asian–Pacific Weed Science Society Conference*, Bangalore, pp. 439–442.

STOLLER, E.N., WAX, L.M. and MATTHIESON, R.L. (1975). Response of yellow nutsedge and soybeans to bentazon, glyphosate and perfluidone, *Weed Science*, **23**(3), 215–221.

SUWANKETNIKOM, R. and PENNER, D. (1978). Effect of ammonium salts on bentazon and glyphosate activity on yellow nutsedge (*Cyperus esculentus* L.), *Abstracts of the 1978 Meeting of the Weed Science Society of America*, p. 73.

TERRY, P.J. (1974a). Field evaluation of glyphosate, asulam and dalapon on African couch grass (*Digitaria scalarum*), *East African Agricultural and Forestry Journal*, **39**(4), 386–390.

TERRY, P.J. (1974b). Long term control of *Cyperus rotundus* with glyphosate, *Proceedings of the 5th East African Weed Control Conference*, Nairobi, pp. 173–188.

THARAWANICH, T. and LINSCOTT, D.L. (1975). Factors influencing the effect of glyphosate on yellow nutsedge, Abstract, *Proceedings of the Northeastern Weed Science Society*, p. 132.

TUCKER, D.P.H. (1977). Glyphosate injury symptom expression in *Citrus*, *HortScience*, **12**(5), 498–500.

TUCKER, D.P.H., BAIRD, D.D. and PHILLIPS, R.L. (1977). Development of glyphosate as a herbicide for Florida citrus, *Proceedings of the International Society of Citriculture*, **1**, 148–152.

VANUNU, E., AMIR, J. and LIFSHITZ, N. (1976). Control of *Cynodon dactylon* (L.) Pers. in peanuts with glyphosate, *Phytoparasitica*, **4**(2), 150.

WILSON, A.K. (1981). Commelinaceae—a review of the distribution, biology and control of the important weeds belonging to this family, *Tropical Pest Management*, **27**(3), 405–418.

WILSON, H.P. and HINES, T.E. (1981). Preliminary studies in early planted no-tillage soybeans, Abstract, *Proceedings of the Northeastern Weed Science Society*, **35**, 51.

WONG, P.W. (1975a). Commercial development of Roundup post emergence herbicide as a one-shot treatment for control of lalang (*Imperata cylindrica*) in Malaysian rubber cultivation, *Proceedings of the 3rd Indonesian Weed Science Society Conference*, Bandung, **I**, 164–179.

WONG, P.W. (1975b). Tolerance of young rubber to Roundup postemergence weedicide, *Planter*, **51**(593), 367–369.

WONG, P.W. (1977). Roundup for weed control in mature rubber planting strips dominated by *Ottochloa nodosa* and *Paspalum conjugatum*, *Planter, Kuala Lumpur*, **53**, 118–124.

WONG, P.W. (1981). Evaluation of the isopropylamine salt of glyphosate for *Imperata cylindrica* (L.) Beauv. control in oil palm, *Proceedings of the 8th Asian–Pacific Weed Science Society Conference*, Bangalore, pp. 273–276.

YEOH, C.H. (1980). Control of *Imperata cylindrica* (L.) Beauv. (lalang) in Malaysia's smallholdings, *Proceedings of the BIOTROP Workshop on Alang-Alang, 1976*, BIOTROP, P.O. Box 17, Bogor, Indonesia, pp. 89–111.

YEOH, C.H. and PUSHPARAJAH, E. (1976). Chemical control of *Imperata cylindrica* (L.) Beauv. (lalang) in Malaysia, *Proceedings of the Rubber Research Institute of Malaysia Planters' Conference*, pp. 250–273.

ZAHRAN, M.K., IBRAHIM, T.S. EL-N., FARAG, F.H. and KOROLLOS, M.A. (1980). Chemical control of *Orobanche crenata* in *Vicia faba*, *FABIS (Faba Bean Information Service) Newsletter*, **2**, 47–49.

ZAMBIA (1980). Weed control in minimum tillage maize, *Annual Report of the Weed Control Research and Extension Team—1979*, Mt. Makulu Research Station, Chilanga, Zambia, pp. 37–40.

ZANDSTRA, B.H. and NISHIMOTO, R.K. (1975). Effect of undisturbed soil period on glyphosate control of *Cyperus rotundus* L, *Proceedings of the 5th Asian–Pacific Weed Science Society Conference*, Tokyo, pp. 130–133.

ZANDSTRA, B.H. and NISHIMOTO, R.K. (1977). Movement and activity of glyphosate in purple nutsedge, *Weed Science*, **25**(3), 268–274.

Chapter 26

Efficacy of glyphosate for weed control in grassland, turf grass and amenity grassland and for renovation of pastures

R.J. Haggar
Weed Research Organization, Oxford, UK

Introduction

The wide spectrum of activity of glyphosate against both perennial grasses and broad-leaved weeds (Baird *et al.*, 1971), coupled with its rapid inactivation by soil, makes it ideally useful for killing weeds and old swards prior to sowing forage grasses and legumes. Replacement of unwanted vegetation by new crops is referred to variously as direct drilling, direct planting, no-tillage planting or zero tillage. The potential benefits of this technique compared with ploughing include: more economical use of time, energy and labour; reductions in moisture loss and soil erosion; maintenance of surface consolidation (see also Chapter 27).

Good weed control is vital for the success of direct-drilling or reduced-tillage systems. Glyphosate is effective in killing most perennial weeds present in crop stubbles and fallows, e.g. *Agropyron repens, Cirsium arvense, Cyperus* spp. and *Sorghum halepense* (Hoagland and Duke, 1981). Thus, a high success rate has been reported for establishing a wide range of forage crops in stubbles sprayed with glyphosate (Linscott, 1979). The comparatively few incidents of failures have been attributed variously to damage caused by decaying crop and weed residues (Lynch, 1980), predation caused by pests and diseases (Clements, 1980), as well as competition from invading annual grass weeds (Linscott, 1979). Notwithstanding these limitations, the direct drilling of grasses and forage legumes into stubbles is generally successful and large areas have been sown in the USA and elsewhere.

By comparison, drilling seed directly into chemically killed swards presents a different set of problems. This will be a major aspect dealt with in this chapter.

Pasture renovation, as opposed to direct drilling, generally refers to the partial suppression of the old sward (sod), either overall or in strips, followed by the introduction of desirable legumes and grasses. Other terms used as variants of pasture renovation include sod-seeding, interseeding, overseeding, overdrilling, strip-tillage seeding, minimum-tillage seeding, etc. After reviewing the use of glyphosate in pasture renovation, some consideration will be given to the use of glyphosate in turf-grass renovation, as well as vegetation control in amenity grassland—including its selective use through directional application to tall growing weeds in grassland.

The name glyphosate in this chapter refers to the isopropylamine salt of N-(phosphonomethyl)glycine used as the commercial formulation Roundup.

Killing swards with glyphosate prior to no-tillage seeding

The UK is unique in having a high proportion of old grass replaced by new grass leys at frequent intervals. Scientists here have established guidelines for direct drilling grass-into-grass, based initially on the use of paraquat (Allen, 1981). The main requirements are a well-drained, fertile soil of good structure, with adequate moisture and temperature, and freedom from weeds, pests, diseases and toxic compounds. Old swards containing stoloniferous grasses which are difficult to eradicate and perennial weeds, are outside the guidelines and have to receive prior treatment with appropriate herbicides.

Many investigators have compared the quick-acting paraquat with the slower acting, but readily translocated, glyphosate. For instance, Oswald (1972), using logarithmic doses on an old permanent pasture, showed that glyphosate was generally more effective in killing grasses like *Festuca rubra* and *Agrostis stolonifera* than paraquat. Cromack *et al.* (1978) also found that glyphosate was slower in action than paraquat, but gave an improved kill of the old sward, particularly of *Rumex* spp.

Glyphosate is a foliar-applied (acting) herbicide. It is therefore only effective when plants are growing actively and have a reasonable leaf area. With permanent grass swards in England, this refers to mid-summer (Oswald, 1976), although it can be effective until late autumn. For broad-leaved weeds, the optimum timing varies from early June to mid-August, depending on species, climate, location and sward management.

Amounts of glyphosate required to kill swards depend largely on the species of grasses present. For example, annual grasses and some non-stoloniferous crop grasses can be killed by less than 1 kg a.e. ha^{-1} of glyphosate. Stoloniferous grasses require higher amounts (*Table 26.1*) and if *A. repens* is present, rates need to be increased to at least 1.4 kg ha^{-1}, rising to over 2 kg ha^{-1} if certain ecotypes are present (Westra and Wyse, 1978; Wyse, 1978). With this species, Ernst and Weber (1975) found no dose-related response in the range of 1.08–2.16 kg ha^{-1}. Even higher rates are needed for killing fine-leaved grasses like *Festuca rubra* (Oswald, 1976).

Where swards are contaminated with broad-leaved weeds, glyphosate rates necessary for control will depend on the species present, as indicated in *Table 26.1*.

Drilling seeds immediately into old swards, desiccated with glyphosate, often leads to problems of poor germination and indifferent establishment, especially at sites of high organic matter. Phytotoxicity, caused directly by the herbicide in the dying sward or thatch, is rarely the problem (Hurts and Turgeon, 1979), rather it is due to breakdown products from the decaying swards such as acetic acid (Gussin and Lynch, 1981) or tannins and phenolic compounds (Habeshaw, 1980). Often these harmful phytotoxic substances predispose the young plants to fungal attack, especially under low temperatures. *Fusarium* is a widely distributed pathogen causing root rot in seedlings. *F. culmorum* and, especially, *F. nivale* can both have a marked effect on the growth of young ryegrass seedlings, although there are several other microorganisms which can retard seedling root growth. Such attacks can be countered by the use of fungicide seed dressings (Edwards, 1982; see also Chapter 11).

Formation and dissipation of these phytotoxic compounds are controlled by microbial activity which is, in turn, influenced by temperature, pH (Toai and Linscott, 1979) and other factors. These are time-dependent processes and

TABLE 26.1   Amounts of glyphosate needed to kill certain weed and grass species

Species	Glyphosate (kg ha⁻¹)	Reference
Agropyron repens	1.4–2.1	Wyse (1978)
Agrostis palustris	1.7	Klingman and Murray (1977)
Bromus inermis	2.6	Mueller-Warrant and Koch (1980)
Cirsium arvense	2.0	Davison (1972)
Cynodon dactylon	2.2	Johnson (1976a)
Dactylis glomerata	1.1	Mueller-Warrant, Koch and Mitchell (1979)
Digitaria spp.	2.2	Burt (1975)
Equisetum arvense	8.0	Davison (1972)
Festuca arundinacea	2.2	Falb and Stroube (1976)
F. rubra	3.7	Oswald (1976)
Holcus mollis	1.5	Williams (1979)
Hordeum murinum	0.54	Allen and Butler (1980)
Juncus spp.	1.4–2.2	Moore, Yortt and Atkinson (1980)
Nassella trichotoma	5.0	Campbell and Gilmour (1979)
Paspalum dilatatum	2.2	Scherp and Sarfaty (1975)
Pennisetum clandestinum	1.1	Read (1977)
Poa annua	0.3	Johnson and Ware (1978)
P. pratensis	1.5	Daniel and Freeborg (1974)
Pteridium aquilinum	2.0	Williams (1977)
Ranunculus repens	1.0	Davison (1972)
Rubus fruticosus	1.4–3.0	Yortt and Atkinson (1980)
Rumex obtusifolius	1.0	Davison (1972)
Taraxacum officinale	2.2	Waddington and Bowren (1976)
Trifolium repens	4.0	Jagschitz (1978)
Urtica dioica	1.0	Davison (1972)
Ulex europaeus	2.0	Preest (1980)
Zoysia japonica	2.2	Klingman and Murray (1977)

necessitate a separation of spraying and drilling operations. By increasing the interval between spraying and drilling from 0 to 21 days, Davies and Davies (1981) reported a linear increase in establishment of perennial ryegrass seedlings. These benefits extend to intervals of up to, at least, 28 days. This agrees with the results of Welty *et al.* (1981) (*Figure 26.1*).

A further reason for extending the spray-drill interval to 4, and preferably 6, weeks is to reduce the great risk of damage by frit-fly larvae. However, because such a delay negates much of the advantage of direct drilling, the insecticide chlorpyrifos has been used successfully as a tank mix with glyphosate (Clements and Haggar, 1982). In the USA, carbofuran granules have proved helpful in the no-till establishment of lucerne following sward kill by glyphosate (Peters and Zapozalka, 1981). Other predators which need to be controlled are leatherjackets (*Tipula* spp.), slugs (*Deroceras* spp.) and wireworms (*Agriotes* spp.).

Where surface trash (thatch) is a problem, burning soon after spraying can be helpful (Davies, Jackson and Johnson, 1980) as can mowing or soil cultivation (Hurts and Turgeon, 1979). Other aids have been investigated, including the use of calcium peroxide in high rainfall areas. This treatment of grass seed improved grass establishment (Davies and Davies, 1981). Calcium peroxide probably helped to overcome the oxygen deficiency in the immediate vicinity of the seed as well as neutralize acidity in the seed microenvironment and act as a fungicide (J.M. Lynch, personal communication).

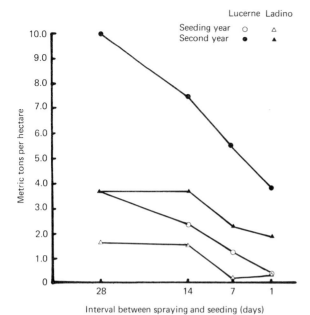

Lucerne Ladino

Seeding year   ○   △
Second year   ●   ▲

Figure 26.1. Effect of spray–plant interval on forage yields of
two sod-seeded legumes at Kalispell, Montana (from Welty
et al., 1981, by courtesy of the Editor of *Agronomy Journal*)

In practice, the rate of decomposition of matted swards can be speeded up by
surface cultivation (Barber *et al.*, 1978). In many cases, however, autumn-sprayed
swards may have to be left to over-winter to allow complete breakdown of organic
matter and reduce the risk of toxins being present at drilling time in spring.

Renovating pastures by partial spraying

Spraying and overdrilling seed

Pasture renovation or sod-seeding is a special application of direct drilling (zero
tillage) since, with both techniques, seed is drilled into a non-tilled seed-bed. The
distinguishing feature is that with direct drilling, seedlings emerge into a relatively
weed-free environment, whereas with sod-seeding, seedlings emerge into an
existing sward. Sod-seeding is used either to renovate damaged or low-yielding
pastures, or to introduce more desirable species.

The early sod-seeding machines failed because competition from the existing
sward was not controlled adequately. With the advent of paraquat, band spraying,
coupled with overdrilling, became a possibility (Blackmore, 1962). Further
improvements in sod-seeding equipment followed (Decker, Retzer and Swain,
1964) leading to the production of a band-spraying, powered rotaseeder (Taylor *et
al.*, 1964). Several million hectares of pasture land in the USA were sod-seeded
with legumes such as red and white clovers (*Trifolium pratense, T. repens*), lucerne
(*Medicago sativa*), birdsfoot trefoil (*Lotus corniculatus*) and crown vetch (*Coronilla
varia*) (Decker *et al.*, 1969).

This early work on pasture renovation was most successful on relatively open swards in the north central states of the USA. When glyphosate was introduced it became possible to deal with dense and difficult swards containing stoloniferous and rhizomatous grasses in the more northerly states. For instance, glyphosate was used to establish lucerne in *A. repens*-dominant swards (Linscott and Hagin, 1976; Mueller-Warrant and Koch, 1980), red clover was sod-seeded into *Poa pratensis* pasture (Hartwig, 1976) and birdsfoot trefoil was sod-seeded into swards dominated by *Bromus* sp. (Rayburn, Hunt and Linscott, 1981a).

Several workers have found glyphosate to be more efficient than paraquat in killing dense swards (e.g. Peters and Lowance, 1979; Nichols and Peters, 1980). Reporting on 28 no-tillage forage legume trials on farms in New York State, Rayburn, Hunt and Linscott (1981b) found that, where glyphosate was compared with paraquat, plant densities at 30 days were equal to paraquat in 85% of the cases and greater than paraquat in 15% of the cases. Weed control was greater with glyphosate in 90% of the trials; glyphosate treatment produced significantly greater yields than paraquat in 5 out of 8 trials and legume content was greater in 6 out of 8 experiments.

However, in many situations where glyphosate has provided adequate sward suppression, establishment densities have been inadequate or lacking in vigour (Welty *et al.*, 1981), suggesting that factors other than removal of competition are limiting successful establishment of small-seeded legumes and grasses. These factors do not include any direct toxic effect of glyphosate (Moshier and Penner, 1978), but are more likely to be due to toxic release from the breakdown of organic matter (Toai and Linscott, 1979), plus attack by molluscs, insects, fungi, etc. (Dowling and Linscott, 1981).

One way of reducing the harmful effects associated with the breakdown of mat and trash is a renovation technique developed at the Weed Research Organization called slot-seeding (Squires, Haggar and Elliott, 1979). This involves spraying an 8–12 cm wide band of glyphosate at 1.4 kg ha^{-1}, cutting and *removing* a central 2 × 2 cm slot of turf, thus exposing the soil, and sowing seed with fertilizer and pesticides, all in a one-pass operation. Development work carried out prior to commercial introduction of this technique has been reviewed by Edwards (1980). Crops which have been successfully slot-seeded into permanent swards using glyphosate as a band spray include perennial and Italian ryegrass (*Lolium perenne, L. multiflorum*) (Haggar and Squires, 1982a; 1982b) plus red clover (Haggar and Koch, 1982) and white clover (Boatman, Haggar and Squires, 1980)—see *Figures 26.2–26.4* and *Table 26.2*.

Other recent developments in band-spraying drill design have been made in New Zealand. For instance, Baker (1976) has produced a band-spraying drill with chisel coulters, designed specifically to minimize surface disturbance and so reduce moisture loss. Using this drill, comparisons were made between the speed of action of glyphosate and paraquat + dicamba, applied as band sprays, to swards dominated variously by *Paspalum dilatatum*, *Agrostis tenuis* and white clover.

Spraying and surface sowing

Broadcasting seed of leguminous species is a common method of renovating swards in many parts of the world, notably in Australia. Success with this technique depends on the non-legume vegetation being suppressed or killed using a

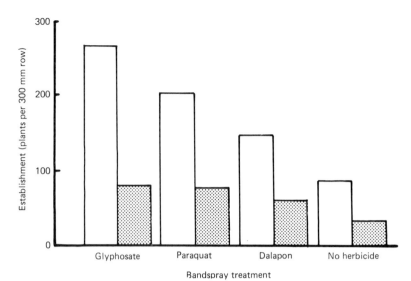

Figure 26.2. Effect on grass (shaded) and clover (unshaded) establishment of band-spraying on either side of the sowing trench

Figure 26.3. Rear view of the Gibbs slot-seeder

Figure 26.4. Rows of white clover (*Trifolium repens*) 2 months
after slot-seeding

TABLE 26.2   Mean effect of herbicide, dose and band-spray width on seedling vigour and development of slot-seeded red clover (*Trifolium pratense*), measured at various dates after sowing (after Haggar and Koch, 1982)

Main factors	Seedling vigour*		Seedling development†	
		Days after sowing		
	38	51	58	76
Paraquat	5.30	5.46	2.46	2.45
	‡	n.s.	n.s.	‡
Glyphosate	6.05	5.73	2.41	2.36
Low dose	5.44	5.26	2.30	2.30
	‡	‡	‡	‡
High dose	5.91	5.93	2.57	2.50
Narrow width	5.48	4.86	2.33	2.26
	n.s.	‡	‡	‡
Wide width	5.86	6.33	2.54	2.54

*1 = small, pale green; 9 = large, deep green.
†From Carlson (1966).
‡ = 0.05.
n.s. = not significant.

wide-spectrum herbicide like glyphosate, which has little or no apparent residual activity in soil, followed by surface sowing immediately after spraying. To check on this, Campbell (1974) placed grass and clover seed onto pasture at various times after spraying with 1.5 kg ha^{-1} of glyphosate. The spray did not affect germination of the sown species, but did reduce establishment. However, the residual effects disappeared 15–30 days after spraying. A shorter spray–sow interval could be contemplated if the seed is covered with a thin layer of soil, as judged by the results of Egley and Williams (1978). In practice, Moshier and Penner (1978) concluded that a 3-day lapse between spraying and sowing lucerne in *Poa pratensis* was adequate.

Several workers have shown that spraying glyphosate onto exposed seed does not necessarily affect germination, although it will usually inhibit radical and shoot growth and so reduce establishment (e.g. Klingman and Murray, 1976; Moshier, Turgeon and Penner, 1976). Moreover, because glyphosate sprayed onto turf is not inactivated as readily as when sprayed onto soil, seedling growth may be inhibited when treated foliage collapses (Moshier and Penner, 1978).

Renovating pastures without seeding

When used at sub-lethal rates, glyphosate can be used to change selectively the botanical composition of swards. Although the margin of selectivity is usually narrow, the differences in sensitivity among grasses is often sufficient to alter the balance of species growing in a mixed sward. For example, Oswald (1972), working on an old permanent pasture, found that *Festuca rubra* was moderately resistant to 1.5 kg a.e. ha^{-1} glyphosate, whereas *Agrostis stolonifera* was relatively susceptible. In upland swards, *F. rubra* was also shown to be relatively more tolerant than *Holcus mollis* and *Molinia caerulea* (Williams, 1979). This relatively high resistance of *F. rubra* to low rates of glyphosate has been utilized to control selectively *A. alba* (Comes, 1976) and *Phalaris arundinacea* (Marquis, Comes and Yang, 1979) in *F. rubra* swards. The resistance of *F. rubra*, which appears to be caused by restrictions in translocation of glyphosate in this species, is apparent at a very early stage. When 4-month-old grasses were treated with 0.28 kg ha^{-1} of glyphosate, *F. rubra* and *Poa pratensis* were tolerant, *Dactylis glomerata* and *L. perenne* were moderately susceptible and *A. tenuis* was very susceptible (Bingham, Segura and Foy, 1980).

Cynodon dactylon* is another grass which can tolerate low rates of glyphosate. For instance, acceptable control of *Paspalum notatum* was obtained when glyphosate at 0.6 kg ha^{-1} was applied immediately after cutting for hay (Smith and Powell, 1980). The same rate of glyphosate was used to control selectively *P. annua* and other winter annual weeds in dormant *C. dactylon* (Johnson, 1976b). On the other hand, the selective control of *Sporobulus poiretii* in *C. dactylon* proved much more difficult (Meyer and Baur, 1979) than that of other weeds.

In New Zealand, Allen and Butler (1980), attempting to control selectively *Hordeum murinum*, found that the rates of glyphosate required to kill this species (0.54 kg ha^{-1}) were too damaging to *Lolium perenne*-dominant swards. However, using a slightly higher rate, namely 0.8 kg ha^{-1} in early spring, Haggar and Bastian (1980) have demonstrated that the substantial suppression in *L. perenne* growth can be put to good use in encouraging white clover growth later in the year. They observed that the herbicide caused a marked increase in stolon branching and concluded that this technique could have relevance in the production of clover seed from grass–clover swards. It has been reported (Baur, 1979) that application of sub-lethal amounts of glyphosate produce growth responses normally associated with auxins and plant growth regulators. As white clover is becoming increasingly important in extensively managed grassland, low-dose glyphosate could well find a place in the manipulation of mixed swards towards increased legume content, although more research is necessary to confirm the reliability of the technique (Elliott, 1978).

Renovating fine turf-grass

Turf-grass renovation refers to the practice of converting an existing stand of mixed grass species and weeds into turf of acceptable species and quality for lawns, golf greens, sports fields, etc., In the USA, research has focused on chemical renovation, with glyphosate being used to remove *A. repens, C. dactylon, F. arundinacea* and *Pennisetum clandestinum*, as well as other difficult-to-control perennial weeds, and replace these with *Poa pratensis* or *Lolium perenne*.

An early example of such chemical renovation (Newman, 1974) involved the autumn application of up to 3 kg ha^{-1} of glyphosate to kill actively growing *A. repens*, followed by ploughing and seeding; there was no evidence that glyphosate affected either turf-grass seed germination or seedling development. Similarly, Freeborg and Daniel (1974) treated old turf with glyphosate at 1.5 and 3 kg ha^{-1}, oversowed with *L. perenne* and recorded 98% cover of this species 55 days later. Later, Jagschitz (1978) carried out field experiments in Rhode Island, from 1974 to 1978, comparing glyphosate with cacodylic acid and paraquat for killing a range of perennial grasses. Glyphosate provided the most consistent and complete kill as well as giving the best control of *Taraxacum officinale*.

One week after killing turf with glyphosate, removal of the dying foliage and thatch, using a vertical mower, may be all that is necessary for preparation of a seed-bed for turf-grasses like *P. pratensis, L. perenne* and *F. rubra* (Bingham, 1977); however, irrigation is often desirable. Klingman and Murray (1977), working at Beltsville, found that stands of turf-grass, seeded into old turf and sprayed with glyphosate, were as good as those on seed-beds that were rototilled and raked. Daniel and Freeborg (1974) used 1.5 kg ha^{-1} glyphosate to kill turf consisting of *Agrostis* sp., *Zoysia* sp. and *Poa pratensis* and successfully overseeded *L. perenne* by placement of seed in slits within 6–10 days from spraying. Using rates of glyphosate appropriate for killing unwanted grasses, Moshier, Turgeon and Penner (1976) found that germination and seed-bed growth of *P. pratensis, A. palustris* and *F. rubra* were unaffected under field conditions; however, when very high rates of glyphosate were sprayed on seed lying on the soil surface, *F. rubra* germination was reduced and shoot growth of all three species was inhibited. Riden and Duich (1977) compared 4 rates of glyphosate on 5 dates for the chemical renovation of mature stands of *A. tenuis, A. palustris* and *P. pratensis* and found that groove-seeded *L. perenne* was not significantly affected by any of the treatments. Further south, Johnson (1976a) successfully renovated a poor quality *C. dactylon* turf by spraying with glyphosate, and spring planting improved *C. dactylon*. In practice, renovation treatments which ensured good seed–soil contact result in significantly improved stands of *L. perenne*, as shown by Kaufmann (1977), who compared 5 different reseeding techniques.

Guidelines to successful turf-grass renovation have been devised by Hanson, Elmore and Baldwin (1980). They stress the need to spray glyphosate only when the old turf is growing actively, preferably in July or August, and has adequate leaf cover (i.e. allow turf to grow 2 weeks without mowing). They suggest waiting 2 weeks after spraying before rototilling and sowing seed.

However, major problems still encountered during turf-grass renovation using glyphosate include: (1) the need to delay spraying until optimum leaf areas have been reached, (2) poor germination of *P. pratensis* in mid-season, and (3) rapid emergence of weed species, necessitating the use of selective herbicides (Bingham, 1977). In this context, the results of Hanson, Elmore and Baldwin (1980) point to the benefit of applying siduron for controlling selectively a range of germinating grass weeds.

In addition to renovating turf, glyphosate can be used to trim lawn edges and control a large number of weed species in golf course sand traps, including *C. dactylon* and *Cyperus rotundus* (Murdoch and Nishimoto, 1974).

A further use for glyphosate is the selective control of winter annual weeds in dormant turf-grass. Early work by Troutman, Frans and King (1974) showed that outstanding control of various winter annuals growing in dormant *C. dactylon* could be achieved by spraying glyphosate in February. Their findings were confirmed later by Johnson and Ware (1978) and Johnson (1980). Similarly, Batten (1981) applied glyphosate at 1 kg ha^{-1} in early March when 10% of *C. dactylon* was starting to regrow, and achieved 87% control of *P. annua* without injuring the turf. Also, repeat applications of glyphosate at 0.28 kg ha^{-1} proved successful in the selective removal of *Panicum repens* in established *C. dactylon* turf (Fleming, Palmertree and Houston, 1978).

Efforts to select *F. rubra* genotypes tolerant to glyphosate have not proved successful so far (Fisher, 1976).

Glyphosate in coarse turf and amenity grassland

This section deals with the use of glyphosate in less intensively mown turf, characterized by urban parks, road verges, airfields, cemeteries, golf 'roughs', etc. Where such areas are being created or landscaped, perennial rhizomatous weeds and woody species often survive the operations of heavy machinery. Applications of glyphosate at 2 or 3 kg ha^{-1}, before earth-moving operations start, destroys most of the problem weeds (Denninger, 1979).

Choice of species for these various amenity areas will obviously vary from site to site and depend largely on climatic limitations. For instance, in the USA, *F. arundinacea* is often a popular grass for parks and commercial areas in the transitional zone between cool and warm humid regions; Johnson (1976b) showed that it could be successfully seeded into *C. dactylon* turf, sprayed 10 days previously with glyphosate, although a single application did not give complete control.

The major management objective for road verges, airfields, etc., is to maintain complete vegetation to prevent erosion, at the same time as preventing vegetation from growing so tall as to restrict visibility. Similarly, in leisure parks and nature reserves, management is concerned principally with regulating vegetation height, to provide public access, to control scrub ingress and to create a visually attractive landscape.

In the past, hebicides like glyphosate have not been considered as options in vegetation management, and their use has been restricted to controlling weeds on pathways, along fencelines, etc., as spot treatment to control noxious weeds, or on small areas where a particularly aggressive grass threatens a species-rich plant community (Haggar, 1980). However, as knowledge and experience in the use of such herbicides continues to grow, so their use as options in vegetation management is likely to increase. For instance, glyphosate can be used to trigger off flushes of growth of attractive dicotyledonous species and, used as a band-spray, it can act as an aid to seeding wild flowers into established amenity grassland (Marshall, 1982).

Killing tall weeds in grassland

Since tall-growing weeds are a consistent feature of amenity areas (as well as a widespread problem in agricultural grassland), glyphosate has a great potential for their control now that application techniques based on plant height differential are being devised (see also Chapter 16).

The foliar uptake and rapid translocation of glyphosate makes it particularly suitable for use in applicators that selectively apply the herbicide to tall weeds growing above crop canopies. Several such applicators have been developed recently, using either rollers or rope wicks to smear glyphosate onto weeds. For instance, Wyse and Habstritt (1977) used a carpet-covered horizontal roller, impregnated with glyphosate, to kill selectively *A. repens* and *Phalaris arundinacea* in *Poa pratensis*. Alternatively, recirculating sprayers (Supak and Abernathy, 1977) can be used to spray narrow jets of glyphosate across the top of the pasture; herbicide not intercepted by tall growing weeds is caught and recirculated (see also Chapter 16).

A recirculating sprayer was compared with two rope applicators for applying herbicides to late *Eupatorium* spp. growing in pasture (Peters and Dale, 1978). The recirculating sprayer was more effective than the rope devices for applying glyphosate, but some injury to the forage species occurred with the sprayer due to drift, dripping and splashing.

All of these applicators used relatively small amounts of herbicide and proved to be an economical means of treating pasture, especially where the weed density was low.

Low-cost, rope-wick applicators have recently become very popular for weed control in grassland. For instance, Peters (1981) applied glyphosate in a water–herbicide concentration of 2:1 with a rope-wick applicator to kill up to 65% of *Solidago nemoralis* growing in a pasture containing *Poa pratensis;* early treatments and applications in two directions were most effective. In this way, wiper applicators use low rates of glyphosate, often as low as 0.1 kg ha^{-1}, depending on weed density. Although glyphosate has been used in most experiments, other translocated herbicides can also be applied (Rolston, 1979). Although most tall-growing weeds can be killed more effectively, with smaller amounts of herbicide, with wiper applicators than with conventional broadcast applicators, some problems still remain—a major one being that immature plants and establishing seedlings are not touched. Further work is also needed to determine minimum amounts of herbicide needed to kill the major weeds of grassland. In this connection, Oswald (1978) found that 2.5 ml of 10% glyphosate in 3% sodium alginate solution (i.e. a gel), smeared onto a single leaf of *Rumex obtusifolius,* was sufficient to kill the whole plant. Later, Oswald (1980) successfully used a 1% glyphosate solution, although noting that the treated plants tended to kill some underlying grasses as they collapsed and died.

Conclusions

The broad-spectrum efficacy of glyphosate and its rapid inactivation in soil makes it a valuable herbicide for controlling hard-to-kill weeds and unwanted vegetation, including old swards, prior to seeding new crops. Problems associated directly or indirectly with the decomposition of dead and dying plants, plus pests and diseases, remain as hindrances to the establishment of forage crops direct drilled in grass swards, although these limitations are not nearly so acute with legumes sown directly into cereal stubbles.

Pasture renovation, involving partial suppression of existing swards by applying glyphosate either overall or in bands and the sowing of desirable forage legumes, has been successfully carried out in the USA and elsewhere. Reliability has been greatest with red clover introduced into relatively open swards and least with interseeding lucerne into dense swards. For both pasture and turf-grass renovation to be successful, site deficiences in soil pH, drainage and nutrient availability need to be rectified.

These uses of glyphosate, coupled with its directed application to tall-growing weeds, makes this an outstanding herbicide in grassland.

References

ALLEN, F.C. and BUTLER, J.H.B. (1980). Weed control in pastures, *Annual Report 1978/79*, New Zealand, Ministry of Agriculture and Fisheries, Agriculture Research Division, p. 238.
ALLEN, H.P. (1981). *Direct Drilling and Reduced Cultivations*. Ipswich; Farming Press.

BAIRD, D.D., UPCHURCH, R.P., HORNESLEY, W.B. and FRANZ, J.E. (1971). Introduction of a new broad spectrum post-emergence herbicide class with utility for herbaceous perennial weed control, *Proceedings of the 26th North Central Weed Control Conference*, pp. 64–68.

BAKER, C.J. (1976). Experiments relating to techniques for direct drilling of seed into untilled dead turf, *Journal of Agricultural Engineering Research*, **21**, 133–144.

BARBER, D.D., GREENWOOD, M., GREEN, R., SAVOURS, D. and SERUBULA, J. (1978). Direct drill grass in chemically destroyed grassland, in *Summary of Experiments, Studies and Surveys, 1977*. London; Ministry of Agriculture, Fisheries and Food, pp. 39–41.

BATTEN, S.M. (1981). Post-emergence control of annual bluegrass (*Poa annua*) in dormant bermudagrass turf, *Report No. PR-3831-3851: Texas Turf-Grass Research 1979–80*, Texas Agricultural Experiment Station, pp. 89–90.

BAUR, J.R. (1979). Reduction of glyphosate-induced tillering in sorghum (*Sorghum bicolor*) by several herbicides, *Weed Science*, **27**, 69–73.

BINGHAM, S.W. (1977). Turf-grass renovation using glyphosate, *Abstracts of the 1977 Meeting of the Weed Science Society of America*, pp. 50–51.

BINGHAM, S.W., SEGURA, J. and FOY, C.L. (1980). Susceptibility of several grasses to glyphosate, *Weed Science*, **28**, 579–585.

BLACKMORE, L.W. (1962). Band spraying: a new overdrilling technique, *New Zealand Journal of Agriculture*, **104**, 13–19.

BOATMAN, N.D., HAGGAR, R.J. and SQUIRES, N.R.W. (1980). Effect of band spray width and seed coating on the establishment of slot-seeded grass and clover, *Proceedings of the 1980 British Crop Protection Conference—Weeds*, pp. 503–509.

BURT, E.O. (1975). Control of weeds in warm-season turf-grass with herbicides, *Annual Report, Institute of Food and Agriculture Sciences*, Florida, p. 323.

CAMPBELL, M.H. (1974). Effects of glyphosate on the germination and establishment of surface-sown pasture species, *Australian Journal of Experimental Agriculture and Animal Husbandry*, **14**, 557–560.

CAMPBELL, M.H. and GILMOUR, A.R. (1979). Effect of time and rate of application of herbicides on serrated tussock (*Nasella trichotoma*) and improved pasture species I. Glyphosate and 2,2-DPA, *Australian Journal of Experimental Agriculture and Animal Husbandry*, **19**, 472–475.

CARLSON, G.E. (1966). Growth of clover leaves—developmental morphology and parameters at ten stages, *Crop Science*, **6**, 293–294.

CLEMENTS, R.O. (1980). Grassland pests—an unseen enemy, *Outlook on Agriculture*, **10**, 219–223.

CLEMENTS, R.O. and HAGGAR, R.J. (1982). Impact and control of pests, weeds and diseases on sward establishment and herbage production, *Proceedings of the 9th Meeting of the European Grassland Federation*, pp. 69–75.

COMES, R.D. (1976). Response of three ditchbank grasses to glyphosate, dalapon and amitrole-T, *Weed Science Society of America, 1976 Meeting, Abstract No. 5*.

CROMACK, H.T.H., DAVIES, W.I.C., ROWLANDS, A., PRYTHERCH, E.I. and DAVIES, J. (1978). The replacement of old swards using herbicides and cultivation techniques, *Proceedings of the 1978 British Crop Protection Conference—Weeds*, pp. 333–339.

DANIEL, W.H. and FREEBORG, R.P. (1974). Turf renovation with glyphosate, *Abstracts of the 1974 Meeting of the Weed Science Society of America*, p. 19.

DAVIES, W.I.C. and DAVIES, J. (1981). Varying the time of spraying paraquat or glyphosate before direct drilling grass and clover seeds with and without calcium peroxide, *Grass and Forage Science*, **36**, 65–69.

DAVIES, W.I.C., JACKSON, M.V. and JOHNSON, J. (1980). Direct drilling of grass and clover into chemically destroyed sward, *Proceedings of the 1980 British Crop Protection Conference—Weeds*, pp. 495–502.

DAVISON, J.G. (1972). The response of 21 perennial weed species to glyphosate, *Proceedings of the British Weed Control Conference*, **1**, 11–16.

DECKER, A.M., RETZER, H.J. and SWAIN, F.G. (1964). Improved soil openers for the establishment of small-seeded legumes in sod, *Agronomy Journal*, **56**, 211–214.

DECKER, A.M., RETZER, H.J., SARNA, M.L. and KERR, H.D. (1969). Permanent pastures improved with sod-seeding and fertilization, *Agronomy Journal*, **61**, 243–247.

DENNINGER, C. (1979). Weed control before establishing amenity areas, *Compte Rendu de la 10e Conference de COLUMA*, pp. 621–628.

DOWLING, P.M. and LINSCOTT, D.L. (1981). Effect of chemicals on the establishment of direct planted alfalfa, *Proceedings of the Northeastern Weed Science Society*, **35**, 42–43.

EDWARDS, R.V. (1980). Slot-seeding—development to commercial introduction, *Proceedings of the 1980 British Crop Protection Conference—Weeds*, pp. 637–644.

EDWARDS, R.V. (1982). Establishing swards by direct drilling into pastures treated with the IPA salt of glyphosate, *Proceedings of the 9th Meeting of the European Grassland Federation*, pp. 121–124.

EGLEY, G.H. and WILLIAMS, R.D. (1978). Glyphosate and paraquat effects on weed seed germination and seedling emergence, *Weed Science*, **26**, 249–251.

ELLIOTT, J.G. (1978). The role of herbicides in temperate grassland, *Proceedings of the Roundup Seminar*, Madrid, pp. 102–111.

ERNST, P. and WEBER, O. (1975). The control of couch (*Agropyron repens* L.) in intensively used permanent pasture, *Mitteilungen aus der Biologischen Bundesanstalt für Landund Forstwirtschaft*, Berlin-Dahlem, no. 165, 195–196.

FALB, L.N. and STROUBE, E.W. (1976). Turfgrass renovation with glyphosate, *Proceedings of the North Central Weed Control Conference*, **30**, 175.

FISHER, R. (1976). Selective control of undesirable grasses in amenity grassland, *Journal of the Sports Turf Research Institute, 1977*, no. 53, p. 113.

FLEMING, D.C., PALMERTREE, H.D. and HOUSTON, D.W. (1978). Screening herbicides for torpedograss control in turf, *Proceedings of the 31st Annual Meeting of the Southern Weed Science Society*, p. 136.

FREEBORG, R.P. and DANIEL, W.H. (1974). Roundup for turf renovation. 1974 results, *Proceedings of the North Central Weed Control Conference*, **29**, 67.

GUSSIN, E.J. and LYNCH, J.M. (1981). Microbial fermentation of grass residues to organic acids as a factor in the establishment of new grass swards, *New Phytologist*, **89**, 449–457.

HABESHAW, D.B. (1980). Indigenous growth and germination inhibitors and their role in grass survival and pasture establishment, *Grass and Forage Science*, **35**, 69–70.

HAGGAR, R.J. (1980). Weed control and vegetation management by herbicides, in *Amenity Grassland* (Eds. I.H. Rorison and R. Hunt). Chichester, Wiley, pp. 163–173.

HAGGAR, R.J. and BASTIAN, C.J. (1980). Regulating the content of white clover in mixed swards using grass-suppressing herbicides, *Grass and Forage Science*, **35**, 129–137.

HAGGAR, R.J. and KOCH, D.W. (1982). Slot-seeding investigations. 3. The productivity of slot-seeded red clover compared with all-grass swards receiving nitrogen, *Grass and Forage Science*, **38**, 45–53.

HAGGAR, R.J. and SQUIRES, N.R.W. (1982a). Slot-seeding investigations. 1. Effect of level of nitrogen fertilizer and row spacing on establishment, herbage growth and quality of perennial ryegrass, *Grass and Forage Science*, **37**, 107–113.

HAGGAR, R.J. and SQUIRES, N.R.W. (1982b). Slot-seeding investigations. 2. Time of sowing, seed rate and row spacing of Italian ryegrass, *Grass and Forage Science*, **37**, 115–122.

HAGGAR, R.J., SQUIRES, N.R.W., ELLIOTT, J.G. and OSWALD, A.K. (1978). Improving sward composition by selective herbicides and one-pass seeding, *ARC Research Review*, **4**, 46–50.

HANSON, D.L., ELMORE, C.L. and BALDWIN, R.L. (1980). Turf-grass renovation, *Proceedings of the 32nd Annual California Weed Conference*, pp. 84–88.

HARTWIG, N.L. (1976). Weed control and sod suppression for no-tillage legume seedlings into bluegrass pastures, *Proceedings of the Northeastern Weed Science Society*, **30**, 31.

HOAGLAND, R.E. and DUKE, S.O. (1981). Glyphosate: a unique herbicide, *Weeds To-day*, **12**, 21–23.

HURTS, K.A. and TURGEON, A.J. (1979). Effect of thatch on residual activity of non-selective herbicides used in turf-grass renovation, *Agronomy Journal*, **71**, 66–71.

JAGSCHITZ, J.A. (1978). Turf-grass renovation with cacodylic acid, glyphosate and paraquat, *Proceedings of the Northeastern Weed Science Society*, **32**, 317.

JOHNSON, B.J. (1975). Glyphosate for weed control in dormant bermudagrass, *Weed Science*, **24**, 140–143.

JOHNSON, B.J. (1976a). Turf-grass renovation with chemicals, *Abstracts of the 1976 Meeting of the Weed Science Society of America*, pp. 33–34.

JOHNSON, B.J. (1976b). Timing of glyphosate for conversion of bermudagrass turf to tall fescue, *Crop Science*, **16**, 598–599.

JOHNSON, B.J. (1980). Post-emergence winter weed control in bermudagrass (*Cynodon dactylon*) turf, *Weed Science*, **28**, 385–392.

JOHNSON, B.J. and WARE, G.O. (1978). Dates of glyphosate treatments on weeds and bermudagrass (*Cynodon dactylon*), *Weed Science*, **26**, 523–526.

KAUFMANN, J.E. (1977). Turf-grass renovation with glyphosate, *Abstracts of the 1977 Meeting of the Weed Science Society of America*, p. 51.

KLINGMAN, D.L. and MURRAY, J.J. (1976). Germination of seeds of turf-grass as affected by glyphosate and paraquat, *Weed Science*, **24**, 191–193.

KLINGMAN, D.L. and MURRAY, J.J. (1977). Herbicidal use and effectiveness for renovation of turf, *Abstracts of the 1977 Meeting of the Weed Science Society of America*, pp. 49–50.

LINSCOTT, D.L. (1979). Projections for no-tillage forage systems for the north-east, Abstract, *Northeastern Branch Meeting, American Society of Agronomy*, pp. 10–12.

LINSCOTT, D.L. and HAGIN, R.D. (1976). A progress report on no-tillage planting of legumes, *Proceedings of the Northeastern Weed Science Society*, **30**, 32–33.

LYNCH, J.M. (1980). Effects of organic acids on the germination of seeds and growth of seedlings, *Plant, Cell and Environment*, **3**, 255–259.

MARQUIS, L.Y., COMES, R.D. and YANG, C.P. (1979). Selectivity of glyphosate in creeping red fescue and reed canarygrass, *Weed Research*, **19**, 335–342.

MARSHALL, E.J.P. (1982). A feasibility study on the use of chemicals for rural amenity area management—second interim report—1981, *Internal Report No. 148*, Weed Research Organization, Oxford.

MEYER, R.E. and BAUR, J.R. (1979). Smutgrass (*Sporobolus poiretii*) control in pasture with herbicides, *Weed Science*, **27**, 361–366.

MOORE, R.W., YORTT, M.L. and ATKINSON, G.C. (1980). Rush and Australian sedge control with glyphosate, *Proceedings of the 33rd New Zealand Weed and Pest Control Conference*, pp. 63–66.

MOSHIER, L. and PENNER, D. (1978). Use of glyphosate in sod-seeding alfalfa (*Medicago sativa*) establishment, *Weed Science*, **26**, 163–166.

MOSHIER, L., TURGEON, A.J. and PENNER, D. (1976). Effects of glyphosate and siduron on turf-grass establishment, *Weed Science*, **24**, 445–448.

MUELLER-WARRANT, G.W. and KOCH, D.W. (1980). Establishment of alfalfa by conventional and minimum-tillage seeding techniques in a quackgrass–dominant sward, *Agronomy Journal*, **72**, 884–889.

MUELLER-WARRANT, G.W., KOCH, D.W. and MITCHELL, J.R. (1979). Chemical control of orchardgrass preceding a no-till alfalfa seeding, *Proceedings of the Northeastern Weed Science Society*, **33**, 31–32.

MURDOCK, C.L. and NISHIMOTO, R.K. (1974). Use of glyphosate (*N*-phosphonomethyl glycine) for edging and controlling weeds in golf course sand traps, *University of Hawaii, Honolulu, Hort. Science, 1974*, **9**(3), section 2, p. 32.

NEWMAN, R.C. (1974). Glyphosate for quackgrass control prior to turf-grass seeding, *Proceedings of the North Central Weed Control Conference*, **29**, 68–69.

NICHOLS, R.L. and PETERS, R.A. (1980). Effect of timing and herbicides on the no-tillage establishment of red clover, alfalfa and birdsfoot trefoil, *Proceedings of the Northeastern Weed Science Society*, **34**, 91.

OSWALD, A.K. (1972). Effects of April and July applications of glyphosate, paraquat and dalapon on old permanent pasture, *Proceedings of the 11th British Weed Control Conference*, pp. 994–1001.

OSWALD, A.K. (1976). The effects of seasonal applications of glyphosate on a mixed sward, *Proceedings of the 13th British Weed Control Conference*, pp. 961–969.

OSWALD, A.K. (1978). The control of *Rumex obtusifolius* in grassland by selective application of herbicides, *Proceedings of the 1978 British Crop Protection Conference—Weeds*, pp. 475–481.

OSWALD, A.K. (1980). Progress in the development of the selective application of herbicides to control *Rumex obtusifolius* in grassland, *Proceedings of the 1980 British Crop Protection Conference—Weeds*, pp. 209–215.

PETERS, E.J. (1981). Effectiveness and safety of translocated herbicides applied to pasture weeds with a rope wick-applicator, *Summary, 14th International Grassland Congress*, p. 296.

PETERS, E.J. and DALE, J.E. (1978). Rope application and a recirculating sprayer for pasture weed control, *Proceedings of the North Central Weed Control Conference*, **33**, 127.

PETERS, E.J. and LOWANCE, S.A. (1979). Herbicides for renovation of pastures and control of tall ironweed (*Veronica altissima*), *Weed Science*, **27**, 342–345.

PETERS, R.A. and ZAPOZALKA, J. (1981). Impact of carbofuron treatment on no-tillage alfalfa establishment, *Proceedings of the Northeastern Weed Science Society*, **35**, 76.

PREEST, D. (1980). Seasonal variation in gorse susceptibility to four herbicides, *Proceedings of the 33rd New Zealand Weed and Pest Control Conference*, pp. 165–169.

RAYBURN, E.B., HUNT, J.F. and LINSCOTT, D.L. (1981a). Herbicide and tillage effects on legume establishment in bromegrass sod, *Proceedings of the Northeastern Weed Science Society*, **35**, 67–68.

RAYBURN, E.B., HUNT, J.F. and LINSCOTT, D.L. (1981b). Three year summary of no-till forage establishment research on New York farm sites, *Proceedings of the Northeastern Weed Science Society*, **35**, 65–66.

READ, J.W. (1977). The use of herbicide and sod-seeding in pasture establishment, *Proceedings of the International Conference, Energy Conservation in Crop Production*, Palmerston North, New Zealand, pp. 39–42.

RIDEN, W.M. and DUICH, J.M. (1977). Chemical renovation of cool-season turf-grass species with glyphosate, *Proceedings of the Northeastern Weed Science Society*, **31**, 377.

ROLSTON, M.P. (1979). A review of novel techniques in herbicide usage, *Proceedings of the 32nd New Zealand Weed and Pest Control Conference*, pp. 202–206.

SCHERP, L.A. and SARFATY, A.B. (1975). *Paspalum* control in Australasia, *Proceedings of the 28th New Zealand Weed and Pest Control Conference*, pp. 169–172.

SMITH, A.E. and POWELL, J.D. (1980). Bahiagrass control in coastal bermudagrass hay fields, *Research Report No. 356*, Georgia Agricultural Experiment Station, 18pp.

SQUIRES, N.R.W., HAGGAR, R.J. and ELLIOTT, J.G. (1979). A one-pass seeder for introducing grasses, legumes and fodder crops into swards, *Journal of Agricultural Engineering Research*, **24**, 199–208.

SUPAK, J.R. and ABERNATHY, J.R. (1977). Recent innovations in recirculating sprayer development, *Proceedings of the 30th Annual Meeting of the Southern Weed Science Society*, pp. 409–411.

TAYLOR, T.H., ENGLAND, J.M., POWELL, R.E., FREEMAN, J.F., KLINE, C.K. and TEMPLETON, W.C. (1964). Establishment of legumes in old *Poa pratensis* L. sod by use of paraquat and strip-tillage for seedbed preparation, *Proceedings of the 7th British Weed Control Conference*, pp. 792–803.

TOAI, T.V. and LINSCOTT, D.L. (1979). Phytotoxic effect of decaying quackgrass (*Agropyron repens*) residues, *Weed Science*, **27**, 595–598.

TROUTMAN, B.C., FRANS, R.E. and KING, J.W. (1974). Post-emergence weed control in dormant bermudagrass, *Proceedings of the 27th Annual Meeting of the Southern Weed Science Society*, p. 57.

WADDINGTON, J. and BOWREN, K.E. (1976). Pasture renovation by direct drilling after weed control and pasture suppression by herbicides, *Canadian Journal of Plant Science*, **56**, 985–988.

WELTY, L.E., ANDERSON, R.L., DELANEY, R.H. and HENSLEIGH, P.F. (1981). Glyphosate timing effects on establishment of sod-seeded legumes and grasses, *Agronomy Journal*, **73**, 813–817.

WESTRA, P. and WYSE, D.L. (1978). Control of quackgrass biotypes with glyphosate, *Proceedings of the North Central Weed Control Conference*, **33**, 106.

WILLIAMS, G.H. (1977). Qualitative effects of asulam and glyphosate on swards dominated by bracken (*Pteridium aquilinum* (L.) Kuhn), *Journal of the British Grassland Society*, **32**, 149–155.

WILLIAMS, G.H. (1979). Effect of time of spraying of glyphosate on the vegetation of upland deep peat soil, *Grass and Forage Science*, **34**, 317–318.

WYSE, D.L. (1978). Perennial weed control systems, *Minutes of the 32nd Meeting of the Expert Committee on Weeds*, Eastern Canada, pp. 27–29.

WYSE, D.L. and HABSTRITT, C. (1977). A roller herbicide applicator, *Proceedings of the North Central Weed Control Conference*, **32**, 144–145.

YORTT, M.L. and ATKINSON, G.C. (1980). Blackberry control with glyphosate, *Proceedings of the 33rd New Zealand Weed and Pest Control Conference*, pp. 177–180.

Chapter 27

Efficacy of glyphosate in arable situations

M.G. O'Keeffe
Monsanto, Leicester, UK

R.J. Makepeace
Oxford Agriculture Group, Oxford, UK

Introduction

In temperate agricultural crops consisting of predominantly small grain cereals, glyphosate is used as a non-selective herbicide between cropping seasons or before harvest when weeds are actively growing in certain cereal and oilseed crops. For many perennial grasses and broad-leaved herbaceous perennial weeds, active growth and regrowth is occurring prior to harvest, and in the period following harvest, until periods of frost induce senescence. The onset of senescence varies according to the weed species; volunteer potato (*Solanum tuberosum*) is frost sensitive and killed by temperatures in the region of $-3°C$ (Lutman, 1979a; 1979b), but *Agropyron repens* is much less frost sensitive and will continue to grow, even into the winter (Cussans, 1972). Thus, from before harvest until the onset of winter glyphosate may be used for weed control. In the spring, temperatures rise and active growth will recommence; this provides another possible period for herbicide treatment with glyphosate, provided that there is time for sufficient growth before soil cultivation begins.

Initial reports by Baird *et al.* (1971), Baird and Begeman (1972) and Baird and Upchurch (1972) have described the utility of glyphosate, since when many studies have been carried out to find the most effective time of application of glyphosate relative to crop and weed growth and environmental conditions. The term glyphosate in this chapter refers to the isopropylamine salt of *N*-(phosphonomethyl) glycine used as the commercial formulation Roundup.

Efficacy of glyphosate post-harvest in the autumn and spring

Several comparisons of results from spring versus autumn applications for the control of a number of weed species in differing climatic conditions have been carried out. In field trials by Hodgson (1974), glyphosate applied in the spring gave over 90% weed control of *A. repens*, assessed 15 weeks after treatment. There were significant yield increases in crops sown 1–2 weeks after treatment. Similar rates of application ($1.12–4.48$ kg ha^{-1}) were less effective for autumn applications, possibly due to poorer plant growth, than compared with the spring. Favourable results were obtained in studies by Fiveland (1979), in which spring applications were made prior to sowing. The control of *A. repens* achieved was 70–90%. Highest levels were obtained from treatments applied 8 days prior to spring sowing of cereals. In field trials repeated by French and Riveland (1980) in North Dakota, USA, early spring applications of glyphosate were more effective than applications in autumn. Other results favour treatment carried out in the autumn rather than the spring.

Comparisons of weed control from spring treatments with those in the autumn carried out by Sprankle and Meggitt (1972) indicated that application in May was less effective in the long term than in September, although the initial response was quicker from the spring treatment. Spurrier (1973) reported that, under temperate conditions, *A. repens* control with glyphosate was more complete, with less rhizome regeneration, if applications were made in early autumn rather than in the spring. This was also reported by Brockman, Duke and Hunt (1973). Nuyken (1976) obtained more successful control of *A. repens* in stubble with application rates of glyphosate of 2.24 kg ha^{-1} made in the autumn than in the spring, in trials carried out in Germany. Aamisepp (1976; 1978) also reported a greater efficacy of control of *A. repens* and *Holcus mollis* in stubble when herbicide treatment was carried out in the autumn rather than in the spring in Norway. Similar results were obtained by Rioux (1981) and Ivany (1975; 1981). The studies by Ivany were carried out in Atlantic Canada where there is a short growing season. Spring treatment with glyphosate of weeds at optimum susceptibility delayed planting beyond the optimum time for the crop. In addition, autumn applied treatments gave better weed control than the same rate of glyphosate in the spring.

The consensus of published information indicates better weed control from applications of glyphosate made in the autumn than in the spring. Treatment with glyphosate, pre-sowing in the spring, although of use, does not give the same level of reliable weed control and is therefore less used than autumn applications. The emphasis on autumn post-harvest applications has been further increased by the general swing in temperate areas to autumn sowing of wheat (*Triticum aestivum*), barley (*Hordeum vulgare*) and oilseed rape (*Brassica napus*). In the UK, for example, from 1974 to 1979 the area of winter-sown cereals increased from 1.3 to 2.2 million ha, and by 1982 it had become 2.4 million ha (MAFF, 1978; 1983).

Timing of application in stubble during autumn

The most effective time for treatment during the autumn, after harvesting or prior to cultivation or sowing in fallow land, has been widely studied. The optimum stage of weed regrowth for effective herbicide translocation is related to the total leaf area and stage of plant development. In perennial grasses this has been found to be the 4–6 leaf stage (Baird *et al.*, 1971; Baird and Begeman, 1972; Spurrier, 1973; Rioux, Bandeen and Anderson, 1974). Studies by Ivany (1975) reported 95% control of *A. repens* when glyphosate was applied at the 4–6 leaf stage. Similar rates of application at the 1–3 leaf growth stage gave only 50% control.

The percentage total regrowth is also important for overall control, and this varies with the depth of the storage organs and the weed species. For much of Europe, southern England and America, the minimum susceptible regrowth stage is attained within 4–6 weeks of harvesting the crop. Fiveland (1976) obtained maximum control of *A. repens* when treatments were carried out 3–4 weeks after harvest. Wicks (1977) found optimum control of *Echinochloa crus-galli* when treatment was carried out 6 weeks after harvest. This is the longest recommended interval prior to tillage. Aamisepp (1977) obtained 95% control of *A. repens* and *H. mollis* when glyphosate treatment occurred just 6 days after harvest. Lutman (1979a; 1979b) obtained optimal control of *S. tuberosum* when glyphosate was applied 3–4 weeks after the harvest of cereals. Nuyken (1976) reported the most rapid potato regrowth when the straw produced in harvesting cereals was removed rather than chopped or burnt (see also Chapter 11).

Efficacy of glyphosate in relation to tillage interval in cereals

The cultivation procedures carried out after treatment affect the efficacy of the herbicide. The optimum system for weed control varies with the weed species being treated, but certain general treatment–tillage time intervals have been suggested by field trials. Not all results concur and further research may be necessary. Results of studies by Brockman, Duke and Hunt (1973) on *S. halepense* indicated that rotary tillage, as early as 1 day after glyphosate application, had no effect on the efficacy of glyphosate for weed control. Similar results were obtained by Brecke *et al.* (1974) for the control of *A. repens*. However, others have recommended a longer tillage interval for optimal herbicide activity. Baird and Begeman (1972), in the USA, studied the efficacy of the control of *A. repens* with intervals between the application of glyphosate and tillage of 3, 7, 14 and 21 days. At a rate of application of 2.24 kg ha^{-1} an interval of 3 days gave only 10% control when measured 27 weeks after treatment, but 50–90% control was obtained with an interval of 14 days and 68–96% control with an interval of 21 days. They recommended a 3-week tillage interval after treatment of *A. repens* with glyphosate. A minimum tillage interval of 2 weeks for optimal herbicide activity was recommended by Behrens and Elakkad (1972), Aamisepp and Gummesson (1974), Nuyken (1976), Fiveland (1976) and Kemmer (1978). Nuyken (1976) removed rhizomes of *A. repens* 3, 8, 15 or 25 days after treatment and recorded maximum glyphosate uptake 25 days after treatment. Blair (1975), however, reported that with rates of application of glyphosate of 0.75, 1.5 and 3.0 kg ha^{-1}, a significant reduction in rhizome regrowth of *A. repens* occurred and that results were not affected by cultivation carried out 8 days after treatment.

Tillage immediately after glyphosate application may reduce the level of control of perennial grasses, including *A. repens*. Cultivation after a set time interval following application does not improve the efficacy of glyphosate for the control of *A. repens*. Reports by Wilson (1978), Bailey (1978), Ivany (1981) and Sandberg and Meggitt (1977), however, indicate that tillage subsequent to the treatment of *Convolvulus arvensis* with glyphosate increased the level of control, where rates of application were low (below 0.4 kg ha^{-1}). Results reported by Selleck and Kline (1978) using higher doses gave results in line with those obtained with *A. repens;* soil cultivation following treatment with glyphosate at 2.27 and 3.41 kg ha^{-1} reduced the efficacy of control.

Levels of application of glyphosate in stubble

Many of the early studies of the efficacy of glyphosate in arable situations used varying levels of glyphosate per unit area. The lowest rate of application tested was 0.18 kg ha^{-1}, for the control of wild oats (*Avena fatua*) in fallow. Even at this rate, short-term high levels of control were obtained (Fellowes, Anderson and Chin, 1979). Rates of 0.5 kg ha^{-1} gave high levels of control of *S. tuberosum* (Lutman, 1979a; 1979b) and *A. repens* (Evans, 1972). For *A. repens* this did not prevent regrowth. Long-term control may be obtained with higher rates. Increases in dosage generally gave corresponding increase in weed control; for example, the highest rate of application in trials by Lutman (1979a; 1979b) was 3 kg ha^{-1} and this gave nearly 90% control compared to 70% with an application of 0.5 kg ha^{-1}. In trials reported by Pessala (1979), in Finland, applications of 1.44 kg ha^{-1} gave a variable response of 60–80% control of *A. repens*, whereas rates of 2.16 kg ha^{-1} resulted in at least 80% control, when applications were made 7–18 days after harvest. Harvey, Attwood and Potts (1981), in trials in the UK for the control of *A. repens*, obtained 72% control 1 year after treatment from application rates of 0.72 kg ha^{-1} of glyphosate, but 82% control with 1.44 kg ha^{-1}.

Many other reports of variation in control with different rates of application of glyphosate have been published. Applications of over 1.44 kg ha^{-1} seem generally to give acceptable levels of weed control of *A. repens*. Rates over 3 kg ha^{-1} seem not to significantly increase levels of control, except with certain semi-resistant weed species (see also Chapter 15 for discussion of the use of low rates with additives). The control of *A. repens* with rates between 1.44 and 3 kg ha^{-1} will be effective for 3 years post-treatment, without need for retreatment unless conditions during the initial treatment were sub-optimal due to insufficient weed growth or unsuitable environmental conditions (see also Chapter 7).

Rates of application of glyphosate in stubble are not critical in relation to subsequent crop growth or yield. An interval of only 1–2 days is required between herbicide application and sowing of crops, as reported by Brecke *et al.* (1974), Kapusta and Strieker (1976), Fellowes, Anderson and Chin (1979) and others. Aamisepp (1978) found, in trials carried out in Sweden, no crop damage resulting from spraying, immediately before or after sowing a range of crops with glyphosate at 4 kg ha^{-1}. The crops tested included wheat, barley, oat (*Avena sativa*), rye (*Secale cereale*), broad bean (*Vicia faba*), runner bean (*Phaseolus coccineus*), red beet (*Beta vulgaris*), swede (*Brassica napus*), lettuce (*Lactuca sativa*), turnip (*Brassica rapa*), pea (*Pisum sativum*), cabbage (*Brassica oleracea*) and red fescue (*Festuca rubra*).

The level of weed control obtained with treatments of glyphosate at all rates varies according to the weather conditions at the time of application (see also Chapter 7). Percentage control was highest when conditions included cool temperatures prior to spraying, high relative humidity during and after spraying and no rainfall for at least 6 h after spraying (Coupland and Caseley, 1981). Reduction in control with loss of optimal conditions has been reported in the field by Brockman, Duke and Hunt (1973) and Blair (1975). Heavy rainfall within 6 h of treatment may reduce weed control to nil (Spurrier, 1973; Coupland and Caseley, 1981).

Treatment apparatus in stubble situations

A conventional hydraulic nozzle sprayer is most commonly used in field trials for applications of glyphosate in stubble. Studies have compared conventional application techniques with controlled drop application. The level of weed control obtained with glyphosate applied during a controlled drop application was variable but higher than from conventional applications of similar rates (Harvey and Potts,

1978; MAFF, 1978). The formulation used is critical and related specifically to the Roundup formulation (Caseley, Coupland and Simmons, 1976; Turner and Loader, 1978). Only the conventional method of application is recommended by the manufacturer. The application of glyphosate is discussed in detail in Chapter 16.

Conservation tillage

The control of perennial weeds in stubble with glyphosate is effective for the majority of common weeds, without the need for cultivation procedures following application. As a result, glyphosate has a crucial role in minimum tillage systems where perennial grass weeds have often limited the success of the system (Blair, 1975). In minimum tillage or non-tillage systems, herbicide treatment replaces the cultivations normally needed for weed control prior to sowing. High costs of labour and fuel have made conventional cultivation procedures more expensive than minimum tillage or non-tillage systems. Blair (1975) recommended glyphosate for late autumn control of perennial weeds in minimum tillage systems in the UK.

Reduced cultivation procedures have been widely adopted in North America, particularly for the production of maize and soya bean (*Glycine max*). Kapusta and Strieker (1976) reported that maize yields comparable to those obtained with conventional tillage methods were obtained with non-tillage planted maize after the application of glyphosate in the stubble. No residual effects were found in the crop, and weed control was reported as excellent during the 4 years in which trials were carried out.

Seeney and Eady (1978) and Peters (1977) also reported successful control of several grass and perennial broad-leaved weeds with glyphosate in minimum tillage, direct-drilling systems in North America. Tydens (1979) supports the use of glyphosate as being valuable for conservation tillage systems in Australia. He stated that control of weeds with glyphosate, rather than cultivation, is both cost effective and beneficial in conserving moisture and reducing soil erosion. He also outlined the value of glyphosate for seedbed salvage in wet soil conditions. Such conditions preclude cultivation and seedbed preparation, although aerial spraying of glyphosate allows successful weed control. Restrictions on aerial spraying may apply in some countries.

Pre-harvest application of glyphosate

In certain situations, the control of weeds with glyphosate in stubble has been found to give low levels of efficacy. In late harvested crops or under very dry conditions, the time taken for weeds to regrow after harvest may be too long, overlapping with the time for sowing winter cereal or overlapping with the onset of cold weather conditions. In these situations, the treatment of weeds with glyphosate has to be carried out before sufficient regrowth has occurred, reducing the efficacy of weed control. This occurs commonly in northern England and Scotland (Harvey, Attwood and Potts, 1981). To overcome these difficulties, an alternative method of application has been reported (O'Keeffe, 1980). This involves the application of glyphosate to the standing crop of small grain cereals, oilseed rape and peas pre-harvest. When cereal grains reach their maximum dry matter content, the moisture content is about 37% (Mitchell *et al.*, 1980). From this stage the grain matures and exists independently of the rest of the plant, and the grain moisture content decreases. When the bulk moisture content of the crop is 30%, 95% of individual grains, by weight, will have less than a 34% moisture content (O'Keeffe, 1980). This is termed the hard dough stage of maturation. The risk of reducing crop yield or damaging the grain by application of glyphosate at or after this stage has been found to be negligible.

The majority of perennial grass weed species in cereal crops in the UK mature much later than seeded cereals and so may be successfully treated at this pre-harvest stage of growth (O'Keeffe, 1980). A number of perennial broad-leaved weeds which do not have the capacity to regrow after harvest to a susceptible stage are also susceptible.

The correct 'safe time' for application to both crop and treated grain is indicated by the bulk moisture content of the grain. In field trials this has been measured by a wet tone moisture meter. In farm situations, the period between 12 and 7 days prior to harvest seems most efficient, according to reports by O'Keeffe (1980; 1981a; 1981b; 1982), Orson (1982) and Azlin and McWhorter (1981), for maximum weed control and no crop damage.

Rates of application recommended for efficient weed control are similar to those used in stubble treatments. The currently recommended rate for control of *A. repens* in pre-harvest treatments (Orson, 1982) is 1.44 kg ha^{-1}.

Pre-harvest application of glyphosate—effect on cereal yield and grain quality

Grain yields were not affected by rates of glyphosate from 0.36 kg ha^{-1} up to 4.32 kg ha^{-1} when applied between 7 and 17 days prior to harvest in trials (O'Keeffe, 1980; 1981a; 1981b). Macarez (1981) found that rates of use from 2.16 to 8.64 kg ha^{-1}, applied between 8 and 10 days pre-harvest, also did not affect grain yields in trials. There was no fall in the thousand grain weight from crops treated with glyphosate, as compared with untreated crops (O'Keeffe, 1980; 1981b; Macarez, 1981; Sheppard *et al.*, 1982). Lower levels of grain moisture content were recorded for treated grain than for untreated grain in trials by O'Keeffe (1981b) and Sheppard *et al.* (1982). Treated grain was between 0.5% and 2% lower in moisture content than untreated. However, in Canadian trials (Clarke, 1981), glyphosate at rates of 0.5 and 1 kg ha^{-1}, applied pre-harvest when grain moisture content was less than 43% at time of application, did not increase grain desiccation more than that of control grain or straw. The reduction of grain moisture content may be the result of a reduction of green matter in the crop by lowering environmental moisture levels. It is undoubtedly a benefit to the grower.

No significant differences have been recorded in the germination capacity of treated grain as compared with untreated grain (O'Keeffe, 1981b; Macarez, 1981). Slight germination depression was reported by Sheppard *et al.* (1982) for grain treated pre-harvest with application rates of 1.44 kg ha^{-1} glyphosate on one occasion only. This has led to some caution in recommending this use on some cereals grown for seed. Germination depression was not found in the same trials with rates of 0.72 kg ha^{-1}.

The malting quality of barley and the bread-making quality of wheat treated with glyphosate pre-harvest were also discussed by O'Keeffe (1981b). Glyphosate applied pre-harvest at rates of 1.44 or 2.88 kg ha^{-1} did not affect the energy potential, crude protein percentage or tetrazolium data, as used in the determination of malting quality, in barley. The crude protein percentage was also tested to assess effects on potential milling quality and found not to differ statistically from levels in untreated grain. *Tables 27.1–27.3* show grain quality results of pre-harvest treated cereals compared with untreated cereals (O'Keeffe, 1980).

A report by Laermann and Lundehn (1980) indicates that when poor weather conditions lead to the lodging of treated crops, glyphosate may be absorbed into the cereal grain husks. The actual levels were found to vary considerably over a period of 7–28 days after treatment with glyphosate. In barley, where the lemma and palea are not shed during threshing, higher residue levels were recorded.

TABLE 27.1   Effects of pre-harvest application of glyphosate on wheat and barley crops (after O'Keeffe, 1980).

Rate of application (kg ha^{-1})	Thousand grain weight (g)	Yield relative to control	Grain moisture content (%)	Thousand grain weight (g)
0.0	41.4	100	15.7	41.1
0.36	40.6	100	15.7	40.6
0.72	40.9	104	15.2	40.9
1.44	41.2	100	15.5	41.2
2.16	40.7	100	15.2	40.7
2.88	40.7	102	15.2	40.7

TABLE 27.2   Effects of pre-harvest application of glyphosate on malting barley (after O'Keeffe, 1980)

Rate of application (kg ha^{-1})	Energy	Germination (% capacity)	Tetrazolium	Crude protein (%)
0.0	99.5	99.5	99.3	11.8
1.44	98.5	98.9	99.3	13.1
2.88	99.0	99.3	99.1	13.3

TABLE 27.3   Effects of pre-harvest application of glyphosate on milling wheat—mean of four cultivars (after O'Keeffe, 1980)

Rate of application (kg ha^{-1})	Crude Protein (%)	Hagberg falling number
0.0	10.8	200
0.36	11.1	231
0.72	10.5	188
1.44	11.1	221
2.16	11.1	232
4.32	11.1	245

Pre-harvest treatment of *S. halepense* and other broad-leaved weeds has been studied in crops of soya bean by Azlin and McWhorter (1981) and Carringer, Fawcett and Bryant (1980). Results indicated that glyphosate, applied more than 14 days before full maturity, was harmful to soya bean yields and resulted in reduced levels of germination and seed discoloration. Within 7–12 days of harvest, the soya beans were sufficiently mature for the application of glyphosate without harmful effects. The highest levels of control of *S. halepense* were obtained for rates of application between 1.12 and 1.68 kg ha^{-1}, reported by Azlin and McWhorter (1981).

Efficacy of pre-harvest weed control with glyphosate

The treatment of crops pre-harvest with glyphosate has resulted in significant yield increases in the following crops on the same land. Sheppard *et al.* (1982) reported yield increases for crops of barley, oats, swedes and wheat in fields of wheat and barley treated pre-harvest with glyphosate the year before. In trials reported by O'Keeffe (1980; 1981b), yield increases of 30–60% were recorded in cereals following pre-harvest treated wheat and barley.

Weed control with pre-harvest application of glyphosate has been shown to be outstanding. Results for individual species are given in *Table 27.4*. Over 90% control of seven broad-leaved perennial weeds was recorded in trials by O'Keeffe

TABLE 27.4   Effect of pre-harvest applications of glyphosate on weed control in cereals and soya beans

Weed species	Percent control assessed 1 year after application (Pre-harvest application rates, kg ha^{-1})					Reference
	0.3–0.7	0.72–1.4	1.41–2.1	2.11–3.0	Over 3	
Agropyron repens			94	98		O'Keeffe
Convolvulus arvensis			93	95		(1980)
Calystegia sepium			97	99		
Mentha arvensis			97	99		
Polygonum amphibium			98	98		
Solanum tuberosum			93	93		
Sonchus arvensis			97	97		
A. repens		99	99	96		O'Keeffe (1981a)
A. repens		94	95			O'Keeffe
Phragmitis australis			98			*et al.* (1981)
Agrostis gigantea		89	95	94		
Arrhenatherum elatius		52	59	66		
Polygonum amphibium			95	95		O'Keeffe
S. tuberosum			92	94		(1982)
Calystegia sepium			97	99		
Tussilago farfara				97		
Cirsium arvense			97			
Sonchus arvensis			95			
A. repens	95–99		97–99			Sheppard *et al.* (1982)
A. repens	80–95		99			Orson (1982)
Apocynum cannabinum					92	Carringer *et al.* (1980)

(1980), measured 1 year after treatment. Glyphosate was applied pre-harvest at a rate of 1.44 kg ha^{-1}. The broad-leaved weeds included *S. tuberosum, Cirsium arvense* and *Convolvulus arvensis*. Over 95% control of five perennial grasses, including *A. repens*, was recorded in trials by O'Keeffe (1981), measured 2 years after treatment. Glyphosate had been applied pre-harvest of wheat and barley at a rate of 1.44 kg ha^{-1}. Similar levels of weed control, recorded 1 year after treatment, were obtained in trials by Sheppard *et al.* (1982) after pre-harvest application of glyphosate in barley at a rate of 1.44 kg ha^{-1}. A similar rate of application, applied post-harvest in stubble, gave reduced control, varying from minimal to 75%, in the same trials (Sheppard *et al.*, 1982).

Pre-harvest treatment of weeds in soya bean with 3.36 kg ha^{-1} of glyphosate gave nearly 100% control of broad-leaved perennial weed species, including *Apocynum cannabinum* (92% control), recorded 1 year after treatment (Carringer, Fawcett and Bryant, 1980).

Efficacy of harvesting after treatment of weeds with glyphosate

The high levels of control obtained by pre-harvest treatment of perennial grasses, broad-leaved perennial weeds and also annual weeds result in much cleaner crops at harvesting (O'Keeffe, 1981). In wheat and barley, treated pre-harvest, separation losses at the sieve stage of the harvester were up to 50% lower than for untreated cereals (O'Keeffe, 1981a; 1981b; Sheppard *et al.*, 1982). This would enable an increase of 11–31% in the area harvested per unit time for treated cereals with similar grain losses to untreated cereals (Sheppard *et al.*, 1982).

Damage to crops by tractor tyres during pre-harvest treatments has been estimated as a 2–5% yield loss by O'Keeffe, Richards and Sheppard (1981) and Sheppard *et al.* (1982). This problem may be overcome by the preparation of tramlines at drilling or soon after crop emergence. Pre-harvest application of glyphosate for the control of perennial grasses and broad-leaved weeds with a rate of application of approximately 1.44 kg ha^{-1} is generally recommended, especially where it provides more reliable weed control in climates where cereal harvests are late and the onset of winter early. It may also widen the opportunities for subsequent choice of crops and date of sowing after harvest. When such treatment is to be carried out on a regular basis to improve annual weed control and harvesting efficiency, a lower rate of application, of the order of 0.72 kg ha^{-1}, may be sufficient and will occasionally give effective control of perennial weeds, as reported by Orson (1982).

New recommendations for pre-harvest use of glyphosate

Later trials on the efficacy of glyphosate as a pre-harvest weed treatment indicated that it may be used in crops other than cereals and soya bean. M.G. O'Keeffe (unpublished) has observed successful control of annual and perennial weeds pre-harvest of oilseed rape, mustard (*Sinapis alba*) crops and peas for dry harvesting. Oilseed rape should be treated when the moisture content of the seed is below 30%. This usually coincides with the stage when pod colour is yellow/green and seed colour is yellow/brown—approximately 4 or 5 days prior to normal swathing time. Treatment with glyphosate ensured a standard level of foliar death, even seed moisture content and prevention of pod shattering. All varieties, both winter and spring planted, may be treated pre-harvest with glyphosate. Glyphosate applied at a rate of 1.44 kg ha^{-1} in these trials gave 95% control of *A. repens*, measured 1 year after treatment. At this rate of application, the percentage viability of treated seed was 90% of an untreated control. Crops grown for seed production for resowing should not be treated. However, seed quality and oil quality for processing was not significantly different from that of untreated crops. Peas to be harvested dry can also be treated when their moisture content is below 30%. At this stage the pea pods are mature. Harvesting may be carried out after a minimum of 7 days from treatment.

The optimum time-lapse after application, for maximum harvesting efficacy, is reported as 10–14 days. Glyphosate was applied at the same rate as in trials for oilseed rape and similar levels of control of *A. repens* were obtained. At this rate, treated peas compared with untreated peas showed no significant difference in moisture content at harvest, yield, thousand seed weight, percentage waste and stain, percentage seed germination, percentage protein content or taste in canned samples. Mustard crops should be treated when seed moisture content is below 30% and the seeds have lost their green colour. This occurs approximately 3 or 4 days after normal swathing time, but as with treated oilseed rape swathing is not required to ensure even levels of foliar death and seed moisture content at harvest. Application should be carried out between 8 and 10 days after treatment. In oilseed rape and pea trials observed by M.G. O'Keeffe (unpublished), treated crops showed no significant differences in germination percentage or seed quality compared with seeds harvested by the standard technique (*Table 27.5*)

Pre-harvest treatment of oilseed rape, peas and mustard has received full clearance from the Pesticides Safety Scheme and approval from the Agricultural Chemicals Approval Scheme of the UK. Work has been done on pre-harvest use in herbage seed crops, but no recommendations made.

Efficacy of glyphosate for the control of problem weed species

Control of *Agropyron repens*

Agropyron repens is one of the major weed problems in arable land in the UK (Ingram, 1975). In Scotland it has been recorded as infesting 88% of all cereal crops. The density of infestations was variable, but nearly 25% of the total cereal area studied contained *A. repens* at a density of one inflorescence per 2 m^2 or denser (Elliott *et al.*, 1979; O'Keeffe; 1981a). Control of infestations of *A. repens* at

TABLE 27.5   Weed control from pre-harvest application of glyphosate to oilseed rape and peas (from M.G. O'Keeffe, unpublished)

Rate of application	Weed species	Percent level of control 1 year after treatment	Treated crop
1.44 kg ha^{-1}	*Agropyron repens*	97	Oilseed rape
	A. repens	99	Peas
	Convolvulus arvensis	60	Peas
	Sonchus arvensis	50	Peas
	Rumex spp.	50	Peas

this density by the application of glyphosate has resulted in yield increases of over 60% in autumn sown crops harvested the year after treatment (O'Keeffe, 1980). This gives an indication of the competitive ability of *A. repens*.

Throughout northern parts of Europe, *A. repens* has been recorded as one of the most important agricultural weeds (Pessala, 1979). In Finland, for example, 47% of spring cereal fields are infested with *A. repens* at an average density of 25 aerial shoots per m^2 (Pessala, 1979). Of the winter cereal fields, 38% were recorded as infected by *A. repens* at an average density of 9.6 aerial shoots per m^2 (Pessala, 1979).

The efficacy of control of *A. repens* with glyphosate applied either in the stubble after crop harvest or pre-harvest has been widely reported. Where poor weather conditions retard the regrowth of *A. repens* after harvest (see also Chapter 7), or where tillage has resulted in variable depths of rhizomes and thus variable regrowth, glyphosate is most efficient when applied to *A. repens* pre-harvest. With the increase in short-strawed cereal varieties grown throughout Europe, the leaf area of the weed present pre-harvest is sufficient for high levels of absorption and rapid translocation by the weeds to occur (O'Keeffe, 1980; 1981a; 1981b; 1982). The recommended rate of application of glyphosate for both the pre-harvest and stubble treatment of *A. repens* is 1.44 kg ha^{-1}. This dose is also recommended for the control of other perennial grass weeds (O'Keeffe, 1981a), including *Agrostis gigantea*, *Arrhenatherum elatius* and *Phragmites australis*. The control of *A. repens* in other crops is discussed in other chapters (see, for example, Chapter 19).

Control of volunteer crops

Self-seeded or volunteer crop plants are classed as weeds in arable situations. They compete with slow-growing crops, contaminate those grown for seed or for processing and interfere with harvesting. They may also adversely affect the health of subsequent crops of the same species by acting as carriers for disease. Glyphosate has been recommended for the control of volunteer potatoes (*S. tuberosum*) by Lutman (1976; 1977, 1979a; 1979b), Lumkes and Sitjsma (1972), beet-bolters by Vigoureux and Stallen (1975), volunteer sunflowers (*Hilanthus annuus*) by Abernathy, Hollingsworth and Keeling (1977) and volunteer cereals by Furrer *et al.* (1980) and Carlson and Burnside (1981) among others. The control procedure, utilizing glyphosate, varies according to volunteer species. In Europe, parts of North America and Australasia, volunteer potatoes are classed as important weeds. Studies in the early 1970s found them to be frequently resistant to commonly used herbicides, often emerging too late to be treated by post-emergence herbicides (Lumkes and Sitjsma, 1972). Volunteer potatoes are still growing vigorously at the time of cereal harvest, and plants cut back by the harvester regrow, producing new aerial shoots in the stubble after harvest.

Volunteer potatoes have been successfully treated with glyphosate applied 7–10 days pre-harvest, in trials reported by O'Keeffe (1980; 1982). Here, over 92% control, measured after 1 year of treatment with rates of application of 1.44 and 2.16 kg ha^{-1}, was reported. Successful control has also been obtained from treatment of regrowth of volunteer potatoes with glyphosate in cereal stubbles. Baart and Sijtsma (1978) reported that glyphosate applied at 1.44 kg ha^{-1} to vigorously growing potatoes in stubble produced a high proportion of rotting tubers. Adequate regrowth was found to occur within 3–4 weeks after the harvest of winter barley (Lutman, 1979a; 1979b) with 70–80% control obtained for rates of application between 0.5 and 3 kg ha^{-1}. Glyphosate applied at a rate of 1.8 kg ha^{-1} to cereal stubble, in trials by Maykuhs (1980), gave 100% control of top growth and 92% tuber-kill of volunteer potatoes. The regrowth of volunteer potatoes in barley stubble has been studied by Lutman (1976; 1979a; 1979b). He reported considerable variation in the pattern of potato regrowth under different trial conditions. The size of the parent tuber affected potential regrowth. Potatoes 2–3 cm in diameter produced up to 70% regrowth. Trials in years when June was a very dry month gave a very low percentage of regrowth.

Tolerance to drought was particularly noticeable in spring barley crops which were less competitive to initial tuber development than winter barley and so produced greater potato growth early in the spring. Crops at a high planting density had a greater competitive effect on regrowth in winter barley. Where restricted early growth of volunteer potatoes occurred, regrowth was higher in stubble and so stubble treatment was recommended by Lutman (1979a; 1979b). In good summer weather conditions and in less competitive crops, e.g. spring barley, percentage stubble regrowth was greatly reduced and the treatment of volunteer potatoes with glyphosate is more effective pre-harvest. (For a more complete discussion of general effects of weather on efficacy see Chapter 7).

DIRECTED APPLICATION OF GLYPHOSATE

Volunteer plants, including potatoes, have been successfully treated by directed applications of glyphosate above the crop. When the growth is standing above the crop, the weed may be treated selectively in this way.

Excellent control of volunteer sunflowers was reported by Abernathy, Hollingsworth and Keeling (1977) with the application of glyphosate at a rate of 2.24 kg ha^{-1} applied with horizontal jets above cotton by a recirculating sprayer. Volunteer sunflowers are not controlled by conventional chemical techniques, but treatment with glyphosate prior to sowing cotton resulted in 86% of control (Abernathy, Hollingsworth and Keeling, 1977). The recirculating spray technique for application of glyphosate was also found to give acceptable control of certain weeds in soya beans (see also Chapter 16). Evetts *et al.* (1976) applied glyphosate at rates between 1.12 and 4.48 kg ha^{-1} to *Asclepias syriaca* and *S. halepense* and obtained acceptable control. Rates of application of 0.56–1.12 kg ha^{-1} gave significant control of annual weeds. Similar results were obtained by Carlson (1977) without obvious crop damage. In studies by Hauser and Buchanan (1978), glyphosate applied by the recirculating spray technique, at a rate of application of 1.25 kg ha^{-1}, gave 95% control of two species of broad-leaved weeds in a crop of peanuts (*Arachis hypogaea*), without injury to the crop, where the spray was applied at least 10–15 cm above the crop. Carlson and Burnside (1981) reported 75–100% control of volunteer maize in soya beans after the application of glyphosate at 1.1–4.5 kg ha^{-1}, 4.5 cm above the crop, by recirculating sprayer. Significant crop damage occurred when drip and splash were not prevented.

Glyphosate may also be applied by means of a rope-wick applicator (see also Chapter 16). It was first reported as being efficient for selective weed control with glyphosate by Dale (1978) and since then has been found to give effective control of volunteer maize (*Zea mays*) by Furrer *et al.* (1980). The level of control of volunteer maize was 75–82% and without visible injury to crops. The control of *S.*

bicolor with glyphosate applied by this method was reported by Furrer *et al.* (1980). Levels of control ranged from 73% to 96%, with up to 7% crop injury.

Over 50% control of volunteer potatoes was obtained without damage to a crop of sugar beet (*Beta vulgaris*) when application of glyphosate was made with an inter-row dribble bar (Elema, 1980). The direct treatment of grass weeds in crops, with glyphosate, has proved successful. The control of volunteer crops, volunteer and bolted weed beet and broad-leaved weed species has been successful. Provided the target plant is taller than the crop plant and that there are not leaks or splashes from the applicator, many other uses can be envisaged for this method of applying glyphosate selectively.

Control of perennial broad-leaved weeds

CONVOLVULUS ARVENSIS

Convolvulus arvensis and *Calystegia sepium* are often of some importance as crop weeds and effective control measures have been studied by a number of authors. The control of bindweed in other crops is discussed in other chapters (see, for example, Chapter 19). Fischer *et al.* (1974) studied the efficacy of glyphosate for the control of *C. arvensis* in cropped and non-cropped areas in America. The optimum rate of application for effective control of *C. arvensis* was reported as 4.48 kg ha^{-1}, higher than the optimum required for perennial grass weeds such as *A. repens*. The optimal rate of application gave 80–95% control, measured 1 year after treatment. Control of *C. arvensis* was also obtained with application of glyphosate at a rate of 1.12 kg ha^{-1} (Sandberg and Meggitt, 1977). *Calystegia sepium* was controlled with a single application, but *C. arvensis* required an additional application the year following treatment to maintain suppression, possibly due to sub-optimal application rates. Application of glyphosate gave effective control until the onset of winter frosts, which completely reduced control in both species.

Cultivation prior to the application of glyphosate reduced the control of *C. arvensis* and caused proliferation of buds at the nodes of the crowns, roots and stems. However, cultivation after treatment improved performance when the initial control was poor. The combination of sub-tillage and glyphosate application was reported by Wilson (1978) to result in excellent control of *C. arvensis*. Glyphosate applied at rates of 3.36 kg ha^{-1} gave 95% control measured 1 year after treatment. *Convolvulus arvensis* control by late autumn application of glyphosate was reported by Runyan and Peeper (1980) as giving 90–100% control, measured the following May, with significant crop yield increases in winter wheat planted after treatment. Swan (1982) also obtained excellent crop yields, compared with other herbicide treatments to *C. arvensis*, when glyphosate was applied at rates of 4.5 kg ha^{-1}; 85% control was measured 1 year after treatment. Pre-harvest application of glyphosate at rates of 1.44 and 2.16 kg ha^{-1} (O'Keeffe, 1980) gave over 95% control of both *C. arvensis* and *Cal. sepium*, measured 1 year after treatment. In terms of percentage control, this is the most efficient control method.

SEMI-RESISTANT WEED SPECIES

Although glyphosate provides effective control of many perennial grasses and perennial broad-leaved weeds (*Table 27.4*), some perennial weeds are semi-resistant to glyphosate and require very high levels of treatment for control.

These include *Potentilla arvensis, Tussilago farfara, Polygonum convolvulus* and *Equisetum arvense* (Evans, 1972). O'Keeffe (1982), however, obtained 97% control of *T. farfara* with 1.44 kg ha^{-1} glyphosate applied pre-harvest. *Cynodon dactylon*, a problem grass weed in France, also requires high rates of dosage for effective control with glyphosate. Rates of application of over 3.24 kg ha^{-1} were required for efficient weed control (Bouchet, 1977; see also Chapter 15 for effects of additives).

Conclusions

Glyphosate has been shown to be an effective herbicide for the control of annual and perennial weeds in agricultural crops in a widely divergent range of temperate climates. Perennial graminaceous weeds, especially *A. repens*, are more susceptible to glyphosate than perennial dicotyledonous weeds. Rates of 0.5–2.24 kg ha^{-1} will control graminaceous weeds, whereas doses of 2.24–8.8 kg ha^{-1} are necessary to control perennial dicotyledonous weeds.

The major factor affecting the performance of glyphosate, and hence the necessary dose, is the stage of weed growth in relation to environmental conditions. The timing of the application is important, with the highest levels of control obtained from treatments applied to plants which are building up food reserves and which can be said to be at the sink stage of development. Late summer and autumn treatments have therefore given better control than spring treatments (see also Chapter 7).

Recommendations now exist in the UK and some other northern European countries for the treatment of weeds in standing crops of cereals, oilseed rape and peas prior to the harvest of these crops. Adopting the same rates of use as employed in the autumn, higher levels of weed control have been obtained. This timing has proved particularly useful for the control of perennial dicotyledonous weeds. Little or no effect has been found on the subsequently harvested grain or seed and both germination and processing qualities have not been adversely affected.

Although the herbicide is non-selective, control of weeds growing above a crop is possible, with the application of glyphosate to the weeds by contact action using wiper applicators.

References

AAMISEPP, A. (1976). Control of *Agropyron repens* in cereal stubble. *Proceedings of the 17th Swedish Weed Conference*, Pt 1; Pt 2; pp. D12, 17–18.

AAMISEPP, A. (1977). Control of *Agropyron repens*. *Proceedings of the 18th Swedish Weed Conference*, Pt 1; Pt 2; pp. H1–H5, 5–9.

AAMISEPP, A. (1978). Control of *Agropyron repens*. *Proceedings of the 19th Swedish Weed Conference*, Pt 1; Pt 2, pp. C29–C32; 6–8.

AAMISEPP, A. and GUMMESSON, G. (1974). Control of *Agropyron repens* and *Holcus mollis*. *Proceedings of the 15th Swedish Weed Conference*, Pt 1; Pt 2, pp. D15–D17, 4–8.

ABERNATHY, J.R., HOLLINGSWORTH, D. and KEELING, J.W. (1977). Control of volunteer sunflower in rotational crops. *Progress Report No. 3438*, Texas Agricultural Experiment Station, pp. 1–3.

AZLIN, W.R. and MCWHORTER, C.G. (1981). Preharvest effects of applying glyphosate to soybeans (*Glycine max*). *Weed Science*, **29**, 123–127.

BAART, E.A.D. and SIJTSMA, R. (1978). The possibility of the control of volunteer potatoes with paraquat in maize and glyphosate in stubble. *Proceedings of the British Crop Protection Conference—Weeds*, **2**, pp. 379–384.

BAILEY, J.A. (1978). Control of *Convolvulus arvensis* with cultivations and/or glyphosate. *Proceedings of the British Crop Protection Conference—Weeds*, **1**, pp. 231–235.

BAIRD, D.D. and BEGEMAN, G.F. (1972). Postemergent characterization of a new quack grass herbicide. *Proceedings of the Northeastern Weed Science Society Meeting*, **1**, pp. 100–106.

BAIRD, D.D. and UPCHURCH, R.P. (1972). Postemergence characterisation of a new herbicide, MON0468, on johnson grass. *Proceedings of the 25th Annual Meeting of the Southern Weed Science Society*, **1**, pp. 113–116.

BAIRD, D.D., UPCHURCH, R.P., HOMESLEY, W.B. and FRANZ, J.E. (1971). Introduction of a new broadspectrum post-emergence herbicide class with utility for herbaceous perennial weed control. *Proceedings of the 26th North Central Weed Control Conference*, **1**, pp. 64–68.

BEHRENS, R. and ELAKKAD, M. (1972). Herbicides for quackgrass control. *29th Annual Report North West Central Weed Conference*, **1**, pp. 40–41.

BLAIR, A.M. (1975). The control of *Agropyron repens* (L.) Beauv. in the stubble using glyphosate. *Weed Research*, **15**, 83–88.

BOUCHET, F. (1977). Techniques for the control of *Agropyron repens*. *Proceedings of the European Weed Research Society Symposium on the different methods of weed control and their integration*, pp. 163–170.

BRECKE, B.J., HUNT, J.F., FAY, P.K. and DUKE, W.B. (1974). The influence of sod density and time of plowing on quackgrass control with glyphosate. *Proceedings of the Northeastern Weed Science Society*, **28**, 35–40.

BROCKMAN, F.E., DUKE, W.B. and HUNT, J.F. (1973). Agronomic factors influencing the effectiveness of glyphosate for quackgrass control. *Proceedings of the Northeastern Weed Science Society*, **27**, 21–29.

CARLSON, D.R. (1977). Use of recirculating sprayer for selective control of common milkweed. *Proceedings of the North Central Weed Control Conference*, **32**, 110–112.

CARLSON, D.R. and BURNSIDE, O.L. (1981). Use of recirculating sprayer to control tall weed escapes in crops. *Weed Science*, **29**, 174–179.

CARRINGER, R.D., FAWCETT, R.S. and BRYANT, W.E. (1980). Perennial broadleaf weed control with pre-harvest applications of glyphosate. *Proceedings of the North Central Weed Control Conference*, **34**, 56.

CASELEY, J.C., COUPLAND, D. and SIMMONS, R.C. (1976). Effect of formulation, volume rate and application method on the performance and rain-fastness of glyphosate on *Agropyron repens*. *Proceedings of the British Crop Protection Conference—Weeds*, **2**, pp. 407–412.

CLARKE, J.M. (1981). Effect of diquat, paraquat and glyphosate on pre-harvest drying of wheat. *Canadian Journal of Plant Science*, **61**, 909–913.

COUPLAND, D. and CASELEY, J.C. (1981). Environmental influences on the effect of glyphosate on *Agropyron repens*. *Proceedings of the Conference on Grass Weeds in Cereals in the United Kingdom*, Association of Applied Biologists, Warwick, UK, pp. 177–186.

CUSSANS, G.W. (1972). A study of the growth of *Agropyron repens* (L) Beauv. during and after the growth of spring barley as influenced by the presence of undersown crops. *Proceedings of the 11th British Weed Control Conference*, **2**, pp. 689–697.

DALE, J.E. (1978). The rope-wick applicator, a new method of applying glyphosate. *Proceedings of the 31st Annual Meeting of the Southern Weed Science Society*, pp. 332–337.

ELEMA, H.M. (1980). A new implement for killing volunteer potato plants. *Landbouwmechanisatie*, **31**, 121–125.

ELLIOTT, J.G., CHURCH, B.M., HARVEY, J.J., HOLROYD, J. and HULLS, R.H. (1979). Survey of the presence and methods of control of wild oats, blackgrass and couchgrass in cereal crops in the United Kingdom during 1977. *Journal of Agricultural Science*, **92**, 617–634.

EVANS, D.M. (1972). Field performance of glyphosate derivatives in the control of *Agropyron repens* and other perennial weeds. *Proceedings of the British Weed Control Conference*, **1**, pp. 64–70.

EVETTS, L.L., RIECK, W.L., CARLSON, D. and BURNSIDE, O.C. (1976). Application of glyphosate with the recirculating sprayer. *Proceedings of the North Central Weed Control Conference*, **31**, 69.

FELLOWES, R.W., ANDERSON, R.D. and CHIN, M.L. (1979). Evaluation of glyphosate for control of emerged wild oats (*Avena* spp.) in fallow land. *Proceedings of the 7th Asian–Pacific Weed Science Society Conference*, pp. 437–439.

FISCHER, B.B., LANGE, A.H., MAY, D.M. and JOHNSON, D.E. (1974). *Towards More Effective*

Bindweed Control. A Progress Report, 1974. University of California Co-operative Extension Service, Fresno County, USA, 30 pp.

FIVELAND, T.J. (1976). Couch control with glyphosate. *Proceedings of the 4th Conference on Plant Protection*, Vollebekk, Norway, **1**, pp. 56–62.

FIVELAND, T.J. (1979). Couch control with glyphosate 1972–1977. *Forskning og forsoek i Landbruket*, **30**, 1–16.

FRENCH, E.W. and RIVELAND, N. (1980). Chemical fallow in a spring wheat fallow rotation. *North Dakota Farm Research*, **38**, 12–15.

FURRER, J.D., LUESCHEN, W.E., MARTIN, A.R. and BURNSIDE. O.C. (1980). The use of glyphosate in rope-wicks and roller applicators for controlling shattercane and volunteer corn in grain sorghum. *Proceedings of the North Central Weed Control Conference*, **35**, 58–59.

HARVEY, J.J., ATTWOOD, P.J. and POTTS, M.J. (1981). The control of *Agropyron repens* in cereal stubbles with glyphosate. *Proceedings of the Conference on Grass Weeds in Cereals in the United Kingdom*, Association of Applied Biologists, Warwick, UK, pp. 155–165.

HARVEY, J.J. and POTTS, R.J. (1978). A cost effective approach to the control of *Agropyron repens* in cereal stubbles with glyphosate. *Proceedings of the British Weed Conference*, 49–55.

HAUSER, E.W. and BUCHANAN, G.A. (1978). Progress report: control of broadleaf weeds in peanuts with the recirculating spray technique. *Proceedings of the 31st Annual Meeting of the Southern Weed Science Society*, pp. 330–335.

HODGSON, J.M. (1974). Quackgrass control and crop protection with herbicides. *Proceedings of the Western Society of Weed Science*, **27**, 17–19.

INGRAM, G.H. (1975). The distribution and importance of perennial weed grasses in the arable regions of the United Kingdom. *Proceedings of the European Weed Research Society Symposium Status, Biology and Control of Grass Weeds in Europe*, **1**, 1–8.

IVANY, J.A. (1975). Effects of glyphosate application at different growth stages on quackgrass control. *Canadian Journal of Plant Science*, **55**, 861–863.

IVANY, J.A. (1981). Quackgrass (*Agropyron repens*) control with fall-applied glyphosate and other herbicides. *Weed Science*, **29**, 382–386.

KAPUSTA, G. and STRIEKER, C.F. (1976). Herbicidal weed control in no-till planted corn. *Weed Science*, **24**, 605–611.

KEMMER, A. (1978). Results of many years of tests with the use of Roundup in the control of couchgrass (*Agropyron repens*) in crop farming. *Gesunde Pflanzen*, **30**, 182–188.

LAERMANN, H.T. and LUNDEHN, J.R. (1980). Weed control in lodged cereals—efficiency and residue situation. *Nachrichtenblatt des Deutschen Pflanzenschultz-dienst*, **32**, 125–127.

LUMKES, L.M. and SIJTSMA, R. (1972). The possibilities of controlling volunteer potatoes in a mature crop and of destroying their haulms. *Landbouwen Plantenziekten*, (**i**), 17–36.

LUTMAN, P.J.W. (1976). The control of groundkeeper potatoes. *Seed Potato*, **16**, 18–19.

LUTMAN, P.J.W. (1977). Investigations into some aspects of the biology of potatoes as weeds. *Weed Research*, **17**, 123–132.

LUTMAN, P.J.W. (1979a). The control of volunteer potato plants in the autumn in cereal stubbles. Factors affecting potato regrowth. *Annals of Applied Biology*, **93**, 41–47.

LUTMAN, P.J.W. (1979b). The control of volunteer potato plants in the autumn in cereal stubbles. II The performance of glyphosate and aminotriazole. *Annals of Applied Biology*, **93**, 49–54.

MACAREZ, R. (1981). Use of the isopropylamine salt of glyphosate to control perennial weeds before harvesting cereals. *Compte Rendu de la 11e Conference du Columa*, **1**, 133–142.

MAFF (1978). *June Returns*. Ministry of Agriculture, Fisheries and Food, HMSO, London.

MAFF (1983). *June Returns*. Ministry of Agriculture, Fisheries and Food, HMSO, London.

MAYKUHS, F. (1980). When potatoes are only troublesome weeds. *DLG-Mitteilungen*, **95**(14), 785.

MITCHELL, B., ARMSTRONG, C., BLACK, M. and CHAPMAN, J. (1980). Physiological aspects of sprouting and spoilage in development of *Triticum aestivum* L (wheat) grains, in *Seed Production*, Butterworths, London, pp. 339–356.

NUYKEN, W. (1976). Possible uses of glyphosate to control *Agropyron repens* L.B. *Mededelingen van de Faculteit Landbouwwetenschappen, Rijksuniversiteit, Gent*, **41**, 1155–1163.

O'KEEFFE, M.G. (1980). The control of *Agropyron repens* and broadleaved weeds preharvest of wheat and barley with isopropylamine salt of glyphosate. *Proceedings of the 1980 British Crop Protection Conference—Weeds*, **1**, pp. 55–60.

O'KEEFFE, M.G. (1981a). The control of perennial grasses by preharvest applications of glyphosate. *Proceedings of the Conference on Grass Weeds in Cereals in the United Kingdom*, Association of Applied Biologists, Warwick, UK, pp. 137–144.

O'KEEFFE, M.G. (1981b). The effect of preharvest application of the isopropylamine salt of glyphosate on treated crops. *Proceedings of the Conference on Grass Weeds in Cereals in the United Kingdom*, Association of Applied Biologists, Warwick, UK, pp. 145–153.

O'KEEFFE, M.G. (1982). The control of perennial broad-leaved weeds by the application of the isopropylamine salt of glyphosate pre-harvest in wheat and barley. *Aspects of Applied Biology*, **1**, 97–102.

O'KEEFFE, M.G., RICHARDS, M.C. and SHEPPARD, B.W. (1981). The effect on crop safety and weed control from applications of the isopropylamine salt of glyphosate preharvest of cereals. *Proceedings of the Conference on Crop Protection in Northern Britain*, Dundee, 1981, British Crop Protection Council, Croydon, UK, pp.51–56.

ORSON, J.H. (1982). The control of *Agropyron repens* pre-harvest of wheat and barley with the isopropylamine salt of glyphosate. *Proceedings of the 1982 British Crop Protection Conference—Weeds*, pp. 653–660.

PESSALA, B. (1979). Control of *Agropyron repens* (L) Beauv. in some field experiments. *Proceedings of the European Weed Research Society Symposium on Different Method of Weed Control and their Integration*, pp. 213–220.

PETERS, R.A. (1977). Options for quackgrass control in no-tillage silage corn. *Proceedings of the Northeastern Weed Science Society*, **31**, 71–74.

RIOUX, R. (1981). The influence on barley productivity of the timing of couch control with glyphosate. *Canada Agriculture*, **26**, 20.

RIOUX, R., BANDEEN, J.D. and ANDERSON, G.W. (1974). Effects of growth stage on translocation of glyphosate in quackgrass. *Canadian Journal of Plant Science*, **54**, 397–401.

RUNYAN, T.J. and PEEPER, T.F. (1980). Herbicide combinations and application timing for field bindweed control in winter wheat. *Proceedings of the 33rd Annual Meeting of the Southern Weed Science Society*, p. 24.

SANDBERG, C.L. and MEGGITT, W.F. (1977). A summary of field studies for the control of field bindweed with glyphosate. *Proceedings of the North Central Weed Control Conference*, **32**, 113.

SEENEY, R.D. and EADY, F.C. (1978). Control of winter weeds with glyphosate prior to direct drilling of winter cereals in Victoria. *Proceedings of the 1st Conference of the Council of the Australian Weed Science Society*, pp. 223–228.

SELLECK, G.W. and KLINE, W.L. (1978). Factors affecting efficacy of glyphosate for hedge bindweed (*Convolvulus sepium* L) control on Long Island. *Abstracts of the Meeting of the Weed Science Society of America*, p. 34.

SHEPPARD, B.W., PASCAL, J.A., RICHARDS, M.C. and GRANT, H. (1982). The control of *Agropyron repens* by the pre-harvest application of glyphosate and its effect on grain yield, moisture, germination and harvesting. *Proceedings of the 1982 British Crop Protection Conference—Weeds*, pp. 953–960.

SPRANKLE, P. and MEGGITT, W.F. (1972). Effective control of quackgrass with fall and spring applications of glyphosate. *Resource Report, North Central Weed Control Conference*, pp. 27–54.

SPURRIER, E.L. (1973). Glyphosate—a new broadspectrum herbicide. *PANS*, **19**, 607–612.

SWAN, D.G. (1982). Long term field bindweed (*Convolvulus arvensis*) control in two cropping systems. *Weed Science*, **30**, 476–480.

TURNER, D.J. and LOADER, M.P.C. (1978). Controlled drop application of glyphosate, difenzoquat and dichlorprop. *Monograph No. 22*, British Crop Protection Council, pp. 179–185.

TYDENS, N.M (1979). Conservation Tillage using 'Roundup'. *Australian Weeds*, **1**(i), 29–30.

VIGOUREUX, A. and STALLEN, E. VON (1975). Results of chemical treatment of normal beet bolters and annual weed beet. *Proceedings of the 27th International Symposium on Crop Protection*, **40**, pp. 987–994.

WICKS, G.A. (1977). Control of weeds with herbicides in stubble 10 months prior to planting corn or sorghum. *Proceedings of the North Central Weed Control Conference*, **32**, 87–88.

WILSON, R.G. (1978). Field bindweed control in Western Nebraska. *Proceedings of the North Central Weed Control Conference*, **33**, 142–144.

Chapter 28

Efficacy of glyphosate in non-crop situations

R.W. Bovey
USDA, Texas, USA

Introduction

Glyphosate, *N*-(phosphonomethyl)glycine, effectively controls a wide spectrum of plant species *(Table 28.1)*. Directed sprays of glyphosate allow the selective control of a large number of weed species with an otherwise non-selective herbicide. Since it does not provide residual weed control, retreatment is sometimes needed to control weeds regenerating vegetatively or from seeds. Repeat treatment may also be necessary if heavy rainfall occurs within 6 h after spraying and glyphosate is washed from plant surfaces.

Glyphosate sprays control a wide range of annual and perennial weeds in such areas as airports, around notice boards, ditch banks, dry ditches, around electrical equipment and poles, around farms, fence rows, firebreaks, factories, shops, golf courses, highways and roadsides, industrial plant sites, lumberyards, parking areas, parks, petroleum tanks and pumping installations, pipelines, power and telephone rights-of-way, railways, schools, storage areas, ammunition dumps, vacant holding sites and other public or non-cropland areas (Anon., 1983a).

In addition to conventional power or hand-held spray equipment, glyphosate can be applied to non-crop areas with shielded, carpet-wiper or rope-wick applicators (see also Chapter 16).

The name glyphosate in this chapter refers to the isopropylamine salt of *N*-(phosphonomethyl)glycine used as the commercial formulation Roundup.

Early work

Baird *et al.* (1971) reported on the effectiveness of a new broad-spectrum post-emergence herbicide, glyphosate, for perennial weed control. Derting *et al.* (1973) indicated, from extensive testing of glyphosate in Southern USA on non-crop areas, that it was superior to monosodium methanearsonate (MSMA) and dalapon (2,2-dichloropropionic acid) for control of *Sorghum halepense*, especially as late summer or fall treatments. Other weeds controlled with rates of 1.1–3.4 kg ha^{-1} included *Andropogon virginicus*, *Rumex crispus*, *Paspalum dilatatum*, *P. urvillei*, *Panicum maximum*, *P. repens* and *Cyperus rotundus*. A minimum of 3.4 kg ha^{-1}, either as a single or as repeat treatments, was required to

TABLE 28.1 Partial list of herbaceous and woody plants found on non-cropland and their response to glyphosate

Common and scientific name	Type*	Response†	Reference
HERBACEOUS SPECIES			
African couch grass (*Digitaria scalarum*)	P	G	Terry (1974)
Alligatorweed (*Alternanthera*)	P	P	Derting *et al.* (1973)
Annual sowthistle (*Sonchus oleraceus*)	A	E	Klingman *et al.* (1983)
Bermudagrass (*Cynodon dactylon*)	P	G	Derting *et al.* (1973); Andrews, Billman and Timmons (1974); Burr, (1974); Anon. (1983a).
Blackberry (*Rubus* spp.)	P	G	Anon. (1983a)
Black nightshade (*Solanum nigrum*)	A or B	E	Klingman *et al.* (1983)
Blue vervain (*Verbena hastata*)	P	F	McHenry *et al.* (1980)
Broadleaf dock (*Rumex obtusifolius*)	P	E	Davison (1972); Klingman *et al.* (1983)
Broadleaf plantain (*Plantago major*)	P	G	Klingman *et al.* (1983)
Broomsedge (*Andropogon virginicus*)	P	G	Derting *et al.* (1973); Peters, Lowance and Mattas (1975)
Buckhorn plantain (*Plantago lanceolata*)	P	E	Andrews, Billman and Timmons (1974); Klingman *et al.* (1983)
Canada thistle (*Cirsium arvense*)	P	G	Davison (1972); Andrews, Billman and Timmons (1974); Burr (1974); Anon. (1983a).
Cattail (*Typha* spp.)	P	G	Derting *et al.* (1973); Anon. (1983a)
Cleavers bedstraw (*Galium aparine*)	A	E	Klingman *et al.* (1983)
Cogongrass (*Imperata cylindrica*)	P	F	Dickens and Buchanan (1975)
Coltsfoot (*Tusselago farfara*)	P	F	Davison (1972)
Common chickweed (*Stellaria media*)	A	E	Klingman *et al.* (1983)
Common dandelion (*Taraxacum officinale*)	P	E	Davison (1972); Anon. (1983a); Klingman *et al.* (1983)
Common mallow (*Malva neglecta*)	A or B	G	Davison (1972)
Common milkweed (*Asclepias syriaca*)	P	G	Link *et al.* (1979a); Anon. (1983a)
Creeping bentgrass (*Agrostis stolonifera*)	P	E	Oswald (1976)
Creeping buttercup (*Ranunculus repens*)	P	E	Davison (1972)
Creeping cinquefoil (*Potentilla reptans*)	P	E	Davison (1972)
Curly dock (*Rumex crispus*)	P	G	Derting *et al.* (1973); Anon. (1983a); Klingman *et al.* (1983)
Dallisgrass (*Paspalum dilatatum*)	P	E	Derting *et al.* (1973); McHenry and Smith (1973); Anon. (1983a)
Dalmatian toadflax (*Linaria dalmatica*)	P	G	Burr (1974)

TABLE 28.1   continued

Common and scientific name	Type	Response	Reference
Desert saltgrass (*Distichlis stricta*)	P	G	Burr (1974)
European blackberry (*Rubus fruticosus*)	P	E	Davison (1972)
Field bindweed (*Cirsium arvense*)	P	F	Davison (1972); Anderson *et al.* (1975); Allen (1979a); Anon. (1983a)
Field horsetail (*Equisetum arvense*)	P	P	Davison (1972)
Goldenrod (*Solidago* spp.)	P	G	Derting *et al.* (1973); Andrews, Billman and Timmons (1974)
Guineagrass (*Panicum maximum*)	P	E	Derting *et al.* (1973); Anon. (1983a)
Hairy willowweed (*Epilobium hirsutum*)	P	E	Davison (1972)
Hoary cress (*Cardaria draba*)	P	G	Burr (1974)
Hogpotato (*Hoffmanseggia densiflora*)	P	F	Anderson *et al.* (1975)
Hogweed cowparsnip (*Heracleum sphondylium*)	P	E	Davison (1972)
Horsenettle (*Solanum carolinense*)	P	G	Derting *et al.* (1973); Anon. (1983a)
Johnsongrass (*Sorghum halepense*)	P	E	Derting *et al.* (1973); Andrews, Billman and Timmons (1974); Burr (1974); Anderson *et al.* (1975); Allen (1979b); Allen and Gregorczyk (1982); Anon. (1983a)
Kentucky bluegrass (*Poa pratensis*)	P	E	Davison, (1972); Anon. (1983a)
Kikuyugrass (*Pennisetum clandestinum*)	P	G	Anon. (1983a)
Kudzu (*Pueraria lobata*)	P	F	Andrews, Billman and Timmons (1974); Chappell and Will (1974); Anon. (1983a)
Leafy spurge (*Euphorbia escula*)	P	F	Burr (1974); Strand (1975); Alley (1977); Klingman *et al.* (1983)
Meadow foxtail (*Alopecurus pratensis*)	P	F	Oswald (1976)
Musk thistle (*Carduus nutans*)	B	E	Lee and Alley (1973); Anon. (1983a)
Napiergrass (*Pennisetum purpureum*)	P	G	Orsenigo (1975); Anon. (1983a)
Orchardgrass (*Dactylis glomerata*)	P	E	Davison (1972); Anon. (1983a)
Paragrass (*Brachiaria mutica*)	P	G	Derting *et al.* (1973); Anon. (1983a)
Perennial ryegrass (*Lolium perenne*)	P	P	Oswald (1976)
Prickly lettuce (*Lactuca serriola*)	P	E	Andrews, Billman and Timmons (1974); Anon. (1983a)
Puncturevine (*Tribulus terrestris*)	A	E	Klingman *et al.* (1983)
Purple nutsedge (*Cyperus rotundus*)	P	G	Derting *et al.* (1973); Anon. (1983a)
Quackgrass (*Agropyron repens*)	P	G	Davison (1972); Burr (1974); Anon. (1983a)

TABLE 28.1 continued

Common and scientific name	Type	Response	Reference
Ragweed (*Ambrosia* spp.)	A	E	Andrews, Billman and Timmons (1974)
Red fescue (*Festuca rubra*)	P	P	Oswald (1976); Anon. (1983a)
Redvine (*Brunnichia cirrhosa*)	P	G	Derting *et al.* (1973)
Reed canarygrass (*Phalaris arundinacea*)	P	G	Burr (1974); Anon. (1983a)
Roughstalk bluegrass (*Poa trivialia*)	P	F	Oswald (1976)
Rush skeletonweed (*Chondrilla juncea*)	P	P	Belles *et al.* (1978)
Russian knapweed (*Centaurea repens*)	P	G	Burr (1974); Anon. (1983a)
Silverleaf nightshade (*Solanum elaegnifolium*)	P	E	Cooley and Smith (1973); Anderson *et al.* (1975); Anon. (1983a)
Silverweed cinquefoil (*Potentilla anserina*)	P	E	Davison (1972)
Southern sandbur (*Cenchrus echinatus*)	A	E	Klingman *et al.* (1983)
Spring aster (*Aster spinosus*)	P	G	Anderson *et al.* (1974)
Stinging nettle (*Urtica diocia*)	P	G	Davison (1972)
Strangler vine (*Morrenia odorata*)	P	G	Derting *et al.* (1973)
Swamp smartweed (*Polygonum coccineum*)	P	E	McHenry, Smith and Buschmann (1974); Anon. (1983a)
Tansy ragwort (*Senecio jacobaea*)	P	G	Burr (1973)
Texas blueweed (*Helianthus ciliaris*)	P	G	Anderson *et al* (1975)
Torpedograss (*Panicum repens*)	P	G	Derting *et al.* (1973); Somaratne and Manipura (1974)
Trumpet creeper (*Campsis radicans*)	P	G	Derting *et al.* (1973); Andrews, Billman and Timmons (1974); Anon. (1983a)
Vaseygrass (*Paspalum urvillei*)	P	G	Derting *et al.* (1973); Andrews, Billman and Timmons (1974); Anon. (1983a)
Velvetgrass (*Holcus lanatus*)	P	E	Oswald (1976)
White clover (*Trifolium repens*)	P	P	Oswald (1976); Anon. (1983a)
Wild buckwheat (*Polygonum convolvulus*)	A	G	Klingman *et al.* (1983)
Wild garlic (*Allium vineale*)	P	F	Troutman, King and Frans (1981)
Wild licorice (*Glycyrrhiza lepidota*)	P	F	Anderson *et al.* (1975)
Yellow nutsedge (*Cyperus esculentus*)	P	G	Derting *et al.* (1973); Burr (1974)
WOODY SPECIES			
Alder (*Alnus* spp.)	P	G	Anon. (1983a)
Apple (*Malus* spp.)	P	G	Bovey (1977)

TABLE 28.1   continued

Common and scientific name	Type	Response	Reference
Ash (*Fraxinus* spp.)	P	G	Chappell *et al.* (1979)
Black locust (*Robinia pseudacacia*)	P	G	Chappell *et al.* (1979)
Blackberry (*Rubus* spp.)	P	G	Andrews, Billman and Timmons (1974)
Cherry (*Prunus* spp.)	P	E	Chappell *et al.* (1979)
Dogwood (*Cornus* spp.)	P	P	Chappell *et al.* (1979); Anon. (1983a)
Elderberry (*Sambucus* spp.)	P	G	Bovey (1977)
Elm (*Ulmus* spp.)	P	G	Bovey (1977)
Grape (*Vitis* spp.)	P	G	Bovey (1977)
Hickory (*Carya* spp.)	P	F	Chappell *et al.* (1979); Anon. (1983a)
Honeysuckle (*Lonicera* spp.)	P	G	Andrews, Billman and Timmons (1974); Bovey (1977); Anon. (1983a)
Lontana (*Lantana camara*)	P	G	Anon. (1983a)
Oaks (*Quercus* spp.)	P	G	Bovey (1977); Chappell *et al.* (1979); Anon. (1983a)
Pine (*Pinus* spp.)	P	P	Chappell *et al.* (1979)
Poison ivy (*Rhus radicans*)	P	G	Bovey (1977); Anon. (1983a)
Poison oak (*Rhus toxicodendron*)	P	G	Bovey (1977); Anon. (1983a)
Poplar (*Populus* spp.)	P	E	Chappell *et al.* (1979)
Red maple (*Acer rubrum*)	P	G	Chappell *et al.* (1979); Anon. (1983a)
Rose (*Rosa* spp.)	P	G	Bovey (1977); Ahrens (1979); Anon. (1983a)
Sassafras (*Sassafras albidum*)	P	E	Chappell *et al.* (1979)
Sourwood (*Oxydendrum arboreum*)	P	E	Chappell *et al.* (1979)
Sumac (*Rhus* spp.)	P	E	Chappell *et al.* (1979)
Tanoak (*Lithocarpus densiflorus*)	P	P	King and Radosevich (1978)
Willow (*Salix* spp.)	P	E	Dickerson (1980); Anon. (1983a)

*A, annual; B, biennial; P, perennial.

†Response—control ratings of weeds:
Excellent (E) Over 95% of the weed population killed by a single treatment.
Good (G) One treatment per year maintains 85–94% suppression of top growth; or over 95% of the weed population killed by 2 or 3 treatments.
Fair (F) From 60 to 85% of the weed population killed by a single treatment; or 2 or 3 treatments per year maintains 85–94% suppression of top growth.
Poor (P) From 10 to 59% of the weed population killed by 1 treatment; or 2 or 3 treatments per year maintains 60–84% suppression of top growth.

control *Typha* spp., *Solidago* spp., *Solanum carolinense*, *Morrenia odorata*, *Cyperus esculentus, Brachiaria mutica* and *Cynodon dactylon*.

Rights-of-way

On railway rights-of-way in Southeastern USA, Andrews, Billman and Timmons (1974) found that all annual weeds were suppressed with glyphosate at 2.2 kg ha^{-1}. *S. halepense* control was better in mid-June than from mid-May treatments at 3.4 kg ha^{-1}. Control of *Cynodon dactylon* was highest with autumn applications. Glyphosate plus residual herbicides such as bromacil [5-bromo-6-methyl-3-(1-methyl-*n*-propyl)uracil], prometon (4,6-bisisopropylamino-2-methoxy-1,3,5-triazine), diuron [*N'*-(3,4-dichlorophenyl)-*N,N*-dimethylurea] or simazine (2-chloro-4,6-bisethylamino-1,3,5-triazine), provided a less effective control of *S. halepense* and *C. dactylon* than did glyphosate alone, but glyphosate plus diuron or bromacil produced excellent control of *Paspalum urvillei*. Link *et al.* (1979b) indicated that the antagonism between glyphosate and simazine was not pronounced at threshold rates and could be alleviated by increasing the amount of the triazine component. *Rubus* spp. sprayed in May and September, 1973, and *Lonicera japonica* treated in May, were difficult to control with glyphosate (Andrews, Billman and Timmons, 1974).

   S. halepense control along highways and roadsides is a major problem (Fisher, 1977; Allen, 1979b; Johnston and Dickens, 1979; Link *et al.*, 1979b; Tripp and Huffine, 1981; Allen and Gregorczyk, 1982). Other perennial noxious weeds receiving attention along highways included control of *Pueraria lobata* (Chappell and Link, 1977) and *Convolvulus arvensis* (Allen, 1979a). Glyphosate, fosamine ammonium (ammonium ethyl carbamoyl phosphonate) or 2,4,5-T [(2,4,5-trichlorophenoxy)acetic acid] did not completely control *P. lobata* because of its resistance and rapid growth rate. This suggested the need for repetitive treatments with glyphosate (Chappell and Link, 1977). Glyphosate effectively controlled *C. arvensis* when applied from 27 June to 25 August (Allen, 1979a). Even when applied at optimum dates, without repeat treatments, species such as *S. halepense, Paspalum dilatatum* and *Cynodon dactylon* may reinfest the area (Allen and Gregorczyk, 1982).

Ditchbanks and aquatic areas

Kempen (1976) reported excellent control of *C. dactylon* and *S. halepense* on ditchbanks with autumn treatments of glyphosate, but control of the grasses allowed *Chenopodium album* to invade the treated plots. Other winter annuals such as *Hordeum jubatum, Erodium cicutarium* and *Amsinckia* spp. were prevalent in untreated plots. *S. halepense* and *C. dactylon* control was much poorer from spring treatments, especially below the water line which fluctuated in the ditch. Anderson *et al.* (1975) applied glyphosate to mixed stands of perennial weeds established on an irrigation canal bank. *S. halepense* was effectively controlled by glyphosate at 2.2 kg ha^{-1}; moderately susceptible species, such as *Helianthus ciliaris* and *Solanum elaeagnifolium* required 3.4–4.5 kg ha^{-1} and least susceptible species, such as *Convolvulus arvensis* and *Aster spinosus*, required 4.5–6.7 kg ha^{-1}

for control. *Hoffmanseggia densiflora* and *Glycyrrhiza lepidota* were not controlled at rates of 6.7 kg ha^{-1} glyphosate.

Glyphosate applied at 25 ml per 3.8 l of water plus 20 ml of detergent killed 90–95% of the *Sagittaria latifolia, Jussiaea repens,* var. *Glabrescens* and *Nymphaea tuberosa* within the treated area (Hiltibran, 1979). *Potamogeton nodosus* and *Justicia americana* were also affected, but more slowly. Aspects of weed control in water are discussed in Chapter 24.

Hiltibran (1978) found that glyphosate applied at 30–75 ml per 3.8 l of water was very effective against the immersed aquatic macrophytes *Scirpus validus, Jussiaea repens,* var. *Glabreacens, Typha angustifolia* and the *Nymphaea* spp. Welker and Riemer (1982) found that glyphosate at 2.2 kg ha^{-1} controlled *N. odorata* from a single application. Seeds that germinated either during the year of the glyphosate treatment or the following spring were controlled with a second application of glyphosate.

Woody plant control

Chappell and Will (1974) reported that August treatments of glyphosate appeared promising for control of *Quercus* spp., *Acer rubrum, Rhus* spp., *Pinus* spp. and *Robinia pseudoacacia* on power line and highway rights-of-way using ground equipment. Aerial application (Chappell *et al.,* 1979) of glyphosate also proved effective for control of several woody species similar to those reported by Chappell and Will (1974), with the addition of *Carya* spp., *Sassafras albidum, Prunus* spp., *Fraximus* spp., *Populus* spp. and *Oxydendrum arboreum* on an electric transmission line in Virginia, when compared to 2,4,5-T or picloram (4-amino-3,5,6-trichloropicolinic acid) plus 2,4-D [(2,4-dichlorophenoxy)acetic acid] (1:4). The optimum rate of glyphosate was 14 l ha^{-1}. Herbicides were applied in September 1977 and control ratings were made in October 1978.

Campbell (1980) reported that, after two growing seasons, glyphosate when injected into stems caused more canopy reduction of *Liquidambar styraciflua, Carya tomentosa* and *Quercus marilandica* than equivalent amounts (1 or 2 ml per injection) of picloram plus 2,4-D (1:4), fosamine (ethyl hydrogen carbamoyl phosphonate), hexazinone (3-cyclohexyl-6-dimethylamino-1-methyl-1,3,5-triazine-2,4-dione) or triclopyr (3,5,6-trichloro-2-pyridyloxyacetic acid). Two millilitres per incision (1 incision for 10.2 cm diam. trees, 2 for 17.8 cm diam. trees and 3 for 25.4 cm diam. trees) killed all but the *Carya* sp., which was highly resistant to all treatments. Similar data were reported by Mann (1979) for control of unwanted hardwoods. Glyphosate was superior to 2,4-D amine and picloram plus 2,4-D amine (1:4).

Preliminary data by Holt and Seifert (1979) indicated that glyphosate defoliated several deciduous tree species in the central hardwood forest of the USA using a knapsack mist blower. Glyphosate, at 2.2 kg ha^{-1} was noticeably more effective than at lower rates. Hardwoods were treated in September 1978 and 1979 and evaluated for percentage of defoliation 1 year after treatment.

Mayeux, Scifres and Crane (1980) reported that *Ericameria austrotexana* in Texas was controlled by glyphosate applied at 2.2 kg ha^{-1} in June 1975 and May 1976. Glyphosate was applied by tractor-mounted sprayer and control of this small shrub lasted at least 4 years. Glyphosate also controlled *Iscoma drummondii,* a serious subshrub in South Texas, at 1.1 kg ha^{-1}, when sprayed in May or June (Mayeux and Scifres, 1981).

Ahrens (1979) indicated that foliar sprays of glyphosate at 0.68 or 1.4 kg per 379 l of diesel oil in June or August were very effective for controlling *Rosa multiflora* in Connecticut.

The aforementioned research illustrates that the use of glyphosate on non-cropland is sometimes feasible for brush control using different methods of application. Glyphosate is especially effective in killing woody plants by injection.

Dangers of glyphosate drift

Since glyphosate is highly effective for killing or injuring some woody species, is there danger of glyphosate injury from herbaceous weed control around shade trees and ornamentals or from spray drift from nearby applications?

The herbicide label recommends glyphosate for weed control in established groves or orchards or for site preparation prior to transplanting (Anon., 1983a). Tree crops include avocado (*Persea americana*), grapefruit (*Citrus maxima*), kumquat (*Fortunella margarita*), lemon (*C. limonia*), lime (*C. aurantifolia*), orange (*C. sinensis*), tangelo (*C. reticulata* × *C. paradisi*), tangerine (*C. nobilis*), apple (*Malus* spp.), cherry (*Prunus* spp.), pear (*Pyrus* spp.), almond (*Prunus* spp.), filbert (*Corylus arellana*), macadamia (*Macadamea ternifolia*), pecan (*Carya illinoensis*), pistachio (*Pictacia vera*) and walnut (*Juglans regia*). It is recommended that spray, drift or mist of glyphosate should not be allowed to contact the green foliage, green bark or suckers of grape vines less than 3 years of age. Spray contact, other than on mature bark of the main trunk, can seriously damage the plants (Anon., 1983a).

Trees, ornamentals, vine crops and other valuable plants can be very sensitive to glyphosate and there may be risk of spraying non-cropland near or adjacent to ornamental or crop plants. Proper application equipment, timing and weather factors and application of directed sprays should prevent damage to the plants. Ornamentals and crops highly susceptible to glyphosate should be approached with extreme caution (see also Chapters 21–23 and Appendix I for further details).

Additives and other herbicides

The need to minimize cost of weed control on non-cropland is paramount. Results of several investigations on herbicide additives and residual herbicides in combination with glyphosate have been reported (see also Chapter 15).

Peters, Dest and Triolo (1974) stated that nitrogen at 179 kg N ha^{-1} in 330 l of solution as a carrier for glyphosate enhanced injury of rye (*Secale cereale*). However, on perennial sod species only initial injury was enhanced, with complete recovery occurring within 6 weeks.

Phytotoxicity of glyphosate is increased in non-crop situations, as it is in cropped areas, by the addition of ammonium sulphate and various surfactants. This aspect is described in detail in Chapter 15.

The quality of water used also affects glyphosate performance, O'Sullivan, O'Donovan and Hamman (1981) showed that glyphosate was less phytotoxic to barley (*Hordeum vulgare*) when applied in tap water (45 µg g^{-1} Ca^{2+} equivalent) compared with distilled water. Effectiveness of low rates of glyphosate was reduced with increasing spray volumes, and this reduction was more evident in tap than distilled water.

When glyphosate was applied to *Cyperus rotundus*, in combination with a range of other herbicides, most tended to have an antagonistic effect on glyphosate, especially those which inhibit photosynthesis (Suwunnamek and Parker, 1975; see also Chapter 15). Selleck (1975) reported that glyphosate at 2.2 kg ha^{-1} was superior to glyphosate combinations with bromacil plus diuron, bromacil, diuron and atrazine (2-chloro-4-ethylamino-6-isopropylamino-1,3,5-triazine) for controlling *Asclepias syriaca* and *Saponaria officinalis*. All herbicides except atrazine reduced the control of *Linaria vulgaris* when tank-mixed with glyphosate. Antagonism was not evident for control of *Poa pratensis*, *Solidago* spp. or *Rubus* spp. Antagonism between glyphosate and residual herbicides has also been reported for *Sorghum halepense* and *Cynodon dactylon* control on railroad rights-of-way in Southeastern USA, but glyphosate plus diuron or bromacil produced excellent control of *Paspalum urvillei*, *Rubus* spp., *Lonicera japonica* (Andrews, Billman and Timmons, 1974; see also Chapter 23).

Interaction of glyphosate with the environment

Run-off of glyphosate caused by natural rainfall following early spring treatment indicated that the highest concentration of glyphosate in run-off (5.2 mg l^{-1}) occurred 1 day after application (Edwards, Triplett and Kramer, 1980). Glyphosate concentration was 2 µg l^{-1} in run-off 4 months after treatment. Maximum transport by run-off water was 1.85% of the amount applied, most of which occurred during a single storm on the day after glyphosate application. Herbicide transport in the first run-off event following treatment accounted for 99% of the total run-off transport on one watershed in each of the three study years. Glyphosate residues in the upper 2.5 cm of the treated soil decreased logarithmically with the logarithm of time; they persisted several weeks longer than in run-off water. Extrapolation of these data to non-cropland situations is difficult but, based on the high rates of herbicide used in this study (Edwards, Triplett and Kramer, 1980), the occurrence of rainfall soon after treatment of glyphosate should not pose a problem relative to its movement from site of application to cropland, water sources or other sensitive areas (see also Chapter 13).

As indicated earlier, certain additives, spray volumes and water sources used as a carrier for glyphosate can alter its herbicide effect. Rainfall or irrigation can wash glyphosate from plant surfaces for as much as 6 h after treatment, reducing its effect. Treating weeds under poor growing conditions such as drought stress, disease or insect damage may reduce the effectiveness of the herbicide. Reduced results may also occur when treating weeds heavily covered with dust such as along roadsides.

Wyse and Higgins (1975) found that glyphosate applied at 2.2 kg ha^{-1} gave good control of *Agropyron repens* even though the plants were drought stressed. Glyphosate applied at rates lower than 2.2 kg ha^{-1} were not as effective on drought-stressed plants as the higher rate. This aspect, and the effect of humidity, temperature and light, are discussed in Chapter 7.

Time of application

The performance of glyphosate is affected by the time of application. Derting *et al.* (1973) found the best *S. halepense* control with glyphosate occurred from late summer and autumn treatments. Andrews, Billman and Timmons (1974) indicated that control of *C. dactylon* was highest with autumn applications. Whitwell and Santelmann (1978) reported that glyphosate at rates of 3.4 kg ha^{-1} or more was effective for controlling *C. dactylon* from July to early October in Oklahoma. Spring applications were ineffective even at 5.0 kg ha^{-1}. Substantial foliage (>17 cm tall) had to be present to obtain control in August. Cool temperatures (5 days at 20°C) did not decrease *C. dactylon* control with glyphosate, but dry soil conditions or wilted plants significantly reduced effectiveness. Effective *C. dactylon* control with glyphosate requires actively growing plants with the major portion of the photosynthates moving into the stems and roots. Plant stress prior to treatment reduced control.

Baird *et al.* (1973) indicated that more glyphosate is required for long-term control of *A. repens* with an increase in rhizome concentrations and/or length. Mowing the foliage 1 day before and after glyphosate application reduced the effect of glyphosate. Mowing *A. repens* 1 day before treatment had a much more pronounced effect on reducing glyphosate effectiveness than mowing 1 day after. Mowing 1 or 2 weeks after glyphosate application did not appear to influence its activity, compared with unmowed glyphosate-treated plants.

These data strongly suggest the necessity to treat actively growing weeds with sufficient foliar development for maximum effectiveness (see also Chapter 7).

Recommended uses of glyphosate (non-crop situations)

A general outline of application methods, rates required and species controlled with glyphosate are given in *Table 28.2* (Anon., 1983b). Readers are also referred to *Table 28.1* and other chapters of this book for further details on application methods and weed species controlled.

Conclusions

Glyphosate is a highly effective herbicide for use in non-crop situations because of the wide spectrum of plants it controls, the low rates required for activity and the lack of residual activity in the soil. Some weedy species are resistant to glyphosate, however, and repeated treatments may be necessary to control these plants. Other species, including many woody plants such as shade trees and ornamentals, are not affected by glyphosate at normal field rates. Glyphosate can be applied to vegetation, with standard aerial- and ground-application techniques. Glyphosate lends itself, particularly in cropland situations, to recirculating sprays and wipers. The wiper or wick method may be especially useful in non-crop situations to prevent herbicide spray drift and selectively retain certain desirable species not contacted by the wiper.

TABLE 28.2 General guidelines for glyphosate use on non-cropland (after Anon., 1983b, by courtesy of the Meister Publishing Co.)

Rate per treated acre	Weeds controlled (common names)	Remarks/areas of application
Handgun and high volume: mix 3.8 l glyphosate in 379 l clean water and apply to foliage of vegetation to be controlled Boom equipment: use 1.9–3.8 l glyphosate in 187–280 l water as broadcast spray Aerial application: apply recommended rates per weed species in 47–140 l ha^{-1} of water on rights-of-way only	Controls perennial weeds such as johnsongrass, quackgrass, Canada thistle, milkweed, hemp, dogbane, bermudagrass, paragrass, dallisgrass, vaseygrass, fescues, common mullein, wirestem muhly and field bindweed, plus many other problem annual and perennial grasses and broad-leaved weeds. Also controls woody brush species such as alder, blackberry, dewberry, elderberry, honeysuckle, kudzu, maple, multiflora rose, oak, trumpetcreeper, willow. Provides canopy reduction plus destruction of underground plant parts including rootstocks, rhizomes, etc. Repeat treatments may be necessary to kill resistant species or where regeneration from seed causes reinfestation of the species	Not a residual herbicide; therefore, follow with a label-approved programme for effective annual and perennial seedling weed control. Apply to the foliage of actively growing broad-leaved weeds and grasses at the recommended growth stage. Do not mix with other herbicides. Do not allow spray or spray drift to contact desirable plants. Do not mow or till prior to glyphosate treatment. Do not apply if rainfall is imminent Railroad, highway, pipeline, powerline and telephone line rights-of-way. Other areas of application include petroleum-tank farms and pumping installations, lumberyards, parking areas, industrial plant sites, roadsides, storage areas, fence rows, schools, parks, golf courses, other public areas, airports and similar industrial or non-crop areas. Labelled for aerial applications on rights-of-way only
Hand sprayer: mix 57 g per 3.8 l water and spray per 90 m^2 for control of perennial weeds listed on label		If spraying areas adjacent to desirable plants, use a shield made of cardboard, sheetmetal or plyboard while spraying to help prevent spray from contacting foliage of desirable plants
mix 85 g per 3.8 l water and spray per 90 m^2 for control of perennial weeds listed on label		Use around farmstead building foundations, along and in fences, in shelterbelts and for general non-selective farmstead weed control
1.9 l of glyphosate broadcast spray of 1% solution with hand-held equipment	Multiflora rose	Apply when canes are actively growing and at or beyond the early to full bloom stage of growth

References

AHRENS, J.F. (1979). Chemical control of multiflora rose, *Proceedings of the Northeastern Weed Science Society*, **33**, 213–217.

ALLEN, T.J. (1979a). Studies on field bindweed control along Texas highways, *Proceedings of the Southern Weed Science Society*, **32**, 227.

ALLEN, T.J. (1979b). Studies on Johnsongrass control along Texas highways, *Proceeding of the Southern Weed Science Society*, **32**, 228.

ALLEN, T.J. and GREGORCZYK, D. (1982). Effect of DPX-5648 and glyphosate on roadside vegetation, *Proceedings of the Southern Weed Science Society*, **35**, 258-263.

ALLEY, H.P. (1977). Leafy spurge control. Project I. Perennial herbaceous weeds, *Research Progress Report of the Western Society of Weed Science*, pp. 6–7.

ANDERSON, W.P., SHRADER, T.H., CLARY, M. and LOYA, R. (1975). Perennial weed control with glyphosate, *Research Progress Report of the Western Society of Weed Science*, pp. 116–117.

ANDREWS, O.N., JR., BILLMAN, R.C. and TIMMONS, F.D. (1974). Glyphosate control of railroad rights-of-way vegetation in the southeast, *Proceedings of the Southern Weed Science Society*, **27**, 251–258.

ANON. (1983a). *Monsanto 1983 Crop Chemical Label Guide*. St. Louis, Missouri, USA Monsanto, p. 86.

ANON. (1983b). *1983 Weed Control Manual*. Willoughby, OH; Meister, p. 338.

BAIRD, D.D., PHATAK, S.C., UPCHURCH, R.P. and BEGEMAN, G.F. (1973). Glyphosate activity on quackgrass as influenced by mowing and rhizome density, *Proceedings of the Northeastern Weed Science Society*, **27**, 13–20.

BAIRD, D.D., UPCHURCH, R.P., HOMESLEY, W.B. and FRANZ, J.E. (1971). Introduction of a new broadspectrum postemergence herbicide class with utility for herbaceous perennial weed control, *Proceedings of the Northcentral Weed Control Conference*, **29**, 64–68.

BELLES, W.S., WATTENBARGER, D.W., BAYSINGER, O.K. and LEE, G.A. (1978). Rusk skeletonweed control, *Research Progress Report of the Western Society of Weed Science*, pp. 16–17.

BOVEY, R.W. (1977). Response of selected woody plants in the United States to herbicides, *Agricultural Handbook No. 493*, US Department of Agriculture, Agricultural Research Service, p. 101.

BURR, R.J. (1973). Tansy ragwort control, *Research Progress Report of the Western Society of Weed Science*, p. 10.

BURR, R.J. (1974). Perennial weed control with glyphosate, *Research Progress Report of the Western Society of Weed Science*, p. 8.

CAMPBELL, T.E. (1980). A comparison of five tree-injected herbicides, *Proceedings of the Southern Weed Science Society*, **33**, 127–131.

CASELEY, J. (1972). The effect of environmental factors on the performance of glyphosate against *Agropyron repens*, *Proceedings of the British Weed Control Conference*, **11**, 641–647.

CHAPPELL, W.E., COARTNEY, J.S., HIPKINS, P.L. and LINK, M.L. (1979). Aerial applications of glyphosate for the control of brush in rights-of-way, *Proceedings of the Southern Weed Science Society*, **32**, 242–244.

CHAPPELL, W.E. and LINK, M.L. (1977). Kudzu control on Virginia highways, *Proceedings of the Southern Weed Science Society*, **30**, 299.

CHAPPELL, W.E. and WILL, J.B. (1974). Brush control studies in rights-of-way, *Proceedings of the Southern Weed Science Society*, **27**, 259-265.

COOLEY, A.W. and SMITH, D.T. (1973). Silverleaf nightshade response to glyphosate, *Proceedings of the Southern Weed Science Society*, **26**, 59.

DAVISON, J.G. (1972). The response of 21 perennial weed species to glyphosate, *Proceedings of the 11th British Weed Control Conference*, **11**, 11–16.

DERTING, C.W., ANDREWS, O.N., JR., DUNCAN, R.G. and FROST, K.R. JR. (1973). Two years of perennial weed control investigations with glyphosate, *Proceedings of the Southern Weed Science Society*, **26**, 44–50.

DICKENS, R. and BUCHANAN, G.A. (1975). Control of cogongrass with herbicides, *Weed Science*, **23**, 194–197.

DICKERSON, G.W. (1980). Effects of glyphosate and other herbicides on willows in northern New Mexico, *Research Progress Report of the Western Society of Weed Science*, pp. 342–343.

EDWARDS, W.M., TRIPLETT, G.B. JR. and KRAMER, R.M. (1980). A watershed study of glyphosate transport in runoff, *Journal of Environmental Quality*, **9**, 661–665.

FISHER, W.T. (1977). Johnsongrass control on Virginia highways, *Proceedings of the Southern Weed Science Society*, **30**, 297–298.

HILTIBRAN, R.C. (1978). Aquatic plant control research—1978, *Research Report of the Northcentral Weed Control Conference*, **35**, 77–78.

HILTIBRAN, R.C. (1979). Illinois 1979 aquatic plant control research report, *Research Report of the Northcentral Weed Control Conference*, **36**, 22–23.

HOLT, H.A. and SEIFERT, J.R. (1979). Initial woody plant control results with glyphosate and fosamine applied with a mistblower, *Northcentral Weed Control Conference*, **34**, 85–86.

JOHNSTON, W.J. and DICKENS, R. (1979). Evaluation of herbicides and application systems for highway weed control, *Proceedings of the Southern Weed Science Society*, **32**, 235.

KEMPEN, H.M. (1976). Ditchbank perennial weed control with glyphosate, *Research Progress Report of the Western Society of Weed Science*, p. 188.

KING, M.G. and RADOSEVICH, S.R. (1978). Effectiveness of various foliar applied herbicides on tanoak resprouts, *Research Progress Report of the Western Society of Weed Science*, pp. 35–36.

KLINGMAN, D.L., BOVEY, R.W., KNAKE, E.L., LANGE, A.H., MEADE, J.A., SHROCK, W.A., STEWART, R.E. and WYSE, D.L. (1983). Systemic herbicides for weed control—phenoxy herbicides, dicamba, picloram, amitrole and glyphosate, U.S. Department of Agriculture, Extension Service AO-BU-2281, 16 pp.

LEE, G.A. and ALLEY, H.P. (1973). Muskthistle (*Carduus nutans* L.) control in Wyoming, *Research Progress Report of the Western Society of Weed Science*, p. 12.

LINK, M.L., COARTNEY, J.S., CHAPPELL, W.E. and HIPKINS, P.L. (1979a). Control of common milkweed on highway right-of-way, *Proceedings of the Southern Weed Science Society*, **32**, 229–234.

LINK, M.L., COARTNEY, J.S., CHAPPELL, W.E. and HIPKINS, P.L. (1979b). Antagonistic aspects of glyphosate-residual herbicide tank mixes, *Proceedings of the Southern Weed Science Society*, **32**, 241.

MANN, W.F., JR. (1979). Glyphosate is highly effective for tree injection, *Research Paper SO-150*, U.S. Department of Agriculture Forest Service, Southern Forestry Experiment Station, New Orleans, LA, p. 7.

MAYEUX, H.S., JR. and SCIFRES, C.J. (1981). Drumond's goldenweed and its control with herbicides, *Journal of Range Management*, **34**, 98–101.

MAYEUX, H.S., JR., SCIFRES, C.J. and CRANE, R.A. (1980). *Ericameria austrotexana* and associated range forage responses for herbicides, *Weed Science*, **28**, 602–606.

MCHENRY, W.B. and SMITH, N.L. (1973). Response of dallisgrass (*Paspalum dilatatum* Poir.) to dalapon, glyphosate and MSMA, *Research Progress Report of the Western Society of Weed Science*, p. 19.

MCHENRY, W.B., SMITH, N.L. and BUSCHMANN, L.L. (1974). Control of swamp smartweed (*Polygonum coccineum* Muhl.) on a ditchbank with glyphosate, 2,4-D and asulam, *Research Progress Report of the Western Society of Weed Science*, pp. 138–139.

MCHENRY, W.B., SMITH, N.L., WILSON, C.B. and BUSCHMANN, L. (1980). Response of blue vervain to four foliage-applied herbicides, *Research Progress Report of the Western Society of Weed Science*, p. 344.

ORSENIGO, J.R. (1975). Napiergrass response to glyphosate, *Proceedings of the Soil and Crop Science Society of Florida*, **34**, 125–127.

O'SULLIVAN, P.A., O'DONOVAN, J.T. and HAMMAN, W.M. (1981). Influence of non-ionic surfactants, ammonium sulfate, water quality and spray volumes on the phytotoxicity of glyphosate, *Canadian Journal of Plant Science*, **61**, 391–400.

OSWALD, A.K. (1976). The effects of seasonal applications of glyphosate on a mixed sward, *Proceedings of the 1976 British Crop Protection Conference—Weeds*, **13**, 961–969.

PETERS, E.J., LOWANCE, S.A. and MATTAS, R. (1975). Response of broomsedge to herbicides, *Research Report of the North Central Weed Control Conference*, **32**, 47.

PETERS, R.A., DEST, W.M. and TRIOLO, A.C. (1974). Preliminary report on the effect of mixing liquid fertilizers and residual herbicides with paraquat and glyphosate, *Proceedings of the Northeastern Weed Science Society*, **28**, 35–40.

SELLECK, G.W. (1975). Antagonistic effects with glyphosate herbicide plus residual herbicide combinations, *Proceedings of the Northeastern Weed Science Society*, **29**, 327.

SOMARATNE, A. and MANIPURA, W.B. (1974). The control of *Panicum repens* (L.) Beauv. with glyphosate, *Tea Quarterly, Sri Lanka*, **44**, 86–94.

STRAND, O.E. (1975). Leafy spurge control with herbicides, Pine County, Minnesota, *Research Report of the North Central Weed Control Conference*, **32**, 73.

SUWUNNAMEK, U. and PARKER, C. (1975). Control of *Cyperus rotundus* with glyphosate: the influence of ammonium sulfate and other additives, *Weed Research*, **15**, 13–19.

TERRY, P.J. (1974). Field evaluation of glyphosate, asulam and dalapon on African couch grass (*Digitaria scalarium*), *East African Agricultural and Forestry Journal*, **39**, 381–390.

TRIPP, T.N. and HUFFINE, W.W. (1981). Evaluation of mixtures of herbicides for the roadside control of seedlings and rhizomatous Johnsongrass, *Proceedings of the Southern Weed Science Society*, **34**, 213–220.

TROUTMAN, D.C., KING, J.W. and FRANS, R.E. (1981). Wild garlic (*Allium vineale*) control with glyphosate, *Weed Science*, **29**, 717–722.

WELKER, W.V. and RIEMER, D.N. (1982). Fragrant waterlily (*Nymphaea odorata*) control with multiple applications of glyphosate, *Weed Science*, **30**, 145–146.

WHITWELL, T. and SANTELMANN, P.W. (1978). Influence of growth stage and soil conditions on bermudagrass susceptibility to glyphosate, *Agronomy Journal*, **70**, 653–656.

WYSE, D.L. and HIGGINS, M. (1975). Control of drought stressed quackgrass with fall-applied herbicides at Rosemount, Minnesota in 1975, *Research Report of the Northcentral Weed Control Conference*, **32**, 34.

Part VIII

Summary

Chapter 29

Glyphosate: a summing-up

K. Holly
Weed Research Organization, Oxford, UK

Introduction

During the past three decades the search for new agrochemicals has been intense, with each major firm screening many thousands of new chemical molecules each year for usable biological activity. Herbicidal activity has been much sought after because of the total size of the world herbicide market as compared with that for other biocides. In consequence, about 170 distinct herbicides have been brought to commercial availability during that time.

Many of these herbicides have depended for success upon their ability to occupy a hitherto unfilled niche in controlling a particular group of weeds or in being selective in one or two important crops. Others have behaved like already established herbicides, but have offered the chance to compete for and take over a slice of the established market.

A very few have been truly significant discoveries, providing herbicides with a wide range of uses and substantially affecting the course of development of techniques of agricultural production. Such major herbicides have made substantial sales throughout the life of the patents protecting them and have gone on to become commodity herbicides destined to be important components of the weed control armoury for many years to come. Among such herbicides have been the phenoxyacetic acids MCPA and 2,4-D, the phenoxypropionic acids mecoprop and dichlorprop, the triazines simazine and atrazine, and paraquat. Without doubt, glyphosate is destined to join this select band of truly great herbicides.

Properties

Glyphosate possesses a combination of near unique properties. The most impressive is its very high degree of mobility following entry into foliage, coupled with an extreme effectiveness at sites of action in buds. This gives it an unparalleled efficiency for the control of perennial weeds. Where, previously, farmers and horticulturalists had struggled to achieve useful levels of control of *Agropyron repens* with herbicides such as dalapon and paraquat, glyphosate has made long-term control of this major world grass weed easy. In the same way, control of many dicotyledonous perennial weeds has been facilitated through the addition of

451

glyphosate to the previous armoury of herbicides such as 2,4-D, 2,4,5-T, picloram and triclopyr which often required use under very closely defined conditions in order to be successful.

When glyphosate is applied to the foliage there are few species really resistant to it. Hence there is a lack of true selectivity, although diligence has revealed some limited selectivity between pasture grasses, and in conifer crops. The minimal entry through mature bark permits very valuable selectivity for weed control in woody crops.

The lack of significant biological activity once glyphosate has reached the soil, its comparative safety from toxicological standpoints and its lack of major environmental side-effects have all made glyphosate an attractive herbicide to use.

Crop production

Glyphosate has already played a major role in furthering change and improvement in the technology of crop production. The widespread availability of paraquat was an important ingredient for the successful initial development of minimum cultivation and direct drilling techniques for stubbles and newly killed swards. Glyphosate overcomes the limitation of paraquat in being more successful in the control of established perennial plants. In consequence, it has facilitated greatly the swing to sequential winter cereal crops through a combination of quick and effective vegetation control with minimum cultivation techniques. One relevant new approach has been the meteoric rise of application of glyphosate a few days prior to harvest of cereals and other crops, in order to secure maximum effectiveness on perennial weeds, an easy and efficient harvest and the swiftest possible move towards preparation for the next crop.

Application machinery

There is another instance where glyphosate has followed, widened and diversified a trail first initiated by paraquat. This is in the broadening of approaches to the application of herbicides. Paraquat provided the stimulus to development of a variety of sprayers involving crop shielding devices, and to devices such as the 'Vibrajet' for forming large drift-free drops. Glyphosate, in turn, has provided an excellent herbicide for use in conjunction with a host of direct herbicide application devices, of which the plethora of rope-wick and roller applicators are examples. In this way glyphosate has instigated much activity in small agricultural engineering firms and in farm workshops around the world to develop application machinery for specific purposes.

On the scientific side, glyphosate has attracted a great deal of interest among physiologists and biochemists as well as weed scientists. It breaks much new ground in its mode of action upon plants and is distinctive from most other herbicides in this way.

All these topics, and more, have been reviewed authoritatively and at length in this book. It will be an introduction to, a source book for, and a synthesis of, most of the knowledge on the uses and properties achieved during the first decade of availability of glyphosate. Any attempt at detailed summing-up could only lead to trivialization.

The future

The one thing remaining to be said, perhaps, is in brief answer to the question 'What of the future?'. Glyphosate, in common with most other new chemicals, was introduced at a price the market would bear for the priority uses and markets on which the discovering company initially concentrated its attention. This is a practice aimed at maximizing the chances of recovering the high costs of research and development within a reasonable period of time. Glyphosate is now assuredly through this phase and into one in which it can be available at a price for an effective dose which permits its consideration for a very wide range of uses throughout the world, both in countries with highly mechanized cost-effective agricultural production technologies and in developing countries with a variety of other simpler agricultural systems. There is no reason to doubt that the aspiration of Monsanto for glyphosate to become the first 'thousand million dollar annual sales proprietary molecule' will be fulfilled.

On the technical side, we shall see adaptation to particular forms of use. Concepts of weed management may develop with adaptation of level of dose applied to level of effect or control desired. More formulations will become available, tailored to specific forms of application and to the more efficient control of those species showing some degree of resistance. The latter may well include improvement aimed at control of woody plants. Likewise, formulation technology may well overcome the current weakness of glyphosate in requiring several hours without major rainfall in order to give maximum biological effectiveness. Glyphosate is an obvious candidate for bringing together the skills of the plant breeder, the genetic engineer and the agrochemist to give us varieties of major crop plants resistant to a herbicide which will control virtually all weeds in that crop. Finally, there are still enough unanswered questions on the mode of action of glyphosate to provide topics for student and postgraduate projects in the university sector for many years to come.

The outcome of all the above must surely be that, in a few years' time, there will be need for further review of our knowledge on the diversity of uses and properties of glyphosate.

Appendix I

Glyphosate damage symptoms and the effects of drift

D. Atkinson
East Malling Research Station, UK

Introduction

As a herbicide, glyphosate is unique in many ways, but in relation to its potential to cause accidental damage its ability to be translocated through the plant is of particular interest, especially in perennial species. Lange *et al.* (1975) found that glyphosate drift caused fewer immediate symptoms but more eventual plant damage than other translocated herbicides in peach, plum and seedless grapevines. Similarly, Lange and Schlesselman (1975) found that glyphosate caused more drift damage than 2,4-D oil-soluble amine, MSMA, aminotriazole, cacodylic acid, paraquat or dalapon. Assessment of the foliage response showed that glyphosate moved further into the unsprayed portion of the tree than any other translocated herbicide tested (see *Figures A.12, A.15* and *A.16*). Accidental damage can occur either by drift during weed control operation within a crop or by drift from one field to another.

In experimental studies, drift has usually been simulated by directed applications to limited parts or the whole of a plant. Considerations of its ease of translocation and the long list of reported actual or potential instances of damage due to glyphosate in a range of species, e.g. cane fruits (Davison, 1975), cotton (Anon., 1973; Kleifeld, 1976; Tollervey, Paniagua and Gonzalez, 1980), maize (Cooper, 1975), plantain (Liu, Rodriguez-Garcia and Semidey-Laracuente, 1981), *Prunus* spp. (Rom and Talbert, 1973), sugar cane (Ching *et al.*, 1976), tanier (*Xanthosoma sagittifolium*) (Liu and Acevedo-Borrero, 1980), tea (Magambo and Kilavuka, 1982), tomato (Romanowski, 1974), Valencia orange (Toth and Morrison, 1977) and vine (Barralis *et al.*, 1973; Kafadarof and Poisson, 1973), suggest that damage due to drift is likely to be more common and more severe with glyphosate than with other herbicides. Instances of particular problems are detailed in the individual commodity chapters in this volume.

This appendix reviews some factors influencing the severity of drift damage and the probability of its occurrence, and presents a series of figures to illustrate the appearance of both acute (immediate) and longer term symptoms of glyphosate damage in a range of crops. Additional evidence for the practical importance of drift with this herbcide is shown by the emphasis which has been placed on the development of methods of application to minimize drift (see also Chapter 16). Costa (1981), Evetts *et al.* (1976), Kafadarof and Poisson (1973), Liu and

Acevedo-Borrero (1980), Peters and Dale (1978) and Wills and McWhorter (1981) all discuss this point and describe machinery to limit accidental applications to crops. Although direct drift damage can be serious, it does not cause the damage associated with vapour transfer found with some other compounds (Wiese, 1976; Shaw and Bruzzere, 1979).

Factors influencing damage from drift

The effect of drift has been analysed in detail for a number of situations. Many of the factors affecting damage to crop species are the same as those influencing efficacy on weed species (see also Chapters 7 and 15). Rate and timing of application seem especially important. Magambo and Kilavuka (1975) compared the damage to tea resulting from both accidental drift during weed control and direct application. They found that, after 2 weeks, young leaves became chlorotic and young shoots scorched (see *Figures A.2* and *A.4*), but that damage was more severe with the directed application. After 6 weeks there were still symptoms on the directed-spray plants, but not those affected by genuine drift. San Juan, Blancaver and Rodriguez (1981) assessed the effect of simulated drift at a rate of 1.64 or 3.28 kg ha^{-1} on coconut. Both rates caused damage on the three oldest but not succeeding leaves. San Juan and Rodriguez (1980) investigated the effect of the drift of solutions containing from 0.38 to 3.8 kg a.i. ha^{-1} on to either 30- or 90-day-old coconut seedlings. They found both tolerated a 0.77 kg ha^{-1} application, but that 1.9 and 3.8 kg ha^{-1} solutions caused slight drying of the tips of the lower leaves in both groups of seedlings. The effect of a range of application rates on apple, blackcurrant and raspberry was investigated by Clay (1972) (see Chapter 19 for full discussion). On apple, a 0.56% solution caused prolonged dormancy in the spring and an increase in the number of lateral shoots on the leader shoots of the tree (see *Figures A.9, A.18* and *A.19*). A 2.24% solution reduced leaf expansion and shoot growth (see *Figures A.9, A.11* and *A.12*).

The timing of contact with drift is important in relation to the amount of damage caused. This has implications for whole farm management, especially in small multi-crop horticultural enterprises. One crop may limit the freedom to act on another unless drift can be prevented (see also Chapter 7). Romanowski (1974) studied the hazard to vegetable crops incurred as a consequence of glyphosate being used on an adjacent industrial site. An application of 0.11 kg a.i. ha^{-1} in July injured processing tomatoes. The chemical caused chlorosis of the central part of the leaf, stunting, white rather than yellow flowers, base-end cracks in the fruit and loss of yield. Applications in August were well tolerated. Ching et al. (1976) reported that, in sugar cane, phytotoxic effects of drift depended upon cane age, with older plants being less susceptible. The potential for drift from older to younger fields is therefore a practical problem.

The probability of drift occurring and the amount likely to be deposited are both affected by the method of spray application (see also Chapter 16). Yates, Akesson and Bayer (1978) studied the potential losses of glyphosate sprays, with and without a polymer thickener, when made from a boom-nozzle ground sprayer, a helicopter and fixed wing aircraft. The downwind transport and diffusion of the spray loss was assessed with mylar fallout sheets, high volume air samplers and 4-leaf wheat test plants. Lowest drift losses, <10 mg ha^{-1} on fallout sheets at 100 m, occurred with deflector fan nozzles at low pressure, 7 kPa, on the ground sprayer. A helicopter with microjet nozzles gave relatively similar losses, 30 mg ha^{-1}. Other nozzle types and methods of application gave more drift, the highest, 5 g ha^{-1}, being with D4 jet nozzles directed downwards from a helicopter. The polymer gave some reduction of airborne drift.

Symptoms of glyphosate injury

Accidental applications of glyphosate, as drift, may result in the death of part or the whole of the affected plant. Typical acute damage symptoms are shown in *Figures A.1–A.6*. With glyphosate, damage often spreads well beyond the immediately affected part (see also Chapters 7 and 19). In perennial crops, symptoms of glyphosate damage may be exhibited for a number of years. Typical symptoms of chronic or persistent glyphosate injury are shown in *Figures A.8–A.13* and *A.15–A.20*. Glyphosate is not unique in producing some of these symptoms. The damage caused by fosamine-ammonium (Atkinson, Hyrycz and Petts, 1978) is illustrated for comparison (*Figure A.14*).

The symptoms resulting from accidental glyphosate applications and the time course of their development and persistance have been detailed in a number of papers for a range of crop species. In cotton (Kleifeld, 1976), an application of 4 kg ha^{-1} near to 3-week-old plants caused a growth retardation and reddish coloration of the leaves. A 360 mg l^{-1} spray to 3-year-old highbush blueberries caused terminal die-back, foliar damage and delayed flowering (see *Figures A.7, A.9* and *A.11*). In the subsequent year, growth was normal (Hodges, Talbert and Moore, 1978). Applications to individual young tree branches by Lange and Schlesselman (1975) caused burn, splitting and exudation (see *Figure A.17*). In both trees and vines, sub-lethal doses released adventitious and lateral buds but stunted surviving shoots (see *Figures A.19* and *A.20*). Although total growth was reduced, some treated trees and vines developed normal foliage within 1–2 years of the sub-lethal application. In peach (Toth and Morrison, 1977), 2.8 kg a.i. ha^{-1} caused leaf shed within 7 days and death in 4 weeks (see also Chapter 19). In contrast, in Valencia oranges there was some leaf shed at 7 days, but although abnormal and reduced growth and shoot fasciation were recorded for 2 years, subsequent growth was normal (see *Figures A.12, A.18* and *A.20*). With tea (Magambo and Kilavuka, 1982), applications of 2–8 kg ha^{-1} caused a reduction in internode length in young shoots and after 1 week post-spraying the production of curled needle-like leaves. Symptoms of this type persisted for 3 months post-spraying. New shoots developing below the canopy were normal and mature leaves unaffected (see *Figures A.12, A.15* and *A.20*). Sub-lethal effects are persistent and mainly involve shoot retardation, bud proliferation and leaf deformation. Some of these effects can be induced by other herbicides, e.g. fosamine-ammonium (Atkinson, Hyrycz and Petts, 1978).

The effect of sub-lethal damage has been quantified. Its importance is often related to the contribution of new shoots to cropping. Where new growth is not a controlling factor, i.e. mature temperate fruit trees, then effects may be small. In time, damaged growth is replaced (see *Figure A.7*). In annual species, effects on growth may be more significant. In tomato, Romanowski (1980) found that glyphosate at 100 g ha^{-1} applied either early or mid-season reduced yields from 80 t ha^{-1} to 47 and 53 t ha^{-1}, respectively.

Conclusions

Research carried out with glyphosate in a range of crops indicates that where drift onto the whole or part of the crop plant occurs, damage is likely to be much more extensive and more persistent than with many other herbicides. Very great care and perhaps modified methods of application are thus needed to reduce the frequency of occurrence, the extent of the incident and the severity of effects in affected plants. These are influenced by method, rate and timing of applications. The risk of drift may influence the siting of particular plantings in a multi-crop situation, i.e. nursery stock (see also Chapter 22). Acute damage due to glyphosate can be similar to that caused by several herbicides, but chronic residual symptoms are relatively typical of this type of herbicide.

References

ANON. (1973). Progress report for the period April 1972 to March 1973. Institute of Agricultural Research, Melka Werer Research Station, Ethiopia, pp. 157–164.
ATKINSON, D., HYRYCZ, K.J and PETTS, S.C. (1978). Preliminary results on the use of fosamine in fruit trees. *Proceedings of the 1978 British Crop Protection Conference—Weeds*, pp. 197–200.
BARRALIS, G., CHADOUEF, R., RIFFIOD, G., GAGNEPAIN, P., HAMELIN, J., QUICHET, R., BOIDRON, R., COUILLAULT, J.P., MICHAUT, J.C., CUISSET, R. and MONDOVITS, P. (1973). Trials for control of bindweed in the vineyards of Burgundy and Franche-Comte. *Compte Rendu de la 7e Conference du Columa*, pp. 777–786.
CHING, S., NOMURA, N., YAUGER, W., UYEHARA, G. and HILTON, N.W. (1976). Summary of glyphosate use. *Hawaiian Sugar Planters' Association 1975 Annual Report*, pp. 39–40.
CLAY, D.W. (1972). Response of various fruit crops to glyphosate. *Proceedings of the 11th British Weed Control Conference*, pp. 451–457.
COOPER, F.B. (1975). Herbicides for maize. *Report on Field Experiments 1975*, ADAS, E. Midlands Region MAFF, UK, pp. 235–241.
COSTA, V.J. (1981). New methods of applying Roundup by wiping. *Herbicides en Hortofruticultura 13 Jornadas de Estudio de la Asociacion Interprofesional Para el Desarrolo Agrario.*
DAVISON, J.G. (1975). Glyphosate—a new weedkiller for fruit-growers? *ARC Research Review*, 1, 59–62.
EVETTS, L.L., RIECK, W.L., CARLSON, D. and BURNSIDE, D.C. (1976). Application of glyphosate with the recirculating sprayer. *Proceedings of the North Central Weed Conference*, 31, 69.
HODGES, L., TALBERT, R.E. and MOORE, J.N. (1978). Effect of glyphosate on highbush blueberries. *Abstracts of the 1978 Meeting of the Weed Science Society of America*, p. 27.
KAFADAROF, G. and POISSON, J.C. (1973). Glyphosate, a new herbicide for the control of perennial weeds. *Compete Rendu de la 7e Conference du Columa*, pp. 3–13.
KLEIFELD, Y. (1976). Control of *Cynodon dactylon* in cotton. *Phytoparasitica*, 4, 148.
LANGE, A.H., FISHER, B.B., ELMORE, C.L., KEMPEN, H.M. and SCHLESSELMAN, J., (1975). Roundup—the end of perennial weeds in tree and vine crops? *California Agriculture*, 29, 6–7.
LANGE, A.H. and SCHLESSELMAN, J. (1975). Tree and vine responses to glyphosate. *Proceedings of the Western Society of Weed Science*, 28, 49.
LIU, L.C. and ACEVEDO-BORRERO, E. (1980). Chemical weed control in taniers. *Journal of Agriculture of the University of Puerto Rico*, 64, 442–449.
LIU, L.C., RODRIGUEZ-GARCIA, J. and SEMIDEY-LARACUENTE, N. (1981). Glyphosate for weed control in plantains. *Journal of Agriculture of the University of Puerto Rico*, 65, 317–325.
MAGAMBO, M.J.S. and KILAVUKA, C.I. (1975). Effect of Roundup on tea bushes. *Tea in East Africa*, 15, 17–19.
MAGAMBO, M.J.S. and KILAVUKA, C.I. (1982). Effect of glyphosate on shoot growth of tea. *Tropical Pest Management*, 28, 315–316.
PETERS, E.J. and DALE, J.E. (1978). Rope application and a recirculating sprayer for pasture weed control. *Proceedings of the North Central Weed Control Conference*, 33, 127.
ROM, R.C. and TALBERT, R.E. (1973). Field evaluation of herbicides in fruit and nut crops. *Report of the University of Arkansas Agricultural Experiment Station*, 212, 1–30.
ROMANOWSKI, R.R. (1974). Effect of low levels of glyphosate on field grown tomatoes. *Proceedings of the North Central Weed Control Conference*, 29, 73.

(a) Acute sub-lethal and lethal damage due to Roundup drift

Figure A.1. Extensive contact damage on hornbeam (*Carpinus betulus*). Left, damaged; right, green (Photo: E.M. Smith, Ohio State University)

Figure A.2. Severe damage; chlorosis and distortion to basal leaves of a shoot of linden (*Tilia* sp.) (Photo: E.M. Smith, Ohio State University)

Figure A.3 (top). Severe stunting of yew (*Taxus* sp.). Right, treated; left, control (Photo: E.M. Smith, Ohio State University)

Figure A.4 (centre). Leaf death on maple (*Acer* sp.). Left, leaves necrotic; right, necrotic margins only (Photo: E.M. Smith, Ohio State University)

Figure A.5 (bottom). Complete shoot death in apple (*Malus pumila*), due to a directed application to simulate drift. Here, translocation is restricted as the shoot above is unaffected. (Photo: V.F. Hucks, East Malling Research Station)

Figure A.6. Shoot death in tomato (*Solanum lycopersicon*), due to drift (Photo: T. Erlandsen, Norwegian Plant Protection Institute)

(b) Effect of glyphosate applications and drift on growth, post-application

Figure A.7. The regrowth of a new terminal shoot on Norway spruce (*Picea abies*) following the death of the previous leader due to glyphosate application in June (Photo: K. Lund-Høie, Norwegian Plant Protection Institute)

Figure A.8. The production of deformed leaves in potato (*Solanum tuberosum*) treated post-emergence with glyphosate (Photo: R. Skuterud, Norwegian Plant Protection Institute)

Figure A.10. Untreated apple blossoms as a comparison of form, development and size with *Figure A.9* (Photo: J.K. Lewis, East Malling Research Station)

Figure A.13. An untreated plum shoot as a comparison of development with *Figures A.11* and *A.12* (Photo: J.K. Lewis, East Malling Research Station)

Figure A.12. Deformed plum shoot emerging just above scion–rootstock union on a tree which received drift damage 40 cm above this point the previous summer (Photo: J.K. Lewis, East Malling Research Station)

Figure A.9. Deformed apple spur leaves and blossoms, reduced in size and delayed in opening as a result of glyphosate drift damage to the shoot in the previous early summer (Photo: J.K. Lewis, East Malling Research Station)

Figure A.11. Deformed plum (*Prunus domestica*) shoot with typically elongated leaves and up-rolled margins as a result of glyphosate drift damage to the parent shoot in the previous summer (Photo: J.K. Lewis, East Malling Research Station)

Figure A.14 (left). Damage due to the translocation of fosamine-ammonium in pear (*Pyrus communis*) for comparison with *Figures A.9* and *A.11*. This compound also produces narrow elongated leaves with rolled margins (Photo: J.K. Lewis, East Malling Research Station)

Figure A.15 (right). Translocation damage in a cherry (*Prunus avium*) sucker. The sucker was sprayed at the base during the previous year. Buds at the tip died, those near the tip were deformed, while those in the zone of application seemed normal (Photo: V.F. Hucks, East Malling Research Station)

Figure A.16. Damage to the new growth of apple following absorption through a wound in the bark (see *Figure A.17*) (Photo: D.W. Robinson, Kinsealy Research Centre, Eire)

Figure A.17. A wound in apple bark due to cutting back the rootstock following budding which allowed the entry of glyphosate (Photo: D.W. Robinson, Kinsealy Research Centre, Eire)

Figure A.18. Shoot proliferation in raspberry (*Rubus idaeus*) as a consequence of glyphosate application during the previous season (Photo: K. Lund-Høie, Norwegian Plant Protection Institute)

Figure A.20. The persistence of glyphosate damage effects in white ash (*Fraxinus excelsior*) which was damaged by glyphosate drift 2 years previously. Deformed leaves are still visible (Photo: K. Lund-Høie, Norwegian Plant Protection Institute)

Figure A.19. Shoot proliferation in *Epilobium adenocaulon* as a result of a glyphosate application earlier in the same season (Photo: V.F. Hucks, East Malling Research Station)

ROMANOWSKI, R.R. (1980). Simulated drift studies with herbicides on field grown tomato. *HortScience*, **15**, 793–794.

SAN JUAN, N.C., BLANCAVER, R.C. and RODRIGUEZ, C.R. (1981). Preliminary study of the tolerance of coconut seedlings to different rates of glyphosate. *Weed Science Society of Philippines Newsletter*, **9**, 7.

SAN JUAN, N.C. and RODRIGUEZ, C.R. (1980). Tolerance of young coconut seedlings to glyphosate as a herbicide in coconut nurseries or newly developed plantation. *Weed Science Society of Philippines Newletter*, **8**, 10–11.

SHAW, K.A. and BRUZZERE, E. (1979). Herbicide screening trials for control of *Hypericum perforatum*. *Proceedings of the 7th Asian Pacific Weed Science Society*, pp. 185–187.

TOLLERVEY, F.E., PANIAGUA, B.O. and GONZALEZ, B.G. (1980). Herbicide trials in annual crops in Santa Cruz, Bolivia 1978–79. *CIAT Report*, **8**, 28–32.

TOTH, J. and MORRISON, G. (1977). Glyphosate drift damages fruit trees. *Agricultural Gazette of New South Wales*, **88**, 44–45.

WIESE, A.F. (1976). Glyphosate on perennial weeds. *Proceedings of the 29th Annual Meeting of the Southern Weed Science Society*, pp. 88–93.

WILLS, G.D. and MCWHORTER, C.E. (1981). Developments in post-emergence herbicide applicators. *Outlook on Agriculture*, **10**, 337–341.

YATES, W.E., AKESSON, N.B. and BAYER, D.E. (1978). Drift of glyphosate sprays applied with aerial and ground equipment. *Weed Science*, **26**, 597–604.

Common names of crops (cultivated species) together with their equivalent Latin names

Principal source: *Weed Abstracts*, **32**, No. 1 (1983).

CROP	LATIN NAME
acerola cherry	*Malpighia glabra*
alfalfa (*see* lucerne)	
almond	*Prunus amygdalus*
apple	*Malus* spp.
ash	*Fraxinus excelsior*
aspen	*Populus tremuloides*
avocado	*Persea americana, P. gratissima*
banana	*Musa sapientum*
barley	*Hordeum vulgare*
bean, broad, field	*Vicia faba*
bean, bush, dwarf, navy,	
pinto, snap, white	*Phaseolus vulgaris*
bean, mung	*Vigna radiata*
bean, scarlet runner	*Phaseolus coccineus*
beech	*Fagus silvatica*
beet, red, sugar	*Beta vulgaris*
bilberry (whortleberry)	*Vaccinium myrtillus*
birch	*Betula* spp.
bird cherry	*Prunus padus*
black currant	*Ribes nigrum*
blackberry	*Rubus* spp.
blueberry	*Vaccinium* spp.
box	*Buxus sempervirens*
buckwheat	*Fagopyrum esculentum*
bulrush millet	*Pennisetum americanum*
cabbage	*Brassica oleracea*
cantaloupe	*Cucumis melo*
carrot	*Daucus carota*
cherry	*Prunus* spp.
citrus	*Citrus* spp.
clove	*Eugenia caryophyllus*
clover, red	*Trifolium pratense*
white	*Trifolium repens*
cocoa	*Theobroma cacao*
coconut	*Cocos nucifera*
coffee	*Coffea arabica*
corn (*see* maize)	
cotton	*Gossypium* spp.
cowberry	*Vaccinium vitis-idaea*

CROP	LATIN NAME
cranberry	*Vaccinium oxycoccus*
American	*Vaccinium macrocarpon*
cucumber	*Cucumis sativus*
date palm	*Phoenix dactylifera*
filbert	*Corylus maxima*
fir, Douglas	*Pseudotsuga menziesii, P. taxifolia*
flax	*Linum usitatissimum*
gooseberry	*Ribes grossularia*
grape	*Vitis vinifera*
grapefruit	*Citrus paradisi*
groundnut	*Arachis hypogaea*
guava	*Psidium guajava*
hazel	*Corylus avellana*
holly	*Ilex* spp.
Jerusalem artichoke	*Helianthus tuberosus*
juniper	*Juniperus* spp.
kumquat	*Fortunella* spp.
larch	*Larix* spp.
lemon	*Citrus limon*
lettuce	*Lactuca sativa*
lime	*Citrus aurantifolia*
small-leaved	*Tilia cordata*
lucerne (alfalfa)	*Medicago sativa*
macadamia	*Macadamia ternifolia*
maize (corn)	*Zea mays*
mango	*Mangifera indica*
maple, Norway	*Acer plantoides*
mustard, white	*Sinapis alba*
nectarine	*Prunus persica*
oak	*Quercus* spp.
oat	*Avena sativa*
oil palm	*Elaeis guineensis*
olive	*Olea europaea sativa*
onion	*Allium cepa*
orange	*Citrus sinensis*
papaya	*Carica papaya*
parsley	*Petroselinum hortense, P. crispus*
parsnip	*Pastinaca sativa*
pea	*Pisum sativum*
peach	*Prunus persica*
pear	*Pyrus pyraster (communis)*

CROP	LATIN NAME
pecan	*Carya illinoensis*
pine, Eastern white	*Pinus strobus*
lodgepole	*Pinus contorta*
Scots	*Pinus sylvestris*
Swiss mountain	*Pinus montana*
pineapple	*Ananas comosus*
pistachio	*Pistacia vera*
plum	*Prunus domestica*
potato	*Solanum tuberosum*
pumpkin	*Cucurbita pepo*
radish	*Raphanus sativus*
raspberry	*Rubus ideaus*
rhubarb	*Rheum* spp.
rice	*Oryza sativa*
rowan	*Sorbus aucuparia*
rubber	*Hevea brasiliensis*
rum cherry	*Prunus serotina*
rye	*Secale cereale*
ryegrass, Italian or annual	*Lolium multiflorum*
perennial	*Lolium perenne*
safflower	*Carthamus tinctorius*
sorghum	*Sorghum bicolor*
soya bean	*Glycine max*
spinach	*Spinacea oleracea*
spruce, Colorado	*Picea pungens*
Norway	*Picea abies, P. excelsa*
Sitka	*Picea sitchensis*
squash	*Cucurbita pepo, C. maxima*
strawberry	*Fragaria* × *Ananassa*
sugar cane	*Saccharum officinarum, S. officinale*
sunflower	*Helianthus annuus*
swede	*Brassica napus*
tangelo	*Citrus paradisi* × *C. reticulata*
tangerine	*Citrus reticulata*
tanier	*Xanthosoma* spp.
tea	*Camellia sinensis, Thea sinensis*
tobacco	*Nicotiana tabacum*
tomato	*Lycopersicon esculentum*
turnip	*Brassica rapa*
walnut	*Juglans regia*
watermelon	*Citrullus lanatus*
wheat	*Triticum aestivum*
willow	*Salix* spp.
yam	*Dioscorea* spp.
yew	*Taxus baccata, T. cuspidata*

Latin names of weeds together with their equivalent UK and USA common names

The principal sources for the UK and USA common names in this list were *English Names of Wild Flowers* by J. G. Dony, C. M. Rob and F. H. Perring, London: Butterworths (1974) and Composite List of Weeds, *Weed Science*, **19**, 437–476 (1971).

LATIN NAME	UK COMMON NAME	USA COMMON NAME
Acer circinatum Pursh	—*	vine maple
Acer rubrum L.	—	red maple
Aegopodium podagraria L.	ground elder	bishops goutweed
Agropyron repens (L.) Beauv.	common couch	quackgrass
Agrostis gigantea Roth.	black bent	—
Agrostis stolonifera L. (*A. palustris* Huds)	creeping bent	creeping bentgrass
Agrostis tenuis Sibth. [*A. capillaris* L.]†	common bent	common bentgrass
Allium canadense L.	—	wild onion
Allium vineale L.	wild onion	wild garlic
Alnus rubra Bong.	—	red alder
Alopecurus pratensis L.	meadow foxtail	meadow foxtail
Alternanthera philoxeroides (Mart.) Griseb.	—	alligatorweed
Amaranthus retroflexus L.	common amaranth	redroot pigweed
Ampelamus albidus (Nutt) Britt.	—	honeyvine milkweed
Andropogon virginicus L.	—	broomsedge
Anemone nemorosa L.	wood anemone	—
Apocynum cannabinum (L.)	—	hemp dogbane
Arabidopsis thaliana (L.) Heynh.	thale cress	mouseearcress
Arctostaphylos manzanita Parry	—	big manzanita
Aristolochia clematitis L.	birthwort	—
Arrhenatherum elatius (L.) J. & C. Prest.	false oat-grass	tall oatgrass
Artemisia vulgaris L.	mugwort	mugwort
Arundo donax L.	giant reed	giant reed
Asclepias syriaca L.	—	common milkweed
Aster spinosus Banth	—	spiny aster
Avena fatua (L.)	wild-oat	wild oat
Baccharis pilularis DC	—	coyotebush
Betula pendula Ruth. (*B. verrucosa* Ehrh)	silver birch	—

* The symbol — indicates that an equivalent common name could not be found in the principal, and other, sources consulted.

† In species where the Latin name has been changed recently, the name in square brackets is the most recent.

LATIN NAME	UK COMMON NAME	USA COMMON NAME
Brachiaria mutica (Forsk.) Stapf (see also *Panicum purpurascens* Raddi)	—	paragrass, tall panicum
Bromus catharcticus Vahl [*B. willdenowii* Kunth]	brome grass	rescue grass
Bromus inermis Leyss.	Hungarian brome	smooth brome
Brunnichia cirrhosa Gaertn.	—	redvine
Bryonia dioica Jacq.	white bryony	—
Calendula arvensis L.	field marigold	—
Calluna vulgaris (L.) Hull	heather	heather, ling
Calystegia sepium (L.) R.Br.	hedge bindweed	—
Campsis radicans (L.) Seem.	—	trumpetcreeper
Capsella bursa-pastoris (L.) Medic.	shepherd's purse	shepherdspurse
Cardaria draba (L.) Desv. (*Lepidium draba* L.)	hoary cress	hoary cress
Carduus nutans L.	musk thistle	musk thistle
Carya tomentosa Nutt.	—	mockernut hickory
Cassia obtusifolia L.	—	sicklepod
Catabrosa aquatica L.	water whorl-grass	—
Cenchrus echinatus L.	—	southern sandbur
Centaurea repens L.	—	Russian knapweed
Cerastium vulgatum L.	common mouse-ear	mouseear chickweed
Chamaenerion angustifolium (L.) Scop [*Epilobium angustifolium* L.]	rosebay willowherb	fireweed
Chenopodium album L.	fat-hen	common lambsquarters
Chloris gayana Kunth.	—	rhodesgrass
Chondrilla juncea L.	—	rush skeletonweed
Cirsium arvense (L.) Scop.	creeping thistle	canada thistle
Clematis vitalba L.	traveller's joy	—
Commelina diffusa Burm.f.	—	spreading dayflower
Commelina erecta	—	erect dayflower
Convolvulus arvensis L.	field bindweed	field bindweed
Convolvulus sepium L.	—	hedge bindweed
Cuscuta campestris Yunck.	—	field dodder
Cuscuta indecora Choisy	—	largeseed dodder
Cynodon dactylon (L.) Pers.	bermuda-grass	bermudagrass
Cyperus esculentus L.	—	yellow nutsedge
Cyperus rotundus L.	—	purple nutsedge
Dactylis glomerata L.	cock's-foot	orchardgrass
Deschampsia cespitosa (L.) Beauv.	tufted hair-grass	—
Deschampsia flexuosa (L.) Trin.	wavy hair-grass	—
Desmodium tortuosum (Sw.) DC.	—	Florida beggarweed
Digitaria sanguinalis (L.) Scop	hairy finger-grass	large crab grass
Distichlis stricta (Torr.) Rydb.	—	desert saltgrass
Echinochloa crus-galli (L.) Beauv.	cockspur	barnyardgrass

LATIN NAME	UK COMMON NAME	USA COMMON NAME
Eichhornia crassipes (Mart.) Solms	—	waterhyacinth
Eleusine indica (L.) Gaertn.	—	goosegrass
Elymus repens (L.) Gould (see also *Agropyron repens* (L.) Beauv.)	common couch	quackgrass
Epilobium hirsutum L.	great willowherb	hairy willowweed
Epilobium tetragonum L.	square-stalked willow herb	—
Equisetum arvense L.	field horsetail	field horsetail
Erechtites hieracifolius (L.) Raf.	—	American burnweed
Erodium cicutarium (L.) L'Hér.	common stork's-bill	redstem filaree
Eryngium campestre L.	field eryngo	—
Euphorbia esula L.	leafy spurge	leafy spurge
Euphorbia hirta L.	—	garden spurge
Festuca arundinacea Schreb.	tall fescue	alta fescue
Festuca pratensis Huds.	meadow fescue	—
Festuca rubra L.	red fescue	—
Filipendula ulmaria (L.) Maxim.	meadow sweet	—
Fimbrystilis littoralis Gaud	—	grasslike fimbrystilis
Galium aparine L.	cleavers	catchweed bedstraw
Galium mollugo L.	hedge bedstraw	smooth bedstraw
Glyceria maxima (Hartm.) Holmberg	reed sweet-grass	—
Glycyrrhiza lepidota (Nutt.) Pursh	—	wild licorice
Gnaphalium obtusifolium L.	fragrant everlasting	fragrant cudweed
Hedera helix L.	ivy	English ivy
Helianthus annuus L.	—	sunflower
Helianthus ciliaris DC.	—	Texas blueweed
Heracleum sphondylium L.	hogweed	hogweed cowparsnip
Hoffmanseggia densiflora Benth.	—	hogpotato
Holcus lanatus L.	Yorkshire fog	velvetgrass
Holcus mollis L.	creeping soft-grass	German velvetgrass
Hordeum jubatum L.	foxtail barley	foxtail barley
Hordeum murinum L.	wall barley	wall barley
Hypericum perforatum L.	perforate St. John's-wort	St. Johnswort
Hypericum pulchrum L.	slender St. John's-wort	—
Imperata cylindrica (L.) Beauv.	—	cogongrass
Ipomoea purpurea (L.) Roth	—	tall morningglory
Juncus effusus L.	soft rush	soft rush
Jussiaea repens L.	—	creeping waterprimrose
Justicia americana (L.) Vahl	—	waterwillow
Lactuca serriola L.	prickly lettuce	prickly lettuce

LATIN NAME	UK COMMON NAME	USA COMMON NAME
Lantana camara L.	—	lantana
Lemna gibba L.	fat duckweed	—
Lemna polyrrhiza	greater duckweed	giant duckweed
Linaria dalmatica (L.) Mill.	—	dalmatian toadflax
Linaria vulgaris Mill.	common toadflax	yellow toadflax
Liquidambar styraciflua L.	—	sweetgum
Lithocarpus densiflorus (Hook & Arn.) Rehd.	—	tanoak
Lolium perenne L.	perennial ryegrass	perennial rye grass
Lonicera japonica Thunb.	—	Japanese honeysuckle
Malva neglecta Wallr.	dwarf mallow	common mallow
Malva rotundifolia	small mallow	dwarf mallow (common)
Mentha arvensis L.	corn mint	field mint
Mercurialis annua L.	annual mercury	—
Molinia caerulea (L.) Moench.	purple moor-grass	—
Morrenia odorata Lindl.	—	strangler vine
Murdannia nudiflora (L.) Brenan (*Commelina nudiflora* Merr. L.)	—	spreading dayflower
Nasturtium officinale R.Br.	watercress	watercress
Nelumbo lutea (Willd.) Pers.	—	American lotus
Nuphar advena (Ait.) Ait. F.Br f	—	spatterdock
Nuphar lutea (L.) Sm.	yellow water-lily	—
Nymphaea alba L.	white water-lily	—
Nymphaea odorata Ait.	—	fragrant waterlily
Nymphaea tuberosa Paine	—	white waterlily
Nymphoides peltata (Gml)	fringed water lily	—
Oenothera laciniata Hill	—	cutleaf eveningprimrose
Oxydendrum arboreum (L.) DC.	—	sourwood
Panicum dichotomiflorum Michx.	—	fall panicum
Panicum maximum Jacq.	—	guineagrass
Panicum purpurascens Raddi (Brachiaria mutica (Forsk.) Stapf)	—	paragrass
Panicum repens L.	—	torpedograss
Parthenium hysterophorus L.	—	ragweed parthenium
Parthenocissus quinquefolia (L.) Planch.	—	Virginia creeper
Paspalum conjugatum Berg.	—	sour paspalum
Paspalum dilatatum Poir.	—	dallisgrass
Paspalum distichum L.	—	knotgrass
Paspalum notatum Fluegge	—	Bahia grass
Paspalum urvillei Steud.	—	vaseygrass
Pastinaca sativa L.	wild parsnip	wild parsnip
Pennisetum clandestinum Hochst.	—	kikuyugrass

LATIN NAME	UK COMMON NAME	USA COMMON NAME
Pennisetum purpureum (Schumach.) Schum et Thonn.	—	napiergrass
Phalaris arundinacea L.	reed canary-grass	reed canarygrass
Phalaris canariensis L.	canary-grass	canarygrass
Phleum pratense L.	timothy	timothy
Phragmites australis (Cav.) (Trin. ex Streud.) (*P. communis* Trin.)	common reed	common reed
Pistia stratioties L.	—	waterlettuce
Plantago lanceolata L.	ribwort plantain	buckhorn plantain
Plantago major L.	great plantain	broadleaf plantain
Poa annua L.	annual meadow-grass	annual bluegrass
Poa pratensis L.	smooth meadow-grass	Kentucky bluegrass
Poa trivialis L.	rough meadow-grass	roughstalked blue grass
Polygonum amphibium L.	amphibious bistort	water smartweed
Polygonum aviculare L.	knotgrass	prostrate knotweed
Polygonum bistorta L.	common bistort	—
Polygonum bistortoides Pursh.	—	American bistort
Polygonum coccineum Muhl.	—	swamp smartweed
Polygonum convolvulus (L.) [*Bilderdykia japonica* (L.) Dumort]	black-bindweed	wild buckwheat
Polygonum cuspidatum (Sieb & Zucc.) [*Reynoutria japonica* Houtt]	—	Japanese knotweed
Polygonum persicaria L. .	redshank	ladysthumb
Polypodium vulgare	polypody	—
Pontamogeton natans L.	broad-leaved pond weed	floating-leaf pond weed
Populus gradientata Michx.	—	bigtooth aspen
Portulaca oleracea L.	purslane	common purslane
Potamogeton nodosus Poir	loddon pondweed	American pondweed
Potentilla anserina	silverweed	silverweed cinquefoil
Potentilla reptans	creeping cinquefoil	creeping cinquefoil
Prosopis juliflora var velutina (Woot) Sarg.	—	velvet mesquite
Pteridium aquilinum (L.) Kuhn	bracken	bracken
Pueraria lobata (Willd.) Ohwi	—	kudzu
Quercus marilandica Muenchh.	—	blackjack oak
Ranunculus repens L.	creeping buttercup	creeping buttercup
Raphanus sativus L.	—	garden radish
Rhododendron ponticum (L.)	rhododendron	—
Rhus radicans L.	—	poison ivy
Rhus toxicodendron L.	—	poison oak (sumac)
Robinia pseudoacacia L.	acacia	black locust
Rosa canina L.	dog rose	—
Rottboellia exultata (L.) L.f.	—	itchgrass
Rubia peregrina L.	wild madder	—
Rubus flagellaris Willd.	—	northern dewberry
Rubus fruticosus L.	bramble	European blackberry
Rubus spectabilis Pursh.	—	salmonberry

LATIN NAME	UK COMMON NAME	USA COMMON NAME
Rumex acetosella L.	sheep's sorrel	red sorrel
Rumex crispus L.	curled dock	curly dock
Rumex hastatulus Baldw.	—	heartwing sorrel
Rumex obtusifolius L.	broadleaf dock	broadleaf dock
Sagittaria latifolia Willd.	—	common arrowhead
Sagittaria sagittifolia L.	arrowhead	—
Saponaria officinalis L.	soapwort	bouncingbet
Sassafras albidum (Nutt.) Nees	—	sassafras
Scirpus atrovirens Willd.	—	green bulrush
Scirpus lacustris L. (Schoenoplectus lacustris (L.) Palla)	common club-rush	hardstem bulrush
Scirpus maritimus L.	sea club-rush	—
Scirpus validus Vahl.	—	softstem bulrush
Senecio jacobaea L.	common ragwort	tansy ragwort
Senecio vulgaris L.	groundsel	common groundsel
Sesbania exaltata (Raf.) Cory	—	hemp sesbania
Setaria viridis (L.) Beauv.	green bristle grass	green foxtail
Solanum carolinense L.	—	horsenettle
Solanum elaeagnifolium Cav.	—	silverleaf nightshade
Solanum nigrum L.	black nightshade	black nightshade
Solidago nemoralis Ait.	—	gray goldenrod
Sonchus arvensis L.	perennial sowthistle	perennial sowthistle
Sonchus asper (L.) Hill	spiny sowthistle	spiny sowthistle
Sonchus oleraceus L.	smooth sow-thistle	annual sowthistle
Sorghum bicolor (L.) Moench.	—	shattercane
Sorghum halepense (L.) Pers.	—	johnsongrass
Sparganium erectum L.	branched bur-reed	—
Spiraea tomentosa L.	—	hardhack
Sporobulus poiretii (R. & S.) Hitch.	—	smutgrass
Stellaria media (L.) Vill.	common chickweed	chickweed
Striga lutea Lour. (S. asiatica (L.) Kuntze)	—	witchweed
Tagetes minuta L.	—	wild marigold
Tamus communis L.	black bryony	—
Taraxacum officinale Weber.	dandelion	common dandelion
Tribulus terrestris L.	—	puncturevine
Trifolium repens L.	white clover	white clover
Tussilago farfara L.	colt's-foot	coltsfoot
Typha angustifolia	lesser bulrush	narrowleaf cattail
Ulex europaeus L.	gorse	gorse
Urtica dioica L.	common nettle	stinging nettle
Verbena hastata L.	—	blue vervain
Veronica peregrina L.	American speedwell	purslane speedwell
Xanthiun pensylvanicum Wallr.	—	common cocklebur

Index